Geological Society Special Publications
Series Editor K . COE

<small>Frontispiece</small>: Professor Janet Watson FRS

GEOLOGICAL SOCIETY SPECIAL PUBLICATION NO 27

Evolution of the Lewisian and Comparable Precambrian High Grade Terrains

EDITED BY

R. G. PARK

Department of Geology, University of Keele,
Newcastle, Staffordshire

J. TARNEY

Department of Geology, University of Leicester
Leicester

1987

Published for

The Geological Society by

Blackwell Scientific Publications

OXFORD LONDON EDINBURGH

BOSTON PALO ALTO MELBOURNE

Published for
The Geological Society by
Blackwell Scientific Publications
Osney Mead, Oxford OX2 0EL
8 John Street, London WC1N 2ES
23 Ainslie Place, Edinburgh EH3 6AJ
52 Beacon Street, Boston,
    Massachusetts 02108, USA
667 Lytton Avenue, Palo Alto,
    California 94301, USA
107 Barry Street, Carlton, Victoria 3053,
    Australia

First published 1987

DISTRIBUTORS
USA and Canada
    Blackwell Scientific Publications Inc.
    PO Box 50009, Palo Alto
    California 94303

Australia
    Blackwell Scientific Publications
    (Australia) Pty Ltd.
    107 Barry Street, Carlton,
    Victoria 3053

Typeset by Clowes Computer Composition,
printed and bound in Great Britain by
William Clowes Limited, Beccles and London

British Library Cataloguing in Publication Data

Evolution of the Lewisian.—(Geological Society special
    publication, ISSN 0305-8719)
    1. Geology, Stratigraphic—Pre-Cambrian
    2. Geology—Scotland—Highlands
    I. Park, R. G.   II. Tarney, J.
    III. Geological Society of London
    IV. Series
    551.7′12′094111   QE653

ISBN 0-632-01683-3

Library of Congress Cataloging-in-Publication Data.

(Geological Society special publication; no. 27).
    Papers presented at a conference held at Leicester
University in 1985.
    Bibliography: p.
    Includes index.
    1. Geology,   Stratigraphic—Pre-Cambrian—
    Congresses.   2. Geology—Scotland—
    Congresses.   3. Geology—Congresses.   I. Park,
    R. G. (R. Graham).   II. Tarney, J.
    III. Geological Society of London.   IV. Series.
    QE653.E94   1986   551.7′15′09411   86-20740
    ISBN 0-632-01683-3

Contents

vi   *Contents*

Preface

The first Lewisian conference was held at the University of Birmingham in 1963 at a time when controversy over the chronology of the Lewisian was at a peak. Partly as a result of that conference, interest in the problems of the Lewisian increased rapidly and considerable progress had been made, particularly in geochronology and structural geology, by 1971 when the second Lewisian conference was held at Keele University. This conference resulted in the first 'Lewisian volume' edited by ourselves, which laid the basis for a generally accepted chronology of Lewisian events and attempted to draw comparisons with the allied terrains of Southern Greenland.

A further fourteen years elapsed before the third Lewisian conference took place, this time at Leicester University on 20–22 March 1985, co-sponsored by the Tectonic and Metamorphic Studies Groups of the Geological Society and WG4 of the International Lithosphere Programme. In the intervening period great strides had been made in the understanding of many of those facets of research which contribute to the understanding of a high-grade Precambrian terrain like the Lewisian. Advances in geochemistry and petrogenesis, in structural geology and deformation, in geophysical applications and also, not least, in the basic mapping which resulted in the BGS published map sheets of the Outer Hebrides, all played their part in this expansion of knowledge.

Our aim in holding the third conference was partly to provide for an exchange of ideas but also to enable us to provide an updated 'Lewisian volume' to replace the much-quoted but sadly outdated Park & Tarney (1973). The papers that follow result from that Leicester conference and, we hope, convey the wide spread of interests and specialisations which have contributed to the understanding of the Lewisian over the intervening period.

The preparations for this volume were overshadowed by the death of Professor Janet Watson FRS, whose pre-eminence in Lewisian geology was acknowledged by all. She was prevented by her last illness from attending the Leicester Conference and from reading the introductory paper, which was given on her behalf by her husband Professor John Sutton. It was the wish both of the Geological Society, of which Janet Watson was immediate past president, and of ourselves, that this volume be dedicated to her memory, and the first contribution to the volume is an appreciation of her written at the request of the Society by Professor Don Bowes who had known Janet since they were both students at Imperial College (London). The second contribution consists of the Introduction to the Conference prepared jointly by John Sutton and Janet Watson in what was to be the last of a long series of collaborative ventures.

The third contribution to this volume consists of an introductory paper by ourselves which attempts to summarise and draw together some of the important themes of the conference, and to convey for the benefit of the general reader our impression of the present state of knowledge of the Lewisian complex. We were mindful of the comments of a reviewer of the first Lewisian volume who regretted the absence of such an overview. We also provide a general map and a series of cartoon profiles representing the various steps in the evolution of the Lewisian complex as we currently view them.

The remaining 22 contributions consist of papers read at the conference. The first by Fettes & Mendum reviews the recent BGS work in the Outer Hebrides. There then follows a set of six papers dealing with various aspects of the petrology, geochemistry and petrogenesis of Lewisian rocks, followed in turn by five papers on structural aspects and three on geophysical applications.

Following the pattern of the last Lewisian conference, we have deliberately chosen to take a somewhat wider view of the Lewisian as an example of an early Precambrian high-grade terrain, and the last six papers are included in order that comparisons may be drawn with allied terrains in other parts of the world. The Lewisian after all is such a small outcrop by the standards of the great Precambrian shield regions that we cannot afford to take too parochial a view of it. The obvious comparisons are to be made along-strike in Greenland and Labrador, but other papers deal with Archaean–Early Proterozoic terrains in West Australia, Antarctica and NE China. These examples demonstrate that the Lewisian complex with its lateral equivalents is not unique but is representative of early Precambrian high-grade terrains world wide.

We made the claim in the preface to our first Lewisian volume that the Lewisian complex was probably the best understood piece of early Precambrian crust in the world; this is still our view, and we hope that the papers in this volume will stimulate yet more work which will undoubtedly lead to a greater understanding of the processes of formation of the continental

Preface

crust. We very gratefully acknowledge financial support from the Royal Society and the Geological Society which made the Conference and this volume possible.

R. G. PARK, Department of Geology, Keele University, Newcastle, Staffordshire, UK.
J. TARNEY, Department of Geology, Leicester University, Leicester LE1 7RH, UK.

Janet Watson—an appreciation and bibliography

D. R. Bowes

With the passing of Professor Janet Vida Watson FRS the earth sciences in the U.K., and throughout the world, lost one of its most distinguished and well known personalities. For while Janet Watson spent most of her academic career in London, at Imperial College (after graduation with a First Class General Honours degree at Reading University in 1943), she was known throughout the world not only for her exceptional gift of clear and persuasive exposition both at the lecture bench and the committee table, but also as a major contributor to the advancement of the earth sciences. Her death on 29 March 1985, at the age of 61, brought to an untimely end a distinguished career which had seen many honours showered on her. The Geological Society of London, which had elevated her to the office of President in 1982–84, had previously awarded her, jointly with her husband (Professor John Sutton FRS) both the Lyell Fund (1954) and the Bigsby Medal (1965). They also honoured her with the Lyell Medal (1973) as they had her father (Professor D. M. S. Watson FRS) nearly 40 years previously. The Edinburgh Geological Society awarded her the Clough Medal (1980), she was President of Section C of the British Association for the Advancement of Science (1972), elected a Fellow of the Royal Society of London (1979) and a member of its Council and Vice-President (1983 until her death). To the various offices she held, Janet brought the directness, the precision and the liveliness of mind she had shown in one of the very first offices she had held as an earth scientist, that of a steward at the 18th International Geological Congress held in London, at Imperial College, in 1948—'Tell John (later to be her husband) 1 . . ., 2 . . . and 3 . . .', with each part of the message clearly and precisely stated. Yet perhaps it was not in the professional societies, congresses and committees where she received most recognition, but in the student societies throughout the country. They consistently put her at the top of their lists of speakers to be invited, and she consistently responded by using her talent of clear, precise and persuasive exposition to excite as well as instruct many a budding earth scientist.

It was Scotland that provided Janet with the outdoor laboratory that she loved the most. The initial choice was that of her teacher, mentor and co-author of a number of books, Professor H. H. Read FRS, who first set her to study one of his favourite topics, the migmatites of Sutherland, an aspect of which was the subject of her first publication. He then directed her and her contemporary as a research student, John Sutton, to parts of the Lewisian complex of NW Scotland where there were abundant migmatitic and igneous rocks. This, together with the research being done by Professor W. S. Pitcher and others at Imperial College on the granitic rocks of Donegal, was to test and apply the concepts of place and time in plutonism enunciated by Professor Read in his Presidential Addresses to the Geological Society of London in 1948 and 1949. The young research workers went to the rocks of NW Scotland from which B. N. Peach, J. Horne, C. T. Clough and other members of a distinguished team from the Geological Survey had developed ideas that had made such a big impact on geological thinking at the turn of the century. However, despite such a daunting prospect, both Ph.D. theses were accepted in the summer of 1949, just in time for a wedding, and a honeymoon in the Channel Islands, a venue that accounts for a publication about the Isle of Sark that does not appear to be cognate to their main body of published work. For the next three decades, there flowed from their pens a succession of publications that had a profound impact on geological thinking and the direction of research, particularly in basement complexes, both in the UK and abroad. Many were under the authorship of J. Sutton and J. Watson, but in later years, as her husband progressively became more involved in administrative matters, more of Janet's publications were her own, or with other authors, including a succession of research students and officers of the British Geological Survey with whom she worked on a number of projects.

The initiation of the partnership, both scientific and personal, had really taken place in 1948 when, after separate field studies at Scourie–Loch Laxford (J. W.) and Torridon (J. S.), and joint studies in the former area with their supervisor, they set off by bicycle (on roads that seemed to consist largely of blocks of Torridonian conglomerate) to look at other parts of the Lewisian complex, particularly around Gruinard Bay. They tested their conclusions that the complex contained the products of two separate orogenic episodes (Scourian and Laxfordian) and that chronological subdivision could be made using basic dykes as time markers.

From: PARK, R. G. & TARNEY, J. (eds), 1987, *Evolution of the Lewisian and Comparable Precambrian High Grade Terrains*, Geological Society Special Publication No. 27, pp. 1–5.

Of all the many papers Janet published, there is no doubt that the resulting publication (1951) with her husband had the greatest impact on geology in Britain. Not that the basis used for subdividing the Lewisian complex, or the proposed concept of wholesale reactivation of basement, were not questioned in the discussion that followed the verbal presentation in London early in 1950, and time and again subsequently. But the paper set out to show that a Precambrian 'fundamental complex' was amenable to chronological subdivision using field observations. It also presented a model that could be tested. Subsequently the ideas were 'exported' to Greenland at the time of a major surge of field study, and later tested there, and in Scotland, at a stage of major advancement in isotopic geochemistry. While the isotopes pointed to new crustal additions of mantle-derived products being more widespread than those resulting from wholesale reactivation of existing basement, they clearly demonstrated c. 1 Ga between the Scourian and Laxfordian episodes. However to Janet the size of this time gap seemed secondary to the field evidence that pointed to chronological subdivision. Intuitively she trusted rocks she could see more than isotopes that she could not see and it was to the field that she returned time and again for evidence. It was to the field that her students were directed first. There she imparted to them an enthusiasm to find out for themselves and her own indefinable sense that rocks had 'character'. How could anyone, except someone who had spent time in the field with Janet, understand what 'happy rocks' were?

Only those who knew the earth sciences at Imperial College in the late 1940s can really appreciate the changes that took place during the forty years she spent there. In these changes Janet played no insignificant role. She was part of the research powerhouse that, initially under the inspiration and guidance of H. H. Read, began the major expansion of the research school, the great extension of the range of research interests and facilities and the almost complete rebuilding of the accommodation. There can be little doubt that the type of precise evaluation and clear statement of requirements transmitted to her future husband during the 1948 Congress were in evidence as he progressively assumed more administrative responsibility at Imperial College. Yet her students and research colleagues saw her principally as a research worker who inspired them and also acted as a catalyst for advances in fields other than those which were mainstream to

her at the time. An illustration of such a catalytic effect is in the field of structural geology. Following the work that Janet and her husband had done on the Moine rocks and Moine–Lewisian relationships in northern Scotland in the early–mid 1950s, Professor John Ramsay FRS, who had graduated at Imperial College, was launched into research in these fields. What had been initiated to further understanding of the geology of Scotland became a major advance in understanding processes of rock deformation. In turn this added to the stature of the earth sciences at Imperial College and to its impact on the academic community at home and abroad, things which were constantly in the forefront of Janet's thinking and actions.

While field studies, particularly in the Lewisian complex, were a major part of Janet's work, as instanced by the research group she supervised in the Outer Hebrides and the help she gave to the initiation and carrying out of a programme of mapping there by the Geological Survey, progressively she became involved in other fields, particularly ore genesis and regional geochemistry. In these she worked closely with Dr. Jane Plant and other members of the Geological Survey and she considered that the affinity she had with the Survey partly stemmed from H. H. Read's association with it. She was too modest to claim that her very wide field experience, her breadth of knowledge over such a wide range of aspects of the earth sciences and her outstanding ability to integrate and make a synoptic presentation meant that she had a very great deal to offer co-workers.

To the world-wide earth science community who did not know Janet Watson personally, it will not be the conclusions of field studies in Scotland by which she will be remembered particularly, but the clearly thought out and elegantly written distillations of ideas and concepts over a wide range of topics that embody her exceptional gifts of both written and spoken exposition. For those who knew her, and particularly those who spent time in the field with her, the extensive list of publications will be secondary to the insights gained from her both in agreement and in disagreement, the opportunities provided, the enthusiasm generated and the memories, even of very wet boots being dried by an open fire in a highland cottage near Gruinard Bay. For the rocks would be waiting out there tomorrow, not to have data wrested from them, but to give up more of their secrets to a scientist who communicated with the Earth.

D. R. Bowes, Department of Geology, University of Glasgow, Glasgow G12 8QQ, UK.

Publications of Janet Vida Watson (1923–1985)

1948 Late sillimanite in the migmatites of Kildonan, Sutherland. *Geol. Mag.* **85**, 149–62.

1951 Varying trends in the metamorphism of dolerites. *Geol. Mag.* **88**, 25–35 (J. Sutton & J. Watson).

1951 The pre-Torridonian metamorphic history of the Loch Torridon and Scourie areas in the north-west Highlands, and its bearing on the chronological classification of the Lewisian. *Q. J. Geol. Soc. London*, **106** (for 1950), 241–307 (J. Sutton & J. Watson).

1951 Scourie dykes and Laxfordian metamorphism. *Geol. Mag.* **88**, 299–301 (J. Sutton & J. Watson).

1953 The supposed Lewisian inlier of Scardroy, Central Ross-shire and its relations with the surrounding Moine rocks. *Q. J. Geol. Soc. London*, **108** (for 1952), 99–126 (J. Sutton & J. V. Watson).

1953 Current bedding in the Moine Series of north-western Scotland. *Geol. Mag.* **90**, 377–87 (G. Wilson, J. Watson & J. Sutton).

1954 On the status of certain Lewisian inliers. *Trans. Geol. Soc. Glasgow*, **21**, 480–502 (J. Sutton & J. Watson).

1954 Ice-borne boulders in the Macduff Group of the Dalradian of Banffshire. *Geol. Mag.* **91**, 391–8 (J. Sutton & J. Watson).

1954 The structure and stratigraphical succession of the Moines of Fannich Forest and Strath Bran, Ross-shire. *Q. J. Geol. Soc. London*, **110**, 21–53 (J. Sutton & J. Watson).

1954 A study of the metamorphic rocks of Karema and Kungwe Bay, western Tanganyika. *Bull. Geol. Surv. Tanganyika*, **22**, 1–70 (J. Sutton, J. Watson & T. C. James).

1955 The deposition of the Upper Dalradian rocks of the Banffshire coast. *Proc. Geol. Assoc. London*, **66**, 101–33 (J. Sutton & J. Watson).

1956 The Boyndie syncline of the Dalradian of the Banffshire coast. *Q. J. Geol. Soc. London*, **112**, 103–30 (J. Sutton & J. Watson).

1957 The development of lineation in complex fold systems. *Geol. Mag.* **94**, 1–24 (P. Clifford, M. J. Fleuty, J. G. Ramsay, J. Sutton & J. Watson).

1957 The structure of Sark, Channel Islands. *Proc. Geol. Assoc. London*, **68**, 179–203 (J. Sutton & J. Watson).

1959 Metamorphism in deep-seated zones of transcurrent movement at Kungwe Bay, Tanganyika Territory. *J. Geol.* **67**, 1–13 (J. Sutton & J. Watson).

1959 Structures in the Caledonides between Loch Duich and Glenelg, North-West Highlands. *Q. J. Geol. Soc. London*, **114** (for 1958), 231–57 (J. Sutton & J. Watson).

1962 *Introduction to Geology* Volume 1 *Principles*, 693 pp. London: Macmillan (H. H. Read & J. Watson).

1962 Festoon bedding. *Geol. Mag.* **99**, 286–7 (J. Sutton and J. V. Watson).

1962 An interpretation of Moine–Lewisian relations in central Ross-shire. *Geol. Mag.* **99**, 527–41 (J. Sutton & J. Watson).

1962 Further observations on the margin of the Laxfordian complex of the Lewisian near Loch Laxford, Sutherland. *Trans. R. Soc. Edinburgh*, **65**, 89–106 (J. Sutton & J. Watson).

1963 Structures in shallow-water Precambrian sediments from northwest Scotland. *Sedimentology*, **2**, 207–14 (J. Sutton & J. Watson).

1963 Some problems concerning the evolution of the Caledonides of the Scottish Highlands. *Proc. Geol. Assoc. London*, **74**, 213–58.

1963 Some underwater disturbances in the Torridonian of Skye and Raasay. *Geol. Mag.* **100**, 224–43 (R. C. Selley, D. J. Shearman, J. Sutton & J. Watson).

1964 Some aspects of Torridonian stratigraphy in Skye. *Proc. Geol. Assoc. London*, **75**, 251–89 (J. Sutton & J. Watson).

1964 Conditions in the metamorphic Caledonides during the period of late orogenic cooling. *Geol. Mag.* **101**, 457–65.

1965 Lewisian. In CRAIG, G. Y. (ed.) *The Geology of Scotland*, 49–77. Edinburgh: Oliver & Boyd.

1965 Isotopic age-determinations of rocks from the British Isles, 1955–64. 1. Introduction. *Q. J. Geol. Soc. London*, **121**, 477–87 (P. A Sabine & J. V. Watson).

1966 *Beginning Geology*, 246 pp. London: Macmillan and Allen & Unwin (H. H. Read & J. Watson).

1967 Isotopic age-determinations of rocks and minerals from the British Isles, 1965. 1. Introduction. *Q. J. Geol. Soc. London*, **122** (for 1966), 443–7 (P. A. Sabine & J. V. Watson).

1967 Evidence of mobility in reactivated basement complexes. *Proc. Geol. Assoc. London*, **78**, 211–35.

1968 *Introduction to Geology* Volume 1 *Principles* (2nd edn), 693 pp. London: Macmillan (H. H. Read & J. Watson).

1968 Post-Scourian metadolerites in relation to Laxfordian deformation in Great Bernera, Outer Hebrides. *Scott. J. Geol.* **4**, 53–67.

1969 The Precambrian gneiss complex of Ness, Lewis, in relation to the effects of Laxfordian regeneration. *Scott. J. Geol.* **5**, 269–85.

1969 Remnants of an early metasedimentary assemblage in the Lewisian complex of the Outer Hebrides. *Proc. Geol. Assoc. London*, **80**, 387–408 (M. P. Coward, P. W. Francis, R. H. Graham, J. S. Myers & J. Watson).

1969 Scourian–Laxfordian relationships in the Lewisian of northwest Scotland. *In:* WYNNE-EDWARDS, H. R. (ed.) *Age relations in high-grade metamorphic terrains*, 119–28. *Spec. Pap. Geol. Assoc. Can.* **5** (J. Sutton & J. Watson).

1970 The Alderney Sandstone in relation to the ending of plutonism in the Channel Islands. *Proc. Geol. Assoc. London*, **81**, 577–84 (J. Sutton & J. Watson).

1970 Large-scale Laxfordian structures of the Outer Hebrides in relation to those of the Scottish mainland. *Tectonophysics*, **10**, 425–35 (M. P. Coward, P. W. Francis, R. H. Graham & J. Watson).

1970 Early clastic formations of certain orogenic cycles. *In: Studies in Earth Sciences: West Commemorative Volume*, 10–16. Saugur University, India (J. Sutton & J. Watson).

1970 An apparent age for a member of the Scourie dyke suite in Lewis, Outer Hebrides. *Scott. J. Geol.* **6**, 214–20 (R. StJ. Lambert, J. S. Myers & J. Watson).

1973 The pre-Laxfordian complex of the Outer Hebrides. *In:* PARK, R. G. & TARNEY, J. (eds) *The Early Precambrian of Scotland and Related Rocks of Greenland*, 45–50. University of Keele (J. Watson & R. J. Lisle).

1973 Concluding remarks: the evolution of a polycyclic gneiss complex. *In:* PARK, R. G. & TARNEY, J. (eds) *The Early Precambrian of Scotland and Related Rocks of Greenland*, 191–4, University of Keele.

1973 Effects of reworking on high-grade gneiss complexes. *Phil. Trans. R. Soc. London* A **273**, 433–55.

1973 The Archaean craton of the North Atlantic region. *Phil. Trans. R. Soc. London*, A **273**, 493–512 (D. Bridgwater, J. Watson & B. F. Windley).

1973 Influence of crustal evolution on ore deposition. *Trans. Inst. Min. Metall.* B **82**, 107–13.

1974 Tectonic evolution of the continents in Proterozoic times. *Nature, London*, **247**, 433–5 (J. Sutton & J. Watson).

1974 Torridonian tourmaline–quartz pebbles and the Precambrian crust northwest of Britain. *J. Geol. Soc. London*, **130**, 85–91 (P. Allen, J. Sutton & J. V. Watson).

1975 *Introduction to Geology* Volume 2 *Earth History Part 1 Early Stages of Earth History*, 221 pp. Part 2 *Later Stages of Earth History*, 371 pp. London: Macmillan (H. H. Read & J. Watson).

1975 The Precambrian rocks of the British Isles—a preliminary review. *In:* HARRIS, A. L., SHACKLETON, R. M., WATSON, J., DOWNIE, C., HARLAND, W. B. & MOORBATH, S. (eds) *A correlation of Precambrian rocks in the British Isles*, 1–10. *Spec. Rep. Geol. Soc. London*, **6**.

1975 The Lewisian Complex. *In:* HARRIS, A. L., SHACKLETON, R. M., WATSON, J., DOWNIE, C., HARLAND, W. B. & MOORBATH, S. (eds) *A correlation of Precambrian rocks in the British Isles*, 15–29.

1975 The tectonic evolution of the Lewisian complex in northern Lewis, Outer Hebrides. *Proc. Geol. Assoc. London*, **86**, 45–61 (F. B. Davies, R. J. Lisle & J. Watson).

1976 Vertical movements in Proterozoic structural provinces. *Phil. Trans. R. Soc. London*, A **280**, 629–40.

1976 The Earth's crust in Precambrian times. *Proc. Yorks. Geol. Soc.* **41**, 145–62.

1976 Mineralization in Archaean provinces. *In:* WINDLEY, B. F. (ed.) *The Early History of the Earth*, 443–53. London: Wiley.

1976 Variations in crustal level and geothermal gradient during the evolution of the Lewisian complex of northwest Scotland. *Precambrian Res.* **3**, 363–74 (B. B. Dickinson & J. Watson).

1976 *Eo-Europa*: the evolution of a craton. *In:* AGER, D. V. & BROOKS, M. (eds) *Europe from Crust to Core*, 59–78. New York: Wiley.

1977 Intrusion into moving crust. *In:* SAXENA, S. & BHATTACHARJI, S. (eds) *Energetics of Geological Processes*, 20–30. New York: Springer-Verlag (J. Sutton & J. Watson).

1977 Early basic bodies in the type Laxfordian complex, N W Scotland and their bearing on its origin. *J. Geol. Soc. London*, **133**, 123–31 (F. B. Davies & J. V. Watson).

1977 Precambrian thermal regimes. *Phil. Trans. R. Soc. London*, A **288**, 431–40.

1977 The Outer Hebrides: a geological perspective. *Proc. Geol. Assoc. London*, **88**, 1–14.

1978 Review lecture. Ore deposition through

geological time. *Proc. R. Soc. London,* **A 362**, 305–28.

1978 The basement of the Caledonide orogen in Britain. *In: Caledonian-Appalachian Orogen of the North Atlantic Region*, 75–7. *Geol. Surv. Can. Pap.* 78–13.

1979 Basement–cover relations in the British Caledonides. *In*: HARRIS, A. L., HOLLAND, C. H. & LEAKE, B. E. (eds) *The Caledonides of the British Isles – reviewed*, 67–91. *Spec. Publ. Geol. Soc. London*, **8** (J. Watson & F. W. Dunning).

1979 Regional geochemistry of the Northern Highlands of Scotland. *In*: HARRIS, A. L. HOLLAND, C. H. & LEAKE, B. E. (eds) *The Caledonides of the British Isles – reviewed*, 117–28 (G. S. Johnstone, J. Plant & J. V. Watson).

1979 Caledonian granites in relation to regional geochemistry in northern Scotland. *In*: HARRIS, A. L., HOLLAND, C. H. & LEAKE, B. E. (eds) *The Caledonides of the British Isles – reviewed*, 663–7 (G. S. Johnstone, J. Plant & J. V. Watson).

1979 Regional geochemistry of uranium as a guide to deposit formation. *Phil. Trans. R. Soc. London* **A 291**, 321–38 (J. V. Watson and J. Plant).

1980 Metallogenesis in relation to mantle heterogeneity. *Phil. Trans. R. Soc. London,* **A 297**, 347–52.

1980 The origin and history of the Kapuskasing structural zone, Ontario, Canada. *Can. J. Earth Sci.* **17**, 866–75.

1980 Basement heat flow and metalliferous mineralization in England and Wales. *Nature, London,* **288**, 657–9 (G. C. Brown, J. Cassidy, E. R. Oxburgh, J. Plant, P. A. Sabine & J. V. Watson).

1981 Regional geochemistry in relation to the structures in the south-west Highlands. *Geophys. J. R. astr. Soc.* **65**, 246 (J. Plant & J. Watson).

1982 The role of metalliferous and mineralised uranium granites in the formation of uranium provinces. *In: Proceedings of the Symposium on Uranium Exploration Methods*, 157–68. Paris: Nuclear Energy Agency (P. R. Simpson, J. A. Plant, J. V. Watson, P. M. Green & M. B. Fowler).

1982 Uranium provinces in relation to metamorphic grade and regional geochemistry. *In: Proceedings of the Symposium on Ura-nium Exploration Methods*, 235–47. Paris: Nuclear Energy Agency (J. Watson, M. B. Fowler, J. A. Plant, P. R. Simpson & P. M. Green).

1982 Layered ultramafic-gabbro bodies in the Lewisian of northwest Scotland: geochemistry and petrogenesis. *Earth Planet. Sci. Lett.* **58**, 345–60 (J. D. Sills, D. Savage, J. V. Watson & B. F. Windley).

1983 *Geology and Man—An introduction to applied earth science*, 150 pp. London: Allen & Unwin.

1983 A geochemical study of Lewisian metasedimentary granulites and gneisses in the Scourie-Laxford area of north-west Scotland. *Mineral. Mag.* **47**, 1–9 (P. O. Okeke, G. D. Borley & J. Watson).

1983 Metalliferous and mineralized Caledonian granites in relation to regional metamorphism and fracture systems in northern Scotland. *Trans. Inst. Min. Metall.* **B 92**, 33–42 (J. A. Plant, P. R. Simpson, P. M. Green, J. V. Watson & M. B. Fowler).

1983 Lewisian. *In*: CRAIG, G. Y. (ed.) *Geology of Scotland* (2nd Edn), 23–47. Edinburgh: Scottish Academic Press.

1984 The ending of the Caledonian orogeny in Scotland. *J. Geol. Soc. London,* **141**, 193–214.

1984 Continental crustal regimes as factors in the formation of sedimentary ore deposits. *J. Geol. Soc. London,* **141**, 215–20.

1984 Variscan–Caledonian comparisons: late orogenic granites. *Proc. Ussher Soc.* **6**, 2–12 (J. Watson, M. B. Fowler, J. A. Plant & P. R. Simpson).

1984 Moine–Dalradian relationships and their palaeotectonic significance. *Proc. R. Soc. London,* **A395**, 185–202 (J. A. Plant, J. V. Watson & P. M. Green).

1985 Northern Scotland as an Atlantic-North Sea divide. *J. Geol. Soc. London,* **142**, 221–43.

1986 Architecture of the continental lithosphere. *Phil. Trans. R. Soc. London,* **A317**, 5–12.

1987 The Lewisian complex: questions for the future. *In: The Evolution of the Lewisian and Comparable Precambrian High Grade Terrains*, 7–11. *Spec. Publ. Geol. Soc. London*, **27**, 7–11. Blackwell Scientific Publications, Oxford.

The Lewisian complex: questions for the future

John Sutton & Janet Watson

The study of the Lewisian is entering a third phase. The first was the mapping of the complex by the Geological Survey. The second was the dating of the main events which demonstrated the long time span, almost one third of geological time, which separated the early Scourian crustal accretion from the latest Laxfordian igneous activity. This chronology and comparable advances in Canada, Greenland and Scandinavia made it possible for the first time to view the Lewisian not as an isolated fragment of Precambrian, which was the situation when we first took up this problem nearly forty years ago, but as a component in the Precambrian of the northern hemisphere. The third phase, which is now under way, is providing information on the processes that produced these remarkable rocks. We can now begin an attempt to reconstruct the settings in which Scourian and Laxfordian events took place. This is going to be a very difficult task; it involves extracting from the rocks evidence as to the nature of the crust and mantle below the sections of the complex visible today and reconstructing the overlying material, at times 45 kilometres thick, which has now vanished. The key to the Lewisian lies in understanding the conditions under which the accretion of the Scourian occurred between 2700 and 2900 million years ago. For these rocks (the 'Old Boy' of the Geological Survey) make up the bulk of the complex, although we now know that they were profoundly modified and received many further additions during the 1500 million years that elapsed before the formation of the Lewisian was complete. As Teall wisely remarked in the introduction to the North West Highland Memoir, 'The Lewisian gneiss is not a geological formation in the ordinary sense of the word'.

The original mapping of the Lewisian, initiated just over a century ago, was one of the great accomplishments in field geology. It revealed for the first time a section through the lower crust in all the detail that 6″ to the mile mapping in the hands of experts can provide. In many ways it was a more remarkable achievement than the somewhat later work of the Geological Survey that demonstrated the make-up of the dissected Tertiary volcanoes, which is often taken as the finest example of Survey work in the Scottish Highlands. In the latter instance the Surveyors knew very well that they were uncovering the roots of volcanoes, whereas the earlier workers

on the Lewisian were deciphering a structure for which no model existed. To map correctly, as Clough and his colleagues did, a feature as complex as the Lewisian, was a feat no-one had achieved elsewhere at that time. The Lewisian chapters of the North West Highland Memoir published in 1907 and the accompanying maps provide the first detailed analysis of a section through the lower crust.

Occasionally in the history of science, something is accomplished so effectively that no-one at that moment can improve upon it. A long pause in the study of the Lewisian followed. The Geological Society did not publish a single paper on the foreland Lewisian in the first half of this century. It is true that during that period much was learned about the Lewisian of the Scottish Highlands. Davidson's paper on South Harris broke new ground with its petrological detail and his recognition of Lewisian charnockites. But general understanding of the Lewisian remained much as it had stood in 1907.

Elsewhere, particularly in Scandinavia and Canada, many new ideas on Precambrian complexes emerged in the first half of the century. Sederholm and his successors in Finland, Wegmann both in Finland and Greenland, Holmes through his dating of Precambrian belts in Africa and elsewhere, and investigators in North America showed how great shields could be analysed, and recognized the roles of igneous activity, metamorphism and migmatization within Precambrian terrains.

In 1950, in our account of the Scourian and Laxfordian to the Geological Society, we were able to draw on all this work overseas and apply it to the results of the Geological Survey. We used the Scourie basic dykes as a time marker in distinguishing an older Scourian and a younger Laxfordian complex and went on to argue that a long time interval separated the two complexes. The discussion of that paper shows the mixed reception with which that argument was received. While H. H. Read observed that the authors had now applied vast draughts of time to the dead rocks of the Lewisian and that the two time periods, Scourian and Laxfordian, were recorded in the Lewisian rocks with as much faithfulness as if they were recorded in sediments; others failed to grasp the immensity of the time span we thought separated Scourian and Laxfordian, which we regarded then as fragments of two

From: PARK, R. G. & TARNEY, J. (eds), 1987, *Evolution of the Lewisian and Comparable Precambrian High Grade Terrains*, Geological Society Special Publication No. 27, pp. 7–11.

orogenic belts. In coming to that conclusion we were much influenced by Noe Nygaard's presentation, at the International Geological Congress held in London in 1948, of his paper on a new orogenic period in Greenland, at which he showed illustrations of changes in basic dykes as they were involved in the Nagssugtoqidian events. With O'Hara's demonstration that some high-grade metamorphic assemblages in the Scourie dykes dated from their initial crystallization, it became clear that our assumption, that the intrusion of the dykes occurred when the present section through the Lewisian stood high in the crust near the surface, was incorrect. We were on sounder ground when we emphasized that the emplacement of a dyke swarm many km wide indicated crustal extension. The first radiometric dating however supported our conclusion that the Scourian and Laxfordian represented two periods of orogeny. Although the igneous effects of the Laxfordian are slight in North West Scotland, more extensive igneous activity is now known to have occurred elsewhere in Laxfordian time in Scandinavia, Greenland and North America. Studies of isotopes in the Lewisian have established the chronology, and made it possible to identify contemporaneous analogues elsewhere which are more perfectly preserved.

The Greenland anorthosites and the remarkable late Archaean thrust stacking which accompanied granite intrusion in South West Greenland for example, provide evidence which can be used to understand the Lewisian. The greatest future contribution from isotope geochemistry is likely to be concerned with identifying the sources of Lewisian igneous rocks and the conditions under which the Lewisian evolved.

A major advance was the demonstration that the Scourian represents an addition to the crust of material that had been transferred from the mantle in the 200 million years that preceded the Scourian metamorphism 2900 million years ago. No material older than this has as yet been identified in North West Scotland.

We thus have the opportunity to study the formation of new Archaean continental crust. The Geological Survey recognized the two essential ingredients of the Scourian, the subordinate metasediments and metabasites, and the calc-alkaline tonalitic gneisses which constitute over 80% of the complex. Geochemical mapping by BGS brings out the salient characters of these rocks, shows the depletion in the granulites as compared with the amphibolite-facies Scourian grey gneiss, shows the chemical make up of the late Scourian (Inverian) intrusions and metasediments and indicates the effects of Laxfordian migmatization, shearing and intrusion of granite

pegmatite bodies. This evidence on bulk composition of Lewisian assemblages can be correlated with physical properties of the rocks and so improves the interpretation of geophysical data. To return to Scourian accretion, if the Moho then lay anywhere near its present depth in northern Scotland, a Scourian crust some 70 km thick is indicated. Scourian metamorphic assemblages suggest an overburden of 45 km above the section exposed at the present day surface, itself some 25 km above the present day Moho. Scourian tectonic thickening of the crust must have taken place. The repeated juxtaposition of rocks of very different origins, the altered sediments, the metabasic rocks which were once quartz-tholeiites (possibly lavas, possibly sills or dykes) and the great mass of tonalites from the mantle, indicates subduction of near-surface material to depths of 45 km, accompanied by intense deformation which followed or accompanied the introduction of the tonalites. Analogies with Andean-type mountain building have been made. But we have to consider the possibility that the Scourian crust-forming took place under conditions which have no present day analogy. Several facts suggest that conditions were in fact different; there was a high heat flow, there was less material in the continental crust in pre-Scourian times than today, the continental crust was deformed throughout its extent, and there were features such as the greenstone belts and associated granite gneisses which have no analogues today. We would support the view that Scourian accretian involved subduction and thrusting but hesitate to accept that an Andean model is the only possibility. One could suggest three scenarios.

Scenario 1. An Andean model; collision of continent and ocean.

Scenario 2. Pre-Scourian (i.e. Katarchaean) continental crust was quite subordinate to an extensive ocean, presumably an Archaean 'Pacific' covering most of the Earth. Tonalites were introduced at active margins in a continental crust-forming episode that substantially increased the proportion of continental crust, *ie* a major accretion of continental crust occurred of which the Scourian is only one example.

Scenario 3. There was an extensive Pre-Scourian crust of which the surviving 3,500 Ma rocks are remnants (though none occur in Scotland). Where Scourian accretion occurred, the Katarchaean crust remained in the upper parts of the crust which was invaded by tonalites, was accordingly uplifted in mountain chains and lost by erosion. On this hypothesis the rarity of Katarchaean relicts is explained by their destruction as the upper parts of late Archaean (*ie* Scourian) collision zones are removed by denudation.

If the third scenario is correct, one might expect to find Katarchaean detritus in areas such as the Ketilidian, or in the cover series farther north in Greenland, in the Nagssugtoqidian belt. On hypothesis 2, the upper parts of accreted Scourian crust would consist of late Archaean marine sediments, basic volcanics and intrusives, with much calc-alkaline plutonic rock but no Katarchaean remains. With hypothesis 1 one should find at least occasional relicts of relatively stable blocks of older Archaean from continents flanking accretion belts, just as the South American shield with its cover and older basement flanks the present day Andes.

Turning from what might have been present above the Scourian as exposed today to what might have lain below, we have several lines of evidence. At the close of the Scourian we might expect rocks which formed ocean floor to extend for several hundred kilometres into the mantle. If the upper mantle travels with the overlying crust we should expect evidence of this to be preserved. If there is a surface of decollement separating the outer part of the lithosphere from deeper rocks, the mantle below that plane may bear no relation to the Scourian subduction. Lewisian magmatic rocks can provide evidence of source rocks within the mantle, enabling the chemical composition and age of components in the lowermost crust and mantle to be deduced.

Lower Palaeozoic and Permocarboniferous intrusions bring xenoliths to light which provide samples of the rocks present below northern Scotland at those times. Already evidence of heterogeneity has been obtained and more will be presented at this symposium. Geophysical measurements, including seismic velocity, electrical conductivity and heat flow, produce evidence of present day conditions at depth. The geochemical surveys of BGS provide evidence on the distribution of some 25 elements through Lewisian rock marking different stages in the evolution of the crust. Thus we have evidence on the bulk composition of the Scourian grey gneiss complex, the granulite complex, and of the effects of Inverian events, of the introduction of the Scourie dyke swarm and of Laxfordian igneous activity and metamorphism. It will be of great interest to see to what extent evidence of conditions deeper in the earth can be correlated with the geochemistry of the various geochemical provinces identified within the Lewisian at the present day surface. If we could understand the modifications produced by later events, we might arrive at a picture of conditions at depth during the Scourian accretion which we regard as the principle objective. For such an investigation to be successful, the depth of the moving lithosphere must extend for several hundred kilometres. However it would be a significant discovery to find that the Scourian rested on an alien mantle separated by a zone of detachment dividing the outermost travelling crust from a convecting mantle. The recently discovered Caledonian thrusts should not produce an insuperable barrier, and Laxfordian modification should be recognizable, for Northwest Scotland lies outside the regions of intense alteration at that time.

We are impressed by three remarkable features of the Scourian: firstly the great volume increase which must have accompanied the introduction of the tonalites; secondly the great depth from which the presently exposed section through the Scourian has risen—Scourie granulites include very high-pressure assemblages; and thirdly, the length of time over which this portion of the crust continued to rise. We do not appear to be dealing solely with the usual rapid uplift after Phanerozoic mountain building. This could well have occurred in immediate post-Scourian time, but why did uplift continue, as the succession of lower-grade metamorphic developments indicates, from 2700 to 1200 Ma? Was additional material added to deep crust during this time or had Scourian subduction produced an anomaly within the upper mantle which took 1200 Ma to be corrected?

We called this introduction 'Questions for the future'. Nowhere is this title more appropriate than when we consider the movement of fluids within the Lewisian. We are all aware of the depletion of the Scourian granulites and of the additions to the crust in Laxfordian times. How do these movements take place? What is the role of the shear belts? What is the relation between the Laxfordian change in grain size as Scourian gneisses are converted to finer grained rocks, sometimes but not always of lower metamorphic grade? To what extent are the changes we can observe in the exposed section of the Lewisian open to study, to be connected with the recently discovered flat-lying features which geophysical work indicates are present deeper within the crust, and which have been interpreted as horizons rich in fluids? These are very much questions for the future.

We are on firmer ground when we consider quite a different topic, namely the place of the Hebridean Craton in the Precambrian of Europe and America and its influence in the later evolution of North West Europe.

The presence of granulites in the sea floor west and north of Scotland is indicated by a distinctive signature on magnetic and gravity maps. There may be a cluster of remnants comparable to the Scourian of the type area, the whole assemblage lying to the east of a much larger pre-Ketilidian block in Greenland. The significance of the Inverian is still far from clear. Does it represent a late phase of the Scourian or are the sediments and basic and anorthositic rocks, and the subsequent localised metamorphism and deformation, related to some major event elsewhere? The restricted though rather different Laxfordian events can now be seen as the marginal events in a major episode of igneous activity, deformation and metamorphism which affected the crust from North America to the Black Sea but which affected the Hebridean Craton only to a limited extent. Here again we are brought up against the long time span of Lewisian events. The late deformation and occasional pegmatites found in the southerly parts of the Lewisian tract, well displayed in the Torridon area, may be as late as 1200 Ma, that is to say 400 or 500 Ma after the main Laxfordian events. An even longer time span covers the Scourian to Inverian. Are we linking events that are in reality distinct, or are we dealing with phenomena that reflect processes taking many hundreds of millions of years to reach completion? Finally let us come back to the longest sequence of all. Why is it, from the Scourian accretion onwards, that the crust is repeatedly metamorphosed for the most part at successively lower temperatures and pressures? Was this a long uplift, or was it interrupted by periods of as yet unrecognized subsidence? Perhaps the Scourian accession of new crust was so remarkable an event that it accounts for the buoyancy of Northern Scotland not only to the end of Laxfordian time but right up to the present day.

The position of rocks as old as the Lewisian at the margin of a widening ocean is unusual and on the eastern seaboard of the Atlantic can only be matched off part of West Africa. It is usual for rifts that develop into oceans to follow younger structures. The explanation has recently become apparent with the recognition of Caledonian thrusts within what was previously thought to be the foreland of the Moine and Caledonian chains. It is now known that younger sedimentary basins formed as renewed movements occurred along some thrusts. The Lewisian has for the first time gained an economic importance as the basement to the petroleum fields north and west of Britain. The study of the response of the Lewisian basement to later orogeny also gains importance because it is now possible to study the ways in which the Lewisian, known from geochemical surveys of BGS to underlie part but not all of the younger metamorphic rock south east of the Great Glen Fault, was converted to the Caledonian basement pierced with granites which underlies parts of the North Sea oil fields. The boundary between less altered Lewisian and 'Caledonised' basement has been traced north of Scotland through the Highlands to the west coast. Young Precambrian granulites have been located below southern Scotland, and a boundary between Lewisian and Grenville may be present in north western Ireland, although its location is complicated by later Caledonian events affecting both groups of rock now largely concealed by Dalradian.

A third British petroleum province is immediately underlain by very late Precambrian or early Palaeozoic deposits of which great thicknesses have been proved below parts of southern England by the Deep Geology Unit of BGS. A crystalline basement is believed to underlie this pile of low-grade metamorphic rocks. It is just possible that it might be Laxfordian rather than Grenville, for pre-Grenville dates have been obtained from rocks exposed in the Channel Islands. Southern England could be underlain at depth by rocks equivalent to the Ketilidian of Southern Greenland, which consists of a supracrustal series metamorphosed at the same time as the Laxfordian but totally unlike the Scottish rocks. The Laxfordian affected a Scourian basement, as did parts of the Nagssugtoqidian farther north in Greenland. However other parts of that belt, and most of the Ketilidian, developed in a previously unmetamorphosed cover series which may well contain relicts of the upper parts of the Greenland pre-Ketilidian and, if it extends eastwards into Europe, detritus from the missing parts of the top 45 km of the Scourian crust.

With the greater understanding of the northern Scotland thrusting recently obtained, the possibility opens up of reconstructing Lewisian floor preserved in the pre-thrust structures that interleaved Lewisian and Moine. In brief, the identification of the main components of the heterogeneous basement below Britain's oil fields is now in sight.

The presence of the Lewisian has exerted two general effects during post-Laxfordian times. One is the buoyancy already mentioned and well illustrated by the closeness of the base of first the Torridonian and secondly the onshore Mesozoic deposits of northern Scotland to present day sea levels. The other is shown by the distinctive response of the mass of the Lewisian to changing stress fields. The relatively sharp north-western boundary of the Caledonian chain contrasts with the diffuseness of the south-eastern boundary everywhere south of Scandinavia. This was in part responsible for the sinistral displacement within the Caledonian at a later date along the Great Glen Fault, which itself may lie near the southeast margin of the Hebridean Craton. The Tertiary opening of the Atlantic close to the outcrop of Lewisian thrust sheets dating from Caledonian times has been mentioned. Tertiary intrusions cutting through Lewisian and Torridonian have been contaminated by their host rocks but comparison of Lewisian and Tertiary granitic geochemistry indicates that the latter did not result from melting of Lewisian crust but represent magmas originating at deeper levels.

To end our introduction, let us go back to what we regard as the most critical problem—an understanding of how the accretion of the Scourian took place. This was not a local event but can be paralleled in many parts of the world. Between about 3200 and 2600 Ma continental accretion occurred in every continent. The time span may be even shorter, but during that period, less than 1/7 of geological time, the earth changed from a regime which produced the association of greenstone belts and granitic gneisses to a regime not greatly different from that of the plate tectonic regime we know today. The phenomenon that accompanied the change was the widespread addition of tonalitic rocks to the crust as shown in the Scourian. Whether this change was due to changes in the circulation of the mantle, or whether it came about when it did because a certain period of geological time was required after the origin of the Earth to establish certain contrasts between continental and ocean crust, or for some other cause not yet identified, is not known. But it was an epoch-making phenomenon as important in understanding continental evolution as sea-floor spreading is now recognized to be in the formation of oceanic crust.

The tiny Scourian fragment we are discussing in this symposium is one of the best known examples of this phenomenon. The way forward must be through the variety of detailed studies that will be reported at this meeting. You have everything going for you, you have new techniques, the ability to study a variety of aspects of the question, and above all, as the number of research groups indicates, you have the critical mass that will be needed to solve what is unquestionably one of the key problems in geology. As we said in our opening words, the study of the Lewisian has entered a new phase. Good luck to you!

The Lewisian complex: a typical Precambrian high-grade terrain?

R. G. Park & J. Tarney

SUMMARY: The main structural, lithological and geochemical features of the Lewisian complex are summarized in relation to available geochronology and an attempt is made to integrate this information into an evolutionary model for the Lewisian from the Archaean through the Proterozoic. The phase of extensive crustal generation which formed the early Lewisian (Scourian) complex occurred at about 2900 Ma and was marked by the production of vast volumes of tonalite which, together with supracrustal components, were affected by strong horizontal thrusting and deformation. The deeper parts of the Lewisian crust were subject to (Badcallian) granulite facies metamorphism culminating at *c.* 2700 Ma. Major NW–SE shear zones developed shortly after this and resulted in the segmentation of the Lewisian crust and juxtaposition of different crustal levels. This marked a period of quite extensive retrogression of the high-grade gneisses, which continued (with further local shearing) during and after the emplacement of the Scourie dyke suite at *c.* 2400 Ma. Extension of the Lewisian crust occurred in the southern (Gairloch) area around 2000 Ma and extensive outpourings of mafic volcanics, with associated exhalative mineralization, took place accompanied by sedimentation in the developing basin to form the Loch Maree Group. Igneous activity related to the South Harris igneous complex may have occurred at this period on the Outer Hebrides. Laxfordian deformation and metamorphism began before 1900 Ma and resulted in major reactivation of the earlier shear zones between and within the juxtaposed crustal blocks. More pervasive deformation accompanied the closure of the Loch Maree volcano-sedimentary basin, with major overthrusting and isoclinal folding. Culmination of Laxfordian metamorphic activity occurred at *c.* 1900 Ma with migmatization and granite injection at Laxford and on Harris, and locally in the southern area. Shear deformation, increasingly more brittle and localized, continued to affect the Lewisian complex until 1400 Ma and probably until 1000 Ma. Interestingly, the main shear zones established at the end of the Archaean crust-forming episode at 2600 Ma continued to be the focus of tectonic, metamorphic and magmatic activity over the following 1500 million years.

Introduction: A summary of Lewisian chronology

The Lewisian outcrop of the NW highlands and islands of Scotland constitutes a relatively narrow but well exposed strip of Precambrian crust bordering the Caledonian fold-belt (Fig. 1). Because the length of the outcrop crosses the strike of the major tectonic features of the Lewisian, a variety of crustal levels, rock types and structures are available for study, and indeed the Lewisian probably represents the best studied segment of an Archaean–Proterozoic high-grade terrain in the world. Our understanding of the evolution of the Lewisian has grown in parallel with such studies, but perhaps even more so under the influence of progress in the understanding of Precambrian crustal growth and development generally. Thus our ideas on the Lewisian have been in a constant state of flux over the last two decades, which may have proved confusing to those not familiar with the geology. It is the purpose of this paper to attempt to clarify some of the major issues and problems which will then serve as an introduction to the more detailed contributions which follow.

The basic features of the Lewisian were recognized almost a century ago by Peach *et al.* (1907) during the Survey mapping of the mainland outcrop: a 'fundamental complex' invaded by Scourie dykes and subjected to later 'pre-Torridonian movements'. The significance of these relationships was realized by Sutton & Watson (1951) who proposed that the Lewisian had been affected by two main orogenic cycles, the 'Scourian' and 'Laxfordian', separated by the phase of dyke intrusion. A wealth of geochronological, structural, geochemical and other information accumulated since then can be integrated into a broad chronological sequence (Table 1), which we will amplify below.

The Archaean evolution of the complex

The Lewisian is similar to many other Archaean high-grade terrains in being composed dominantly of tonalitic–trondhjemitic gneisses with numerous mafic–ultramafic enclaves and local intercalated layered mafic–ultramafic complexes and supracrustal metasediments (Tarney & Win-

From: PARK, R. G. & TARNEY, J. (eds), 1987, *Evolution of the Lewisian and Comparable Precambrian High Grade Terrains*, Geological Society Special Publication No. 27, pp. 13–25.

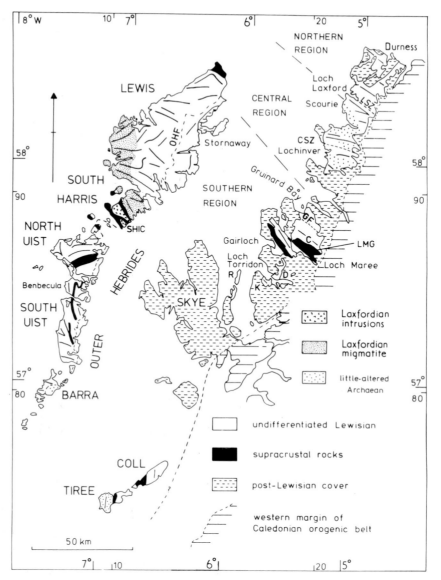

FIG. 1. Location map illustrating the important features of the Lewisian Complex of Northwest Scotland. OHF, Outer Hebrides Fault; SHIC, South Harris Igneous Complex; LSZ, Laxford Shear Zone; CSZ, Canisp Shear Zone; GF, Gruinard 'front'; LMG, Loch Maree Group; C, Carnmore; D, Diabaig; K, Kenmore; R, Rona. Outer Hebrides geology partly after Fettes & Mendum (this vol.).

dley 1977). However, the Lewisian outcrop as a whole comprises a number of juxtaposed crustal levels and the proportions and types of these components appears to differ with crustal level. Thus the granulite-facies terrain of the central region is characterized by a high proportion of intercalated ultramafic and mafic material, and the strongly banded gneisses show a compositional gradation through mafic diorites to tonalite with only a small proportion of silicic trondhjemites (Sheraton *et al.* 1973). The southern part of this central region at Gruinard Bay is largely a bimodal agmatite with numerous mafic enclaves in a sea of trondhjemite (Rollinson & Fowler, this vol.) and the gneisses are now at amphibolite facies. The flanking zones of amphibolite facies gneisses to the north and south of the central region have a much lower proportion of mafic

TABLE 1. *Outline of Lewisian chronology*

Ma	
2900	Formation of early Scourian supracrustal metasediments and mafic–ultramafic rocks and incorporation into developing tonalitic plutonic complex with associated strong horizontal thrusting and deformation
2700	Main Badcallian high-grade granulite-facies metamorphism affecting deeper parts of Lewisian crust
2600?	Initiation of Inverian shear zones associated with uplift and segmentation of Archaean blocks
2500	Late Badcallian (post-Badcallian) biotite pegmatites
2400	Emplacement of Scourie dolerites and norites, and later (?2200Ma) olivine gabbros and picrites. Continuing retrogression of the granulites and intermittent movement on shear zones
2000	Crustal extension with extrusion of voluminous lavas of the Loch Maree Group and associated sedimentation. Emplacement of late Scourie dykes? Formation of S. Harris igneous complex?
1900?	Early Laxfordian deformation and high-grade metamorphism
1800	Early Laxfordian migmatisation and emplacement of granites and muscovite pegmatites
1600–1400	Late Laxfordian deformation and retrogressive metamorphism
1400–1000?	Late– or post–Laxfordian brittle folds and crush-belts

enclaves and very few ultramafic enclaves, and the host gneisses tend to be more silicic and potash-rich than those in the central region. These observations correlate with an increasing mafic composition and density of the Archaean crust with depth, but quartz-bearing silicic rocks are still common in the granulite terrain.

The metasedimentary gneisses are commonly associated with the ultramafic layered complexes, but form a relatively minor component of the gneisses. They are largely semipelitic in composition, but include calc-silicates and possible arkoses (Cartwright & Barnicoat, this vol.; Okeke *et al.* 1983). Although Sutton & Watson (1951), and more recently Lowman (1984), have suggested that the gneiss complex as a whole may have sedimentary precursors, the geochemical evidence (e.g. Weaver & Tarney 1980) demonstrates that the composition of most gneisses is far removed from that of typical sediments and strongly indicates an igneous origin. Interestingly, because of the close association with ultramafic layers, the undoubted Scourian metasediments appear to be more common in the deep crust granulite zones than in sectors representing higher crustal levels.

Origin of the Scourian gneisses

There have been a number of geochemical studies of Lewisian gneisses, either focusing on reasons for the chemical differences between the granulite and amphibolite-facies terrains of the Lewisian (e.g. Tarney *et al.* 1972), or on the petrogenesis of the gneisses (e.g. Weaver & Tarney 1980) or on the origin of specific rock components (e.g. Sills *et al.* 1982). To gain an overall picture it is best to consider the petrogenetic aspects first.

Weaver & Tarney (1980) noted that not only are Lewisian gneisses essentially bimodal in composition, but that the two components have a different petrogenesis. The mafic gneisses show a range of Fe/Mg ratios and have trace element patterns consistent with tholeiitic low-pressure crystal fractionation. Their common association with metasedimentary horizons supports this. Similar features are apparent in other high-grade terrains (e.g. Weaver 1980; Weaver *et al.* 1982) and the most reasonable explanation is that the mafic–ultramafic–sediment association represents material intercalated tectonically during the processes of crustal generation, probably from the subducting ocean floor (Fig. 2A). Compared with modern ocean-floor basalts however, the Archaean basaltic material is not depleted in incompatible trace elements; nor indeed is much of the ultramafic material associated with it (Sills *et al.* 1982).

By contrast the tonalitic and trondhjemitic gneisses of the Lewisian have rare-earth element patterns indicative of magma generation through partial melting of a mafic source under hydrous high-pressure conditions under which hornblende and perhaps minor garnet were stable (Weaver & Tarney 1980). Such conditions would be appropriate to a subduction zone—indeed this is the only environment which would realistically make large amounts of mafic material available for the extensive melting required to generate crust rapidly. However, compared to modern subduction zones, melting would not need to be very deep (see also Rollinson & Fowler, this vol.), hence shallow-angle subduction is implied. An important consequence of hydrous melting at moderate depths is that the generated magmas cannot rise high in the crust (see Tarney & Weaver, this vol.) but would ascend to a level appropriate to their density and the confining pressure. Thus the crust is thickened essentially through underplating by tonalitic magmas.

A number of interesting conclusions follow from the above model which have relevance to understanding the Lewisian. The first is that underplating requires that most crustal components pass through a high-grade (upper amphibolite-facies) metamorphic phase before being uplifted by further magmatic underplating. This concurs with the absence of low-grade rocks in the Scourian crust. The second is that the lower crust remains extremely ductile for long periods, consistent with the observed extreme disruption of mafic–ultramafic layers in the Scourian complex, most of which finish up as rounded enclaves in strongly banded gneisses. The third is that material tectonically stripped from the subducting slab (mafic–ultramafic lenses, with or without sediment) may more easily be emplaced into a ductile deep crustal keel. This accords with the relative abundance of such material in the granulite zone of the Lewisian.

Badcallian metamorphism and the problem of 'depleted' granulites

The amphibolite-facies metamorphic assemblages which characterise Lewisian rocks are easily explicable, using the underplating model, either as a primary feature of any high-grade terrain, or as being superimposed, or re-imposed during subsequent Inverian or Laxfordian events. However, the causes and consequences of the Badcallian granulite-facies metamorphism are more difficult to define. Classical models (e.g. Fyfe 1973) and the andesite model for crustal growth (Taylor & McLennan 1981) regard granulites as a lower-crustal residue from which the granodioritic upper crust has been extracted through partial melting. In theory the lower crust

should be more mafic, be low in lithophile elements and carry a positive Eu anomaly. Lewisian granulites indeed have some of these characteristics, but when considered in detail (Weaver & Tarney 1980, 1981a; Rollinson & Fowler, this vol.) such models fall down because it is the silicic component of the gneisses which carries the positive Eu anomaly (see Tarney & Weaver, this vol.). A careful comparison of equivalent rock types in the granulite- and amphibilite-facies terrains of the Lewisian (Weaver & Tarney 1981a) demonstrates that the essential differences lie in the much lower contents of the heat-producing elements K, Rb, Th and U. Hence, although melting is not discounted (Cartwright & Barnicoat, this vol.), it has been more common in recent years to appeal to the removal of these elements along with the fluids expelled during granulite-facies metamorphism. The fact that many granulite terrains contain CO_2-rich fluid inclusions (Hansen *et al.* 1984) has been taken as evidence that CO_2-rich fluids may have played an important role (Tarney & Windley 1977, Tarney *et al.* 1982).

Lewisian granulites probably rank amongst the most 'depleted' of Archaean high-grade terrains in terms of their extremely low contents of U, Th, Rb and K. There are two problems however in accepting either of the above explanations as a reason for this depletion in heat-producing elements. The first is that the complementary K-, Rb-, Th- and U-rich component, supposedly removed, is not very evident in the higher crustal-level sectors of the Lewisian. The second is that the Gruinard gneisses (Rollinson & Fowler, this vol.) appear to have undergone a loss of heat-producing elements but have suffered only hornblende-granulite facies metamorphism. Additionally there are several granulite terrains worldwide which show very little evidence of removal of heat-producing elements. The possibility arises that granulite-facies metamorphism and removal of heat-producing elements are two separate processes that, because they mostly apply to or affect the deeper crust, often coincide. This possibility is explored by Tarney & Weaver (this vol.). In the present context it is worth noting that Sm–Nd mineral data tend to constrain the termination of Badcallian granulite-facies metamorphism at shortly after 2700 Ma (Humphries & Cliff 1982), as do zircon ages (Pidgeon & Bowes 1972) and Pb/Pb whole-rock isochrons for the granulites (Chapman & Moorbath 1977). On the other hand whole-rock Pb/Pb isotope data for Lewisian gneisses (Moorbath *et al.* 1969) and for the amphibolite-facies gneisses in particular (Whitehouse & Moorbath 1986) suggest that uranium loss from the Lewisian gneisses or their igneous precursors occurred at 2900 Ma, which is, within experimental error, the age of generation of the gneisses—both granulite- and amphibolite-facies—based on Sm/Nd isotope systematics (Hamilton *et al.* 1979). The evidence suggests then that the Badcallian granulite-facies metamorphism occurred, or certainly extended, some 200–250 Ma after the time of crust generation.

P-T conditions deduced for the Badcallian event are amongst the highest recorded for granulite terrains. The available data are summarised and discussed by Barnicoat (this vol.), Cartwright & Barnicoat (this vol.) and Sills & Rollinson (this vol.). The highest *P-T* estimates, originally giving temperatures over 1000°C and pressures up to 15 kb, are partly based on mineral data from the late intrusive trondhjemite sheets. However these high temperatures may reflect intrusive temperatures rather than those of metamorphic equilibration, as the trondhjemite sheets appear to have been emplaced near the peak of the Badcallian event (Sills & Rollinson, this vol.). Determinations based on the cores of coarse-grained crystals in mafic rocks also yield high *P-T* estimates (*c*. 950°C and 11 kb) which may indicate peak metamorphic conditions (Cartwright & Barnicoat, this vol.). By contrast, crystal-rim compositions and determinations based on symplectite reactions yield much lower *P-T* estimates (less than 800°C and less than 8 kb), presumably indicating re-equilibration to lower-grade conditions by the end of the Badcallian event. By the start of the Inverian, and before the Scourie dykes were intruded at 2.4 Ga, temperatures in the central granulite zone had fallen to less than 600°C (Sills & Rollinson, this vol.).

The causes of granulite-facies metamorphism are difficult to constrain (Barnicoat, this vol.), but it is a problem that is not specific to the Lewisian. The apparent 200 Ma gap between crustal generation and the peak of granulite-facies metamorphism suggests that the processes of crustal generation are not responsible. There are no obvious major additions of magma at the time of the Badcallian event to supply the thermal energy. Tectonic thickening (Barnicoat, this vol.) may be responsible, but lacks supporting tectonic evidence. Enhanced heat flow to the base of the crust may be a normal consequence of the higher thermal regime in the Archaean (?perhaps accompanied by CO_2 flushing which would encourage dehydration reactions), but high heat flow could also be more specifically connected with the thermal effects of active additions of low-density mantle material to the sub-continental lithosphere.

The Proterozoic evolution of the complex

The Inverian event

Peach *et al.* (1907) and Sutton & Watson (1951) considered that the fundamental chronological break within the Lewisian complex was represented by the intrusion of the Scourie dykes. However it became clear from the work of Tarney (1963), Evans & Tarney (1964), Park (1964), Evans (1965) and Cresswell (1972) that a major tectono-metamorphic event intervened between the granulite-facies Scourian event of the central region and the intrusion of the Scourie dykes. This event was named the Inverian by Evans (1965), and is now generally recognised in the mainland Lewisian. Although Inverian events have not hitherto been specifically described from the Outer Hebrides, it is now recognised that this is probably because of widespread and intense reworking by the later Laxfordian deformations (see Fettes & Mendum, this vol.).

The similarity of style, orientation and metamorphic facies between the Inverian and Laxfordian structures has led to considerable confusion in the past, and structures can only be confidently assigned to one or the other event where Scourie dykes can be seen either to cut or to be deformed by the structures in question. Park (1970) suggested that the division between the early Scourian (Badcallian) and the Inverian represented the major tectonic break within the Lewisian timespan, and this is now regarded as the Archaean–Proterozoic boundary.

Only the Inverian structures of the mainland are described here; those of the Outer Hebrides are not well enough known. The mainland structures may be divided into three categories: (1) broad shear-zones relatively unaffected by Laxfordian reworking, (2) narrow shear-zones cutting the Archaean rocks of the central region, and (3) regions of inferred Inverian high strain now intensely reworked during the Laxfordian.

A major steep NW–SE shear zone of type 1 occurs between Scourie and Loch Laxford, corresponding to the Claisfearn and Foindle zones of Sutton & Watson (1951), and has a minimum width of 4 km (see Beach *et al.* 1974; Davies 1978). On its southwestern side it cuts undeformed Badcallian structures, but on the northeast it is itself affected by strong Laxfordian deformation in the north-eastern part of the Laxford shear zone. A zone of inferred Inverian high strain extends from here to Durness. A second major steep shear zone, the Canisp Shear Zone (see Attfield, this vol.), cuts through the middle of the central block in a WNW–ESE direction. The third major shear zone occurs in the north-eastern part of the southern region between the Gruinard River and Fionn Loch. This steep NW–SE belt is a mirror image of the Claisfearn zone, and on its southwestern side it is overprinted and obscured by the major Laxfordian belt of deformation which extends from here to the south-west limit of the region. The Inverian high-strain zone is probably co-extensive with this belt.

Thus the mainland Lewisian in Inverian times appears to consist of a central stable block, cut by relatively minor steep shear zones and by the rather larger Canisp zone, and bounded on both sides by major steep NW–SE zones (Figs 1 and 2B). Coward & Park (this vol.) suggest that these steep zones link at depth with a major, flat-lying, mid-crustal shear zone which underlies the central block. The sense of movement on these major belts indicates an overall reverse dip-slip (over-thrust) movement with a small dextral component, indicating a dextral transpressional regime (Coward & Park, this vol.).

Reconstitution of Archaean granulite-facies rocks in these Inverian shear zones took place under amphibolite-facies conditions and was accompanied by an influx of volatiles and by metasomatic activity (see Beach 1976, Beach & Tarney 1978). In the central zone considerable retrogression of the granulites took place before the intrusion of the Scourie dykes, but continued on a diminishing scale after dyke intrusion so that the early dykes are more metamorphosed than the later ones (Tarney 1963, 1973). Although minor movement on shear zones took place during dyke metamorphism, this metamorphism was essentially static. Later Laxfordian deformation is largely confined to major pre-existing shear zones.

The timing of the Inverian event has always been difficult to resolve because of the apparent absence of new crustal material of that age, and because of overprinting by the Laxfordian. The only satisfactory constraints on the age are the date of the pre-Inverian pegmatites at Scourie (*c.* 2500 Ma, Giletti *et al.* 1961) and the date of the earlier Scourie dykes (*c.* 2400 Ma; Chapman 1979) which would appear to bracket the Inverian event. However it has been suggested by Moorbath (pers. comm.) that the comparable Greenland Early Proterozoic belts were initiated contemporaneously with the cratonisation of the Archaean complex at *c.* 2700 Ma, and it is possible that a similar situation existed in the Lewisian. The date of 2600 Ma in Table 1 may be regarded as a compromise estimate.

The emplacement of the Scourie dykes and the Loch Maree Group

The emplacement of the Scourie dykes was one of the most remarkable events in the evolution of the Lewisian crust. Huge volumes of mafic magma were emplaced and in certain areas adjacent to the Gairloch supracrustal belt, up to one-third of the surface area of the complex is occupied by these dykes, which for the most part appear to be emplaced dilatationally, implying major crustal extension.

Significant differences in both size and frequency occur throughout the Lewisian complex. The dykes decrease in abundance northwards towards Durness, westwards in the Outer Hebrides, and to the southwest are apparently absent in Coll and Tiree. They are thickest and most numerous between Gruinard Bay and Torridon in the southern region, although they are significantly affected by pre-existing structure, being thinner, more frequent and often sub-concordant within the Inverian shear zones (Park & Cresswell 1972, 1973). In the region south of the Gruinard river, the dykes show clear signs of intrusion under a dextral shear regime (Park *et al.*, this vol.), which may have applied generally in the mainland during the dyke emplacement.

The petrography, geochemistry and petrogenesis of the dykes are dealt with in detail by Tarney and Weaver (this vol.). They define four dyke types on petrological and geochemical grounds: bronzite-picrites, norites, olivine-gabbros and quartz-dolerites, the last being by far the most abundant. The ubiquitous main 'epidiorite' suite of Peach *et al.* (1907) represents the metamorphosed equivalents of these quartz-dolerites. In the central region, where fresh dykes are better preserved, there is evidence of emplacement at depth into hot country rocks.

The dykes typically are enriched in light rare-earth and large-ion lithophile elements, but with prominent negative Nb anomalies: features typical of island arc lavas or crustal material generally (Weaver & Tarney 1981*b*). This 'crustal' trace-element signature cannot however have arisen through contamination with granulite crustal material at the time of intrusion (Tarney & Weaver, this vol.) and the trace-element characteristics are ascribed to inheritance from the sub-continental lithosphere. Geochemical evidence indicates derivation from at least two distinct mantle sources, one more Mg-rich and refractory for the picrites and norites, and the other more Fe-rich and fertile for the olivine-gabbros and quartz-dolerites. Tarney & Weaver suggest that the sub-continental lithosphere may have suffered enrichment in crustal components at or near the time of Lewisian (Badcallian) crustal generation at 2900 Ma. Similar features are apparent in other early Proterozoic dyke swarms and in Phanerozoic flood basalts (Tarney & Weaver, this vol.).

The Rb-Sr date of *c.* 2400 Ma (Chapman 1979) obtained from certain of the large 'epidiorite' (quartz-dolerite) Scourie dykes probably applies to the major part of the swarm. However certain minor dyke types which were considerably less metamorphosed were considered to be younger by Tarney (1963). Two such dykes gave K-Ar ages of *c.* 2000 Ma (Evans & Tarney 1964).

The Loch Maree Group (LMG) is described in summary by Park (1978). It consists of a thick sequence of metavolcanics and metasediments of predominantly metagreywacke type but including minor layers of marble, banded-iron-formation and graphite-schist. The banded-iron-formation has been recently discussed by Al Ameen (1979) and Williams (1984). The original thickness and extent is impossible to determine because of severe Laxfordian deformation, but the minimum thickness is 3 km. The LMG comprises the only supracrustal succession in the Lewisian that has definitely been assigned to the Early Proterozoic, both on structural (Park 1964) and on geochronological grounds (O'Nions *et al.* 1983). The 2000 Ma Sm-Nd model age obtained by O'Nions *et al.* gives a maximum age of derivation of the sediments. If this age also reflects the emplacement of the LMG, then this event may be coeval with the younger Scourie dykes of Evans & Tarney (1964) but is about 400 Ma later than the emplacement of the main swarm. Recent geochemical studies (Johnson *et al.*, in press) have shown that the LMG mafic volcanics have flat rare-earth profiles and primitive chemistry in contrast with the much more chemically evolved Scourie dykes. It is proposed that around 2400 Ma a period of slow crustal extension allowed the emplacement of the main Scourie dyke swarm into the middle regions of the crust, possibly not reaching the surface. Subsequently, and up to 400 Ma later, a period of much more rapid extension was localised in the Gairloch–Loch Maree region, where a much greater degree of lower-crustal thinning was accompanied by upper crustal rifting and basin formation with rapid emplacement of the primitive tholeiitic mafic volcanics (Fig. 2C). Some Scourie dyke-type magma was still available during the later stages of this process, since the supracrustal rocks are cut by minor sills with typical Scourie dyke chemistry.

The Early Proterozoic plutonic igneous complex of South Harris in the Outer Hebrides (Dearnley 1963, Cliff *et al.* 1983), consisting mainly of gabbro, anorthosite and tonalite, also appears to have been emplaced at this time, but has no obvious genetic relationship with the LMG volcanics.

Apart then from the limited rift zone of the Gairloch–Loch Maree district, the present outcrop appears to represent a rather deep crustal level during this period of Lewisian history and no large vertical movements of the crust are required between the mid-crustal Inverian event and the early Laxfordian.

The early Laxfordian events

Most Lewisian workers, following Peach *et al.* (1907) and Sutton & Watson (1951), have used the Scourie dykes as markers to define the beginning of the Laxfordian period. Thus Laxfordian deformation by definition affects Scourie dykes. This simple stratigraphic approach may no longer be valid owing to the length of time (*c.* 2400–2000 Ma) during which the dyke suite may have been emplaced, and the probable existence of coeval deformation suggested by the evidence for shear movements during emplacement (Park *et al.*, this vol.). It is likely therefore that 'Laxfordian' structures affecting earlier members of the dyke suite may pre-date later members (cf. Bowes 1968) although there is no unequivocal structural evidence of this.

The early Laxfordian deformation produces fabrics in the dykes which are associated generally with amphibolite-facies metamorphic recrystallisation. Assemblages appear to represent lower temperatures and higher crustal levels in the central mainland block compared with the northern and southern regions and with the Outer Hebrides. The highest metamorphic grades are represented by the South Harris granulites (Dearnley 1963, Cliff *et al.* 1983). This variation is consistent with the structural evidence which indicates that the central block was at a higher crustal level than the rest of the complex during dyke intrusion and has been moved downwards in relation to the adjoining areas along the boundary shear zones (see Fig. 2B).

The timing of the early deformation is difficult to establish precisely. An upper limit is given by the 2400 Ma age of the early quartz dolerites and a lower limit by the post-tectonic granites and pegmatites dated at ca 1800 Ma (van Breemen *et al.* 1971, Lyon *et al.* 1973) at Laxford. The intense deformation of the Loch Maree Group must be later than 2000 Ma on the basis of the Sm-Nd age of the metasediments discussed above. It is provisionally suggested that the main deformation took place in the interval 2000–1800 Ma.

The Laxfordian structures have been described in detail over much of the Lewisian outcrop by a number of workers. A summary and kinematic interpretation is provided by Coward & Park (this vol.). Many observers have noted the extreme heterogeneity of the Laxfordian structures which is attributed by Coward and Park to their development in a major, mid-crustal shear-zone network which separates and encloses more stable crustal blocks whose relative movement gives rise to the observed structures (Fig. 2D).

The main Laxfordian belts of the mainland are situated in the northern and southern regions; Laxfordian deformation in the central region is restricted to narrow shear zones (see Attfield, this vol.). The Laxfordian of the southern region is summarised by Park *et al.* (this vol.), who attribute the early Laxfordian structure to two phases of deformation, D1 and D2, related to movements on a major sub-horizontal mid-crustal shear-zone which crops out in the southwest, around Kenmore. One branch of this zone descends below the central block by means of inclined shear-zone ramps at Diabaig and Gairloch, and the other branch extends above the central block (see also Coward 1974). The distinction between D1 and D2 is based on evidence of refolding of steep S1 fabrics in the dykes by recumbent F2 folds and flat-lying fabrics at Kenmore and in the hinge zone of the Tollie antiform. The distinction probably reflects progressive deformation as the main shear zone widens.

The orientation of linear fabrics in zones of high strain associated with these deformations is consistently NW–SE to E–W after allowing for the effects of subsequent deformation. This implies that the movement direction in the early Laxfordian has a large component of strike-parallel displacement.

The northern Laxfordian belt occupies the whole of the northern mainland region. The SW margin of Laxfordian deformation occurs within the Laxford shear zone (which was initiated as an Inverian structure) about 4 km north of its SW margin. The Laxfordian shear zone is steeply inclined to the SW in the Laxford area but becomes flat-lying to the NE, although refolded by later Laxfordian folds. The Laxfordian structure of the northern region thus presents a mirror-image of that in the southern region. The inclined shear zones on both sides of the central block appear to show a significant component of dip-slip (extensional) movement during the early Laxfordian deformation. Coward and Park (this vol.) suggest that the strongly convergent dextral compressional regime of the Inverian is replaced during dyke emplacement and early Laxfordian times by a transtensional regime with a strong dextral strike-slip component.

In the Outer Hebrides the structures developed during this period are generally recumbent (Fettes & Mendum, this vol., Coward 1973), and are interpreted as the outcrop of the major shear-zone flat (Coward 1984) which on the mainland is represented only in the north and south.

The granitic injection complexes of Harris, Laxford and the SW mainland region (e.g. Kenmore and Rona) are all clearly post-tectonic to the main early Laxfordian deformations D1 and D2 (Park *et al.* this vol., Fettes & Mendum, this vol.). These injection complexes are spatially and chronologically associated with a period of Laxfordian migmatisation, dated at *c.* 1800 Ma, which is indistinguishable chronologically from the date of the peak Laxfordian metamorphism (Pidgeon 1973). Beach *et al.* (1974) and Coward (1984) relate these local occurrences of migmatisation to movements on the main shear zones. Although assigned to the 'late Laxfordian' by Dearnley (1963), it seems more logical to regard all these chronologically indistinguishable and probably genetically related effects as belonging to the same protracted event, the early Laxfordian.

The later Laxfordian events

Laxfordian upright folds with NW–SE trend are ubiquitous except in the central mainland region. These folds were designated F3 by Coward (1973) in the Outer Hebrides and in the mainland are recognised in the southern region (Park *et al.*, this vol.) and also in the northern region, north of the steep Laxford shear zone (Beach *et al.* 1974). They refold the generally flat-lying early

FIG. 2. Cartoon sections, drawn perpendicular to the strike of the Proterozoic structures, illustrating the possible tectonic evolution of the Lewisian Complex.

(A) The Badcallian gneiss-generating event. (B) The Inverian event. Note that deep-crustal granulites from A are transferred to A'. (C) Emplacement of Scourie dykes and Loch Maree Group (LMG). Extension is oblique to line of section. (D) Laxfordian D1 and D2 events. The movement direction is approximately perpendicular to the line of section. Note that the relative positions of the Outer Hebrides and Mainland sections is speculative, but that the former represents a deeper crustal level. CB—Central Block. (E) The Laxfordian D3 event. The movement direction is oblique to the line of section (there is a strike-slip component on both the Langavat and Gairloch shear zones). Outer Hebrides sections in D and E are after Coward (1984).

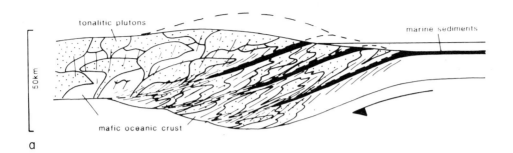

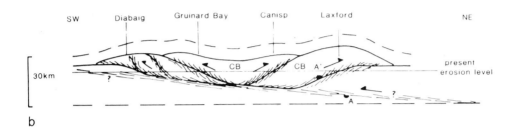

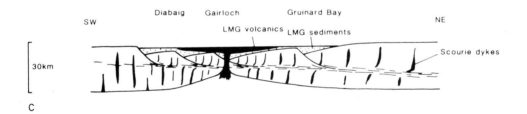

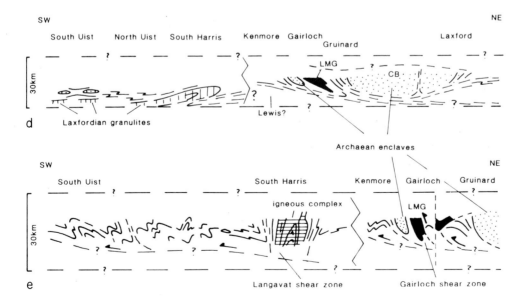

Laxfordian fabrics and recumbent folds (Fig. 2E) and are associated on the mainland with retrogression to greenschist-facies. The major steep NW–SE shear zones of South Harris and Gairloch result from this deformation. Park *et al.* (this vol.) and Coward & Park (this vol.) suggest that the formation of these structures indicates a return to a general dextral transpressional regime, now representing a higher crustal level than in the case of the D1 and D2 structures. The Outer Hebrides folds south of Harris show a general southwestwards vergence, as do those of the southern mainland region. However the northern mainland region exhibits a mirror-image pattern of northeastwards vergence.

The dating of the D3 event at *c.* 1600 Ma on the mainland was based on the widespread evidence of resetting of K–Ar ages in the period 1600–1400 Ma (Moorbath & Park, 1971). The K–Ar ages in the southern mainland region show a considerable spread, with two peaks at 1600 and 1400 Ma, the more heavily retrogressed rocks tending to give the lower ages. However, Fettes & Mendum (this vol.) state that in the Outer Hebrides folds of F3 type are coeval with the 1800 Ma pegmatite sheets. There also appear to be differences in metamorphic facies between the Outer Hebrides and the mainland, which may be attributable to the deeper crustal level of the former. There is thus a possibility that all the D3 events belong to the early Laxfordian period at *c.* 1800 Ma. Alternatively the D3 structures of the southern mainland region may represent a quite separate and later event. A third possibility is that the resetting of K–Ar ages on the mainland may be associated with D4 events.

Abundant but localised steeply-plunging brittle folds and associated crush belts with widespread pseudotachylite development are assigned to D4 by Park *et al.* (this vol.) and are considered to represent a late phase of sinistral strike-slip movements in the southern mainland, provisionally dated at *c.* 1400 Ma. Similar late structures are reported from other parts of the complex, but it is not yet clear whether these represent the same regional event. A second possibility suggested by Park *et al.* is that these late movements may be wholly or partly of Grenville age. Many of the crush-belts are overlain by undisturbed Torridonian rocks, and boulders of pseudotachylite occur in the basal Torridonian conglomerates.

The Outer Hebrides fault zone, described by White & Glasser (this vol.) and Fettes & Mendum (this vol.) is a major crustal dislocation, exhibiting both brittle and ductile characteristics, which is generally considered to be of Caledonian age. However this structure may well have been initiated in late Lewisian time coevally with the late brittle movements described above. Critical geochronological evidence is lacking.

A comparison with other high grade terrains

It is implied by the title of this volume that we believe that the Lewisian complex can best be understood by reference to general Precambrian processes and models, which are often better illustrated in other terrains, and this point is emphasised by Sutton and Watson (this vol.) in their introduction.

Archaean evolution

A remarkable facet of the Archaean is the way essential geological features are repeated on many different Archaean cratons. This applies to high-grade terrains as much as to the greenstone belts, which suggests that similar tectonic processes were operating on a global scale. This can be no better illustrated than by comparisons with a region as far removed from the Lewisian as possible: East Antarctica (Harley & Black, this volume). The granulites of the Napier Complex, Vestfold Block and southern Prince Charles Mountains are broadly similar in age to those of the Lewisian, and equilibrated under similar *P–T* conditions. There is a similar range of rock types, their petrogenesis being in most cases the same as for Lewisian ones (Sheraton & Black 1983, Sheraton & Collerson 1984), and many of the granulites show extreme depletion in the heat-producing elements U, Th, Rb and K. Moreover the complexes are cut by dykes of the same age and petrographic and geochemical character as the Scourie dykes (Sheraton & Black 1981). The main difference is that the uplift/cooling paths of the two complexes are very different (compare Harley & Black (this vol.) with Sills & Rollinson (this vol.)), which reflects the segmentation of the Lewisian and juxtaposition of different crustal levels at the start of the Inverian.

The Lewisian is therefore not unique; indeed similar petrogenetic models to those proposed for the Lewisian (Weaver & Tarney 1980) have been invoked for high-grade terrains in India (Weaver 1980, Condie & Allen 1984) and NE China (Jahn & Zhang 1984) and elsewhere, although not all high-grade granulite terrains show the strong depletion in heat-producing elements which is characteristic of Lewisian granulites. The reasons for this may be, as we have argued earlier, that low concentrations of U, Th, Rb and K may be in part a primary feature of tonalitic magmas emplaced deep in the crust—a feature which may be enhanced by later granulite-facies metamorphism. However, where granulite-facies metamorphism is superimposed on more normal granitic (as opposed to tonalitic) rock types, elemental depletion is more difficult to achieve (Tarney *et al.* 1972).

West Greenland offers the closest comparison to the Lewisian in terms of its magmatic, metamorphic and thermal evolution (Wells 1979). In both regions a strong horizontal thrusting regime accompanied the major phase of crustal generation at *c.* 2·9–3·0 Ga (Bridgwater *et al.* 1974) and resulted in the predominant flat-lying foliation which characterises the Lewisian (Sheraton *et al.* 1973) and much of the West Greenland Archaean (Bridgwater *et al.* 1974).

Early Proterozoic evolution

The Nagssugtoqidian of both East and West Greenland, and the West Nain province of Labrador, which are described by Myers (this vol.) and by Korstgård *et al.* (this vol.) are closely comparable with the Lewisian complex in several important respects. The sequence of early shear zones followed by dyke swarm emplacement and then by the main deformation is common to all four regions, as is the predominance of reworked Archaean rocks, the generally high metamorphic grade, and the rarity of Early Proterozoic granitoid plutons. The whole width of the belt, 240 km, is seen in East Greenland, bordered on both sides by Archaean cratons.

The deformed and metamorphosed Early Proterozoic shelf cover sequences seen in Greenland and Labrador have no recognised counterpart in the Lewisian. The Loch Maree Group however bears some resemblance to the allochthonous Sarfartop Nuna supracrustal sequence near the southern boundary of the belt in West Greenland, and to the Ramah Group in Labrador, both of which may represent products of extensional basins near the margin of the belt.

The Archaean–Early Proterozoic boundary in Labrador differs from that in West Greenland in that the major post-dyke shear zone is strike-slip rather than overthrust, although the sense of movement is not known. Overthrusts and other structures indicating E–W compression are also found in the Labrador belt but their age relationship to the strike-slip shear zone has not been determined.

Coward & Park (this vol.) discuss a kinematic model for the evolution of the Lewisian complex in its North Atlantic setting. The Lewisian lies directly along strike of the Nagssugtoqidian belt of East Greenland, once the effects of Atlantic opening have been removed (see Myers, this vol.) and forms part of a regional system of Early Proterozoic shear zones established at around 2·7–2·6 Ga (Watterson 1978) in the North Atlantic region (see also Korstgård *et al.*, this vol.). Watterson suggested that the orientation and sense of displacement of these zones indicated a general N–S compression. N–S convergence is consistent with the dextral transpressional regime in the Scottish Inverian and with sinistral transpression in the Nag.I phase in West Greenland. However a change to NW–SE convergence is suggested to explain the dominantly overthrust Nag.II regime in West Greenland and the dominantly strike-slip early Laxfordian regime in Scotland. This direction of convergence is also consistent with the major N–S to NNW–SSE strike-slip shear zone in Labrador. A further change to an approximately NNW–SSE convergence direction in Scotland is indicated by the widespread evidence of dextral transpressional movements in the later Laxfordian.

This kinematic synthesis implies a belief that the Early Proterozoic Nagssugtoqidian–Lewisian 'orogenic belt' is primarily due to shear-zone displacements brought about by the relative movements of more stable blocks or cratons, and that the belts are essentially intraplate in nature. Whereas the evidence for this is fragmentary, contrary evidence of subduction-related magmatism is lacking and there is no reason to suspect the existence of a hidden collisional suture either in the Lewisian or, more critically, in East Greenland. However, as Sutton and Watson (this vol.) point out, a quite different regime exists in the coeval Ketilidian belt in South Greenland, which may reflect an Early Proterozoic plate margin, but passing to the south of the present Lewisian outcrop in Scotland.

References

AL-AMEEN, S. I. 1979. Mineralogy, petrology and geochemistry of the banded iron formation, Gairloch, N.W. Scotland. *Unpubl. M.Sc. thesis*, Univ. Keele.

BEACH, A. 1976. The interrelationships of fluid transport, deformation, geochemistry and heat flow in early Proterozoic shear zones in the Lewisian complex. *Phil. Trans. R. Soc London*, **A280**, 569–604.

—— & TARNEY, J. 1978. Major and trace element

patterns established during retrogressive metamorphism of granulite facies gneisses, NW Scotland. *Precambrian Res*, **7**, 325–348.

——, COWARD, M. P. & GRAHAM, R. H. 1974. An interpretation of the structural evolution of the Laxford front. *Scott J Geol*, **9**, 294–308.

BOWES, D. R. 1968. An orogenic interpretation of the Lewisian of Scotland. *XXIII International Geological Congress*, **4**, 225–236.

BREEMAN, O. VAN, AFTALION, M. & PIDGEON, R. T. 1971. The age of the granitic injection complex of Harris, Outer Hebrides. *Scott J Geol*, **7**, 139–152.

BRIDGWATER, D., McGREGOR, V. R. & MYERS, J. S. 1974. A horizontal tectonic regime in the Archaean of Greenland and its implications for early crustal thickening. *Precambrian Res*, **1**, 179–198.

CHAPMAN, H. J. 1979. 2390 Myr Rb-Sr whole rock age for the Scourie dykes of north-west Scotland. *Nature, London*, **277**, 642–643.

—— & MOORBATH, S. 1977. Lead isotope measurements from the oldest recognised Lewisian gneisses of north-west Scotland. *Nature, London*, **268**, 41–42.

CLIFF, R. A., GRAY, C. M. & HUHMA, H. 1983. A Sm-Nd isotopic study of the South Harris igneous complex. *Contrib Mineral. Petrol.*, **82**, 91–98.

CONDIE, K. C. & ALLEN, P. 1984. Origin of Archean charnockites from southern India. *In:* KRONER, A., HANSEN, G. N. & GOODWIN, A. M. (eds) *Archean Geochemistry* (Springer, Berlin), 182–203.

COWARD, M. P. 1973. Heterogeneous deformation in the development of the Laxfordian complex of South Uist, Outer Hebrides. *J geol Soc London*, **129**, 137–160.

—— 1974. Flat lying structures within the Lewisian basement gneiss complex of N.W. Scotland. *Proc geol Assoc London*, **85**, 459–472.

—— 1984. Major shear zones in the Precambrian crust; examples from NW Scotland and southern Africa and their significance. *In:* KRONER, A. & GREILING, S. R. (eds) *Precambrian tectonics illustrated*, Stuttgart. 207–235.

CRESSWELL, D. 1972. The structural development of the Lewisian rocks on the north shore of Loch Torridon, Ross-shire. *Scott J Geol*, **8**, 293–308.

DAVIES, F. B. 1978. Progressive simple shear deformation on the Laxford shear zone, Sutherland. *Proc geol Assoc London*, **89**, 177–196.

DEARNLEY, R. 1962. An outline of the Lewisian complex of the Outer Hebrides in relation to that of the Scottish mainland. *Quart J geol Soc London*, **118**, 143–166.

—— 1963. The Lewisian complex of South Harris; with some observations on the metamorphosed basic intrusions of the Outer Hebrides. *Quart J geol Soc London*, **118**, 243–312.

EVANS, C. R. 1965. Geochronology of the Lewisian basement near Lochinver, Sutherland. *Nature, London*, **207**, 54–56.

—— & TARNEY, J. 1964. Isotopic ages of Assynt dykes. *Nature, London*, **204**, 638–641.

FYFE, W. S. 1973. The granulite facies, partial melting and the Archaean crust. *Phil Trans R. Soc London*, **A273**, 457–462.

GILETTI, B. J., MOORBATH, S. & LAMBERT, R. ST. J. 1961. A geochronological study of the metamor-

phic complexes of the Scottish Highlands. *Quart J geol Soc London*, **117**, 233–264.

HAMILTON, P. J., EVENSEN, N. M., O'NIONS, R. K. & TARNEY, J. 1979. Sm-Nd systematics of Lewisian gneisses: implications for the origin of granulites. *Nature, London*, **277**, 25–28.

HANSEN, E. C., NEWTON, R. C. & JANARDHAN, A. S. 1984. Fluid inclusions in rocks from the amphibolite-facies to charnockite progression in southern Karnataka, India: direct evidence concerning the fluids of granulite facies metamorphism. *J Metamorphic geol*, **2**, 249–264.

HUMPHRIES, F. J. & CLIFF, R. A. 1982. Sm-Nd dating and cooling history of Scourian granulites, Sutherland. *Nature, London*, **295**, 515–517.

JAHN, B-M. & ZHANG, Z. Q. 1984. Archaean granulite gneisses from eastern Hebei province, China: rare-earth geochemistry and tectonic implications. *Contrib Mineral. Petrol.*, **85**, 224–243.

JOHNSON, Y., PARK, R. G. & WINCHESTER, J. A. In preparation. Geochemistry, petrogenesis and tectonic significance of the Early Proterozoic Loch Maree amphibolites. *In:* PHAROAM, T. C., BECKINSALE, R. D. & RICKARD, D. T. *Geochemistry and Mineralization of Proterozoic volcanic suites.* Geol. Soc. Lond. Spec. Publ.

LOWMAN, P. D. 1984. Formation of the earliest continental crust: inferences from the Scourian Complex of Northwest Scotland and geophysical models of the lower continental crust. *Precambrian Res*, **24**, 199–215.

LYON, T. D. B., PIDGEON, R. T., BOWES, D. R. B. & HOPGOOD, A. M. 1973. Geochronological investigation of the quartzofeldspathic rocks of the Lewisian of Rona, Inner Hebrides. *J geol Soc London*, **129**, 389–402.

MOORBATH, S. & PARK, R. G. 1971. The Lewisian chronology of the southern region of the Scottish mainland. *Scott J Geol*, **8**, 51–74.

MOORBATH, S., WELKE, H. & GALE, N. H. 1969. The significance of lead isotope studies in ancient high grade metamorphic basement complexes, as exemplified by the Lewisian rocks of N.W. Scotland. *Earth planet Sci Lett*, **6**, 245–256.

O'HARA, M. J. 1961. Petrology of the Scourie dyke, Sutherland. *Mineralog. Mag*, **32**, 848–865.

—— 1962. Some intrusions in the Lewisian complex near Badcall, Sutherland. *Trans London geol Soc Edinburgh*, **19**, 201–207.

OKEKE, P. O., BORLEY, G. D. & WATSON, J. V. 1983. A geochemical study of Lewisian metasedimentary granulites and gneisses in the Scourie–Laxford area of north-west Scotland. *Mineralog. Mag*, **47**, 1–9.

O'NIONS, R. K., HAMILTON, P. J. & HOOKER, P. J. 1983. A Nd isotope investigation of sediments related to crustal development in the British Isles. *Earth planet Sci Lett*, **63**, 229–240.

PARK, R. G. 1964. The structural history of the Lewisian rocks of Gairloch, Western Ross. *Quart J geol Soc London*, **120**, 397–434.

—— 1970. Observations on Lewisian chronology. *Scott J Geol*, **6**, 379–399.

—— 1978. The Tollie and Gairloch districts (Lewisian). *In:* Barber, A. J. & others (eds) *The Lewisian and*

Torridonian rocks of North-West Scotland (Geologist's Association Guide 21), 59–72.

—— & CRESSWELL, D. 1972. Basic dykes in the early Precambrian (Lewisian) of NW Scotland: their structural relations, conditions of emplacement and orogenic significance. *Reports of the 24th International Geological Congress, Montreal*, **1**, 238–245.

—— & —— 1973. The dykes of the Laxfordian belts. *In*: PARK, R. G. & TARNEY, J. (eds) *The Early Precambrian of Scotland and related rocks of Greenland.* University of Keele, pp. 119–130.

PEACH, B. N., HORNE, J., GUNN, W., CLOUGH, C. T., HINXMAN, L. W. & TEALL, J. J. H. 1907. The geological structure of the north-west Highlands of Scotland. *Mem geol Surv Great Britain*, 668 pp.

PIDGEON, R. T. 1973. Rb-Sr, K-Ar and U-Pb age studies in the Lewisian of Scotland. *In*: PIDGEON, R. T. et al. (eds) *Geochronology and isotope geology of Scotland.* 3rd European Congress of Geochronologists, University of Oxford, D1–12.

—— & BOWES, D. R. 1968. Zircon U-Pb ages of granulites from the central region of the Lewisian, north-west Scotland. *Geol mag*, **109**, 247–258.

SHERATON, J. W. & BLACK, L. P. 1981. Geochemistry and geochronology of Proterozoic tholeiitic dykes of East Antarctica: evidence for mantle metasomatism. *Contrib Mineral. Petrol.*, **78**, 305–317.

—— & —— 1983. Geochemistry of Precambrian gneisses: relevance for the evolution of the East Antarctic Shield. *Lithos*, **16**, 273–296.

—— & COLLERSON, K. D. 1984. Geochemical evolution of Archaean granulite-facies gneisses in the Vestfold Block and comparisons with other Archaean gneiss complexes in the East Antarctic Shield. *Contrib Mineral. Petrol.*, **87**, 51–64.

——, SKINNER, A. C. & TARNEY, J. 1973. Geochemistry of the Scourian gneisses of the Assynt district. *In*: PARK, R. G. & TARNEY, J. (eds) *The Early Precambrian of Scotland and related rocks of Greenland.* University of Keele. pp. 13–30.

SILLS, J. D., SAVAGE, D., WATSON, J. V. & WINDLEY, B. F. 1982. Layered ultramafic-gabbro bodies in the Lewisian of northwest Scotland: geochemistry and petrogenesis. *Earth planet Sci Lett*, **58**, 345–360.

SUTTON, J. & WATSON, J. V. 1951. The pre-Torridonian metamorphic history of the Loch Torridon and Scourie areas in the North-West Highlands and its bearing on the chronological classification of the Lewisian. *Quart J geol Soc London*, **106**, 241–296.

TARNEY, J. 1963. Assynt dykes and their metamorphism. *Nature, London*, **199**, 672–674.

—— 1973. The Scourie dyke suite and the nature of the Inverian event in Assynt. *In*: PARK, R. G. & TARNEY, J. (eds) *The Early Precambrian of Scotland and related rocks of Greenland.* University of Keele. pp. 105–118.

—— & WINDLEY, B. F. 1977. Chemistry, thermal gradients and evolution of the lower continental crust. *J geol Soc London*, **134**. 153–172.

——, SHERATON, J. W. & SKINNER, A. C. 1972. A geochemical comparison of major Archaean gneiss units from North-west Scotland and East Greenland. *Reports of the 24th International Geological Congress, Montreal*, **1**, 162–174.

——, WEAVER, B. L. & WINDLEY, B. F. 1972. Geological and geochemical evolution of the Archaean continental crust. *Revista Brasileira Geociencias*, **12**, 53–59.

TAYLOR, S. R. & McLENNAN, S. M. 1981. The composition and evolution of the continental crust: Rare earth element evidence from sedimentary rocks. *Phil Trans R. Soc London*, **A301**, 381–399.

WATTERSON, J. 1978. Proterozoic intraplate deformation in the light of South-east Asian neotectonics. *Nature, London*, **273**, 636–640.

WEAVER, B. L. 1980. Rare-earth element geochemistry of Madras granulites. *Contrib Mineral. Petrol.*, **71**, 271–279.

—— & TARNEY, J. 1980. Rare-earth geochemistry of Lewisian granulite-facies gneisses, northwest Scotland: implications for the petrogenesis of the Archaean lower continental crust. *Earth planet Sci Lett*, **51**, 279–296.

—— & —— 1981a. Lewisian gneiss geochemistry and Archaean crustal development models. *Earth and Plan Sci Let*, **55**, 171–180.

—— & —— 1981b. The Scourie dyke suite: petrogenesis and geochemical nature of the Proterozoic subcontinental mantle. *Contrib Mineral. Petrol.*, **78**, 175–188.

—— & —— 1983. Chemistry of the sub-continental mantle: inferences from Archaean and Proterozoic dykes and continental flood basalts. *In*: HAWKESWORTH, C. J. & NORRY, M. J. (eds) *Continental Basalts and Mantle Xenoliths.* Shiva Publications, Nantwich, pp. 209–229.

—— & —— 1985. Major and trace element composition of the continental lithosphere. *In*: POLLACK, H. N. & MURTHY, V. R. (eds) *Structure and Evolution of the Continental Lithosphere.* Physics and Chemistry of the Earth, **15**, pp. 39–68.

——, ——, WINDLEY, B. F. & LEAKE, B. E. 1982. Geochemistry and petrogenesis of Archaean metavolcanic amphibolites from Fiskenaesset, S.W. Greenland. *Geochim Cosmochim Acta*, **46**, 2203–2215.

WELLS, P. R. A. 1979. Chemical and thermal evolution of Archaean sialic crust, southern West Greenland. *J Petrol.* **20**, 187–226.

WHITEHOUSE, M. J. & MOORBATH, S. 1986. Pb-Pb systematics of Lewisian gneisses—implications for crustal differentiation. *Nature, London*, **319**, 488–489.

WILLIAMS, P. J. 1986. Petrology and origin of iron-rich silicate-magnetite-quartz rocks from Flowerdale near Gairloch, Western Ross. *Scott J Geol*, **21**, *in press*.

R. G. PARK, Department of Geology, University of Keele, Newcastle, Staffordshire ST5 58G, UK.

J. TARNEY, Department of Geology, University of Leicester, Leicester LE1 7RH, UK.

The evolution of the Lewisian complex in the Outer Hebrides

D. J. Fettes & J. R. Mendum

SUMMARY: The oldest rocks of the Outer Hebrides are a supracrustal sequence of metasediments, metavolcanics and associated layered basics which formed at c. 2900 Ma. These rocks were buried or carried to deep levels in the crust where they were intruded by an extensive series of granodioritic and tonalitic magmas, probably during the period 2800–2900 Ma. These rocks were subjected to the polyphasal Scourian event which led to extensive migmatization, high-grade metamorphism and the development of a pervasive gneissic foliation. The culmination of this event occurred in the period 2600–2700 Ma. The pattern of gneiss types resulting from these events defined a NNE–SSW grain in the rocks which is reflected in the present distribution of metamorphic facies. This pattern, which reflects either original compositional variations or the effects of Scourian metamorphism, has controlled much of the later metamorphic and structural evolution of the Lewisian of the Outer Hebrides.

The late Scourian period was marked by the emplacement of a suite of dioritic intrusions followed by numerous granitic bodies, the two events being separated by a period of deformation. This deformation died out to the extreme SE and did not affect the eastern part of Barra. These intrusive events probably marked the end of crustal formation and the accompanying deformation is the first evidence of the reworking of a crystalline crust with the development of zones or 'augen' of low deformation.

The granitic intrusion was followed by a deformational event which, in the now more rigid crust, resulted in the development of localized steep shear zones in the period 2400–2600 Ma. The later stages of this event coincided with the intrusion of a widespread suite of metadoleritic and metanoritic rocks—the Younger Basics of 'Scourie dyke' age. The overlap of deformational phases from the late Scourian to the early Laxfordian highlights the difficulty of regarding the Scourian–Laxfordian boundary as one of major importance. Also there may well have been a considerable period (c. 400 Ma) of relative crustal stability before the main Laxfordian events.

There is no evidence that the late Scourian shearing events were associated with substantial uplift, although geochronological evidence from S Harris (Cliff et al. 1983) does suggest a gradual uplift and cooling, at least in that area, at about this time. Certainly the early Laxfordian events appear to have been deep-seated. The intrusion of the late Laxfordian granites at c. 1700 Ma and the associated deformation signalled the first movements which led to substantial uplift, thrusting and unroofing of the complex.

The geological history draws attention to the interesting evolution of deformational style and the generation of lineaments with the changes in crustal level. Features such as the Langavat belt of S Harris may result from an early Scourian lineament that has been re-activated many times. In general the Scourian gneiss terrains are broad zones with localized sub-vertical shear zones only becoming established in the late Scourian. The Laxfordian is typified by such zones of reworking, accompanying recrystallization commonly under hydrous conditions. Ductile shear zones are found, although on a local scale the deformation pattern is typically heterogeneous. After the late Laxfordian granitic intrusion the deformation became localized in restricted mylonite zones or along brittle thrusts. The Caledonian reactivation and faulting is largely controlled by the position of this major thrust zone, with mylonization and related low-grade alteration overprinting the late Laxfordian thrust features.

Introduction

The Outer Hebrides, covering nearly 3000 km², comprise by far the largest area of Lewisian rocks exposed in the British Isles. The study of the geological evolution of the area, therefore, provides a major contribution to the understanding of the Lewisian complex. Despite its major importance the Outer Hebrides received little systematic mapping or detailed examination (apart from notable contributions from Jehu &

Craig 1923, 1925, 1926, 1927, 1934 and Dearnley 1962, 1963) until a joint project was carried out in the 1970s by BGS in collaboration with Prof. Janet Watson and her students (Imperial College, London). The results of that work are contained in 4 maps at 1:100 000 (published 1981) and an accompanying memoir (Fettes et al. in press). This paper draws largely on data that arose from the joint project.

Broadly speaking, the geological history of the Lewisian of the Outer Hebrides is comparable to

From: PARK, R. G. & TARNEY, J. (eds), 1987, Evolution of the Lewisian and Comparable
Precambrian High Grade Terrains, Geological Society Special Publication No. 27, pp. 27–44.

that of the mainland and the same overall terminology is used. A list of the main events is given in Table 1.

The rocks of the complex can be divided into a number of major lithological groups: firstly, a series of metasediments and metabasic rocks which together with the quartzo-feldspathic gneiss and their associated intrusives form the fundamental complex; secondly, a series of basic and ultrabasic intrusives (the Younger Basics) of 'Scourie dyke' age, and thirdly, the granitic complexes of late Laxfordian age. It is the

TABLE 1. *The main Lewisian events in the Outer Hebrides*

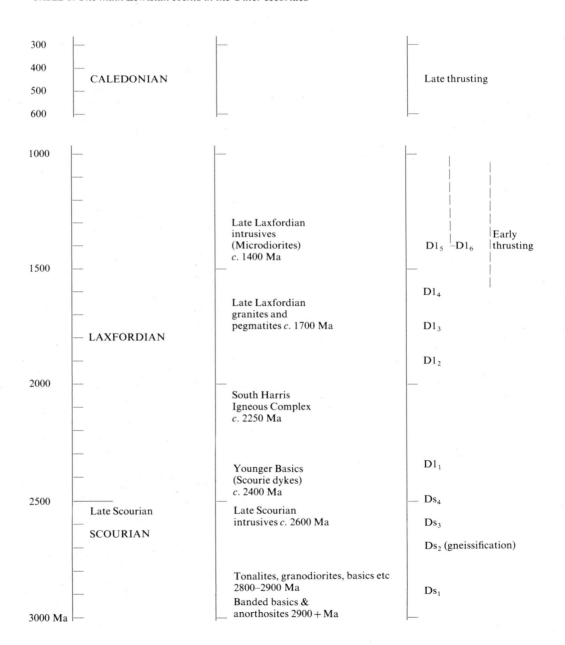

purpose of this paper to examine the data provided by these groups on the evolution of the Lewisian. The South Harris Igneous Complex is not considered here because it is anomalous and its nature and evolution do not relate simply to the adjoining Lewisian terrain. The Corodale Gneiss (Coward 1972) is also omitted because its age, history and original relationships to the other groups are still uncertain.

Formation of the early complex

Before considering the early evolution of the Lewisian rocks and the formation of the gneiss complex it is necessary to examine the nature of the two fundamental units as seen at the present time.

Scattered throughout the islands, but most common in the Uists and Harris (Fig. 1), are the remnants of a supracrustal sequence (Coward *et al.* 1969, Fettes *et al.* in press). This group has its greatest development in the Langavat and Lever- burgh belt flanking the South Harris Igneous Complex. They comprise a series of quartzites, marbles, graphitic schists, kyanite-garnet-pelitic schists, quartzo-feldspathic gneisses and fine- grained interbanded amphibolites (interpreted as meta-volcanics). These rocks have been described by, among others, Dearnley (1963), Myers (1968) and Dickinson & Watson (1976). Outside South Harris the group is most commonly observed as a series of rusty weathering schists characteristi- cally rich in biotite and garnet with locally kyanite-sillimanite- and orthoamphibole-bearing assemblages. These normally occur as thin (2– 3 m) bands or lenses with an along-strike length of only a few tens of metres but concentrated in zones traceable for several kilometres. In addition to these rather exotic rock types there are large areas of fine-grained hornblendic quartzo-feld- spathic gneisses and flaggy quartz-rich rocks of possible sedimentary parentage. The Ness assem- blage of Watson (1969) belongs to this latter group as also does a broad belt trending ENE– WSW across N Uist. Commonly associated with this supracrustal sequence is a suite of banded metabasics which, like the metasediments, are found as scattered lenses, bands and sheets within the gneiss, with individual bodies being only a few tens of metres in size but traceable along strike for considerable distances. These basics, which are particularly well-seen on the west coasts of Benbecula and S Uist, show a character- istic banding on all scales from centimetres up to metres and range in composition from ultramafic to anorthositic. The mineralogy ranges from hornblende-garnet-(clinopyroxene) with subsidi- ary plagioclase (locally confined to coronas on

garnet) through to plagioclase with subsidiary hornblende. The textures are wholly metamor- phic, commonly near equigranular, and although the layering is regarded as representing modified igneous layering no relict cumulate textures have been observed. Overall the chemistry shows the suite to be *Q*-normative with a strong iron- enriched trend typical of modern tholeiites (Table 2).

The quartzo-feldspathic gneisses show a broad homogeneity throughout the islands. They are largely biotite- and hornblende-biotite acid gneisses, but rare occurrences of pyroxene- bearing gneiss are found on the east coast of Barra and adjacent islands to the north (*eg* Fuday), and in a small area on S Uist (Coward 1973). The gneisses contain a wide variety of ultrabasic, basic and acid intrusions and also show a variable degree of migmatization. The majority of the gneisses are typified by the assemblage plagioclase-quartz-biotite-(horn- blende)-(potash feldspar) but range from grano- blastic textured plagioclase-quartz-clinopyrox- ene-(orthopyroxene)-hornblende rocks common in NE Barra to schistose plagioclase-quartz-blue green hornblende-biotite assemblages, particu- larly common in NW Lewis. Chemically the gneisses are granodioritic or tonalitic in compo- sition comparable to the Laxfordian areas of the mainland (Table 2). In detail Fettes *et al.* (in press) have shown that on Lewis and Harris the gneiss chemistry shows a systematic variation from SSE–NNW in certain element ratios (Fig. 2), ie an increase in K/Ba and a decrease in K/ Rb, Ca/Sr, Ca/Y and Ba/Rb values. Restricted analytical data for the Uists indicate that the gneisses are more depleted in lighter elements than those of eastern Lewis and Harris with higher K/Rb, Ba/Rb, Ca/Sr and Ca/Y values and lower K/Sr, K/Ba, Rb/Sr and Ba/Sr ratios. In some respects the Uist gneisses have a chemistry intermediate between the gneisses of Lewis and Harris and the Scourian block of the mainland (Table 2). Fettes *et al.* (in press) infer that this pattern of higher values of lithophile elements in the north and east was in existence before the Scourian migmatization and represents a funda- mental feature of the crust. Whatever the cause, by the end of the Scourian the Lewisian complex of the Outer Hebrides had developed a strong NNE–SSW grain which then exerted a strong influence on the subsequent evolution of the area.

This NNE–SSW grain is also reflected in the variation of gravity throughout the islands (McQuillin & Watson 1973) which shows an increase in density towards the south and east (Fig. 1). The same pattern is also echoed in the metamorphic grades currently exhibited by the

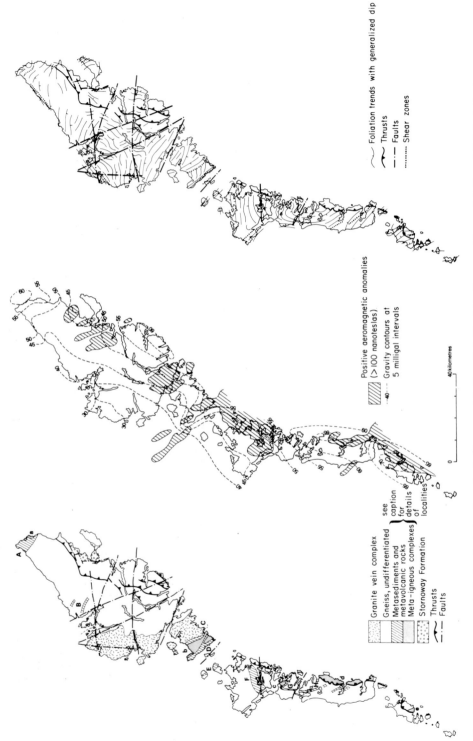

Fig. 1. Sketch maps to show principal geological and geophysical features of the Outer Hebrides (after Fettes *et al.* in press). Left, main lithological units: metasedimentary and metavolcanic rocks; A, Ness; B, Laxavat; C, Langavat; D, Leverburgh; E, Sound of Harris; F, N Uist; G, Benbecula; H, S Uist; meta-igneous complexes; a, Ness; b, S Harris; c, Market Stance; d, Corodale Gneiss; e, E Barra. Centre, main geophysical features (after McQuillin & Watson, 1973). Right, main structural features.

TABLE 2. *Analyses of representative rocks of the Lewisian complex*

	1	2	3	4	5	6	7		8	9	10	11	12	13	14
SiO_2	68.72	68.00	67.1	69.4	61.22	75.0	70.9	SiO_2	51.4	47.0	55.6	60.10	54.39	50.21	51.7
TiO_2	0.32	0.36	0.34	0.4	0.54	0.10	0.28	TiO_2	1.5	1.20	1.90	0.66	0.29	1.46	2.0
Al_2O_3	15.07	15.29	15.48	14.7	15.64	13.6	14.0	Al_2O_3	13.0	18.29	17.6	18.68	7.30	13.57	14.4
Fe_2O_3	0.73	1.70	1.26	0.9	3.07	0.6	1.0	Fe_2O_3	3.7	4.14	3.0	2.43	0.63	3.60	5.4
FeO	1.87	1.65	2.38	2.1	2.57	0.6	1.5	FeO	11.1	6.40	5.6	2.06	8.13	10.17	6.7
MnO	0.04	0.04	0.05	0.05	0.08	0.03	0.3	MnO	0.25	0.14	0.09	0.04	0.18	0.25	0.17
MgO	1.19	1.20	1.44	1.6	3.36	0.2	0.52	MgO	5.3	5.77	2.8	1.11	19.88	5.86	4.2
CaO	2.29	3.51	4.81	3.1	5.57	1.2	1.42	CaO	9.8	8.46	5.2	2.63	6.49	9.63	6.5
Na_2O	4.27	4.20	4.62	4.4	4.42	3.8	3.7	Na_2O	1.8	3.83	4.7	4.22	1.25	2.65	3.2
K_2O	2.70	2.27	1.5	2.0	1.03	5.0	5.2	K_2O	0.4	1.73	2.5	6.34	0.26	0.84	2.7
P_2O_5	0.11	0.13	—	0.1	0.18	0.02	0.09	P_2O_5	0.12	0.49	0.88	0.24	0.04	0.13	1.6
CO_2	—	—	—	—	—	—	—	CO_2	—	0.45	—	0.15	0.06	—	—
Ba	797	787	809	795	757	409	1191	Ba	48	1100	1272	3500	105	199	1719
Ce	—	—	—	65	48	—	—	Ce	—	—	—	—	—	—	—
Co	28	19	66	35	—	20	22	Co	72	40	35	23	90	67	35
Cr	39	25	26	<50	88	52	34	Cr	138	25	1	<10	2650	128	61
Cu	31	15	25	35	—	6	11	Cu	119	65	58	27	35	173	69
Ga	12	10	15	15	—	18	12	Ga	14	24	18	18	9	7	22
La	53	50	43	55	20	28	132	La	0	—	137	—	—	7	142
Li	29	14	22	—	—	16	20	Li	—	10	1	8	16	15	49
Mo	—	—	—	—	—	—	—	Mo	—	—	0	—	—	—	0
Nb	—	—	—	4	5	—	—	Nb	—	—	—	—	—	—	—
Ni	17	21	23	25	58	7	3	Ni	87	41	15	<10	440	78	39
Pb	19	46	6	—	13	23	17	Pb	0	—	0	—	—	120	0
Rb	122	83	41	85	11	462	288	Rb	8	—	102	—	14	27	92
Sr	564	466	370	530	569	125	334	Sr	158	1100	1282	950	95	222	1341
V	—	—	—	—	—	—	—	V	—	180	173	82	155	352	214
Y	8	7	11	—	9	8	10	Y	32	—	18	—	5	22	35
Zn	48	71	35	45	—	28	45	Zn	101	—	140	—	60	121	140
Zr	171	176	185	135	202	120	357	Zr	191	100	847	300	40	125	310
								CIPW norm							
K/Rb	188	257	309	195	763	90	150	Q	8.55	—	3.79	4.77	0.20	1.58	5.93
K/Sr	59.9	57.6	25.11	31.3	15.5	332	125	or	2.36	10.22	14.77	37.46	1.54	4.96	15.95
K/Ba	41.0	28.9	15.69	20.9	11.3	101	36	ab	15.22	25.36	39.75	35.69	10.57	22.41	27.06
Rb/Sr	0.31	0.22	0.11	—	0.19	3.70	0.86	an	26.21	27.61	19.55	10.53	13.54	22.66	16.96
Ba/Rb	6.8	9.9	19.7	9.4	68	0.88	4.14	c	—	—	—	1.02	—	—	—
Ca/Sr	43	54	61	—	70	68	30	ne	—	3.81	—	—	—	—	—
Ba/Sr	1.71	1.92	0.79	—	1.3	—	—	di	17.97	9.0	0.41	—	14.69	20.03	3.91
Ca/Y	3068	3817	3125	—	4400	—	—	hy	19.56	—	11.60	3.52	56.75	18.44	13.42
								ol	—	12.02	—	—	—	—	—
								mt	5.37	6.00	4.35	3.52	0.91	5.22	7.83
								il	2.85	2.28	3.61	1.25	0.55	2.77	3.80
								ap	0.28	1.16	2.09	0.57	0.09	0.31	3.79

Analyses from Fettes *et al.* (in press) unless stated otherwise. (1) and (2) include data from Soldin (1978) and Skinner (1970). 1) Average of 31 analyses of quartzo-feldspathic gneiss from Lewis and Harris west of grid easting [NB 1100]. 2) Average of 118 analyses of quartzo-feldspathic gneiss from Lewis and Harris east of grid easting [NB 1100]. 3) Average of 5 analyses of quartzo-feldspathic gneiss from S Uist. 4) Estimated average of gneiss from Laxfordian areas of the mainland (Bowes 1972). 5) Average of 254 gneisses from the Drumbeg area of the mainland Scourian (Tarney *et al.* 1972). 6) Average of 18 leucogranites ($SiO_2 > 74.0\%$) from the Uig Hills, Lewis. 7) Average of 59 granites ($SiO_2 < 74.0\%$) from the Uig Hills, Lewis. 8) Average of 5 banded basics. 9) Late-Scourian microdiorite dyke (pl-hbl-bi). Leanish, Barra. 10) Late-Scourian microdiorite dyke (pl-bi-hbl-qz). Kilbride, S Uist. 11) Late-Scourian 'granitic' vein (pl-kf-bi-hbl-qz). Earsary, Barra. 12) 'Norite' of the Younger Basic suite (opx-cpx-bi-hbl-pl). Lundale, Lewis. 13) Average of 24 metadolerites of the Younger Basic suite. 14) Late-Laxfordian quartz-microdiorite dyke (hbl-pl-bi). Garry-a-siar, Benbecula.

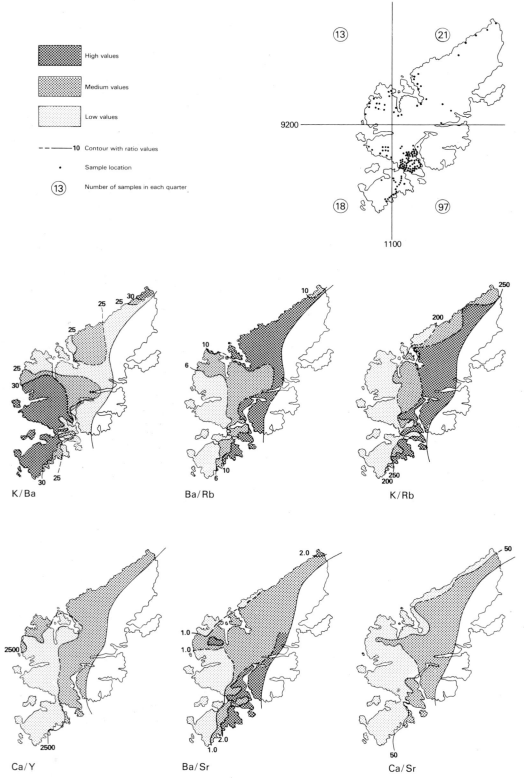

FIG. 2. Distribution of various elemental ratios, showing low, medium and high range values. The top map shows the number of samples within each quarter. See text for explanation. After Fettes *et al.* (in press).

gneisses; with granulite facies assemblages confined to the south and east. It is interesting to consider how fundamental the metamorphic pattern is and how it may relate to the variations in the gneiss chemistry. Two alternative metamorphic sequences seem possible: 1) the gneisses were originally all metamorphosed to granulite facies during the Scourian (or early Laxfordian) and subsequently downgraded, 2) the chemical differences reflect the restriction of Scourian granulite facies conditions to the south and east.

The chemistry of the gneisses in Lewis and Harris are relatively rich in lithophile elements and thorium (Tarney *et al.* 1972) which seems to argue against their having been subjected to high-grade conditions with accompanying depletion, unless subsequent uniform downgrading and re-introduction of elements is argued. Perhaps the strongest argument against regional granulite facies conditions in the north, however, lies in the data presented by Moorbath *et al.* (1975). These indicate that the gneisses of S Uist suffered extreme depletion during the Scourian unlike the gneisses in N Uist. This may be taken to indicate that granulite facies conditions may have extended northwards from Barra to S Uist, the latter subsequently being downgraded. It should be emphasized that these conclusions are based solely on the evidence from the gneisses, because the Leverburgh metasediments do show evidence of granulite facies conditions, presumably related to anomalous conditions associated with the South Harris Igneous Complex. It is possible that the Scourian migmatites in the north and west resulted in part from some enrichment in lithophiles as a consequence of fluid migration from areas undergoing granulitic facies conditions.

The relative age of the supracrustals and the banded basics to the host gneisses is not clearly demonstrated in the Outer Hebrides. Coward *et al.* (1969) suggested that the metasedimentary rocks were closely associated with basic rocks and might represent hornfelses. However, although there is a general association of the two rock types in their mode of occurrence they are by no means always found together. The supracrustal lenses and bands commonly have sharp across-strike contacts with the gneisses even where the latter are highly migmatitic. Along strike, however, the metasediments may pass into the gneisses, an observation which indicated an age prior to the main Scourian events to Coward *et al.* (1969). Also, on the west coast of S Harris the metasediments on the north edge of the Langavat belt appear to pass northwards into Scourian migmatites (Myers pers. comm.); similar relationships can also be seen on the east coast NE of Finsbay. The banded basic rocks

locally show evidence of deformation and migmatization and in two such cases they are cut by Younger Basics, at Sloc Dubh on L Eynort (M. P. Coward pers. comm.) and at Roneval in S Uist (Fettes *et al.* in press). On N Harris about 1 km SW of Loch Chliostair [NB 055 085] anorthosite relics from a layered basic sequence occur in Scourian migmatitic gneisses which are discordantly intruded by members of the Younger Basic suite (Myers pers. comm.)

This general association of metasediments and banded basics both in their spatial coincidence, and the fact that they predate the Scourian migmatization, is reminiscent of relationships seen on the mainland (Davies 1974; Davies & Watson 1977) and in the Fiskenaesset region of Greenland (Windley *et al.* 1973; Myers 1976). This comparison is regarded as valid even though there are major chemical differences between the layered basics of the Outer Hebrides and those of Fiskenaesset. The former are Q-normative, iron-enriched tholeiites (Table 2) the latter *ol*-normative with a calc-alkaline trend (Myers 1975). The comparison leads to the conclusion that the supracrustals and the associated basics are the oldest part of the Outer Hebrides complex. This follows from observations in Greenland by Myers (1976, 1978) of a deformed supracrustal and layered gabbro sequence invaded by notably abundant subconcordant sheets and vein networks of tonalite and granodiorite, these latter intrusions subsequently becoming gneissic. Myers (1978) suggested that such rocks in Greenland formed, and were deformed and migmatized in the period 2800–3000 Ma. Similar conclusions were reached by Moorbath *et al.* (1975) who suggested that the parents of the Outer Hebrides gneisses were derived from upper mantle sources at *c.* 2800 Ma. Like their Greenland analogues, therefore, the supracrustal rocks found in the Outer Isles are most probably large xenolithic relicts within the granitoid orthogneisses.

The exact nature of the igneous parents of the Hebridean gneisses is not known; there was almost certainly a series of intrusive events probably separated by deformational phases and/ or periods of metamorphic recrystallization. The supracrustal sequence was originally deposited at the surface, although the nature of the basement at this stage is unclear. It also follows from the high degrees of migmatization and the metamorphic grade associated with the main Scourian events that by that stage the rocks were at considerable depths in the crust. The crustal level or levels at which the gneiss parents were intruded is also unknown, although the models of Windley & Weaver suggest that the rocks may have been deeply buried during the intrusive events. Fettes *et al.* (in press) suggest that their first Scourian deformational phase (Ds_1) is confined to the supracrustal sequence, that is, predating the gneiss parental intrusions. It may therefore be that these structures in the metasediments are the only relics of the burial mechanism. Similar effects were widespread across the North Atlantic craton at this time. The second Scourian deformational phase (Ds_2 of Table 1) was a major Scourian event. It was accompanied by extensive recrystallization and migmatization, and resulted in the development of the gneissic foliation. The event was polyphasal and accompanied by a sequence of acid veining, veins being folded and cut by later veins in a poorly documented but undoubtedly complex sequence of agmatization, deformation, migmatization *etc.* Despite, or perhaps because of the general intensity of this event no major structures of this age have been identified.

By the end of the Scourian the early evolution of the Lewisian complex of the Outer Hebrides was largely complete. It had acquired the fundamental characteristics which were to persist in varying degrees through the subsequent events, and were to control the nature of those events. Significant in this pattern was the zone of granulite facies rocks to the SE which subsequently resisted much of the reworking; in contrast the relatively potash-rich gneisses of the NW were susceptible to considerable recrystallization and remobilization.

Modification of the complex in the late Scourian

The late Scourian is marked by two widespread, but not abundantly developed, suites of intrusives. The first group is a series of diorites, monzodiorites and microdiorites, the second comprises potash-rich granites, monzonites and pegmatites. The mineralogy of the diorite dykes varies from plagioclase-hornblende-biotite-quartz-(clinopyroxene) to plagioclase-hornblende-potash feldspar-quartz. Chemically they range from Q-normative to *ne*-normative with typical alkaline trends. The granites consist of potash feldspar-plagioclase-quartz-biotite and are chemically similar to syenites. Although members of the two series have been identified at localities throughout the islands, occurring as both major and minor intrusives (Fig. 1) their relationships are best seen in the eastern part of Barra where Laxfordian reworking is particularly low. Here a number of 'dioritic' dykes of 20 cm to 1 m width cut the gneissic foliation. These dykes are cut by a number of pegmatitic veins which are in turn cut by members of the 'Younger

Basic' swarm. The pegmatites have yielded a Rb–Sr whole rock age of 2610 ± 50 Ma (Moorbath *et al.* 1975). To the north, on the Isle of Fuday, a thin (5 cm) dioritic dyke is folded together with the gneiss foliation and is cut by an undeformed 10 cm 'Younger Basic' dyke. Nearby, at Rudha Carraigchrom, a folded dioritic dyke with a pronounced axial fabric is cut by a discordant 'Younger Basic' dyke. These exposures conclusively demonstrate a distinct episode of folding (dying out or absent in E Barra) separating the dioritic and granitic intrusions. Elsewhere in the islands highly deformed dykes and major bodies of diorite are found, although the relative age of deformation is less clearly seen. In the Uists and islands to the north members of the granitic suite are locally quite abundant and may be traced in zones for considerable distances. They are mainly augen granites and granitic gneisses. Two important localities can be examined in N Uist; at Beinn Bhreac several lenses of granitic gneiss, locally with feldspar augen, are cut by members of the 'Younger Basic' suite, and on the small island of Hulmetray [NF 981 752] on the south side of the Sound of Harris a 2 m 'Younger Basic' dyke cuts the dominant planar fabric in a granitic gneiss. This again shows that a phase of deformation occurred following granitic intrusion and before the intrusion of the 'Younger Basics'.

Fettes *et al.* (in press) identify two deformational episodes associated with the late Scourian; both evidenced by regional scale structures. The first (Ds_3) produced a series of asymmetric folds with long limbs oriented approximately NNE–SSW and the second (Ds_4) produced a number of sub-vertical shear zones generally oriented NW–SE, but locally also NE–SW. The relationships of the deformational events noted above and associated with the intrusive phases to the regional Ds_3 and Ds_4 is unknown, although it is tempting to equate Ds_3 with the post-dioritic pre-granite event and Ds_4 with the post-granite pre-'Younger Basic' event. This would bracket the Ds_4 event between 2600 Ma and *c.* 2400 Ma (Table 1) and mark it as a correlative of the Inverian of the mainland. This view receives support from the observation that a number of the 'Younger Basic' dykes are intruded into the Ds_4 shear zones during their later stages of movement.

The dioritic dykes in Barra contain hornblende-biotite-(-clinopyroxene) indicative of sub-granulite facies conditions. This implies that the Ds_3 and Ds_4 events may have accompanied a general uplift of the crust and also indicates the absence of Laxfordian granulite facies metamorphism in that region. The absence of extensive late Scourian deformation in E Barra also suggests that even at this early stage the area was acting as a rigid block. This period also appears to mark a change from the regionally penetrative deformation of Ds$_2$ to a tectonic regime where strain was becoming localized in linear belts.

The 'Younger Basic' (Scourie dyke) Suite

Throughout the Outer Hebrides there is a series of basic and ultrabasic intrusions believed to form part of a widely developed Proterozoic dyke suite intruded at *c.* 2200–2400 Ma that is present in basement rocks adjacent to the North Atlantic. This suite encompasses the Scourie dykes of the mainland. In the Hebrides the suite has been termed the 'Younger Basics' by Fettes *et al.* (in press) to differentiate it from the 'Older Basics' of Scourian age. The 'Younger Basics' fall into three broad groups; 1) a series of ultrabasic bodies, 2) a suite of noritic and picritic rocks termed by Fettes *et al.* (in press) the 'Cleitichean Beag' dykes, and 3) an abundant series of metadolerites.

The first group consists largely of peridotites with subordinate dunites. They are found as characteristic yellow-weathering lenses with thin altered margins. They are generally massive and their relationship to the deformational fabrics in the host gneisses cannot normally be determined. The second group, or 'Cleitichean Beag' dykes, are exemplified by the massive dyke at Cleitichean Beag which was described by Jehu and Craig (1934) and Dearnley (1963). It has a two pyroxene-(olivine)-hornblende-plagioclase-ore assemblage and has been dated at 2400 ± 60 Ma by Lambert *et al.* (1970). The dykes or lenses tend to concentrate in two E–W belts in Lewis and Harris. Chemically the suite is *ol*-normative and broadly similar to the norites and picrites of the mainland (Tarney 1973). The third group of metadolerites are the most abundant representatives of the Younger Basic suite. They occur in a wide variety of modes and deformational states varying from concordant sheets and lenses to discordant dykes. On average they are 2–3 m wide and appear to have had original E–W to NW–SE trends. They are composed typically of *Q*-normative to *ol*-normative continental tholeiites (Table 2) with strong iron-enriched trends. Fettes *et al.* (in press) present data which shows that the original chemistry of the dykes has not been greatly altered during the subsequent Laxfordian metamorphic events.

The relative age of the three groups is uncertain. Good examples of metadolerites cutting the 'Cleitichean Beag' dykes can be seen (*eg* at Lundale [NB 181 3261]) but the relationship of these two groups to the ultrabasics is uncertain.

As mentioned above, at least the early metadolerite dykes were intruded into tectonically active shear zones. Excellent examples of this can be seen at Aird Fenish in W Lewis and on the SE coast of Barra. There are, however, fewer examples in the Outer Hebrides of dykes intruded into active shear zones than can be seen on the mainland. Fabrics in the dykes that are associated with the shearing have been ascribed by Fettes *et al.* (in press) to the first Laxfordian deformational event (Dl$_1$) on the strict definition of all post-Scourie dyke age deformation as Laxfordian. Obviously however, Dl$_1$ as defined, is equivalent to the waning stages of Ds$_4$.

One of the most intriguing features of the dykes is the variety of textures and mineral assemblages that they exhibit; this results in part from their intrusion at deep crustal levels (O'Hara 1961, Tarney 1973, cf. Dearnley 1973) and in part from subsequent reworking. Following their intrusion into hot crust, the dykes quenched with the co-precipitation of clinopyroxene and plagioclase to produce ophitic or sub-ophitic textures. They then began immediately to recrystallize to equigranular metamorphic assemblages. In the centres of the largest dykes, recrystallization was only partial, and large laths of plagioclase and clinopyroxene can still be identified. Garnet (average composition—Al$_{60}$ An$_2$ Gr$_{18}$ Py$_{16}$ Sp$_4$) commonly crystallized at the plagioclase–pyroxene interface and metamorphic pyroxene (salite and ferro-hyperssthene) appeared as small grains within the large igneous crystals. In the smaller dykes recrystallization was complete with the formation of two-pyroxene and garnet-clinopyroxene assemblages and the modal amount of amphibole increased towards the margins. Fettes *et al.* (in press) point out that some of the equigranular clinopyroxenes have compositions very close to the large igneous crystals. They suggest that some of the equigranular 'metamorphic' crystals may represent direct crystallization from the residual igneous melts in accord with the ideas of Lambert *et al.* (1970) and Park & Cresswell (1973) for clinopyroxene coronas on olivine, and garnet coronas on pyroxenes, respectively. It is argued by Fettes *et al.* (in press) and Francis (1973) that the host gneisses were never above upper amphibolite facies and that the two-pyroxene assemblages reflect relatively dry recrystallization. On this model the increasing amounts of modal hornblende towards the dyke margins reflect an increasing degree of equilibration with the host rocks. This process of amphibolitization was facilitated by recrystallization and deformation during the Laxfordian, and the degree of initial equilibration is now unknown, although it is probable that some of the thinner dykes recrystallized immediately after intrusion to equigranular hornblende-plagioclase assemblages. Fettes *et al.* (in press) have shown that most of the metadolerites plot in the clinopyroxene–hornblende–plagioclase field on ACF plots close to the hornblende–plagioclase tie line. This would agree with the observation that hornblende-clinopyroxene-plagioclase is a more common stable assemblage than hornblende-garnet-plagioclase. The composition of the plagioclase also varies with the assemblage. The original igneous laths show values of An_{70-90} but with the trend towards hornblende-plagioclase assemblages, the feldspar shows a trend towards an average value of An_{30}.

Fettes *et al.* (in press) present analyses of scapolite and plagioclase from 'Younger Basic' dykes. The specimens commonly show internally consistent values implying that in general equilibrium was attained. The more calcic scapolites with meionite (Me) values ranging from 50% to 75% are in equilibrium with plagioclase in the range An_{44} to An_{61}. There is considerable within-sample variation but there is a crude linear pattern between An value and % Me for these higher metamorphic grade specimens.

Below Me_{50} there is a uniform rapid decrease in An content of plagioclase from An_{50} to An_{29} but only a small concomitant decrease in Me value from Me_{52} to Me_{41}.

TABLE 3. *Structural history*

Age	
	Movements on Outer Hebrides Thrust Zone (c. 450 Ma) Mylonite formation and retrogression
Dl_5–Dl_6	Formation of open warps, restricted cataclasis and local mylonite development. Initiation of thrusting on Outer Hebrides Thrust Zone. Main pseudotachylite formation.
Dl_4	Deformation of restricted extent.
Dl_3	Regional penetrative deformation, steep (mainly NW) axial planes.
Dl_2	Regional penetrative deformation, gently-inclined axial planes.
Dl_1 / Ds_4	Opening of dyke fractures, early fabric in dykes / Major shear zones
Ds_3	Large asymmetrical folds
Ds_2	Regional ductile deformation, development of gneisses
Ds_1	Penetrative deformation in supracrustal gneisses and associated basic rocks.

After Fettes *et al.* in press.

The former steep trend is thought to reflect the varying *PT* conditions at which the igneous material patchily equilibrated with the adjacent gneisses; generally around uppermost amphibolite conditions. The latter decrease in An content with a small decrease in Me content accords with the degree of retrogression seen in the general mineralogy of the specimens. This implies a change from upper to lower amphibolite facies, probably accompanying the Laxfordian event.

The ambient conditions at the time of intrusion have been given by Fettes *et al.* (in press) as c. 700°C and 6–7kb, equivalent to depths of c. 25 km. There is no significant difference between values for Lewis, Harris and the Uists suggesting that the dykes may have been intruded at the same overall structural level throughout the Outer Hebrides. These values contrast with the c. 450°C suggested by O'Hara (1977) as the temperature at the margins of Scourie dykes in the mainland. The Hebridean values are characteristic of upper amphibolite facies conditions implying that the complex had not undergone significant uplift since the Scourian.

Modification of the complex during the Laxfordian

The Laxfordian is defined as the cycle of events following the 'Younger Basic' intrusions. Six phases of deformation have been recognized by Fettes *et al.* (in press) namely Dl_1–Dl_6 (Table 1 and Table 3). However, as discussed above, Dl_1 is confined to planar fabrics in the 'Younger Basics' ($\equiv Ds_4$) probably developing as a result of their intrusion into tectonically active shear zones. Following this there may well have been a period of relative stability (perhaps for 300–400 Ma) before the subsequent Laxfordian event; otherwise the Laxfordian cycle becomes inordinately long—as much as 1000 Ma (see Table 1).

The Dl_2 and Dl_3 events are the main Laxfordian reworking events associated with major deformation and recrystallization. The Dl_2 event produced a series of open to tight folds with sub-horizontal axial planes. In areas of low strain the folds are open with weak axial fabrics, but with increasing strain the folds tighten, Scourian planar fabrics are strongly enhanced, and late Scourian linear fabrics are rotated into parallelism with Laxfordian trends. The 'Younger Basic' dykes may also become rotated into near parallelism and are commonly boudinaged. The Dl_3 phase is characterized by the development of folds with steep axial planes and, locally, very strongly attenuated or sheared limbs. In general the axial planes and associated shear zones trend

NW–SE although locally, in Lewis, they are oriented NE–SW. Large Dl_3 folds may provide spectacular interference patterns in concert with Dl_2 folds (Graham 1970). Where the strain is high the planar fabrics are further enhanced and the 'Younger Basic' dykes further flattened or disrupted. The general change in tectonic style from Dl_2 to Dl_3 has been cited as possible evidence of the rise and unroofing of the Lewisian complex (Fettes *et al.* in press; Graham 1970; Coward 1973; Dickinson & Watson 1976).

Although the effects of Dl_2 and Dl_3 are present throughout the islands, the amount of bulk Laxfordian finite strain is highly variable, and variations of considerable magnitude may occur over very short distances. This phenomenon is well shown by the 'Younger Basic' intrusives which may go from massive cross-cutting dykes to concordant schistose amphibolites over a few metres (see Coward 1973). Equally dramatic are the effects of Laxfordian recrystallization which may result in the intrusion of the dykes by pegmatitic stringers and veinlets leading to the absorption and 'digestion' of the dyke. In the Howmore quarry [NF 766 365] a series of dykes exhibit progressive recrystallization across about 20 m, ranging from massive discrete basic rocks to coarse patches of recrystallized gneiss with relict hornblendic patches and lenses. Similar textural variations are also spectacularly seen at Mangersta Head in West Lewis. Here the potassic gneisses readily recrystallized during the Laxfordian. The dykes commonly developed rather diffuse potash-feldspar porphyroblasts, the basic rock becoming vague and ill-defined. Locally, dykes may grade along their length from massive basic sheets to areas of coarse hornblendic gneiss.

Apart from these areas of extensive recrystallization and fragmentation of the basic sheets the recrystallization and deformational effects of the Laxfordian tended to drive the rocks towards stable hornblende-(garnet)-(clinopyroxene)-plagioclase assemblages. The present day distribution of different mineral assemblages in the 'Younger Basic' dykes therefore largely reflects the degree of Laxfordian reworking, with the dominance of the higher grade assemblages in the south and east, and (apart from an E–W belt in north Central Lewis) the lower grade assemblages in the north and west. This variation of dyke mineralogy closely follows the degree of Laxfordian bulk finite strain as deduced from the various structural elements. Certain anomalies do exist, for example in North Harris where cross-cutting dykes indicative of low reworking exhibit hornblende-plagioclase assemblages (Myers 1970). Such areas may represent parts of the complex which were relatively more hydrated.

The distribution pattern of the mineral assemblages and Laxfordian bulk finite strain mimics the pattern of gneiss types established during the Scourian and suggests an element of control over the development of the Laxfordian structures. It is perhaps important to emphasize that the Laxfordian structures are evidenced by their effects on the Scourian gneissic foliation. Only in cases of very high Laxfordian strain is the foliation completely transposed; elsewhere the Scourian foliation is only destroyed where Laxfordian remobilization of the gneiss is intense. These latter occurrences are usually confined to more potash-rich areas of Scourian migmatites and perhaps reach their greatest development in the Uig Hills area of Lewis where the local regeneration of the gneiss and pegmatitic production and veining is particularly noticeable. In these areas the Dl_3 minor folds are commonly characterized by the development of pegmatites in their attenuated limbs.

There is little direct evidence from the main Laxfordian events to indicate major variations in the depth of burial, with the general metamorphic assemblages during Dl_2 and Dl_3 suggesting little change. However the change of tectonic style between Dl_2 and Dl_3 may have heralded uplift. Significant uplift, however, did not occur before the late Laxfordian events (Dl_5–Dl_6) but before that time there was a substantial intrusion of granitic material.

The late Laxfordian intrusions

The main phase of late Laxfordian igneous activity is reflected in the granite complexes which reach their greatest development in the western hills of N Harris and S Lewis. In this area the granite intrusions form a complex of veins and sheets, the latter commonly many tens of metres thick. Compositionally the granites are all one-mica types and range from porphyritic granite to leucogranite and local aplite veins with pegmatitic cores and *vice versa*. Although the various textural and compositional types form a complex intrusive sequence, generally the porphyritic granites are the earliest and they predominate in the centre of the complex whereas the leucogranite veins tend to be latest and they are predominant in the marginal zones. The granites are, in part, areally associated with potassic gneisses which, as discussed above, show evidence of local remobilization during the Laxfordian with pegmatitic generation and intrusion. This led Myers (1971) to suggest that granite magma was formed by partial melting of the local gneisses. However, Fettes *et al.* (in press) concluded from the granite geochemistry (see Fig. 3)

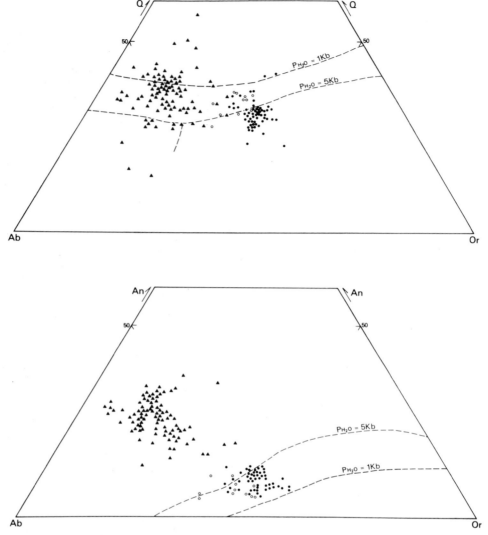

FIG. 3. Compositions of gneiss and late Laxfordian granite in normative *Q–ab–or* and *ab–an–or* diagrams with the 1kb and 5kb cotectics (from Strong 1979). Triangles, quartzo-feldspathic gneiss; dots, granite; circles, leucogranite. After Fettes *et al.* (in press).

that they could not have been derived from the local gneiss.

Texturally the granites all show varying degrees of late-stage low-grade deformation. The degree of deformation is greatest in the youngest leuco-granite veins and in those peripheral to the complex, and is always greater in the granites than in the host gneisses. This implies that deformation may have occurred before the youngest veins fully consolidated, a concept supported by a few veins (*eg* at Aird Fenish, south of Uig) which show massive margins

grading with the increasing development of deformational fabrics inwards to a mylonitic core. These, and similar features, have important implications in dating the thrusting events of the late Laxfordian.

The final phase of the late Laxfordian intrusives is marked by a number of thin microdiorite dykes. One of these at Garry-a-siar [NF 768 535] cuts a late Laxfordian pegmatite which clearly cuts a 'Younger Basic' dyke. The rock is *Q*-normative and similar to the late Scourian microdiorites although richer in sphene and apatite (Table 2). This dyke has been dated by K-Ar mica ages at 1409 ± 25 Ma (Fettes *et al.* in press).

Uplift and thrusting—the Outer Hebrides Thrust Zone

The intrusion of the late Laxfordian granites signals the start of a marked uplift phase which occurred intermittently between *c.* 1700 Ma and *c.* 1100 Ma. Later re-activation is evidenced by Caledonian mylonite formation (Fettes *et al.* in press, Sibson 1977) and the generation of the Minch Fault and related structures in the Permian–Triassic. Phanerozoic dyke intrusion into the rigid basement occurred notably in the Permian–Carboniferous (quartz-dolerites of Barra, camptonites and monchiquites of S Uist) and in the Tertiary (mainly tholeiites). The latter suite is ubiquitous in the Outer Hebrides but concentrations are found in SE Lewis, S Harris and in Barra (Fettes *et al.* in press). Offshore in the Minch, Tertiary sills are common in the Mesozoic sediments.

Concurrent with early uplift was an ESE–WSW directed compressional phase that resulted in the formation of shear zones in the granites and brittle thrusts in the gneisses close to the eastern seaboard of the Outer Hebrides. This culminated in the formation of a complex series of thrusts and crush zones termed the Outer Hebrides Thrust Zone which extends for 172 km from Sandray, south of Barra, to Traigh Mhor near Tolsta in central Lewis (Fig. 1). There is a change both in structural character and thrust products along the length of the zone. The thrust front is best defined in S Uist where a narrow zone of pseudotachylite and cataclasite breccia forms the western boundary of a large overthrust mass of granulite facies metadiorite, the Corodale Gneiss (Coward 1972). The thrust is reflected by a prominent scarp feature in both the Uists and Barra (*eg* Eaval, N Uist; Ben Mhor, S Uist; Heaval, Barra) but in Lewis and Harris where the thrust zone features are more diffuse, the topographical pattern is more complex. Only around Ben Mholach in Central Lewis does a well-defined thrust front occur.

A brief description of the major rock types found in the thrust zone is given below and their distribution both along and across the thrust zone is summarized in Table 4.

Pseudotachylite is a generally devitrified, black isotropic glass that occurs either along low-angle thrusts or as intrusive material adjacent to such features. It results from frictional melting when seismic faulting takes place in dry rock (Sibson 1975, Maddock 1983). Feldspar microlites can be seen, notably in S Uist and Barra, particularly where pseudotachylite veins attain 10 cm in thickness or more. Porphyroclasts of quartz, commonly cracked, and feldspar are both common. Where thick concentrations of pseudotachylite have been reported along thrusts, *eg* 10 m + near Ru Melvick and on Triuirebheinn, S Uist, detailed studies have shown it to consist of a mixture of cataclasite, shattered gneiss and several generations of pseudotachylite veining.

Where retrograded, pseudotachylite and the related cataclasite, and structurally isotropic breccia become pale grey-green to dark grey and resemble ultramylonite. Where inmixed with macroscopic fragments of country rock this lithology has been termed 'mashed' gneiss.

To the east of the main thrust front much of the coherent acid gneiss shows a marked mylonitic/cataclastic fabric of variable intensity. This is typically a recrystallization of biotite and a cataclasis and partial recrystallization of quartz and, rarely, feldspar grains, commonly sub-parallel to the gneissic banding. This 'cataclastic' gneiss is seen on Eaval [NF 897 606] in N Uist and at Seaforth Head [NB 301 164] in SE Lewis to be cross-cut by pseudotachylite veining; in parts the gneiss is broken up and disorientated. Around Loch nan Deaspoirt [NB 305 217] and at Seaforth Head, early mylonites are developed; they represent a notably strong development of this early deformation.

Late-stage mylonites, more correctly termed phyllonites, are also well-developed within the thrust zone. They occur in distinct planar zones 1 m to 250 m thick either sub-parallel to the gneissic banding (in SE Lewis they dip moderately SE) or dipping gently E–ESE. Large basic bodies commonly form a locus for mylonite development. The phyllonites formed subsequent to the thrust products noted above and relate to a zone of retrogression. In places the phyllonites have tight chevron folds. The petrography of the phyllonites is typically quartz, albite, sericite, chlorite, epidote and phengite (muscovite). Albite porphyroblasts are locally common (*eg* East Loch Claidh, SE Lewis; Rudha Rossel, S Uist). Where amphibolite bodies are mylonitized, actinolite, sphene, quartz and epidote are formed; rarely blue-green hornblende is present.

In S Lewis a range of thrusts are seen in a traverse from west to east (Fig. 4). In the west the granite sheets of Uig Hills are foliated, notably at their margins and with increasing intensity towards the periphery of the complex. On the west coast 2 km N of Mangersta [NB 010 334] a gently SE-dipping 5 m thick granite sheet is thrust discordantly over the banded gneiss sequence. The sheet has a strong internal foliation

TABLE 4. *Distribution of the major rock types related to thrusting in the Outer Hebrides*

Area	West of thrust front	At thrust front	East of thrust front
Central Lewis	Early mylonitic fabric (amphibolite facies) common in gneisses. Minor thrusts with pseudotachylite/ultramylonite.	Thick zone of mashed gneiss marks thrust front coincident with the NW limit of general retrogression.	Retrograded 'cataclastic' gneiss of variable intensity. Minor early mylonites. Local later phyllonite bands particularly to the east. (Coherent acid gneisses found extensively in both Central and South Lewis)
South Lewis	Local early mylonitic fabric in gneisses to the north. Upper greenschist facies mylonite zones grading east to ultramylonite and pseudotachylite. Thrusting localized around the margin of the Uig Hills granites and in granite sheets to the east.	Pseudotachylite developed in small thrusts. Early mylonites spatially coincident with major pseudotachylite development at thrust front. Part retrograded to 'mashed' gneiss.	Retrograded 'cataclastic' gneiss of variable intensity. Wide area in which mashed gneiss zones and thick phyllonites are developed (notably L Shell–L Brollum area). Late tight chevron folding with discrete spaced cleavage developed in some phyllonites.
North Harris	Thrust effects largely absent from the gneisses in the west. Minor thrusts located along granite sheets with minor pseudotachylite seen to the east.	Minor pseudotachylite developed along brittle thrusts.	In Scalpay progressive attenuation and retrogression of the gneisses. Minor phyllonite bands.
South Harris	Minor localized pseudotachylite development, often in steep shear zones. Retrogression locally extends northwest of the thrust front. Locally broken gneisses.	'Mashed' gneiss formed from anorthosite marks the thrust front onshore.	Generally brecciated and strongly retrograded anorthosite/grey gneiss with 'mashed' gneiss zones. Basic masses less affected.
North Uist	Forethrusts with pseudotachylite and/or 'mashed' gneiss. Localized upper greenschist facies retrogression.	Thick 'mashed' gneiss zones mark the thrust front with roughly coincident retrogression. Minor phyllonites in Lochportain area.	Retrograded broken and 'cataclastic' gneisses. Minor zones of coherent acid gneiss. Phyllonites zones thin but abundant. Local late tight chevron folding.
South Uist	Minor pseudotachylite in narrow zones in the gneisses.	Thrust front marked by thick pseudotachylite/ cataclasite zones.	Granulite facies metadiorite contains minor pseudotachylite zones. Becomes broken to the east and retrograded. Phyllonites developed from acid gneisses found adjacent to the eastern seaboard. Retrogression here also.
Barra	Pseudotachylite developed sporadically in the gneisses.	Pseudotachylite marks thrust front (possibly major thrust products lie offshore to the east).	Granulite facies gneisses and metaigneous rocks with few thrust features. Mylonites may lie offshore to the east where a deep channel occurs in the sea floor topography.

sub-parallel to its margins. The lower thrust contact and foliated granite are cross-cut by aplogranite veins which themselves show only local shear effects. The sheared granite contains newly-developed epidote, muscovite and chlorite (after biotite). In contrast, in areas west of the Uig Hills, aplogranite and pegmatoid granite veins with a strong internal fabric sub-parallel to their margins, cross-cut granite, which is massive or only weakly foliated, and apparently unmodified banded gneisses, *eg* at Aird Brenish [NB 979 265].

These features imply a close connection between the late phases of Laxfordian pegmatite and aplogranite intrusion and deformation, and thrusting.

East of the Uig Hills, sparse granite sheets act as loci for thrusting; *eg* 2.5 km SE of Kinlochresort [NB 126 152] a 20 m granite sheet shows a strongly foliated centre and ultramylonite at its margins, and 1.8 km farther SE at [NB 142 142] pseudotachylite is well-developed at the lower margin of a 7 m thick granite sheet.

A similar transition from mylonite to ultramylonite and pseudotachylite occurs in moderately SE-dipping shear zones in the gneisses east from Valtos to Grimersta in western central Lewis. Biotite is stable in the shear zones around Grimersta, and discordant veins of pseudotachylite have commonly been observed in ultramylonites formed from both granites and acid gneisses in this area. Figure 4 shows the distribution of mylonite and pseudotachylite in low-angle thrusts across S Lewis. The western limits of pseudotachylite lie along an approximately N–S line which is generally coincident with the increase in grade of the shear zone assemblages, such that biotite is stable. Mylonites do occur east of this line but are typically found in NW trending subvertical shear zones. The geometry of the shear fabric in these zones suggests a sinistral sense of movement. The presence of such mylonites, even within the main thrust zone, may reflect the lower stress necessary to induce failure on transcurrent faults as opposed to thrust faults (see Sibson 1974). In addition, fluid movement can occur readily along these zones, which probably reflects earlier lineaments.

In the thrust zone at Seaforth Head pseudotachylite veins cross-cut the early mylonitic gneisses. Fold structures geometrically related to pseudotachylite veining show no consistent vergence or axial orientation. Several earlier pseudotachylite and ultramylonite veins that developed sub-parallel to the gneissic–mylonitic banding are folded by these open to close minor folds. It seems that pseudotachylite formation here was a multi-stage process resulting from intermittent regional thrusting accompanying uplift.

The spatial coincidence between early mylonite and pseudotachylite in Lewis and parts of N Uist suggests that both are products of the same regional thrusting event.

In the early mylonites at Seaforth Head [NB 315 758] new euhedral to ragged garnets have grown within and across finely recrystallized biotite aggregates. Biotite and recrystallized fine-grained quartz and plagioclase define the mylonitic foliation. Plagioclase and hornblende also show various stages of fracturing and new granular epidote is seen. Garnet–biotite compositions are taken to reflect *PT* conditions during the initial thrust movement phase. Electron probe analyses were taken on several garnet–biotite

pairs and their compositions were used to obtain temperature estimates according to the methods of Thompson (1976) and Ferry and Spear (1978). Values ranged from 535°C to 545°C ($\pm$ 50°C). In addition, plagioclase compositions were taken from both the large relict porphyroclasts and the adjacent recrystallized finer-grained aggregates. Typical anorthite (An) values for porphyroclast/aggregate pairs are An_{30}/An_{25}. However in the notably fine-grained lenticular ribbon aggregates of the matrix, values as low as An_{19} were found. All these compositions are typical of the lower amphibolite facies. Unless an abnormally high geothermal gradient ($> 50°C/km$) is postulated, then depth values in the range 10 km to 15 km must be inferred for thrusting.

In recrystallized pseudotachylite from Aird an Troim [NB 233 165] some 8 km west of Seaforth Head, ovoid porphyroclasts of oligoclase, hornblende and quartz lie in a fine-grained quartz-biotite matrix. Abundant small euhedral garnets lie within the matrix and their composition is similar to those in the mylonites of Seaforth Head. The overall mineralogy again suggests that lower amphibolite conditions prevailed, here subsequent to pseudotachylite formation.

The later mylonitization that resulted in the formation of phyllonite zones is typified by a lower greenschist facies mineralogy. It relates to a zone of hydrous retrogression which in part affected rocks west of the main thrust front. In the Lochportain area of N Uist a weak mylonitic fabric overprints 'catalastic' gneiss and 'mashed' gneiss with local intensification to give thin phyllonites. Sibson (1977) records synkinematic biotite on Scalpay, east of N Harris, but this is atypical of later mylonites.

The development of phyllonites and later, but associated, folding is taken to be of Caledonian age. D. C. Rex (in Sibson 1977) obtained K-Ar whole rock ages from phyllonites of between 394 Ma and 947 Ma, with four of the five dates lying between 394 Ma and 471 Ma. Moorbath (also in Sibson 1977) obtained K-Ar ages of 1120 Ma to 1140 Ma from pseudotachylite west of the thrust base in S Uist.

Open to tight chevron-style folding affects the phyllonites, and in places a dominant strain-slip or spaced cleavage is well-developed (*eg* at [NB 241 037]). The fold asymmetry implies a reverse or down-dip shear couple which is presumed to reflect extension in the late Caledonian event. In fact, White & Glasser (this volume) suggest that the phyllonites may also be a product of low-angle normal faulting.

It is tempting to correlate the pseudotachylite found mainly in sub-vertical shear zones in Lewisian gneisses from the Gairloch area of NW

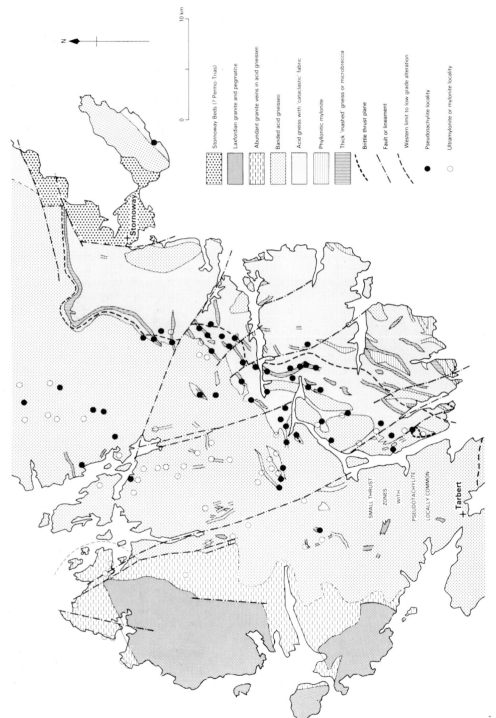

FIG. 4. Map of S Lewis and N Harris showing pseudotachylite and ultra-mylonite/mylonite localities. After Fettes *et al.* (in press).

Scotland with the occurrences in the Outer Hebrides. Moorbath and Park (1971) related the mainland deformation to chloritization of biotite in the adjacent rocks which they dated at *c*. 1150 Ma. Recent work by Consolidated Goldfields Ltd (E. Jones pers. comm. 1982) in this area revealed thrusts dipping about 25°E, marked by pseudotachylite, but cross-cut by Torridonian sandstone 'dykes'.

These features, in total, are a product of thrusting and uplift which marked the later stages of the exhumation of the Lewisian terrain. Re-activation as a result of the proximity of the Outer Hebrides to the Caledonian orogenic margin resulted in the late mylonites forming along the pre-existing thrust zone. Subsequent uplift and possible extension by low-angle faulting formed the late folds in the phyllonites and possibly initiated the early Minch Fault movements (see Brewer and Smythe 1984). This system became re-activated again in the Permian–Triassic when a graben structure formed.

ACKNOWLEDGMENT: This paper is published with the permission of the Director, British Geological Survey (NERC).

References

Bowes, D. R. 1972. Geochemistry of Precambrian crystalline basement rocks, North-West Highlands of Scotland. *24th Sess. Int. Geol. Congr., Canada 1972*, Sect. **1**, 97–103.

Brewer, J. A. & Smythe, D. K. 1984. MOIST and the continuity of crustal reflector geometry along the Caledonian–Appalachian orogen. *J. geol. Soc. London*, **141**, 105–120.

Cliff, R. A., Gray, C. M. & Huhma, H. 1983. A Sm-Nd isotopic study of the South Harris Igneous Complex, the Outer Hebrides. *Contrib. Mineral. Petrol.* **82**, 91–8.

Coward, M. P. 1972. The Eastern Gneisses of South Uist. *Scott. J. Geol.* **8**, 1–12.

—— 1973. Heterogeneous deformation in the development of the Laxfordian complex of South Uist, Outer Hebrides. *J. geol. Soc. London*, **129**, 139–160.

——, Francis, P. W., Graham, R. H., Myers, J. S. & Watson, J. 1969. Remnants of an early metasedimentary assemblage in the Lewisian Complex of the Outer Hebrides. *Proc. Geol. Assoc.* **80**, 387–408.

Davies, F. B. 1974. A layered basic complex in the Lewisian, South of Loch Laxford, Sutherland. *J. geol. Soc. London*, **130**, 279–284.

—— & Watson, J. V. 1977. Early basic bodies in the type Laxfordian complex, NW Scotland, and their bearing on its origin. *J. geol. Soc. London*, **133**, 123–131.

Dearnley, R. 1962. An outline of the Lewisian complex of the Outer Hebrides in relation to that of the Scottish Mainland. *Q. J. geol. Soc. London*, **118**, 143–176.

—— 1963. The Lewisian complex of South Harris, with some observations on the metamorphosed basic intrusions of the Outer Hebrides, Scotland. *Q. J. geol. Soc. London*, **119**, 243–312.

—— 1973. Scourie dykes of the Outer Hebrides. In: Park, R. G. & Tarney, J. (eds), *The Early Precambrian of Scotland and Related Rocks of Greenland*, Univ. of Keele, 131–135.

Dickinson, B. B. & Watson, J. 1976. Variations in crustal level and geothermal gradient during the evolution of the Lewisian complex of NW Scotland. *Precambrian Res.* **3**, 363–374.

Ferry, J. M. & Spear, F. S. 1978. Experimental calibration of the partitioning of Fe and Mg between biotite and garnet. *Contrib. Mineral Petrol.* **66**, 113–117.

Fettes, D. J., Mendum, J. R., Smith, D. I. & Watson, J. V. in press. *The Geology of the Outer Hebrides.* Mem. geol. Surv. U.K.

Francis, P. W. 1969. *Some aspects of the Lewisian geology of Barra and adjacent islands.* Unpublished Ph.D. thesis, Univ. London.

—— 1973. Scourian–Laxfordian relationships in the Barra Isles. *J. geol. Soc. London*, **129**, 161–189.

Graham, R. H. 1970. *A structural analysis of Lewisian rocks in parts of North Uist and the South of Harris, Outer Hebrides.* Unpublished Ph.D. thesis, Univ. London.

Jehu, T. J. & Craig, R. M. 1923. Geology of the Outer Hebrides. Part I—the Barra Isles. *Trans. R. Soc. Edinburgh*, **53**, 419–441.

—— 1925. Geology of the Outer Hebrides. Part II—South Uist and Eriskay. *Trans. R. Soc. Edinburgh*, **53**, 615–641.

—— 1926. Geology of the Outer Hebrides. Part III—North Uist and Benbecula. *Trans. R. Soc. Edinburgh*, **54**, 467–489.

—— 1927. Geology of the Outer Hebrides. Part IV—South Harris. *Trans. R. Soc. Edinburgh*, **55**, 457–488.

—— 1934. Geology of the Outer Hebrides. Part V—North Harris and Lewis. *Trans. R. Soc. Edinburgh*, **57**, 839–874.

Lambert, R. St. J., Myers, J. S. & Watson, J. 1970. An apparent age for a member of the Scourie dyke suite in Lewis, Outer Hebrides. *Scott. J. Geol.* **6**, 214–220.

McQuillin, R. & Watson, J. 1973. Large-scale basement structures of the Outer Hebrides in the light of geophysical evidence. *Nature, London,* **245**, 1–3.

Maddock, R. H. 1983. Melt origin of fault-generated pseudotachylites demonstrated by textures. *Geology*, **11**, 105–108.

MOORBATH, S. & PARK, R. G. 1971. The Lewisian chronology of the southern region of the Scottish mainland. *Scott. J. Geol.* **8**, 51–74.

——, POWELL, J. L. & TAYLOR, P. N. 1975. Isotopic evidence for the age and origin of the "grey gneiss" complex of the southern Outer Hebrides, Scotland. *J. geol. Soc. London*, **131**, 213–222.

MYERS, J. S. 1968. *The tectonic and metamorphic history of the Lewisian migmatite complex of Western Harris, Outer Hebrides, Scotland.* Unpubl. Ph.D. thesis, Univ. London.

—— (with a note by R. J. LISLE) 1970. Zones of abundant Scourie dyke fragments and their significance in the Lewisian Complex of Western Harris, Outer Hebrides. *Proc. Geol. Assoc.* **82**, 365–378.

—— 1971. The late Laxfordian granite–migmatite complex of Western Harris, Outer Hebrides, *Scott. J. Geol.* **7**, 254–284.

—— 1975. Pseudo-fractionation trend of the Fiskenaesset anorthosite complex, southern west Greenland. *Rapp. Grønlands, Geol. Unders.* **75**, 77–80.

—— 1976. Acid and intermediate intrusions, deformation and gneiss formation, north-east of Fiskenaesset. *Rapp. Grønlands. Geol. Unders.* **73**, 7–15.

—— 1978. Formation of banded gneisses by deformation of igneous rocks. *Precambrian Res.* **6**, 43–64.

O'HARA, M. J. 1961. Petrology of the Scourie dyke, Sutherland. *Mineralog. Mag.* **32**, 848–865.

—— 1977. Thermal history of excavation of Archaean gneisses from the base of the continental crust. *J. geol. Soc. London*, **134**, 185–200.

PARK, R. G. & CRESSWELL, D. 1973. The dykes of the Laxfordian belts. *In*; PARK, R. G. & TARNEY, J. (eds), *The Early Precambrian of Scotland and Related Rocks of Greenland*, University of Keele, 119–130.

SIBSON, R. H. 1974. Frictional constraints on thrust, wrench and normal faults. *Nature, London*, **249**, 542–544.

—— 1975. Generation of pseudotachylite by ancient seismic faulting. *Geophys. J. Astr. Soc.* **43**, 775–794.

—— 1977. *The Outer Hebrides Thrust: its structure, mechanism and deformation environment.* Unpubl. Ph.D. thesis, Univ. London.

SKINNER, A. C. 1970. *Geochemical studies of the Lewisian of N.W. Scotland and comparable rocks in E Greenland.* Unpubl. Ph.D. thesis, Univ. Birmingham.

SOLDIN, S. R. 1978. *The tectonic evolution and geochemistry of the Lewisian complex of North Harris.* Unpubl. Ph.D. thesis, Univ. London.

STRONG, D. F. 1979. The Mount Peyton batholith, Central Newfoundland: A bimodal calc-alkaline suite. *J. Petrol.* **20**, 119–138.

TARNEY, J. 1973. The Scourie dyke suite and the nature of the Inverian event in Assynt. *In*: PARK, R. G. & TARNEY, J. (eds), *The Early Precambrian of Scotland and Related Rocks of Greenland*, University of Keele, 195–118.

——, SKINNER, A. C. & SHERATON, J. W. 1972. A geochemical comparison of major Archaean gneiss units from north-west Scotland and east Greenland. *24th Sess. Int. Geol. Congr., Canada 1972*, Sect. **1**, 162–174.

THOMPSON, A. B. 1976. Mineral reactions in pelitic rocks: II Calculation of some P-T-X (Fe-Mg) phase relations. *Am. J. Sci.* **276**, 425–454.

WATSON, J. 1969. The Precambrian gneiss complex of Ness, Lewis, in relation to the effects of Laxfordian regeneration. *Scott. J. Geol.* **5**, 268–285.

WINDLEY, B. F., HERD, R. K. & BOWDEN, A. A. 1973. The Fiskenaesset complex, West Greenland. Part 1. A preliminary study of the stratigraphy, petrology and whole rock chemistry from Qeqertarssuatsiaq. *Bull. Grønlands geol. Unders.* **106**.

D. J. FETTES & J. R. MENDUM, British Geological Survey, Murchison House, West Mains Road, Edinburgh EH9 3LA, UK.

Geochemistry of the Scourian complex: petrogenesis and tectonic models

J. Tarney & B. L. Weaver

SUMMARY: The segmentation of the Lewisian complex which occurred at the end of the Archaean resulted in the juxtaposition of zones representing different crustal levels, including deep crustal granulites. Critical aspects of the geochemistry of Lewisian gneisses are considered in relation to their petrogenesis and tectonic models. Most of the Lewisian is made up of a bimodal suite of tonalitic–trondhjemitic gneisses enclosing mafic–ultramafic enclaves and layered complexes which are often associated with metasediments. These mafic components have a low-pressure petrogenesis and represent tectonic inclusions incorporated into the complex at the time of gneiss generation. They are more abundant in the granulites. The silicic gneisses have a higher pressure petrogenesis and their geochemistry is consistent with hydrous partial melting of amphibolites in a shallow-dipping subducting slab with hornblende as a residual phase.

Granulite metamorphism occurred or peaked some 200 Ma or so after the phase of gneiss generation at 2.9 Ga and terminated about 2.5 Ga. Concentrations of U, Th and Rb are at least an order of magnitude lower in the granulites than in the equivalent amphibolite-facies gneiss zones, and those of K and Pb about 50% lower. Concentrations of other elements are not significantly different. Currently popular models for the removal of these elements from the deep crust through partial melting or transport in a carbonic fluid phase are examined, but each has problems in accounting for all the available data. An alternative model, considering the low contents of heat-producing elements as a primary feature of silicic magmas emplaced into the deep crust, is explored. This relies more on fluid processes removing heat-producing elements from the ocean crust during subduction, followed by hydrous melting of the amphibolite to produce water-saturated magmas which cannot rise to high crustal levels. In contrast to modern subduction zone magmas, which are largely derived from the mantle wedge that has been enriched by addition of a fluid-transported, LIL element, 'subduction component', Archaean sodic tonalite–trondhjemite magmas result from hydrous melting of amphibolite which has lost that component. Granulite-facies metamorphism is an independent process that is commonly superimposed on deep crustal rocks which are already low in heat-producing elements, and during which further loss of these elements may occur, but granulite-metamorphism may also be superimposed on more normal crustal rocks without significant chemical changes.

Introduction

A considerable number of geochemical studies have been carried out on the Lewisian—probably more than on any other Precambrian high-grade terrain—and it is the aim of this paper to focus on critical aspects of Lewisian geochemistry with relevance to the petrogenesis of the gneisses and their subsequent evolution. An immediate issue of concern is whether the Lewisian can be considered as typical of Archaean high-grade terrains and can therefore be used as a model for Archaean crust-generating processes in general (eg Weaver & Tarney 1984), or whether it is somehow unique and unrepresentative (eg Rudnick et al. 1985). In this regard it should be stressed that the period during which the Lewisian complex was generated and evolved in the late Archaean (c. 2.9–2.6 Ga; Hamilton et al. 1979) coincides with perhaps the most voluminous period of crustal generation in Earth history.

On the other hand the Lewisian is unusual in the sense that, as a consequence of the major tectonic activity which terminated the Archaean (ie the start of the Inverian), segments representing different crustal levels were juxtaposed (Sheraton et al. 1973; Park & Tarney, this vol.), and are available for study.

There are some obvious lithological differences between these Lewisian segments. The northern part of the central granulite zone, between Scourie and Achiltibuie, has a particularly high proportion of lensoid mafic and ultramafic masses, and vast numbers of smaller mafic and ultramafic enclaves within the strongly banded tonalitic gneisses which have been derived from these mafic–ultramafic complexes through extreme tectonic disruption at the time of gneiss formation. Gneiss compositions thus range from Mg-rich dunite to silicic trondhjemite, and there is a higher proportion of banded gneisses of intermediate composition than elsewhere (Sheraton et al.

From: PARK, R. G. & TARNEY, J. (eds), 1987, *Evolution of the Lewisian and Comparable Precambrian High Grade Terrains*, Geological Society Special Publication No. 27, pp. 45–56.

1973). In the southern part of the central zone, at Gruinard Bay, where the complex appears to have suffered only hornblende-granulite facies metamorphism (Rollinson & Fowler, this vol.), the host gneisses are mainly silicic trondhjemites with a poorly developed foliation and whereas there are numerous inclusions, these are dominantly mafic rather than ultramafic in composition. In the flanking zones of amphibolite-facies gneisses, in the south at Torridon and in the north at Laxford, the gneisses are generally more potassic, and mafic enclaves are much less common. These observations are at least compatible with geophysical models for the crust which imply an increasingly more basic composition with depth.

Two other points are worth making. The first is that although the average composition of Lewisian granulites is rather more basic than that of the amphibolite-facies segments (Weaver & Tarney 1984, 1985) silicic quartz-bearing tonalites and trondhjemites are still represented. It is the higher proportion of the mafic–ultramafic component which makes the mean granulite composition somewhat more basic than average continental crust estimates. The second is that although obvious metasedimentary gneisses form only a small proportion of the early gneiss complex, these metasedimentary components mostly occur in close association with the mafic–ultramafic bodies. Just as the latter are more common in the granulite zone, metasediments thus appear to be an important, though minor, component of the deeper Lewisian crust, a feature which must have tectonic significance for the evolution of high-grade terrains. Suggestions that the whole Lewisian complex may have a sedimentary parentage (Lowman 1984) find little support from geochemical studies (Weaver & Tarney 1980); the rocks are dominantly orthogneiss.

Lewisian granulites have mineral assemblages which record P–T conditions of at least 8 kb and 800°C (Cartwright & Barnicoat, this vol.; Sills & Rollinson, this vol.), conditions which are appropriate to the deep crust. However, the fact that these granulites are now exposed at the surface, and the present crustal thickness must be at least 25 km, inevitably raises the question of what underlies the granulite terrain. One possible model is to appeal to exhumation of a thickened crustal keel of Andean type, in which case the present granulites might be expected to be underlain by similar material, perhaps with a higher proportion of mafic–ultramafic components. Alternatively the major shear zones which terminated the Archaean may have been listric in form (see Park & Tarney, this vol., fig 2b) leading to ramping of deep crustal granulites

above mid-crustal amphibolite-facies gneisses along the Laxford front, but ramping of granulites above granulites in the middle part of the central granulite zone in Assynt. Of interest in this regard is the distribution of the potash-rich 'Scourian' pegmatites (Sutton & Watson 1951) which were emplaced at *c.* 2.5 Ga (Giletti *et al.* 1961; Evans & Lambert 1974) shortly before the intrusion of the Scourie dykes at *c.* 2.4 Ga (Chapman 1979). These are relatively abundant in the granulite terrain just to the south of the Laxford front, but decrease in abundance southwards and are both rare and more potash-poor in the Assynt region (Sheraton *et al.* 1973). The granulite gneisses are too potash-poor to yield K-feldspar rich pegmatites on partial melting (their melting products tend to be trondhjemitic in composition). However pegmatites in the granulites south of the Laxford front could have resulted from the thermal effects of ramping deep-crustal granulites over mid-crustal amphibolite-facies gneisses, the source of the pegmatites (which have low K/Rb ratios) being the underlying amphibolite-facies gneisses. Thus although these early pegmatites have traditionally (Sutton & Watson 1951) been regarded as the last stage of the Scourian (Badcallian) cycle, they may in reality be linked to the tectonic effects which initiated the Inverian and produced the segmentation of the Lewisian.

Available Sm–Nd and Pb–Pb whole rock geochronological data (Moorbath *et al.* 1969; Hamilton *et al.* 1979; Whitehouse & Moorbath 1986) suggest that the gneisses in both the granulite- and amphibolite-facies zones were generated at 2.92 Ga and that most suffered uranium loss at this time which led to their present unradiogenic Pb compositions. However Sm–Nd mineral isochrons for the granulites give ages of 2.49 Ga (Humphries & Cliff 1982) indicating that grain-size re-equilibration at granulite facies occurred until this time, some 400 Ma after crustal generation. This time of ultimate closure to REE diffusion may mark the uplift associated with Inverian segmentation of the Lewisian complex. Further analysis of the Sm–Nd mineral data led Humphries & Cliff (1982) to suggest that the peak of granulite-facies metamorphism occurred rather earlier at *c.* 2.62 Ga, an age supported by U–Pb zircon data (Pidgeon & Bowes 1972). A Pb–Pb whole rock isochron for the granulites (2.68 Ga: Chapman & Moorbath 1977) is also younger than that for the Lewisian complex as a whole (see also Holland & Lambert 1975), which suggests that U loss from the gneisses continued until this time. It would appear that the peak of Badcallian granulite-facies metamorphism occurred some 250 Ma after the time of formation of the gneisses. When the deeper Lewisian gneisses first attained granulite grade is much less easy to define. Rollinson's data on ilmenite-magnetite intergrowths in late trondhjemite and granite sheets at Scourie (Rollinson 1980) are consistent with more hydrous fluid conditions before attainment of granulite-facies equilibrium.

The above are the main geochronological and geotectonic constraints relating to the age and distribution of different gneiss compositions in the Lewisian within which a petrogenetic discussion must be framed. It is preferable to consider the possible geochemical effects associated with granulite-facies metamorphism after those connected with the primary stage of gneiss generation.

Petrogenesis of Lewisian gneisses

There are a number of comprehensive geochemical studies of Lewisian gneisses, beginning with Sheraton (1970). Tarney *et al.* (1972) and Sheraton *et al.* (1973) first drew attention to the anomalously low contents of heat producing elements U, Th, Rb and (to a lesser extent) K in the granulite-facies gneisses compared with amphibolite-facies equivalents in the Lewisian and elsewhere. Because of the potential mobility of other lithophile elements during the granulite-facies event and later retrogressive phases, emphasis had necessarily to be placed on immobile elements such as the rare-earths in discussing the petrogenesis of the gneiss precursors (Weaver & Tarney 1980, 1981). For instance, although REE mobility occurred on a mineral scale during the granulite-facies event (Humphries & Cliff 1982), the fact that whole rock Sm–Nd isotope data on both granulite- and amphibolite-facies Lewisian rocks faithfully recorded the time of gneiss generation (Hamilton *et al.* 1979), suggested there had not been widespread REE mobility within the gneiss complex. Indeed the 2.92 Ga Sm–Nd isochron in itself tends to argue against significant melting of the Lewisian rocks during the granulite event which, on the evidence cited above, occurred or peaked *c.* 250 Ma later. Thus it can reasonably be assumed that the REE distributions reflect those of the gneiss precursors.

Petrogenetic models for the Lewisian must take account of the bimodal character of the gneisses, which is a feature of Archaean high-grade gneiss terrains worldwide. This bimodal character is less well marked in the granulites owing to extreme tectonic mixing of the two components.

The granulite REE data (Weaver & Tarney 1980) suggest that these two (mafic and silicic)

components have a different petrogenesis. The mafic gneisses show a rather large range of Fe/Mg ratios which correlate positively with REE abundance and have essentially parallel REE distributions, all of which show moderate enrichment in light REE relative to chondrites (Fig. 1). Such patterns are typical of tholeiitic low pressure crystal fractionation involving olivines, pyroxenes and plagioclase. Some have slight negative Eu anomalies. The relative light REE enrichment would be compatible with melting of an 'undepleted' mantle source with chondritic REE distributions. The closely associated ultramafic gneisses also have 'undepleted' REE distributions but most have REE abundances more in keeping with komatiitic liquids than with residual mantle (Weaver & Tarney 1980; Sills *et al.* 1982). The close spatial association of mafic–ultramafic bodies with metasedimentary horizons in the gneisses is also consistent with a low pressure tectonic environment for the primary evolution of these bodies. Mafic gneisses with essentially similar REE characteristics and associations have been described in granulites from Fiskenaesset, West Greenland (Weaver *et al.* 1982), Madras, India (Weaver 1980) and NE China (Jahn & Zhang 1984). The apparently ubiquitous occurrence of such bodies in high-grade terrains, including also genetically-related layered gabbro–anorthosite complexes (Weaver *et al.* 1982), is suggestive of a common origin. The most realistic solution (Weaver & Tarney 1980) is to regard many of them as tectonic inclusions of Archaean ocean floor incorporated penecontemporaneously with crust generation (see Park & Tarney, this vol., Fig. 2*a*). Mafic bodies in the Laxford amphibolite facies gneisses of the Lewisian have essentially the same REE distributions as those in the granulites (Weaver & Tarney 1981) and appear to have a similar origin.

The silicic granulites have very different REE distributions (Fig. 1). They have strongly fractionated REE patterns showing first (compared with the mafic gneisses) enhanced light REE enrichment in the intermediate gneisses, then progressive heavy REE depletion in the tonalitic compositions, followed by both light REE and heavy REE depletion in the trondhjemites. The more silicic gneisses develop a marked positive Eu anomaly and show increased concave-upwards curvature in their heavy REE distributions (Weaver & Tarney 1980). A comparison of granulite- and amphibolite-facies tonalites at equivalent silica contents (Weaver & Tarney 1981) showed that there was no significant difference in their REE distributions. Very similar REE characteristics have now been described from most Archaean high-grade ter-

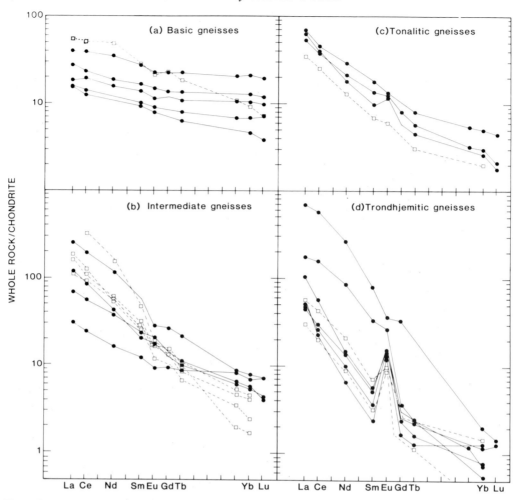

FIG. 1. Rare earth patterns for mafic, intermediate, tonalitic and trondhjemitic Lewisian granulites (full lines—after Weaver & Tarney 1980) and amphibolite-facies gneisses (dashed lines—after Weaver & Tarney 1981).

rains, irrespective of whether they are potash-poor like Lewisian granulites or moderately potash-rich such as the type charnockites from Madras (Weaver 1980; Weaver & Tarney 1983a). By contrast, high level granites from Archaean low-grade terrains tend dominantly to show negative Eu anomalies and have less pronounced curvature in their heavy REE distributions (cf Condie et al. 1986). Most post-Archaean high-level granites have negative Eu anomalies, which contribute to the marked negative Eu anomaly shown by sedimentary REE patterns (Taylor & McLennan 1981).

Rare earth distributions in gabbro–diorite–tonalite–trondhjemite complexes have been at-tributed to hornblende fractionation (Arth et al. 1977). However it is equally possible to reproduce the same REE patterns by differing degrees of partial melting of a mafic source with hornblende and/or garnet in the residue (Tarney et al. 1979; Weaver & Tarney 1980, 1981; Rollinson & Fowler, this vol.). Similar petrogenetic schemes have been proposed for other Archaean high-grade terrains in India (Condie & Allen 1984) NE China (Jahn & Zhang 1984) and East Antarctica (Sheraton & Black 1983; Sheraton & Collerson 1984). The significant petrogenetic point to be made is that the silicic gneisses must be generated under moderately high pressure conditions, in contrast with the low pressure petrogenesis of the mafic gneisses. To explain the voluminous production of tonalitic magmas at this period in earth history, subduction melting of ocean crust is the only viable way of supplying the necessary thermal energy. The higher thermal regime in the Archaean would permit hydrous melting of the downgoing slab in a more active convecting mantle (whereas thermal models of present day subduction zones do not favour significant melting, and element transfer into the mantle wedge is accomplished during dehydration: Anderson *et al.* 1978). Melting would be possible at much shallower depths than at the present day. This provides an important constraint on the evolution of such magmas. Hydrous magmas cannot rise high in the crust because they rapidly congeal as pH_2O falls; hence they will tend to be emplaced into the deeper crust, and crustal growth is accomplished by underplating (*cf* Holland & Lambert 1975). A consequence of continued underplating of tonalitic magmas into the deeper crust is that the crust would remain ductile for long periods, thus being very susceptible to deformation. Mafic material emplaced tectonically into the deeper crust would undergo severe disruption, and the whole complex would develop gneissic characteristics. Moreover, as new crustal material is continually added from beneath, all crustal material in effect passes through a high-grade state (Weaver & Tarney 1980). Such a model does not however produce the thermal conditions for granulite-facies metamorphism.

Modern geochemical equivalents of Archaean tonalites and trondhjemites, with positive Eu anomalies and marked heavy REE depletion are relatively rare. Tonalites with very similar major element compositions are perhaps the dominant pluton in the Andean magmatic belt (*cf* Tarney 1976), but the majority display either no, or slight negative, Eu anomalies and few have the marked heavy REE depletion seen in the tonalites of Archaean high-grade terrains. The majority, of course, are high level plutons. Locally, however, deep sections of both the late Palaeozoic and Mesozoic batholith are exposed (Bartholomew & Tarney 1984) and include a proportion of tonalitic rock types with very similar REE characteristics—positive Eu anomalies and strong heavy REE depletion—to Archaean high-grade tonalitic gneisses (Fig. 2). Moreover such uplifted deep sections tend to be bimodal in nature and the rocks are variably foliated. This suggests that the processes of crustal generation at Cordilleran margins may produce broadly similar hydrous tonalitic magmas which are emplaced into the deeper crust, but which are only rarely exposed.

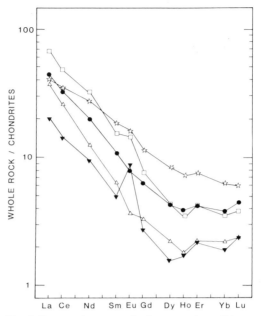

FIG. 2. Rare earth patterns for deep-seated tonalitic granitoids from the Mesozoic Patagonian batholith, Aysen, S. Chile (after Bartholomew & Tarney 1984).

Relationship between granulite-facies metamorphism and element depletion

The relationship between granulite-facies metamorphism and the commonly observed very low concentrations of selected lithophile elements in some (particularly Archaean) granulite terrains (Heier 1973) has been a subject of considerable debate. The issue is confused by two uncertainties. The first is whether granulite-facies metamorphism closely accompanies crustal generation and can be considered a continuation of the crust generating cycle, or whether granulite metamorphism is essentially a separate event which can occur at any time after crustal generation (see Ben Othman *et al.* 1984 and discussion by Moorbath 1984). The second concerns which particular elements are removed during granulite-facies metamorphism and—more important—what processes control this element removal. For instance some granulite terrains, such as the Madras charnockites (Weaver 1980) and the Jequie Complex, Brazil (Sighinolfi *et al.* 1981) show little evidence of removal of Rb, K, *etc.* nor the development of high K/Rb ratios. Studies of various granulite terrains (*eg* Heier & Thoresen 1971; Tarney *et al.* 1972; Barbey & Cuney 1982; Condie & Allen 1984; Jahn & Zhang 1984; Sheraton & Collerson 1984) show that they have experienced various degrees of depletion of U, Th, Rb and K, relative to mean crustal values, a point emphasized by Rudnick *et al.* (1985). Additionally some amphibolite-facies terrains which have not apparently experienced granulite-facies metamorphism have suffered severe U depletion (Taylor *et al.* 1980; Moorbath & Taylor 1981), including segments of the Lewisian (Whitehouse & Moorbath 1986), and others such as the Gruinard gneisses (Rollinson & Fowler, this vol.) are notably Rb poor. This begs the question of whether granulite-facies metamorphism and element depletion are in fact intimately connected, or whether they are two separate processes which, because they relate to or affect deep crustal rocks, frequently coincide. This issue will be addressed further below.

Lewisian granulites have very low Rb, Th and U contents (Tarney *et al.* 1972; Moorbath *et al.* 1969), and have been ranked as the most extreme of all granulites in terms of their very high K/Rb ratios (Rudnick *et al.* 1985), which are well above those of normal igneous rocks (Shaw 1968). Although their major element compositions are broadly calc-alkaline (Sheraton *et al.* 1973) they differ from all calc-alkaline plutonic and volcanic suites in that there is very little change in either K or Rb concentrations between basic and silicic gneisses. Major differences between Lewisian amphibolite- and granulite-facies compositions are apparent for Rb, Th, U and K, and to a lesser extent for Pb, simply by comparing average analyses of the two terrains (Sheraton *et al.* 1973), but this is less sensitive for other elements because the granulite average is biased towards the more abundant basic components. Nonetheless a detailed comparison of element abundances in equivalent tonalitic rock types in the two terrains (Weaver & Tarney 1981) provided no significant additional evidence for major differences in other elements: Rb, Th and U are all more than an order of magnitude lower in the granulites and K and Pb about 50% lower (Fig. 3).

Currently there are two popular models which attempt to provide an explanation for these differences:

Partial melting

Classical models for granite production (*eg* Fyfe 1973) invoke extraction of granite from the lower crust (along with heat-producing elements) leaving a granulite-facies residue depleted in such elements. Extension of this process to crustal development in general (Taylor & McLennan 1981) provides a mechanism for generating upper crustal granites (and derived sediments) with a negative Eu anomaly, whilst the compensating

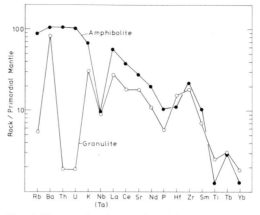

FIG. 3. Element abundances of Lewisian amphibolite-facies tonalites and granulite-facies tonalites compared on primordial mantle normalized multi-element plots (after Weaver & Tarney 1981).

positive Eu anomaly is carried in the plagioclase-rich basic residual granulites. Unfortunately this model is difficult to apply to the Archaean for several reasons: *a*) Archaean sediments in general do not have a negative Eu anomaly and, by implication, neither does the average Archaean upper crust, thus there is *a priori* no reason to extract a granitic melt, *b*) Whereas the Lewisian average granulite does display a positive Eu anomaly, in detail this is carried entirely by the silicic components, not the mafic gneisses (which tend to have negative Eu anomalies): thus melting of these silicic granitic components would provide liquids with positive Eu anomalies, *c*) Removal of granitic liquids would help deplete the residue in Th, U, Rb and K, but would be expected to produce other element fractionations, for instance of Ba relative to Sr; these are not observed, *d*) Significant melt extraction at the time of granulite-facies metamorphism would have severely perturbed the Sm–Nd isotope systematics established *c.* 250 Ma earlier at the time of crust generation; this has not happened.

For these and other reasons Weaver & Tarney (1981) concluded that major melt extraction was not the primary cause of the marked depletion in heat producing elements in Lewisian granulites. This is not to say that melting did not occur on a minor scale during the evolution of the granulite complex. There are numerous trondhjemitic veins, and Weaver & Tarney (1980) proposed that the minor intrusive anorthositic bodies which commonly occur in the Lewisian and other granulite terrains may have been generated through wet melting of the mafic granulites. Rock types with potentially higher aH_2O, such as the metasediments, provide ample evidence of local melting (Cartwright & Barnicoat, this vol.).

Flushing by CO_2-rich fluids

This has become an increasingly popular model in recent years, inspired by the observation that fluid inclusions in granulites are CO_2-rich, and by the spectacular exposures in Kabbaldurga Quarry in southern India where granulite- and amphibolite-facies assemblages co-exist (*cf* Hansen *et al.* 1984). The essence of the model is that as CO_2-rich fluids penetrate the deeper crust from the mantle, the higher CO_2 activity will reduce aH_2O, thus promoting dehydration of hydrous minerals, and at the same time raising the rock solidus to inhibit melting. Elements released as the rock recrystallises are carried upwards by the rising CO_2 front. Whereas the evidence from Kabbaldurga seems beyond dispute as far as the amphibolite–granulite transition is concerned (Friend 1983), the efficacy of the carbonic ichors in element removal has yet to be fully verified experimentally, and their potential may easily be overestimated (*eg* Collerson & Fryer 1978). Geochemical studies at Kabbaldurga (Weaver & Tarney 1983*a*) demonstrated little change in K, Rb contents or K/Rb ratios for the silicic gneisses in the transition to granulite, although the associated basic rocks showed a trend toward high K/Rb ratios.

The carbonic fluid mechanism may inhibit melting, but it does not necessarily prevent it. For instance Weaver (1980) and Weaver & Tarney (1983*a*) proposed that the advancing CO_2 front would be preceded by a H_2O-rich front resulting from the breakdown of hydrous phases which would actually promote K-metasomatism and melting at intermediate crustal levels. Further advance of the CO_2-rich front would convert these K-rich rocks to granulites and account for the potassic nature of the Madras charnockites. This model has been extended by Friend (1983) and Condie *et al.* (1986) to account for the production of granitoid bodies such as the Clospet granite which appear to have been emplaced contemporaneously with charnockite formation. A possible equivalent in West Greenland might be the Qôrqut granite and the associated migmatite terrain.

While CO_2-flushing models may potentially be adequate to account for the conversion of gneisses to granulite facies and to permit local melting, this is not necessarily proof of their efficacy in accomplishing the depletion of the residual granulites in heat-producing elements. For instance there are no comparable granitoid bodies or K-rich granitoid zones in the Lewisian to complement the K-poor granulites. Moreover, Powell (1983) suggests that CO_2 inclusions in granulites might be a natural consequence of the partitioning of H_2O into a melt phase under internal buffering, and do not necessarily provide evidence of widespread CO_2 flushing. More important perhaps is that whereas CO_2 flushing might promote biotite dehydration and release of the Rb (and K) contained in biotite, there is no obvious reason why this should also promote the simultaneous breakdown of U- and Th-bearing phases. Nor indeed why some of these elements are lost at amphibolite facies. At the opposite end of the scale there is the problem of why, if CO_2 fluids are the sole agency of element removal and conversion of rocks to granulite facies under appropriate *P–T* conditions, some granulite terrains such as the Jequie Complex, Brazil (Sighinolfi *et al.* 1981) remain K- and Rb-rich.

Taking an entirely crustal perspective, the above two models of partial melting and fluid transfer are the only ones which are realistically capable of accounting for the production of deep crustal granulites depleted in heat-producing elements. Unfortunately neither fully explains all the available geological and geochemical data. Thus it is worth exploring the extent to which some of the geochemical characteristics of depleted granulites might be primary. This has not been seriously considered previously simply because volcanic rocks with the geochemical characteristics of Archaean granulites do not exist. A necessary consequence of a 'primary' model must therefore be that magmas with these characteristics are constrained by their physical mode of generation to the deeper continental crust: *ie* they must be underplated.

Primary nature of 'depleted' granulites?

Two factors cast some doubt on whether element depletion was achieved *in situ* during granulite-facies metamorphism itself: (1) whole rock Pb isotope data link the timing of major U loss from all Lewisian gneisses with the period of crustal generation rather than with the granulite facies peak *P–T* conditions some 250 Ma later—indeed the U contents of Lewisian zircons are abnormally low (Pidgeon & Bowes 1972); (2) although K/Rb ratios in Lewisian granulites of igneous parentage are uniformly high, the metasediments within the granulites have normal upper crustal K/Rb ratios of about 250 (Sheraton *et al.* 1973). Tarney *et al.* (1972) ascribed this to compositional and mineralogical control; recrystallization reactions leading to Rb and K loss can only take place in diopside-normative rock types (which includes the vast majority of orthogneisses) and are inhibited in corundum-normative metasediments. This difference in K/Rb ratios could however also be interpreted as a primary feature.

Mineralogy exerts a vital control on rock chemistry during extensive fluid activity. For instance Beach & Tarney (1978) demonstrated that during hydrous retrogression of the Lewisian granulites the whole-rock compositions readjusted completely to the new mineralogy, implying element migrations over distances of in some cases above several metres. Minor mineral phases may play an important role, in particular with elements such as U and Th.

The important point to stress however, is that element fractionation resulting from fluid–rock interactions can operate at any one of the several stages involved in the evolution of a magma or its source. The generation of a tonalitic magma for instance, is a product of multistage processes: (1) mantle melting at an ocean ridge to form basalt; (2) hydrothermal activity at the ridge to produce a vertically-zoned series of hydrous assemblages; (3) dehydration during subduction of the ocean lithosphere when the expelled fluids may be in equilibrium with a progressive series of greenschist-, blueschist-, amphibolite- or eclogite-facies mineral assemblages, each with different minor mineral phases; (4) subduction zone melting, in equilibrium with possibly different major and minor phases. Loss of K, Rb, Th or U because of the absence of a suitable retentive mineral phase during any one of these stages could provide a suitable source for the generation of tonalites depleted in heat-producing elements. Unfortunately processes in subduction zones are not well constrained, so that it is difficult to provide more than a qualitative assessment of the likely processes.

During ridge hydrothermal activity there is intake of K and Rb from seawater in the upper layers of the ocean crust where clay minerals and zeolites are stable but, conversely, major loss of K, and particularly Rb, in the deeper layers where hydrothermal activity is more intense and where hornblende is stable. Hornblende accepts some K into its structure, but discriminates against Rb. This results in the deeper layers of ocean crust having very high K/Rb ratios (Sanders *et al.* 1979). However there appears to be a net gain of U by the ocean crust (Aumento 1979).

During subduction there is general agreement that this hydration process is reversed and that as dehydration occurs, selected LIL elements (Pearce 1983), especially Rb and K (Hole *et al.* 1984), are transferred from the subducted ocean crust into the overlying mantle wedge. This LIL element component may either be stabilized as mantle phlogopite or removed as calc-alkaline magmas. Clearly there may be a very great difference in the K and Rb contents and K/Rb ratios of magmas generated from melting of hydrothermally altered ocean crust, after this further stage of dehydration, compared with those in magmas generated from the mantle wedge.

Thermal models for present day subduction zones (Anderson *et al.* 1978, 1980) and experimental data for subduction zone melting under different thermal conditions (see review by Wyllie 1983) indicate that extensive melting of the subducted ocean crust is unlikely, particularly under continental regions, and that small-degree melts that might form after transformation of the ocean crust to eclogite would react and equilibrate with the overlying mantle wedge. They are water-undersaturated. Modern calc-alkaline magmas then are generated from the acceptor regions of the LIL-element enriched subduction component, and this is evident from their trace element patterns (Pearce 1983).

Melting of the donor regions (subducted ocean crust) is much more likely in the Archaean when mantle isotherms were considerably higher than today and, with smaller, more rapidly convecting plates, the subducting ocean crust was warmer. If the subducted slab induces convection in the overlying mantle wedge, the thermal conditions for melting of the ocean crust are even more easily attained. Melts would be water-saturated and generated in equilibrium with hornblende and perhaps residual garnet and, if generated at shallow levels, could be quite silicic. If, as suggested by Green (1975), thermal gradients in the Archaean were too high for the formation of dense eclogite in subducted ocean crust, warm ocean crust would be subducted at a shallow angle. One effect of this would be to extend the zone over which melting with residual hornblende occurs, thus leading to more voluminous magma production under these conditions. Another would be that shallow melting provides less opportunity for magmas to react with the overlying mantle, thus they are more likely to remain water-saturated. Water-saturated magmas would be unable to rise to high crustal levels and would congeal in the deep crust.

Conversely, with a cooler subducting plate, the Benioff zone would be steeper, with melting displaced to deeper levels. Magmas generated from a more steeply inclined subduction zone have more opportunity to react with the higher temperature mantle wedge, take up the LIL element subduction component already transferred to the wedge and, being water-undersaturated, rise to higher crustal levels. This model implies a general correlation between the depth of magma generation and the height to which the magma can eventually rise in the crust. This is dominantly controlled by the degree of water saturation, but is also compatible with the general hydrostatic principle that the height to which a magma column can rise is dependent on the supporting weight of crust + mantle. Modern calc-alkaline magmas, being generated at greater depths and from the mantle wedge, are mostly water-unsaturated and can rise to high crustal levels.

Whereas the above model provides a conceivable explanation of why K- and Rb-poor tonalitic magmas should dominantly be emplaced in the deep crust, the explanation for their low U and Th contents needs further consideration. It may be that during dehydration processes in the subducting slab they are also transferred to the mantle wedge, hence melting of the ocean crust after dehydration would produce magmas low in U and Th (though if Pb had also been removed during dehydration, U/Pb and Th/Pb ratios may not have been seriously affected). Much however will depend on the nature of the minor mineral phases (*eg* sphene, epidote, apatite, zircon) stable during the dehydration stage and also the melting stage. Sphene is stable well into the melting range of hydrous tholeiite compositions (Hellman & Green 1979) as is zoisite. Both sphene and (at higher pressures) rutile are important sinks for high field-strength elements such as Nb and Ta, and the fact that all subduction-zone magmas (and the continental crust generally, irrespective of age—Weaver & Tarney (1985)) display marked negative anomalies for these two elements on mantle-normalized multi-element diagrams (Weaver & Tarney 1983*b*) demonstrates the important role they play in subduction processes. If U and Th can be retained in minor mineral phases in the same way during melting of amphibolite in shallow subduction zones, it might begin to account for the low U and Th contents of high-grade gneisses. Unfortunately experimental data are lacking.

Discussion

Past discussions of the formation of the Scourian gneiss complex have centred on four main issues: *a*) the petrogenesis of the gneisses, *b*) their tectonic development, *c*) the age and causes of the granulite-facies metamorphism, and *d*) the reasons for the anomalously low concentrations of Rb, U, Th and K in the granulites. The traditional approach of linking *d*) with *c*) is not without problems, particularly in accounting for

the pervasive manner in which U, Th, Rb and K have been removed from the granulites, either through melting or fluid transport (later fluid activity affecting the granulites for instance is extensive but very localized). The alternative approach of linking *d*) with *a*) as a primary characteristic has potential, though uncertainties regarding Archaean subduction processes leave it poorly constrained. The main feature of the model is that, in contrast to modern subduction-zone magmas which have their source in the mantle wedge (enhanced in LIL elements through fluid transfer), Archaean tonalitic magmas are derived from melting of ocean crust amphibolite which has suffered complementary loss of LIL elements.

Essentially the process of loss of heat-producing elements from deep crustal rocks is transferred from the granulite-facies event to an earlier stage. This reduces the need to appeal to melt removal from granulites or super-active carbonic fluids pervading the Lewisian deep crust, for which there is meagre evidence. On the other hand this does not mean that further loss of Rb, Th, or U did not occur with the expulsion of fluids during granulite-facies metamorphism. Sheraton (1984) has described the chemical changes in mafic dykes which cut high-grade gneisses and are metamorphosed at amphibolite- or granulite-facies in East Antarctica. The effects are variable. Dykes which were metamorphosed directly to granulite facies show no chemical changes. Most compositional change was seen in dykes which underwent major changes in mineralogy and where there was associated deformation to enhance fluid activity (see also Beach & Tarney 1978). In this regard it should be noted that a subduction zone is an ideal environment for fluid transport; there is continual deformation and recrystallization. In the Lewisian granulites there was extensive deformation before the granulite event and many of the tectonically emplaced mafic gneisses have obviously equilibrated with the silicic gneisses in terms of K/Rb ratios.

If the depletion in U, Th and Rb can be ascribed to subduction rather than crustal processes, there are a number of interesting secondary consequences. First, there is no reason why the deeper crust under many Archaean cratons should not be composed of similar U-, Th- and Rb-depleted material, which will represent a substantial reservoir of low U/Pb, low Th/Pb and low Rb/Sr material with unradiogenic Pb and Sr. Second, the high U/Pb and high Th/Pb complement to this is not necessarily in the upper crust but, if U and Th are stabilized in minor mineral phases (along with Nb and Ta) in the subducted ocean crust, this component is returned to the mantle. Ocean island mantle sources are the only obvious complement to the lower crust in this regard: they have radiogenic Pb compositions which imply that U/Pb ratios of their sources were increased over normal mantle values at least 1.7 Ga ago (Sun 1980); additionally they have distinct positive Nb and Ta anomalies (Wood *et al.* 1981).

Finally, Archaean high-grade terrains have a distinctive tectonic style marked by strong horizontal thrusting and deformation (Bridgwater *et al.* 1974); indeed in Lewisian granulites the foliation is sub-horizontal over large areas (Sheraton *et al.* 1973), which contrasts with the widespread development of sub-vertical shear zones in the Proterozoic. A ductile lower crust is inducive to mobile horizontal tectonics; this would be facilitated by continual underplating of hydrous tonalitic magmas. However, once thermal gradients fall to the extent that voluminous melting of ocean crust is no longer possible, magma generation is restricted to the mantle wedge and is necessarily much less voluminous. Melts produced are then water-undersaturated and can rise to higher crustal levels. The crust adopts a more stable configuration; the permobile regime is at an end. This marks the Archaean-Proterozoic boundary, and is characterized by distinct compositional changes in the sedimentary record (Taylor & McLennan 1981) which largely reflect this change in mode of magma production.

References

ANDERSON, R. N., DELONG, S. E. & SCHWARTZ, W. M. 1978. Thermal model for subduction with dehydration in the downgoing slab. *J. Geol.* **86**, 731–739.

——, —— & —— 1980. Dehydration, asthenospheric convection and seismicity in subduction zones. *J. Geol.* **88**, 445–451.

ARTH, J. G., BARKER, F., PETERMAN, Z. E. & FRIEDMAN, I. 1977. Geochemistry of the gabbro–diorite–tonalite–trondhjemite suite of southwest Finland and its implications for the origin of tonalitic and trondhjemitic magmas. *J. Petrol.* **19**, 289–316.

AUMENTO, F. 1979. Distribution and evolution of uranium in the oceanic lithosphere. *Phil. Trans. R. Soc. London*, **A291**, 423–431.

BARBEY, P. & CUNEY, M. 1982. K, Rb, Sr, Ba, U and Th geochemistry of the Lapland granulites (Fennoscandia). LILE fractionation controlling factors. *Contrib. Mineral. Pet.* **81**, 304–316.

BARTHOLOMEW, D. S. & TARNEY, J. 1984. Geochemical characteristics of magmatism in the southern Andes (45–46°S). *In:* BARREIRO, B. & HARMON, R. S. (eds) *Andean Magmatism.* Shiva Publications, Nantwich, pp. 220–229.

BEACH, A. & TARNEY, J. 1978. Major and trace element patterns established during retrogressive metamorphism of granulite facies gneisses, NW Scotland. *Precambrian Res.* **7**, 325–348.

BEN OTHMAN, D., POLVE, M. & ALLEGRE, C. J. 1984. Nd–Sr isotopic composition of granulites and constraints on the evolution of the lower continental crust. *Nature, London*, **302**, 510–515.

BRIDGWATER, D., McGREGOR, V. R. & MYERS, J. S. 1974. A horizontal tectonic regime in the Archaean of Greenland and its implications for early crustal thickening. *Precambrian Res.* **1**, 179–198.

CHAPMAN, H. J. 1979. 2390 Myr Rb–Sr whole rock age for the Scourie dykes of north-west Scotland. *Nature, London*, **277**, 642–643.

—— & MOORBATH, S. 1977. Lead isotope measurements from the oldest recognised Lewisian gneisses of north-west Scotland. *Nature, London*, **268**, 41–42.

COLLERSON, K. D. & FRYER, B. J. 1978. The role of fluids in the formation and subsequent development of early continental crust. *Contrib. Mineral. Petrol.* **61**, 151–167.

CONDIE, K. C. & ALLEN, P. 1984. Origin of Archean charnockites from southern India. *In:* KRONER, A., HANSEN, G. N. & GOODWIN, A. M. (eds) *Archean Geochemistry.* (Springer, Berlin), 182–203.

—— BOWLING, G. P. & ALLEN, P. 1986. Origin of granites in an Archaean high-grade terrane, southern India. *Contrib. Mineral. Petrol.* **92**, 93–103.

EVANS, C. R. & LAMBERT, R. ST. J. 1974. The Lewisian of Lochinver, Sutherland; the type area for the Inverian metamorphism. *J. geol. Soc. London*, **130**, 125–150.

FRIEND, C. R. L. 1983. The link between charnockite formation and granite production: evidence from Kabbaldurga, Karnataka, southern India. *In:* ATHERTON, M. P. & GRIBBLE, C. D. (eds) *Migmatites, Melting and Metamorphism*, Shiva Publications, Nantwich, pp. 264–276.

FYFE, W. S. 1973. The granulite facies, partial melting and the Archaean crust. *Phil. Trans. R. Soc. London*, **A273**, 457–462.

GILETTI, B. J., MOORBATH, S. & LAMBERT, R. ST. J. 1961. A geochronological study of the metamorphic complexes of the Scottish Highlands. *Q. J. geol. Soc. London*, **117**, 233–264.

GREEN, D. H. 1975. Genesis of Archaean peridotitic magmas and constraints on Archaean geothermal gradients and tectonics. *Geology*, **3**, 15–18.

HAMILTON, P. J., EVENSEN, N. M., O'NIONS, R. K. & TARNEY, J. 1979. Sm–Nd systematics of Lewisian gneisses: implications for the origin of granulites. *Nature, London*, **277**, 25–28.

HANSEN, E. C., NEWTON, R. C. & JANARDHAN, A. S. 1984. Fluid inclusions in rocks from the amphibolite-facies to charnockite progression in southern Karnataka, India: direct evidence concerning the fluids of granulite facies metamorphism. *J. Metamorphic Geol.* **2**, 249–264.

HEIER, K. S. 1973. Geochemistry of granulite facies rocks and problems of their origin. *Phil. Trans. R. Soc. London*, **A273**, 429–442.

—— & THORESEN, K. 1971. Geochemistry of high grade metamorphic rocks, Lofoten-Vesteralen, north Norway. *Geochim. Cosmochim. Acta*, **35**, 89–99.

HELLMAN, P. L. & GREEN, T. H. 1979. The role of sphene as an accessory phase in the high-pressure partial melting of hydrous mafic compositions. *Earth planet Sci. Lett.* **42**, 191–201.

HOLE, M. J., SAUNDERS, A. D., MARRINER, G. F., & TARNEY, J. 1984. Subduction of pelagic sediment: implications for the origin of Ce-anomalous basalts from the Mariana Islands. *J. geol. Soc. London*, **141**, 453–472.

HOLLAND, J. G. & LAMBERT, R. ST. J. 1975. The chemistry and origin of the Lewisian gneisses of the Scottish mainland: the Scourie and Inver assemblages and sub-crustal accretion. *Precambrian Res.* **2**, 161–174.

HUMPHRIES, F. J. & CLIFF, R. A. 1982. Sm–Nd dating and cooling history of Scourian granulites, Sutherland. *Nature, London*, **295**, 515–517.

JAHN, B-M. & ZHANG, Z. Q. 1984. Archaean granulite gneisses from eastern Hebei province, China: rare-earth geochemistry and tectonic implications. *Contrib. Mineral. Petrol.* **85**, 224–243.

LOWMAN, P. D. 1984. Formation of the earliest continental crust: inferences from the Scourian Complex of Northwest Scotland and geophysical models of the lower continental crust. *Precambrian Res.* **24**, 199–215.

MOORBATH, S. 1984. Origin of granulites. *Nature, London*, **312**, 290–291.

—— & TAYLOR, P. N. 1981. Isotopic evidence for continental growth in the Precambrian. *In:* KRONER, A. (ed) *Precambrian Plate Tectonics*. Elsevier, Amsterdam, pp. 491–525.

—— WELKE, H. & GALE, N. H. 1969. The significance of lead isotope studies in ancient high grade metamorphic basement complexes, as exemplified by the Lewisian rocks of N.W. Scotland. *Earth planet Sci. Lett.* **6**, 245–256.

PEARCE, J. A. 1983. Role of the sub-continental lithosphere in magma genesis at active continental margins. *In:* HAWKESWORTH, C. J. & NORRY, M. J. (eds) *Continental Basalts and Mantle Xenoliths*. Shiva Publications, Nantwich, pp. 230–249.

PIDGEON, R. T. & BOWES, D. R. 1972. Zircon U–Pb ages of granulites from the central region of the Lewisian, north-west Scotland. *Geol. Mag.* **109**, 247–258.

POWELL, R. 1983. Processes in granulite-facies metamorphism. *In:* ATHERTON, M. P. & GRIBBLE, C. D. (eds) *Migmatites, Melting and Metamorphism*. Shiva Publications, Nantwich, pp. 127–139.

ROLLINSON, H. R. 1980. Iron-titanium oxides as an indicator of the role of the fluid phase during the cooling of granites metamorphosed to granulite grade. *Mineralog. Mag.* **43**, 623–631.

RUDNICK, R. L., MCLENNAN, S. M. & TAYLOR, S. R. 1985. Large ion lithophile elements in rocks from high-pressure granulite facies terrains. *Geochim. Cosmochim. Acta*, **49**, 1645–1655.

SAUNDERS, A. D., TARNEY, J., STERN, C. R. & DALZIEL, I. W. D. 1979. Geochemistry of marginal basin floor igneous rocks from southern Chile. *Bull. geol. Soc. Am.* **90**, 237–258.

SHAW, D. M. 1968. A review of K-Rb fractionation trends by covariance analysis. *Geochim. Cosmochim. Acta*, **32**, 573–601.

SHERATON, J. W. 1970. The origin of the Lewisian gneisses of northwest Scotland, with particular reference to the Drumbeg area, Sutherland. *Earth planet Sci. Lett.* **8**, 301–310.

—— 1984. Chemical changes associated with high-grade metamorphism of mafic rocks in the East Antarctic Shield. *Chemical Geology*, **47**, 135–157.

—— & BLACK, L. P. 1983. Geochemistry of Precambrian gneisses: relevance for the evolution of the East Antarctic Shield. *Lithos*, **16**, 273–296.

—— & COLLERSON, K. D. 1984. Geochemical evolution of Archaean granulite-facies gneisses in the Vestfold Block and comparisons with other Archaean gneiss complexes in the East Antarctic Shield. *Contrib. Min. Pet.* **87**, 51–64.

——, SKINNER, A. C. & TARNEY, J. 1973. Geochemistry of the Scourian gneisses of the Assynt district. *In:* PARK, R. G. & TARNEY, J. (eds) *The Early Precambrian of Scotland and Related Rocks of Greenland*. Univ. Keele, pp. 13–30.

SIGHINOLFI, G. P., FIGUEREDO, M. C. H., FYFE, W. S., KRONBERG, B. I. & TANNER OLIVERIA, M. A. F. 1981. Geochemistry and petrology of the Jequie granulite complex (Brazil): and Archean basement complex. *Contrib. Mineral Petrol.* **78**, 263–271.

SILLS, J. D., SAVAGE, D., WATSON, J. V. & WINDLEY, B. F. 1982. Layered ultramafic-gabbro bodies in the Lewisian of northwest Scotland: geochemistry and petrogenesis. *Earth planet Sci. Lett.* **58**, 345–360.

SUN, S.-S. 1980. Lead isotopic study of young volcanic rocks from mid-ocean ridges, ocean islands and island arcs. *Phil. Trans. R. Soc. London*, **A297**, 409–445.

SUTTON, J. & WATSON, J. 1951. The pre-Torridonian metamorphic history of the Loch Torridon and Scourie areas in the North-West Highlands and its bearing on the chronological classification of the Lewisian. *Q. J. geol. Soc. London*, **106**, 241–296.

TARNEY, J. 1976. Geochemistry of Archaean high-grade gneisses, with implications as to the origin and evolution of the Precambrian crust. *In:* WINDLEY, B. F. (ed) *The Early History of the Earth*. Wiley, London, pp. 405–418.

——, SHERATON, J. W. & SKINNER, A. C. 1972. A geochemical comparison of major Archaean gneiss units from North-west Scotland and East Greenland. *Reports 24th Int. Geol. Congr., Montreal*, **1**, 162–174.

——, WEAVER, B. L. & DRURY, S. A. 1979. Geochemistry of Archaean trondhjemitic and tonalitic gneisses from Scotland and East Greenland. *In:* BARKER, F. (ed) *Trondhjemites, Dacites and Related Rocks*. Elsevier, Amsterdam, pp. 275–299.

TAYLOR, P. N., MOORBATH, S., GOODWIN, R. &

PETRYKOWSKI, A. 1980. Crustal contamination as an indicator of the extent of early Archaean continental crust: Pb isotopic evidence from the late Archaean gneisses of west Greenland. *Geochim. Cosmochim. Acta*, **44**, 1437–1453.

TAYLOR, S. R. & MCLENNAN, S. M. 1981. the composition and evolution of the continental crust: Rare earth element evidence from sedimentary rocks. *Phil. Trans. R. Soc. London*, **A301**, 381–399.

WEAVER, B. L. 1980. Rare-earth element geochemistry of Madras granulites. *Contrib. Mineral Petrol.* **71**, 271–279.

—— & TARNEY, J. 1980. Rare-earth geochemistry of Lewisian granulite-facies gneisses, northwest Scotland: implications for the petrogenesis of the Archaean lower continental crust. *Earth planet Sci. Lett.* **51**, 279–296.

—— & —— 1981. Lewisian gneiss geochemistry and Archaean crustal development models. *Earth planet Sci. Lett.* **55**, 171–180.

—— & —— 1983a. Elemental depletion in Archaean granulite-facies rocks. *In:* ATHERTON, M. P. & GRIBBLE, C. D. (eds) *Migmatites, Melting and Metamorphism.* Shiva Publications, Nantwich, pp. 250–263.

—— & —— 1983b. Chemistry of the sub-continental mantle: inferences from Archaean and Proterozoic dykes and continental flood basalts. *In:* HAWKESWORTH, C. J. & NORRY, M. J. (eds) *Continental Basalts and Mantle Xenoliths.* Shiva Publications, Nantwich, pp. 209–229.

—— & —— 1984. Estimating the composition of the continental crust: an empirical approach. *Nature, London*, **310**, 575–577.

—— & —— 1985. Major and trace element composition of the continental lithosphere. *In:* POLLACK, H. N. & MURTHY, V. R. (eds) *Structure and Evolution of the Continental Lithosphere. Phys. Chem. Earth, Oxford,* **15**, pp. 39–68.

——, ——, WINDLEY, B. F. & LEAKE, B. E. 1982. Geochemistry and petrogenesis of Archaean metavolcanic amphibolites from Fiskenaesset, S.W. Greenland. *Geochim. Cosmochim. Acta*, **46**, 2203–2215.

WHITEHOUSE, M. J. & MOORBATH, S. 1986. Pb–Pb systematics of Lewisian gneisses—implications for crustal differentiation. *Nature, London*, **319**, 488–489.

WOOD, D. A., TARNEY, J. & WEAVER, B. L. 1981. Trace element variations in Atlantic ocean basalts and Proterozoic dykes from northwest Scotland: their bearing upon the nature and geochemical evolution of the upper mantle. *Tectonophysics*, **79**, 91–112.

WYLLIE, P. J. 1983. Experimental and thermal constraints on the deep-seated parentage of some granitoid magmas in subduction zones. *In:* ATHERTON, M. P. & GRIBBLE, C. D. (eds) *Migmatites, Melting and Metamorphism.* Shiva Publications, Nantwich, pp. 37–51.

J. TARNEY, Department of Geology, University of Leicester, Leicester LE1 7RH, UK.

B. L. WEAVER, School of Geology and Geophysics, University of Oklahoma, Norman, Oklahoma 73019, USA.

The magmatic evolution of the Scourian complex at Gruinard Bay

H. R. Rollinson & M. B. Fowler

SUMMARY: Scourian (Archaean) gneisses at Gruinard Bay form a bimodal suite of trondhjemites and amphibolites in which the trondhjemites form about 75% of the complex. The gneisses form a large-scale agmatite complex in which amphibolite, ultramafic rocks and tonalitic gneiss are enclosed in trondhjemitic and associated granitic gneiss. All lithologies have been metamorphosed to hornblende-granulite facies and subsequently retrogressed. Amphibolites are the earliest recognizable component of the agmatite complex and have a varied geochemistry, which in part reflects the heterogeneous nature of their source. It is postulated that they are fragments of Archaean ocean floor. As such they are potential source rocks for the quartzofeldspathic gneisses, and calculations show that the tonalite and trondhjemite can be derived by 30% and 20–30% partial melting respectively, of a basaltic source, similar in chemistry to the amphibolites, leaving a residue of clinopyroxene, garnet and hornblende. Granitic gneisses associated with the trondhjemite require a slightly lower degree of partial melting (c. 10%) and an eclogitic residue. Comparisons with experimentally determined phase equilibria indicate that the partial melting took place in the pressure range 10–20 kb, significantly shallower than the depth of partial melting in modern subduction zones.

Introduction

The Scourian (Archaean) gneisses at Gruinard Bay form a bimodal suite of trondhjemites and amphibolites, in which the trondhjemitic gneisses dominate to form about 75% of the surface area of the complex. In addition to amphibolite, smaller proportions of ultramafic, tonalitic and granitic gneisses occur. The Archaean geology of the area is not as well known as that in the Scourie–Laxford and Assynt areas. Nevertheless it has special features worthy of discussion, which highlight aspects of the evolution of the Scourian complex, not hitherto reported from these more northerly outcrops.

Previous studies of the geochemistry of the Lewisian complex (Weaver & Tarney 1980, 1981; Tarney et al. 1979) have emphasized the general aspects of the geochemical evolution of the area. The purpose of this paper is to describe in detail the geology and geochemistry of a small part of the Lewisian complex in order to i) determine from the field relationships the sequence of magmatic events amongst the igneous precursors of the gneiss complex, ii) use the major, trace and rare earth element geochemistry of each major suite of rock types to set limits on their fractionation histories and characterize the mineralogical nature of their source, and iii) thus produce a model for the evolution of the Scourian complex in this crustal section, from a knowledge of the relative ages of the igneous components and their petrogenesis.

Geochemical aspects of the post-magmatic high-grade metamorphism, in particular patterns of large ion lithophile (LIL) element depletion (Rollinson & Windley 1980b) are also important to the geochemical evolution of the area, but for reasons of brevity are dealt with elsewhere (Fowler 1986).

Geological setting

The Gruinard Bay area of the Lewisian complex was first described by Peach et al. (1907) and more recently by Davies (1977). A brief description of the geochemistry is given in Holland & Lambert (1973). Whilst no detailed geochronological studies have been made, the Gruinard Bay lithologies are generally accepted as Scourian because the structural relationships of the Scourie dykes indicate little post-intrusion deformation of the gneisses (Sutton & Watson 1951), and the lead isotope composition of the latter falls into the general pattern of the southern region Lewisian (Moorbath & Park 1971).

From a detailed analysis of Scourie dykes, Davies (1977) showed that southeast of Gruinard Bay there is an area of extremely low Laxfordian strain and that intrusive relationships amongst rocks of Scourian age are locally preserved. These are the product of the intrusion of trondhjemite sheets and veins into older gneisses and amphibolites, giving rise to a large-scale agmatite complex in which blocks of amphibolite and older gneiss occur as rafts in trondhjemite and trondhjemitic gneiss. We have studied the geological relationships and collected samples from four small areas in the agmatite complex at Lochan

From: PARK, R. G. & TARNEY, J. (eds), 1987, Evolution of the Lewisian and Comparable Precambrian High Grade Terrains, Geological Society Special Publication No. 27, pp. 57–71.

an Daimh (NG 983 923), Cnoc Bad Nan Cuileag (NG 948 883), Loch an Fhamhair (NG 960 978) and Carn nan con-easan (NG 988 872) (Fig. 1).

Amphibolites

Amphibolites are probably the earliest component of the gneiss complex. They occur as blocks ranging in size from rafts as much as 300 m long to much smaller fragments dispersed in the gneiss, and tend to be organized into both large and small-scale agmatite trains. Their blocky, rather than boudinaged appearance reflects the low strain postdating the trondhjemite emplacement. All amphibolite bodies are penetrated by trondhjemite veins, often most intense at the margins of large blocks. They now have an amphibolite-facies mineralogy, although some samples preserve evidence of an earlier granulite-facies texture. The field relationships provide no firm evidence for the origin of the amphibolites as no pillows or relict igneous textures are preserved. Their original form is, therefore, in some doubt and they could represent fragments of basic lavas or remnants of an early intrusive suite.

The amphibolites are, however, regarded by Davies (1977) as distinct from the layered gabbro-ultramafic complexes, well known from farther

north in the Lewisian complex (Sills *et al.* 1982; Savage & Sills 1980). The latter are also represented at Gruinard Bay by fragments of ultrabasic rocks in the agmatite complex, the best preserved example being at Meall Buidhe (Davies 1977). Amphibolites may be distinguished from these in the field by their medium to fine grain-size and their banded appearance which reflects varying proportions of hornblende and plagioclase. The ultramafic rocks are sometimes cut by thin (1 cm wide) amphibole-rich veins. In one instance, at Lochan an Daimh, a thin lens of ultramafic schist is enclosed in the amphibolite.

Tonalitic gneisses

Rocks of broadly tonalitic composition (61–68% SiO_2) are preserved as banded biotite-rich gneisses at a few localities in the complex. The samples described here were collected at Lochan an Daimh and at Loch an Fhamhair. Enclosed within the tonalitic gneiss are pods of hornblendite and amphibolite a few tens of centimetres long, often showing a slight banding which is discordant to the banding in the tonalitic gneiss. These either intruded into the tonalitic gneiss, or were included in the gneiss during emplacement, and may or may not be related to the larger amphibolite bodies. The tonalitic gneisses are intruded by, and enclosed in, the trondhjemitic gneisses and thus represent an earlier magmatic episode. Their banding is not a feature of the later trondhjemites and thus records an early, pre-trondhjemite deformation. Those collected for this study now show amphibolite-facies mineral assemblages but Field (1978) described granulite-facies tonalites from a locality at the northern edge of the map in Fig. 1 and it is possible that the majority of the tonalites are retrogressed granulites (see petrography, below).

Trondhjemites

Trondhjemite forms the dominant intrusive phase in the gneiss complex and may be divided into two types on the basis of the field relationships: i) areally extensive, relatively homogeneous trondhjemitic gneiss and ii) trondhjemite veins, up to 1 m wide in amphibolite and tonalitic gneiss. The homogeneous trondhjemitic gneiss showing a wispy banding and a weak fabric, is medium to coarse grained and occasionally contains plagioclase megacrysts. It is best seen at Cnoc Bad nan Cuileag (Fig. 1). Trondhjemite veins are found most commonly in the amphibolites, but are also found in the tonalitic gneiss. They often form as apophyses from homogeneous trondhjemitic gneiss and vary from a few cm to

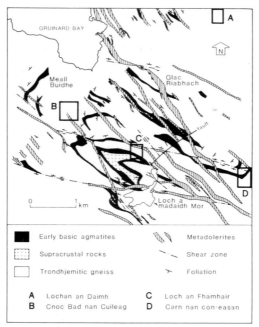

FIG. 1. Geological map of the area southeast of Gruinard bay, showing the sampling areas of this study (after Davies 1977).

about 1 m wide and generally are intruded sub-parallel to the banding of their host. The amount of trondhjemite is variable so that there is a complete gradation from amphibolite with tron-dhjemite veins, through agmatite to trondhjemi-tic gneiss with dispersed amphibolitic blocks. The present mineral assemblage was formed under amphibolite-facies conditions, but the common presence of hornblende-quartz symplec-tites perhaps signals the former presence of pyroxene.

Granitic gneisses

Granitic gneiss is found as irregular patches intimately mixed with trondhjemite. The seven samples collected in this study come principally from the locality at Lochan an Daimh (Fig. 1). Granitic gneisses are recognized in the field by their pink colour imparted by the presence of microcline. They are geochemically distinct from the trondhjemites, although they are closely related with respect to their relative age and mode of emplacement.

Metamorphism

Previous workers have disagreed over the original metamorphic grade of the Scourian rocks at Gruinard Bay (Davies 1977; Field 1978). The results of this study (see section on petrography below) indicate that all the major rock types show some evidence of granulite-facies metamorph-ism, although they are now extensively retro-gressed. Thus a granulite-facies metamorphic event post-dated the emplacement of the tron-dhjemites. What is not clear, is whether an earlier high grade event accompanied the deformation of the tonalitic gneiss prior to the intrusion of the trondhjemites. Preliminary geothermometry (Sills & Rollinson this vol.) suggests a metamor-phic maximum at about $750 \pm 50°C$ for the granulite-facies metamorphism.

The geological history of the area may therefore be summarized as follows: 1. Amphibolites (bas-altic lavas ?) + layered complexes. Tonalitic mag-mas emplaced. 2. Deformation and (?) meta-morphism. 3. Trondhjemite and granite magmas emplaced. 4. Deformation and amphibolite-to hornblende granulite-facies metamorphism. 5. Retrogression.

Unfortunately, as yet, there is little detailed geochronological control on these demonstrably separate components of the Scourian event.

Comparison with the type area at Scourie

In contrast to the Scourian gneisses at Scourie, where the major gneiss-type is tonalite, the

dominant gneiss-type at Gruinard Bay is tron-dhjemite. At Scourie there is apparently a continuum of bulk compositions from acid to basic, whereas Gruinard Bay has an essentially bimodal trondhjemite–amphibolite assemblage (see Fig. 2). Granulite facies metamorphism at Scourie was accompanied by massive depletion of LILEs, in particular the elements K, Rb, Th and U (Weaver & Tarney 1981; Rollinson & Windley 1980*b*), whereas the hornblende granu-lite facies gneisses (*ie* hornblende-two pyroxene gneisses) at Gruinard Bay have LILE abundances transitional between the strongly depleted Scourie granulites and amphibolite facies gneisses at Rhiconich (Fowler 1986). Mafic rocks at Scourie are dominated by the layered gabbro–ultramafic complexes whereas amphibolites of a different character and possibly of supracrustal origin are common at Gruinard Bay.

Despite these differences between the two areas, the sequence of deformation and magma-tism appears to be similar. At Gruinard Bay trondhjemites post-date an early deformation and metamorphism, which involved the tonalites and amphibolites—but the trondhjemites are them-selves deformed, as evidenced by folded agmatite trains within them. Likewise at Scourie, minor trondhjemite sheets cut early Scourian folds, but are themselves deformed and metamorphosed to granulite grade. Thus a similar sequence of events is recorded in both areas and the principal differences are those of degree. It seems likely that the Scourie area represents a slightly deeper level in the crust, into which a relatively small volume of later trondhjemite was emplaced, whereas the Gruinard Bay region was at a higher

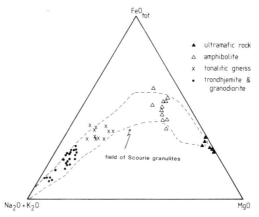

Fig. 2. A–F–M diagram for the Scourian rocks of Gruinard Bay, compared with the field for granulite-facies gneisses from Scourie (Rollinson & Windley 1980*a*).

level in the crust, intruded by a larger volume of trondhjemitic magma.

Petrography

Amphibolites

The amphibolites are principally composed of hornblende and intermediate plagioclase in varying proportions. Clinopyroxene and scapolite are present in some samples, and accessory phases include magnetite, calcite, clinozoisite, biotite, sphene, chlorite and allanite. They are medium grained and many samples are made up of equidimensional grains of hornblende and zoned plagioclase; some hornblende grains are densely sieved with quartz grains and in places overgrow clinopyroxene. The equigranular texture, together with the presence of relict clinopyroxene, scapolite and hornblende sieved with quartz, (typical of hornblende after clinopyroxene), suggests that the amphibolites are retrogressed basic granulites.

Ultramafic rocks

Peridotites also have a granular texture and contain the mineral assemblage olivine (Fo_{88})-orthopyroxene-clinopyroxene-hornblende-green spinel-magnetite. The texture and mineral assemblage are typical of peridotites found at granulite facies in the Scourie area. Pyroxene pairs yield temperatures in the range 800–939°C and 680–850°C on the thermometers of Wood & Banno (1973) and Wells (1977) respectively; these temperatures are typical of those obtained on pyroxene pairs in granulite-facies terrains (Sills & Rollinson this vol.). The wide range in temperatures reflects extensive subsolidus equilibration following the peak of metamorphism (Rollinson 1981). Ultramafic schists, containing the mineral assemblages chlorite-cummingtonite and zoned tremolitic amphibole, are thought to be the retrogressed equivalents of the granulite-facies peridotites.

Tonalitic gneisses

The tonalitic gneisses are principally composed of quartz (21–39%), plagioclase (36–56%) and biotite (10–19%) and there is between 0–5% clinozoisite and hornblende. Accessory minerals include zoned allanite, rutile, sphene, apatite, zircon, chlorite, muscovite, and opaques. Plagioclase is oligoclase (An_{26}) and forms subhedral grains with curved to irregular grain boundaries. It is altered to sericite, scapolite and clinozoisite

and in places is cloudy with a high density of minute grains of clinozoisite. Hornblende is sieved with quartz inclusions and contains oriented exsolution lamellae. Biotite overgrows plagioclase and hornblende and is often intergrown with, and altered to, chlorite and epidote. (001) sections of biotite often show exsolved needles of rutile reflecting an originally high TiO_2 content, typical of hornblende-granulite and granulite-facies biotites (Stephenson 1977). Field (1978) described granulite-facies tonalitic gneisses from Gruinard Bay and, from the evidence of rutile exsolution in biotite and the poikiloblastic hornblende, it is possible that the tonalitic gneisses too are retrogressed granulites.

Trondhjemites

Trondhjemites contain the minerals plagioclase (38–70%), quartz (15–44%), hornblende (0–7%) and biotite (0–9%) (modal percentages). Accessory phases include sphene, zircon, allanite, apatite, garnet and microcline. Plagioclase is a weakly zoned oligoclase (An_{26}) and forms large euhedral grains in a matrix of quartz. It is frequently altered and replaced by sericite and small euhedral grains of clinozoisite and fine antiperthitic lamellae are altered to muscovite. Hornblende may occur as poikiloblastic single grains, sieved with quartz inclusions, or as aggregates of grains, intergrown with quartz. As suggested above, these poikiloblasts are thought to signal the former presence of pyroxene. Biotite overgrows plagioclase and hornblende, but is itself altered to chlorite and intergrown with, or overgrown by, clinozoisite. Phengitic muscovite replaces plagioclase and biotite and is intergrown with calcite. A range of textures reflects varying degrees of post-igneous recrystallization; quartz, plagioclase and hornblende are progressively recrystallized to a granular mosaic, and biotite and chlorite become more dominant.

Granitic gneisses

Granitic gneisses vary in composition between granite and granodiorite on the classification of Streckeisen (1976). They are principally composed of quartz (27–36%), plagioclase (32–43%), microcline (14–23%), muscovite (4–7%) and biotite (2–9%) (modal proportions). Accessory phases include sphene, rutile, epidote, zircon, metamict allanite, pyrite and apatite. Microcline forms large grains with perthitic texture containing blebby lamellae of plagioclase; these lamellae are heavily sericitised. In places microcline grains are recrystallized to aggregates of smaller grains, with irregular grain boundaries and display granular exsolution of plagioclase between grains. Plagioclase is slightly zoned oligoclase (An_{21}) and forms smaller grains than the microcline. The grains are frequently corroded at the margins and often sericitised and altered to clinozoisite and muscovite. Plagioclase–microcline grain boundaries are embayed, the plagioclase is zoned and myrmekite is developed. Quartz forms irregular grains with undulose extinction, although these may be recrystallized to equigranular aggregrates. Both primary and secondary fluid inclusions are present in quartz. Biotite forms fine grained aggregates on plagioclase and is altered to epidote and chlorite. Muscovite grows late on microcline, plagioclase or biotite and quartz-muscovite symplectites are formed at the margins of the larger muscovite porphyroblasts.

Geochemistry

In this section the geochemistry of each of the major units of the Scourian complex at Gruinard Bay is discussed in turn. A total of 58 samples was analysed. These were carefully selected on the basis of their field relationships, from areas of low deformation, in order to obtain rock compositions which show minimal alteration during later deformation. Whilst this study uses only a small number of samples it is important to emphasize that they were carefully chosen to be representative of the original igneous rocks from which the gneiss complex was formed. Representative analyses are given in Table 1 and average analyses in Table 2.

The bimodal nature of the geochemistry is emphasized in the AFM diagram in Fig. 2 which is in strong contrast to the smooth calc-alkaline trend for Scourian gneisses from Scourie and Assynt (Sheraton *et al.* 1973; Rollinson & Windley 1980a). It is possible that the intermediate compositions in the range 50–60% SiO_2 reported at Scourie and Assynt are the product of the 'smearing together' of mafic and intermediate compositions in the gneiss-forming processes; such rocks were therefore deliberately avoided in the sample collection for this study. Alternatively, the smaller volume of tonalitic rocks at Gruinard Bay may have hampered the sampling of the full range of possible compositions. There may, however, be real geochemical differences between Gruinard Bay and the Scourian rocks farther north. There is also a compositional gap between the amphibolites and ultramafic rocks, which is not apparent at Scourie, although this may be a function of the more extensive gabbro–ultramafic complexes present in the Scourie area (Sills *et al.* 1982).

Geochemistry and petrogenesis of amphibolites and ultramafic rocks

The amphibolites are predominantly normative olivine tholeiites. They show a number of chemical similarities to the layered gabbro complexes found farther north and also described at Gruinard Bay (Davies 1977) and it is possible that the two are related via a common parent magma (Rollinson in press). However, the amphibolites are chemically less fractionated and are more likely to represent liquid compositions than the cumulate rocks of the layered complexes. The amphibolites at Gruinard Bay are divisible, on the basis of their trace element chemistry into two groups—one with near chondritic Ti/Zr ratios, and a group of three samples with much higher Ti/Zr ratios.

Chemical alteration

The evidence given above shows that the amphibolites were engulfed in trondhjemitic magma, subsequently metamorphosed to granulite grade and then retrogressed to amphibolite grade. There is, therefore, a strong possibility that their chemistry has been disturbed following emplacement. Plots of major and trace elements against Zr (generally regarded as 'immobile' under the pertinent conditions) show only weak correlations. Limited element mobility may have blurred rather than totally destroyed original inter-element trends. However, incompatible elements such as Rb and Ba, which are expected to correlate with Zr in unaltered basaltic rocks, show a strong scatter reflecting considerable redistribution. On the other hand the elements Ti, Zr, Y and P retain good colinear trends (Fig. 3) which presumably reflect the primary igneous processes which led to their formation.

The REEs (Fig. 4) also show some evidence of mobility. The most striking example is sample 109, which contains a little allanite, resulting in strong enrichment in the light REE. Other evidence comes from sample 115, in which there is strong enrichment of La. Less severe La enrichment is seen in samples 104 and 146 and there is the possibility of some Pr enrichment in samples 115 and 146 although this could result from analytical uncertainty in the determination of Pr. However, with the exception of sample 109, the chief contaminant is La and thus the original REE patterns are not disturbed beyond recognition and can still be used to interpret the petrogenesis. The following discussion will therefore concentrate on elements whose mobility is likely to be minimal, that is Ti, Zr, Y, P and the middle to heavy REEs.

TABLE 1. *Representative analyses of the major lithologies in the Scourian complex at Gruinard Bay*

	Amphibolites					Tonalitic gneiss					Trondhjemite					Granitic gneiss		
Sample no.	104	109	115	146	150	123	135	136	156	159	120	162	168	169	171	131	132	133
SiO_2*	50.64	50.88	50.34	48.24	48.20	68.04	65.06	68.83	64.23	63.30	71.75	70.19	72.63	70.10	68.97	70.72	70.24	73.13
TiO_2	1.55	0.55	0.49	1.21	1.40	0.41	0.29	0.45	0.52	0.65	0.33	0.32	0.35	0.34	0.38	0.25	0.19	0.25
Al_2O_3	11.46	11.53	11.46	10.37	4.23	15.05	15.01	15.38	15.84	16.26	15.44	15.31	14.31	15.18	15.62	15.28	14.86	15.08
FeO_{tot}	13.28	10.91	10.00	12.97	12.82	3.41	3.70	3.36	4.66	5.14	1.75	2.55	2.47	2.60	2.50	1.76	1.26	1.12
MnO	0.23	0.24	0.22	0.24	0.27	0.05	0.05	0.05	0.09	0.17	0.03	0.03	0.03	0.02	0.03	0.02	0.02	0.02
MgO	6.33	8.53	9.76	8.99	11.82	1.47	2.16	1.58	1.58	1.17	0.67	0.82	0.70	0.65	0.71	0.61	0.27	0.25
CaO	10.17	11.10	11.40	11.58	15.83	4.54	6.51	4.87	4.78	4.22	3.24	3.67	3.29	3.57	3.33	1.66	1.15	1.49
Na_2O	2.04	2.57	1.60	1.68	0.63	3.99	3.58	4.01	4.69	4.91	4.66	4.78	4.23	4.92	4.36	4.30	4.18	3.52
K_2O	0.68	0.56	1.63	0.68	0.46	1.23	1.64	1.21	1.47	1.73	1.69	1.15	1.70	1.42	2.49	4.55	4.75	5.25
P_2O_5	0.16	0.03	0.02	0.01	0.10	0.08	0.04	0.08	0.09	0.11	0.07	0.08	0.06	0.08	0.13	0.09	0.04	0.04
TOT	96.53	96.93	96.91	95.97	95.76	98.27	98.04	97.82	97.95	97.56	99.62	98.90	99.77	98.88	98.52	99.25	98.96	100.15
Y†	31	12	12	20	15	1	5	3	9	8	1	3	1	2	2	5	3	2
Sr	184	246	23	123	46	403	333	398	283	363	393	420	355	356	406	623	431	520
Rb	6	5	5	5	3	31	38	29	42	49	27	28	30	29	40	86	82	82
Th	1	1	0	0	1		1	0	2	15	6	9	9	3	1	21	22	19
Pb	2	7	9	11	3	8	8	10	8	13	13	9	7	6	9	22	14	29
Ga	21	13	15	17	14	21	20	20	15	25	20	23	19	21	21	19	20	19
Zn	114	82	117	106	168	35	38	32	8	52	21	31	20	31	32	27	16	27
Ba	174	196	229	204	34	733	504	400	439	616	1081	512	1154	293	1870	1857	1843	2259
Ni	81	146	82	110	358	12	19	18	34	31	3	3	3	2	3	1	0	0
Cr	161	563	402	285	240	29	15	35	69	57	9	10	9	10	12	4	3	2
Zr	114	29	26	19	70	92	75	105	115	156	223	213	177	66	142	193	166	166
Nb	8	1	2	0	9	4	5	7	6	7	2	2	3	3	3	1	0	0
La‡	12.16	17.55	3.98	1.57	13.86	21.26	12.06	11.56	17.35	48.50	39.12	21.85	39.64	39.40	25.74	53.30	39.68	40.73
Ce	24.60	33.45	4.65	4.24	28.08	28.64	20.66	16.01	30.30	80.02	52.21	30.32	56.78	56.84	39.60	86.33	63.48	64.78
Pr	3.39	3.67	0.83	0.82	4.05	2.92	2.49	1.66	3.70	8.04	4.60	2.82	5.09	4.98	3.74	8.80	6.25	6.57
Nd	17.60	13.26	3.46	4.26	20.16	9.79	11.50	7.49	17.00	32.13	15.44	9.62	14.92	14.69	14.17	33.93	22.59	23.79
Sm	4.01	2.23	0.98	1.48	4.19	1.31	2.24	1.26	2.91	3.83	1.32	1.05	1.59	1.66	1.62	3.82	2.47	2.57
Eu	1.21	0.73	0.39	0.68	1.26	0.83	0.66	0.63	0.84	1.12	0.79	0.62	0.92	0.93	0.85	1.14	0.73	0.84
Gd	4.69	2.41	1.45	2.24	3.89	0.93	1.83	1.03	2.30	2.34	0.80	0.33	0.96	1.08	1.01	1.93	1.28	1.37
Dy	5.02	2.91	1.80	2.90	3.20	0.37	1.61	0.72	1.78	1.15	0.28	0.17	0.38	0.44	0.53	0.74	0.53	0.44
Er	3.13	1.95	1.23	1.90	1.52	0.15	0.86	0.40	0.94	0.65	nd	0.16	0.18	0.19	0.23	0.27	0.15	0.14
Yb	2.92	2.03	1.20	1.82	1.22	0.16	0.83	0.40	0.88	0.69	0.14	0.16	0.18	0.18	0.22	0.24	0.16	0.14
Lu	0.43	0.31	0.18	0.27	0.17	0.04	0.12	0.07	0.13	0.12	0.03	0.03	0.04	0.04	0.04	0.04	0.03	0.03

* Major elements expressed as wt %. Analyses made on a Philips PW 1450 XRF spectrometer, using −240 mesh pressed powder discs;
† Trace elements expressed as ppm. Analyses made by XRF on −240 mesh pressed powder discs.
‡ Rare earth elements expressed as ppm. Analyses made using inductively coupled plasma-source spectrometry, following ion exchange REE separation techniques.

Location of individual samples.

Sample no.	Map area (Fig. 1)	Grid Ref.	Sample no.	Map area (Fig. 1)	Grid Ref.	Sample no.	Map area (Fig. 1)	Grid Ref.	Sample no.	Map area (Fig. 1)	Grid Ref.
104	D	NG 987872	150	C	NG 961878	156	C	NG 960787	168	B	NG 947884
109	D	NG 988873	123	C	NG 982923	159	C	NG 960878	169	B	NG 946884
115	D	NG 989873	135	D	NG 983923	120	D	NG 987874	171	A	NG 947884
146	A	NG 984922	136	B	NG 983923	162	B	NG 947885	131	A	NG 984922
									132	A	NG 984923
									133	A	NG 984923

TABLE 2. *Means and standard deviations of analyses of the main Scourian lithologies at Gruinard Bay*

	Amphibolite	High Ti/Zr Amphibolite	Tonalite	Trondhjemitic gneiss	Vein Trondhjemite	Granite
SiO_2	50.53 (0.94)	47.16 (1.2)	64.65 (2.0)	71.00 (2.0)	70.80 (4.3)	70.87 (2.1)
TiO_2	0.72 (0.37)	1.16 (0.06)	0.48 (0.10)	0.34 (0.06)	0.17 (0.14)	0.29 (0.10)
Al_2O_3	11.61 (0.53)	10.38 (0.11)	15.60 (0.63)	15.00 (0.47)	15.95 (2.0)	15.23 (0.41)
FeO_{tot}	10.82 (0.30)	13.14 (0.22)	4.32 (0.73)	2.40 (0.28)	1.53 (1.1)	1.77 (0.67)
MnO	0.21 (0.02)	0.23 (0.01)	0.07 (0.02)	0.03 (0.01)	0.03 (0.03)	0.03 (0.01)
MgO	8.64 (1.3)	8.98 (0.15)	1.75 (0.47)	0.69 (0.10)	0.52 (0.32)	0.59 (0.31)
CaO	10.88 (0.64)	11.96 (0.46)	5.02 (1.2)	3.40 (0.21)	3.68 (0.89)	2.19 (0.93)
Na_2O	2.40 (0.42)	1.60 (0.34)	4.52 (0.49)	4.60 (0.26)	5.57 (0.87)	4.20 (0.62)
K_2O	1.01 (0.37)	0.72 (0.05)	1.34 (0.40)	1.66 (0.41)	0.91 (0.32)	3.87 (1.4)
P_2O_5	0.05 (0.05)	0.01 (0.01)	0.07 (0.03)	0.07 (0.02)	0.01 (0.03)	0.07 (0.04)
Y	17 (8)	17 (3)	6 (4)	1 (0.6)	1 (2.8)	3 (2)
Sr	220 (63)	108 (24)	336 (63)	387 (45)	469 (160)	546 (88)
Rb	15 (10)	4 (2)	36 (13)	31 (5)	16 (8)	67 (19)
Th	1 (2)	1 (1)	3 (5)	5 (7)	1 (1)	16 (13)
Pb	7 (2)	11 (2)	10 (2)	9 (2)	12 (5)	20 (8)
Ga	16 (3)	16 (2)	22 (3)	21 (1)	18 (4)	20 (2)
Zn	106 (20)	127 (20)	42 (15)	26 (6)	19 (9)	28 (7)
Ba	207 (101)	142 (54)	478 (168)	1013 (480)	770 (695)	1909 (877)
Ni	106 (29)	133 (22)	25 (9)	3 (1)	7 (4)	2 (3)
Cr	411 (220)	259 (23)	52 (23)	9 (2)	14 (15)	7 (7)
Ce	19 (12)	6 (3)	31 (15)	51 (18)	22 (13)	75 (28)
La	10 (6)	6 (4)	16 (12)	30 (12)	11 (8)	43 (15)
Zr	48 (29)	20 (3)	133 (53)	190 (52)	199 (192)	198 (65)
Nb	3 (2)	2 (2)	5 (1)	3 (1)	2 (1)	2 (2)
n	9	3	10	10	13	7

Incompatible element ratios

Plots of Ti vs Y, Ti vs Zr, Y vs Zr and P_2O_5 vs Zr are shown in Fig. 3. The ratios Ti/Y, Ti/Zr and Zr/Y for both amphibolites and ultramafic rocks broadly conform to the chondritic values of Nesbitt & Sun (1976), apart from the three samples already noted which are higher. On closer examination however, the best fit line to the Ti–Zr for the main group of amphibolites indicates a ratio of about 83—lower than the chondritic value suggested by Nesbitt & Sun (1976) and lower than that observed in many Archaean mafic rocks (Sun *et al.* 1979), although similar to that observed in some MORBs (Bougault & Treuil 1980). This implies (since the Zr/Y ratios are chondritic) Ti depletion, possibly in the source region. P_2O_5 is colinear with Zr but is consistently below chondritic values.

Rare earth element geochemistry

The most marked feature of the REE patterns of the Gruinard Bay amphibolites is their variability (Fig. 4). There are striking differences between rocks of similar major element composition. Patterns vary from flat, flat and LREE depleted, to steep [$(Ce/Yb)_n = 5.8$ to 0.59]. Eu anomalies are not pronounced, but range from slight positive to slight negative ($Eu/Eu^* = 0.86$ to 1.15).

Petrogenesis

The main group of amphibolites is characterized by a moderate spread of MgO values (6·55–10·5 wt % dry), a wide spread of incompatible element values (Zr = 24–114 ppm) and flat to slightly steepened REE patterns. It is theoretically possible for the bulk of the major and trace element variability to be accounted for by 80% fractionation of the assemblage $olivine_{10}$ $clinopyroxene_{50}$ $plagioclase_{40}$. However, this model is incapable of fully explaining the chemistry of the suite. Rocks containing 9–10% MgO—possible unfractionated basaltic compositions—show a range of Zr (29–45 ppm) and Ni (82–158 ppm) concentrations, suggesting a variety of primary liquid compositions and/or cumulate enriched liquids. It is therefore clear that these samples do not represent a simple comagmatic suite, although the broad uniformity of incompatible element ratios indicates that most samples were derived from a mantle source region with similar chemistry, suggesting that they may be cogenetic. However, the variability of the HREE slope between amphibolites 104 and 115 is not explicable solely in terms of low pressure fractionation

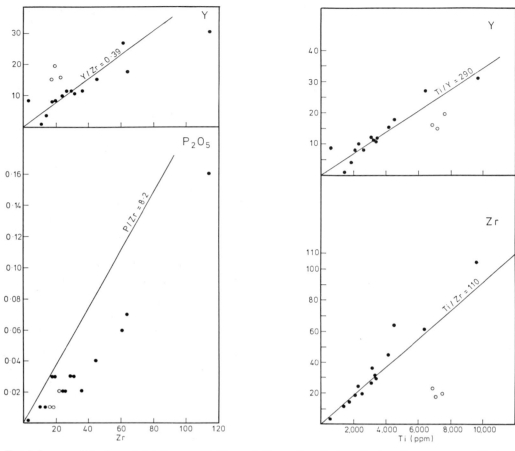

FIG. 3. Incompatible element plots for amphibolites and ultramafic rocks from Gruinard bay compared with the chondritic ratios for Ti/Y, Ti/Zr, Y/Zr and P/Zr (Nesbitt & Sun 1976).

and suggests a derivation from a slightly different mantle source region.

The three samples with high Ti/Zr ratios include amphibolite 146, which, unlike the other REE patterns shown in Fig. 4, is LREE depleted. They contain about 9% MgO and could be relatively unfractionated basaltic liquids. The differences in incompatible element ratios and REE patterns between them and the main group of amphibolites suggest that they are derived from a mantle source region slightly depleted in LREE, Zr, and P relative to Y and the HREE. It is apparent, therefore, that the variability in REE patterns and trace element ratios observed in the Gruinard Bay amphibolites is best explained by heterogeneity in their original source region. There is, however, one other possibility which cannot be fully ruled out, that of crustal contamination. It is possible that the range of REE

patterns is a product of mixing between a LREE depleted basalt and LREE enriched continental crust. However, this is unlikely since the basalts are thought to be one of the earliest components of this segment of continental crust.

The original tectonic setting of the basalts is difficult to establish given our present understanding of Archaean tectonic and igneous process. However, it should be noted that MORBs show a wide range of REE patterns from LREE enriched to LREE depleted (Sun et al. 1979; Saunders 1984), which encompass the range found at Gruinard Bay. Furthermore transitional (T–) type MORB, found on the Mid Atlantic Ridge contains the full range of REE patterns within a restricted area (Saunders 1984). It is possible, therefore, that the Gruinard Bay amphibolites are the product of tectonic processes analogous to those which produce T–type MORB.

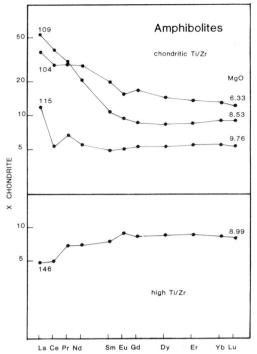

FIG. 4. Chondrite normalized REE patterns (after Nakamura 1974) for amphibolites from Gruinard Bay.

Geochemistry of the quartzo-feldspathic gneisses

Tonalitic gneisses

Tonalitic gneisses form only a small part of the gneiss complex, but an understanding of their origin is vital to any model for the early evolution of this region. Silica contents vary between 61–68 wt% SiO_2, but there are few clear trends on Harker diagrams (not shown), the chief ones being negative correlations between FeO and SiO_2 ($r = -0.787$), Ni and SiO_2 ($r = -0.729$) and a positive correlation between Sr and SiO_2 ($r = 0.861$). REE patterns vary in steepness (($Ce/Yb)_n = 6.3$ to 45.3) and may, or may not, show prominent positive Eu anomalies (Fig. 5). On the basis of these data two groups of samples may be tentatively identified—a group with high silica and prominent positive Eu anomalies (Fig. 5a) and a group with lower silica without Eu anomalies (Fig. 5b). These two groups can be related to one another by hornblende fractionation and this is consistent with the correlations observed in the major and trace element chemistry. However, it is not possible to relate individual samples to one another, thus implying the existence of a range of original tonalitic liquid compositions. It is possible to generate the REE pattern of tonalite 159 by c. 20% fractional crystallization of hornblende from a liquid with a REE pattern similar to tonalite 156 or 135, although with a lower SiO_2 content and higher

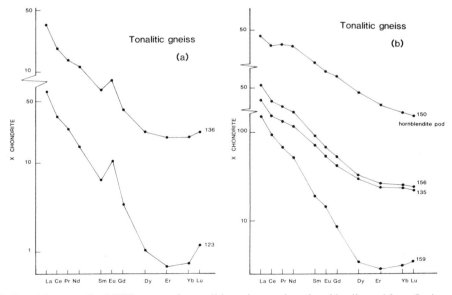

FIG. 5. Chondrite normalized REE patterns for tonalitic gneisses and one hornblendite pod from Gruinard Bay; a) High silica tonalitic gneiss (68–69% SiO_2); b) Low silica tonalitic gneiss (63–65% SiO_2).

total REE content (Fig. 5b). At higher SiO_2 contents the partition coefficients for REE in hornblende increase and lead to patterns with prominent positive Eu anomalies (Fig. 5a). It is interesting to note that a hornblendite pod, from within the tonalitic gneiss (sample 150—Fig. 5b), has an unusual major element chemistry for a rock of possible basaltic parentage (MgO 12%, CaO 10%, Al_2O_3 4%) but has a major element and REE pattern similar to that expected for an amphibole-rich residue from the tonalite. The least fractionated tonalitic liquids, therefore, are samples 156 and 135, which have REE patterns similar to tonalitic gneisses at Assynt (Weaver & Tarney 1980) and Scourie (Rollinson unpubl. data).

Trondhjemites

Two types of trondhjemite are described above and whilst the field evidence suggests that they are related, they are geochemically distinct (Fig. 6). Homogeneous trondhjemitic gneisses have a restricted major element chemistry (SiO_2 contents vary from 70–72·6 wt %) and steep REE patterns

$[(Ce/Yb)_n = 46–95]$ with marked positive Eu anomalies (Fig. 7), similar to trondhjemites described from elsewhere in the Lewisian complex (Weaver & Tarney 1980, 1981). It is interesting to note that the missing positive Eu anomaly, discussed by Condie et al. (1985) and ascribed to the lower continental crust, may in fact reside in trondhjemitic gneisses in the middle of the continental crust.

The trondhjemite veins on the other hand show great chemical diversity (SiO_2 contents vary from 64–76 wt%) and they show REE patterns quite atypical of Archaean trondhjemites (Fig. 8). The mean chemical compositions of both trondhjemite groups are similar (see Table 2) and this, together with the field evidence, indicates that the two are related. The homogeneous trondhjemitic gneisses may therefore be regarded as a parental liquid composition, whereas the chemical variability in the trondhjemite veins is a product of *in situ*, filter press, crystal fractionation operating during their emplacement. This hypothesis is supported by major element mixing calculations (not shown), which indicate that trondhjemite veins depleted in SiO_2 relative to the homogeneous trondhjemitic gneisses could have been produced by *c.* 36% accumulation of the assemblage plagioclase (85%) and hornblende (15%), whereas liquids enriched in SiO_2 could

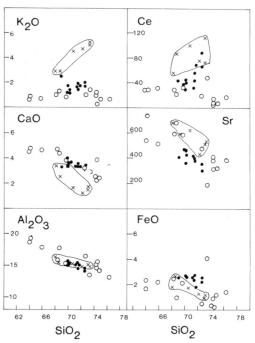

FIG. 6. Harker diagrams for homogeneous trondhjemitic gneiss (solid circles), trondhjemite veins (open circles) and granites (crosses); the field of the granitic gneisses is indicated. (Oxides in wt %, trace elements in ppm.)

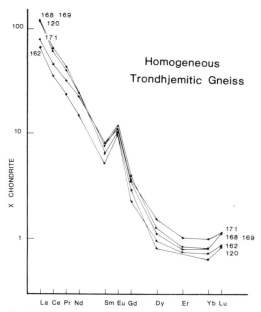

FIG. 7. Chondrite normalized REE patterns for homogeneous trondhjemitic gneiss from Gruinard bay.

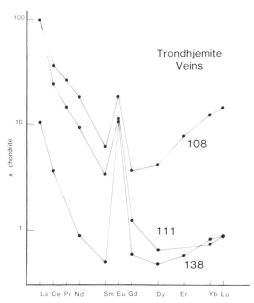

FIG. 8. Chondrite normalized REE patterns for trondhjemite veins from Gruinard Bay.

have been produced by the removal of *c.* 8% biotite together with minor proportions of plagioclase, hornblende and apatite. Minor phases, in particular allanite, apatite, zircon and garnet have exerted a strong control over the trace element chemistry of the trondhjemite veins, resulting in their very unusual REE patterns.

In view of the close association between the trondhjemite veins and amphibolites we investigated the possibility that trondhjemite veins at Gruinard Bay are the product of 'in situ' partial melting of the amphibolites. Using the dacite partition coefficients of Arth (1976) we calculated REE patterns for 5–40% melting of amphibolite assuming a residue of hornblende and plagioclase, in which the proportion of hornblende increases as partial melting proceeds. Our calculations show that there is no close correspondence between the calculated REE patterns and those measured for trondhjemite veins. The presence of a small amount of accessory sphene in the residue serves to reduce the total REE slightly (Green & Pearson 1983) and produce a Eu anomaly, but still cannot duplicate the measured REE patterns. Similarly, Sr values are too low in the melt (up to 320 ppm) compared with a mean value of 469 and a range of 180–740 in the vein trondhjemites. Thus we conclude that trace and REE data preclude the possibility that the trondhjemite veins are the product of partial melting of the amphibolites. A more detailed

discussion of the trondhjemite veins is beyond the scope of this contribution and will be presented elsewhere (Rollinson & Fowler in press).

There are only small systematic variations in the chemistry of the homogeneous trondhjemitic gneisses and these are explicable by minor plagioclase fractionation. The relatively uniform and unfractionated nature of the homogeneous trondhjemitic gneisses suggests that they are relatively unfractionated liquids and are representative of the original magmas. Thus a knowledge of their geochemistry can yield information on the nature of the parental material from which they were derived, and the melting process which operated during their genesis.

Granitic gneisses

Granitic and granodioritic gneisses form diffuse patches, a few tens of metres across, within trondhjemitic gneiss and form only a minor portion of the gneiss complex. Geochemically, they are distinct from the trondhjemitic gneisses (Fig. 6) but their close association suggests that the two are related. Selected Harker diagrams (Fig. 6) show a restricted range of compositions, comparable with the homogeneous trondhjemitic gneiss. The granitic gneisses are therefore unlikely to have undergone extensive crystal fractionation. Moreover, the higher level of Sr in the granitic gneisses, compared with that found in the homogeneous trondhjemites, indicates that they cannot be derived from the latter by plagioclase fractionation. Similarly, the comparable levels of FeO argue against a link via hornblende fractionation. However, for a number of oxides and trace elements they show similar but subparallel trends to the trondhjemites (eg CaO, K_2O, Sr) which might imply similarity of process but a different starting composition. This could be due, for example, to different degrees of partial melting of a common source and/or different source mineralogy. K_2O, Rb and Ba decrease with falling SiO_2 content, whilst CaO, Al_2O_3 and Sr increase. This variability may be explained by a small difference in the degree of partial melting of a source in which Sr is initially retained either in plagioclase or clinopyroxene. It is not possible, however, to rule out some plagioclase fractionation as an additional mechanism.

REE patterns for three samples from the silica-rich end of the range are slightly more fractionated than the trondhjemites, have higher LREE concentrations but similar HREE and lack the prominent positive Eu anomaly (Fig. 9).

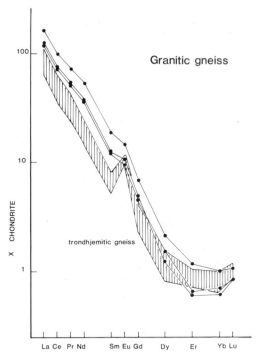

FIG. 9. Chondrite normalized REE patterns for granitic gneiss from Gruinard bay compared with the field of homogeneous trondhjemitic gneiss from Fig. 7.

Petrogenesis of the quartzo-feldspathic gneisses

The origin of Archaean tonalites, trondhjemites and associated magmas has been much debated and the current consensus favours an origin from a basic source either by fractional crystallization (Arth *et al.* 1978) or by partial melting (Barker & Arth 1976; Barker 1979; Arth 1979). The field relationships at Gruinard Bay, where there are large volumes of trondhjemite magma relative to tonalite and gabbro, and where the tonalite formed in an earlier gneiss-forming event, argue strongly for an origin for the trondhjemites via partial melting, rather than for fractional crystallization. The experimental studies of Stern (1974), Helz (1976), Peto & Hamilton (1976), Stern & Wyllie (1978), Holloway & Burnham (1972) and Spulber & Rutherford (1983) support this model and show that the partial melting of wet basalt over a range of pressures will yield trondhjemitic liquids.

In partial melting models for the origin of Archaean tonalites and trondhjemites the basaltic source composition is often equated with that of an Archaean tholeiite. Therefore we have modelled the effects of partial melting on the REE geochemistry of an amphibolite (normative olivine tholeiite) from the agmatite complex, using a batch melting model and partition coefficients from Arth (1976) and Irving & Frey (1978). We have chosen amphibolite 104 for the purposes of modelling as a likely starting composition, since this sample is a relatively unfractionated tholeiite, is unaltered, and has a REE pattern typical of many Archaean tholeiites (Condie 1976).

Tonalitic gneiss

The lack of a Eu anomaly in the REE patterns of the least fractionated tonalitic gneisses indicates that hornblende was not a prominent phase in equilibrium with the melt in the source region. Increasing Sr with increasing SiO_2 (not shown, $r = 0.86$) indicates that Sr is behaving incompatibly and that plagioclase is also not a prominent phase in the source. HREE depletion suggests a small amount of residual garnet. Calculations using the dacite Kd's of Arth (1976) and the highest andesite-basalt value for clinopyroxene yield a good fit, except for Ce, for 30% melting of sample 104 in equilibrium with the residue $clinopyroxene_{70}hornblende_{23}garnet_7$ (Fig. 10). Thus it is possible that the tonalites were generated by the wet melting of basalt leaving a residue containing a small amount of garnet.

Trondhjemite

The highly fractionated REE patterns of the trondhjemites indicate an appreciable amount of residual garnet retaining the HREE. The prominent positive Eu anomaly also suggests hornblende in the residue. Thus there is fair agreement between the observed REE patterns and those calculated for 20–30% equilibrium partial melting of a source with the composition of amphibolite 104 in equilibrium with a residue $clinopyroxene_{35}hornblende_{35}garnet_{30}$. However the fit is not perfect for Eu and the light REE, and a better fit is obtained by 20% partial melting with the residue $clinopyroxene_{70}hornblende_{10}garnet_{20}$, followed by 5% fractional crystallization of hornblende (Fig. 10). It is possible to obtain a similar result by 20% partial melting of a slightly more evolved basaltic parent (basic granulite 20N, Weaver & Tarney (1980)) with 4.3% MgO, with the residue $clinopyroxene_{35}hornblende_{35}garnet_{30}$ followed by 5% fractional crystallization of hornblende.

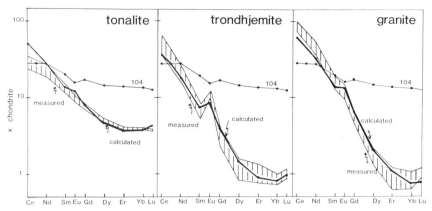

FIG. 10. Calculated values for REE produced by batch melting of a source with the same chemical composition as amphibolite 104. TONALITE—calculated REE pattern for a melt produced by 30% partial melting of amphibolite 104 in equilibrium with a residue of cpx_{70} hbl_{23} gt_7, compared with the field for least fractionated tonalitic gneiss. TRONDHJEMITE—calculated REE pattern for a melt produced by 20% partial melting of amphibolite 104 in equilibrium with a residue of cpx_{70} hbl_{10} gt_{20}, followed by 5% hornblende fractionation and compared with the field of trondhjemitic gneisses. GRANITE—calculated REE pattern for a melt produced by 10% partial melting of amphibolite 104 in equilibrium with a residue of cpx_{70} gt_{30} compared with the field of granitic gneisses.

Granitic gneisses

The close association of the granitic gneisses and the trondhjemites suggests that they were emplaced together. The similarity in their REE patterns is indicative of their derivation via similar processes from a similar source region. In detail, the REE patterns of the granitic gneisses are more fractionated and lack a prominent Eu anomaly. The absence of a Eu anomaly indicates that hornblende was probably not a prominent residual phase and may imply drier melting conditions. If the trondhjemites and granites were derived from a similar source then the higher K_2O content of the granites is indicative of a lower degree of partial melting for the granites than for the trondhjemites.

The results of batch melting calculations on amphibolite 104 show that there is good agreement for the middle and heavy REE for observed and calculated patterns assuming 10% partial melting and an eclogitic residue—clinopyroxene$_{70}$garnet$_{30}$ (Fig. 10). This result, however, does not satisfy the LREE unless the lowest possible Kds are used and it might be necessary to invoke some LREE addition to the melt following the partial melting of a basaltic source.

Condie (1981) suggested that some Archaean granites were produced by the partial melting of tonalites and/or trondhjemites at depth in the continental crust. The arguments presented above, together with the high Sr content of the Gruinard Bay granites, which preclude a plagio-clase-rich source, render this hypothesis untenable in this instance.

Discussion and conclusions

The oldest preserved rocks in the Gruinard Bay agmatite complex are probably the amphibolites. We have shown above that they have a complex and variable geochemistry, which indicates their derivation from a heterogeneous mantle source. In particular their variable REE patterns suggest that they were derived from both LREE enriched and depleted mantle sources possibly via a process analogous to that which produces modern T-type MORB (Saunders 1984). There is, therefore, some very tentative evidence to suggest that these basalts are fragments of Archaean ocean floor (Rollinson in press).

It is equally possible that there is no direct connection between the amphibolites and gneisses, and that the amphibolites are simply typical of mafic magmas produced in the Archaean, emplaced in the gneisses as tectonic or magmatic inclusions. However, in view of the experimental evidence which suggests a basaltic parent for trondhjemitic magmas we wish to draw attention to the fact that the Gruinard Bay amphibolites are potential source rocks and may be equivalent in composition to the material which was partially melted to produce the quartzo-feldspathic gneisses of the area. If the amphibolites are of an ocean floor origin then the high pressure residual mineralogy described above could imply that the quartzo-feldspathic gneisses were produced by the partial melting of wet basalt in a subducting slab. The early tonalitic gneisses were thus derived by *c.* 30% partial melting in equilibrium with the residue clinopyroxene$_{70}$hornblende$_{20}$garnet$_{10}$. The presence of hornblende indicates that the melting took place under hydrous conditions and the compilation of Green (1982) for tholeiite + 5% H_2O would place the residue in equilibrium with the melt in the pressure range 10–20 kb. The later trondhjemites were probably derived by a smaller degree of wet melting of basalt with a residue slightly richer in garnet (and possibly richer in hornblende) than for the tonalites. Granites associated with the trondhjemites were derived either by the hot dry melting of a basaltic source, similar to that of the trondhjemites, and at a similar depth to the trondhjemites (greater than 17 kb), or by wet melting at lower temperatures and higher pressures (greater than 20 kb). Thus the tonalitic and trondhjemitic liquids could have been generated by the partial melting of basalt under slightly different conditions of P–T–XH_2O in a hydrated basaltic slab. Partial melting took place in the pressure interval 10–20 kb, implying a depth of melting significantly shallower than that in modern subduction zones (Dickenson & Hatherton 1967; Marsh 1976).

ACKNOWLEDGEMENTS: This work was initiated during the tenure of NERC studentships which are gratefully acknowledged. HRR also thanks Prof. B. F. Windley for help in the early stages of the project, Prof. J. Tarney, Drs G. Holland and J. Harpum and an anonymous reviewer for thoughtful reviews of the manuscript, Graham Hendry (Univ. Birmingham) for running the XRF analyses and the College of St Paul and St Mary for study leave during which this manuscript was prepared. MBF is indebted to Prof. J. V. Watson and Dr J. A. Plant for their enthusiastic supervision and to Dr J. N. Walsh for provision of the I.C.P. facilities at King's College, London.

References

ARTH, J. G. 1976. Behavior of trace elements during magmatic processes—a summary of theoretical models and their applications. *J. Res. U.S. geol. Survey*, **4**, 41–47.

—— 1979. Some trace elements in trondhjemites—their implications to magma genesis and palaeotectonic setting. *In*: BARKER, F. (ed.) *Trondhjemites, Dacites and Related rocks*. Elsevier. 123–132.

——, BARKER, F., PETERMAN, Z. E. & FRIEDMAN, I. 1978. Geochemistry of the gabbro–diorite–tonalite–trondhjemite suite of southwest Finland and its implications for the origin of tonalite and trondhjemite magmas. *J. Petrol.* **19**, 289–316.

BARKER, F. 1979. Trondhjemite: Definition, environment and hypotheses of origin. *In*: BARKER, F. (ed.) *Trondhjemites, Dacites and Related rocks*. Elsevier. 1–12.

—— & ARTH, J. G. 1976. Generation of trondhjemitic-tonalitic liquids and Archaean bimodal trondhjemite basalt suites. *Geology*, **4**, 596–600.

BOUGAULT, H. & TREUIL, M. 1980. Mid-Atlantic ridge: zero age geochemical variations between Azores and 22°N. *Nature, London*, **286**, 209–212.

CONDIE, K. C. 1976. Trace-element geochemistry of Archaean greenstone belts. *Earth Sci. Rev.* **12**, 393–417.

—— 1981. Geochemical and isotopic constraints on the origin and source of Archaean granites. *Spec. Publ. geol. Soc. Aust.* **7**, 469–479.

——, BOWLING, G. P. & ALLEN, P. 1985. Missing Eu anomaly and Archaean high-grade granites. *Geology*, **13**, 633–636.

DAVIES, F. B. 1977. The Archaean evolution of the Lewisian complex at Gruinard Bay. *Scott. J. Geol.* **13**, 189–196.

DICKENSON, W. R. & HATHERTON, T. 1967. Andesitic volcanism and seismicity around the Pacific. *Science*, **157**, 801–803.

FIELD, D. 1978. Granulites at Gruinard Bay. *Scott. J. Geol.* **14**, 359–361.

FOWLER, M. B. 1986. Large-ion lithophile element characteristics of an amphibolite to granulite facies transition at Gruinard Bay, North-west Scotland. *J. Metamorphic Geol.* **4**, 345–359.

GREEN, T. H. 1982. Anatexis of mafic crust and high pressure crystallisation of andesite. *In*: THORPE, R. S. (ed.). *Andesites*, 465–487. Wiley. New York.

—— & PEARSON, N. J. 1983. Effect of pressure on rare earth partition coefficients in common magmas. *Nature*, **305**, 414–416.

HELZ, R. T. 1976. Phase relations of basalts in their melting ranges at $pH_2O = 5kb$. Part II. Melt compositions. *J. Petrol.* **17**, 139–193.

HOLLAND, J. G. & LAMBERT, R. ST. J. 1973. Comparative major element geochemistry of the Lewisian of the mainland of Scotland. *In*: PARK, R. G. & TARNEY, J. (eds.) *The Early Precambrian of Scotland and related rocks of Greenland*. Univ. Keele. 51–62.

HOLLOWAY, J. R. & BURNHAM, C. W. 1972. Melting relations of basalt with equilibrium water pressure less than total pressure. *J. Petrol.* **13**, 1–29.

IRVING, N. & FREY, F. A. 1978. Distribution of trace elements between garnet megacrysts and host volcanic liquids of kimberlitic to rhyolitic composition. *Geochim. Cosmochim. Acta*, **42**, 771–787.

MARSH, B. D. 1976. Some Aleutian andesites: their nature and source. *J. Geol.* **84**, 27–45.

MOORBATH, S. & PARK, R. G. 1971. The Lewisian chronology of the southern region of the Scottish mainland. *Scott. J. Geol.* **8**, 51–74.

NAKAMURA, N. 1974. Determination of REE Ba, Fe, Mg, Na and K in carbonaceous and ordinary chondrites. *Geochim. Cosmochim. Acta.* **38**, 757–775.

NESBITT, R. W. & SUN, S. S. 1976. Geochemistry of Archaean spinifex textured periodotites and magnesian and low magnesian tholeiites. *Earth Planet. Sci. Lett.* **31**, 433–453.

PEACH, B. N., HORNE, J., GUNN, W., CLOUGH, C. T., HINXMAN, L. W. & TEALL, J. J. H. 1907. The geological structure of the NW Highlands of Scotland. *Mem. Geol. Surv. Gt. Britain* 668 pp.

PETO, P. & HAMILTON, D. L. 1976. Partial fusion of basalts and andesites under vapour excess and vapour deficient conditions at 10 kb total pressure. *In: Progress in Experimental Petrology.* Natural Environment Research Council 45–50. London.

ROLLINSON, H. R. 1981. Garnet-pyroxene thermometry and barometry in the Scourie granulites, N.W. Scotland. *Lithos*, **14**, 225–238.

—— (in press). Early basic magmatism in the evolution of Archaean high-grade gneiss terrains: an example from the Lewisian of N.W. Scotland. *Mineral. Mag.*

ROLLINSON, H. R. & FOWLER, M. B. (in press). Trondhjemite veins in Lewisian agmatiles at Gruinard Bay: crustal melting or filter-press fractionation? *Scott. J. Geol.*

—— & WINDLEY, B. F. 1980a. An Archaean granulite grade tonalite–trondhjemite–granite suite from Scourie, NW Scotland: Geochemistry and origin. *Contrib. Mineral Petrol.* **72**, 265–281.

—— & —— 1980b. Selective elemental depletion during metamorphism of Archaean granulites, Scourie, NW Scotland. *Contrib. Mineral Petrol.* **72**, 251–263.

SAUNDERS, A. D. 1984. The rare earth element characteristics of igneous rocks from the ocean basins. *In:* HENDERSON, P. (ed.) *Rare Earth Element Geochemistry*, 205–236. Elsevier.

SAVAGE, D. & SILLS, J. D. 1980. High pressure metamorphism in the Scourian of N.W. Scotland: evidence from garnet granulites. *Contrib. Mineral Petrol.* **74**, 153–163.

SHERATON, J. W., SKINNER, A. C. & TARNEY, J. 1973. The geochemistry of the Scourian gneisses of the Assynt district. *In:* PARK, R. G. & TARNEY, J.

(eds). *The Early Precambrian of Scotland and Related Rocks of Greenland.* Univ. Keele. 13–30.

SILLS, J. D., SAVAGE, D., WATSON, J. V. & WINDLEY, B. F. 1982. Layered ultramafic-gabbro bodies in the Lewisian of northwest Scotland: geochemistry and petrogenesis. *Earth planet. Sci. Lett.* **58**, 345–360.

SPULBER, S. D. & RUTHERFORD, M. J. 1983. The origin of rhyolite and plagiogranite in oceanic crust: an experimental study. *J. Petrol.* **24**, 1–25.

STEPHENSON, N. C. N. 1977. Coexisting hornblendes and biotites from Precambrian gneisses of the south coast of western Australia. *Lithos*, **10**, 9–27.

STERN, C. R. 1974. Melting products of olivine tholeiite basalts in subduction zones. *Geology*, **2**, 227–230.

—— & WYLLIE, P. J. 1978. Phase compositions through crystallisation intervals in basalt-andesite-H_2O at 30 kbar with implications for subduction zone magmas. *Am. Mineral.* **63**, 641–663.

STRECKEISEN, A. L. 1976. To each plutonic rock its proper name. *Earth Sci. Rev.* **12**, 1–34.

SUN, S. S., NESBITT, R. W. & SHARASKIN, A. YA. 1979. Geochemical characteristics of modern ocean basalts. *Earth planet. Sci. Lett.* **44**, 119–138.

SUTTON, J. & WATSON, J. V. 1951. The pre-Torridonian metamorphic history of th Loch Torridon and Scourie areas in the northwest highlands. *Q. J. geol. Soc. Lond.* **106**, 241–307.

TARNEY, J., WEAVER, B. L. & DRURY, S. A. (1979) Geochemistry of Archaean trondhjemitic and tonalitic gneisses from Scotland and East Greenland. *In:* BARKER, F. (ed). *Trondhjemites, Dacites and Related Rocks.* Elsevier. 275–300.

WEAVER, B. L. & TARNEY, J. 1980. Rare earth element geochemistry of Lewisian granulite-facies gneisses, NW Scotland: implications for the petrogenesis of the Archaean lower continental crust. *Earth planet. Sci. Lett.* **51**, 279–296.

—— & TARNEY, J. 1981. Lewisian gneiss geochemistry and Archaean crustal development models. *Earth planet. Sci. Lett.* **55**, 171–180.

WELLS, P. R. A. 1977. Pyroxene thermometry in simple and complex systems. *Contrib. Mineral. Petrol.* **62**, 129–139.

WOOD, B. J. & BANNO, S. (1973) Garnet-orthopyroxene and orthopyroxene-clinopyroxene relations in simple and complex systems. *Contrib. Mineral. Petrol.* **42**, 109–124.

H. R. ROLLINSON, Department of Geography and Geology, College of St Paul and St Mary, The Park, Cheltenham, Glos. GL50 2RH, UK.

M. B. FOWLER, Department of Geology, Royal School of Mines, Imperial College, Prince Consort Road, London SW7 2BP, UK.

The causes of the high-grade metamorphism of the Scourie complex, NW Scotland

A. C. Barnicoat

SUMMARY: A number of previous studies of the possible causes of Archaean high-grade metamorphism have suggested that the heat source was large bodies of (intermediate) magma emplaced within pre-existing crust. Geochronological data for the Lewisian indicate that there was probably a gap of c. 200 Ma between the cessation of significant igneous activity and the peak of high-grade metamorphism. This is sufficiently long to allow conductive dissipation of magmatic heat and to render a model of the metamorphism relying upon heat transported in by intrusions unsatisfactory. The quantity of deep-derived CO_2 that would be required to make it the primary cause of the metamorphism is larger than petrological considerations allow. Alternative models, based on enhanced basal heat-flow in a static crust or heat derived from the decay of radionuclides resident within the crust coupled with a more normal mantle heat-flow and tectonic crustal-thickening have been erected, and reveal that the P-T conditions and age data recorded by the Scourian granulites can be satisfied by such models.

Thermal models of this nature, and a consideration of the available petrological and geochronological data, suggest a very slow cooling rate which would allow considerable inter-crystalline diffusion to occur. This could give rise to the observed zoning profiles and other forms of re-equilibration found within the granulite-facies rocks of the Lewisian complex.

Using numerical thermal models, it is possible to examine the potential causes of metamorphism and sometimes to constrain the tectono-thermal history of a suite of rocks. Any conclusions are necessarily speculative as the timing and conditions of events are usually poorly constrained, due both to the limited amount of mineral composition and geochronological data available and to the cooling–closure problem which prevents precise estimation of metamorphic conditions. There are potentially two main energy sources for metamorphism (which are not necessarily mutually exclusive)—internal (radiogenic) heat, possibly magnified by tectonic thickening (cf England & Richardson 1977) and external heat, transferred by bodies of magma, deep-derived fluids or enhanced mantle heat flow (cf Oxburgh & Turcotte 1974; Schuiling & Kreulen 1979; Wells 1980). Several workers have previously used models based upon these sources of energy to examine the thermal evolution of the Earth's crust during the Archaean (eg Bickle 1978; England 1979; Wells 1980). Each examined different aspects and stressed a different type of model. Bickle (1978) concluded that as geotherms estimated from metamorphic conditions recorded by Archaean crustal rocks are not dissimilar to those recorded in recent orogenic belts such as the Alps, the palpably greater heat production during the Archaean must have been dispersed by more active plate creation and destruction processes. Wells (1980) demonstrated that models involving the emplacement of large volumes of tonalitic magma into a (thin) pre-existing crustal

pile suggest that the metamorphic conditions recorded are controlled by the large amounts of heat released by the crystallization of the magmas. He concluded that the metamorphic conditions bear little relation to the heat flowing into the crust from the mantle so it is impossible to constrain this 'mantle heat flow'. In a penetrating short analysis, England (1979) puts the case that in the Archaean, as in the Phanerozoic, recorded metamorphic conditions were generally due to transient events giving rise to hotter geotherms than those for the crust in a state of thermal equilibrium, and hence that the inversion from metamorphic conditions to causal process will generally be non-unique without additional data such as high-resolution radiometric dates. These are difficult, if not impossible to obtain for Archaean rocks, so thermal models of the Archaean stages of the Earth's evolution must necessarily remain speculative. In this paper, a number of models of the thermal evolution of the Scourie complex of NW Scotland are examined, with the view to testing them against the metamorphic and geochronological constraints currently available. In particular, peak metamorphic conditions of 1000°C at 10 kb have been assumed as representative of existing P-T data (see Barnicoat 1983 for sources).

Magmatically enhanced heat-flow models

The basal heat-flow into a metamorphic pile may be enhanced by a number of processes. Magmas or deep-derived fluids may transport substantial

From: PARK, R. G. & TARNEY, J. (eds), 1987, *Evolution of the Lewisian and Comparable Precambrian High Grade Terrains*, Geological Society Special Publication No. 27, pp. 73–79.

amounts of heat into the crust. The work of Wells (1980) has shown that the emplacement of large bodies of tonalitic magma into the crust can give rise to granulite-facies conditions. It may be that the cause of the high-grade metamorphism of the Scourie complex was the emplacement of the tonalitic gneisses that form the bulk of the complex. In models of this nature, the peak of metamorphism follows within 35 Ma of the emplacement of the igneous rocks, with temperatures subsequently decreasing to those supported by the basal heat flow and internal heat generation. Only in models of random accretion do post-intrusion temperature maxima at 36 km (c 10 kb) exceed 800°C.

On the basis of Pb-Pb and Sm-Nd studies, Moorbath *et al.* (1969) and Hamilton *et al.* (1979) concluded that the Lewisian was derived from the mantle at about 2.92 ± 0.05 Ga. The metamorphic growth of zircon has been dated at 2.66 ± 0.02 Ga by Pidgeon & Bowes (1972) and Chapman & Moorbath (1977) give a Pb-Pb age of 2.68 ± 0.06 Ga for high-grade metamorphism. A date of 2.62 ± 0.12 Ga for the separation of coarse crystals, now intergrowths of garnet and clinopyroxene, from a finer-grained basic gneiss matrix is given by the Sm-Nd mineral studies of Humphries & Cliff (1982). These geochronological data collectively suggest a period of > 200 Ma between intrusion of igneous rocks and metamorphism, rendering a model for the metamorphism based on the latent heat of tonalitic magmas unlikely.

The rejection of a magmatic heat-source is likely to be valid for most possible heat flows into the base of the crust. As Wells (1980) states, varying this heat flow will affect the absolute temperatures attained, especially at long times after emplacement, and it is quite conceivable that heat flow was of the order of 50 mW m^{-2}, sufficient to give rise to steady-state conditions of 800–1000°C at 35 km. However, post-emplacement erosion is likely to have been significant in the Cordilleran tectonic setting envisaged by Wells (1980) and this will reduce the maximum temperature attained by rocks starting to cool at a specific depth if the erosion starts before thermal equilibrium is achieved. Evidence from the Andes (Pitcher 1979, p. 645) suggests that erosion keeps pace with intrusion in a Cordilleran setting, rendering thermal equilibration in a static tectonic situation unlikely.

A redemption for the magmatism-based model for the Scourian metamorphism would be possible if it could be shown that near-surface emplacement of magma and accompanying burial of underlying material had occurred over an extended time period (of the order of 150–200 Ma)

or at 2.7 Ga, the time of the metamorphism. However, there is no evidence from the Lewisian of large-scale igneous activity over time-spans as long as this, and certainly not at times immediately prior to the peak of metamorphism, so the magmatically enhanced heat-flow model must be set aside.

Deep-derived fluid enhanced heat-flow models

In view of the currently popular model of granulite-facies metamorphism driven by deep-derived CO_2, it is worth investigating the suggestion that mantle-derived CO_2 may be the heat-source for metamorphism in certain instances (*eg* Schuiling & Kreulen 1979). To obtain an order of magnitude estimate for the quantity of CO_2 required, it has been assumed that the metamorphism is caused by temperatures remaining 100°C above equilibrium for 50 Ma. That this is a conservative estimate is shown by the slow cooling demonstrated by the geochronological data (Humphries & Cliff 1982; Humphries, in Cliff 1985). The density of CO_2 at 10 kbar and 1000°C is close to 1100 kg m^{-3}, its heat capacity at constant pressure about 1.6×10^5 J m^{-3} K^{-1} (Bottinga & Richet 1981). Given that the density of rock is about 2800 kg m^{-3} and its heat capacity about 2.5×10^6 J m^{-3} K^{-1} (England & Thompson 1984), it requires one volume of CO_2 200°C hotter than its surroundings to heat the rock by about 12°C and hence $c.$ 8 volumes of CO_2 to give a 100°C rise in rock temperature. To keep the temperature elevated by this amount for 50 Ma against an assumed cooling of 2 K Ma^{-1} would require about 0.2 vols. Ma^{-1}, giving a time-integrated CO_2-rock ratio of $8 + 0.2 \times 50 = 18$. The effect of passing these volumes of CO_2 through the rocks would be to dehydrate the terrain totally, and obliterate any lithological variation in stable isotope ratios (see Valley & O'Neill 1984, for discussion). As neither of these effects are seen in high-grade terrains, hot deep-derived CO_2 cannot be the main thermal cause of high-grade metamorphism.

Enhanced basal heat-flow models

Crustal or lithospheric thinning may increase thermal gradients and heat flows within the crust, as may changing convective regimes within the mantle. Whereas today, basal heat flow is estimated at 30 mW m^{-2} in stable crustal regions, it may have been as high as 50 mW m^{-2} in the Archaean, giving rise to steady-state temperatures of 800–1000°C at 35 km, depending on the internal heat production. Assuming that crust of at least this thickness was stable during the

Archaean, and thermal equilibrium was attained, it is conceivable that the metamorphism of the Scourie complex was the result of equilibration under conditions of high mantle heat flow. However, since the rocks record a steady decrease in pressure and temperature subsequent to the peak of metamorphism, it seems likely that equilibration occurred in a dynamic situation concurrent with uplift and erosion. The effects of this would be to reduce steady-state and transient temperatures attained at a given depth due to the upward transfer of heat by erosive mass-transport and the decrease in crustal thickness concomitant with this. This means that enhanced basal heat-flow alone is unlikely to have produced the metamorphic conditions recorded by the Scourie gneisses.

Tectonic thickening models

An alternative model of the metamorphism, requiring no additional external energy-source other than basal heat-flow is one in which crustal thickening by overthrusting gives rise to elevated temperatures by 'blanketing' the basal heat source. The rocks of the Scourie complex contain evidence for the repetition of the sequence within supracrustal belts by thrusting (Davies 1976; Coward *et al.* 1980). These supracrustal belts, dominated in places by metasediments, contain assemblages cofacial with the surrounding gneisses (Cartwright *et al.* 1985), implying that surface deposits have been transported to at least 35 km during the metamorphism under discussion. In addition, early mineral fabrics are defined by aggregates of quartz, feldspar and pyroxenes (Bowes 1978; Coward *et al.* 1980), suggesting a close inter-relationship between deformation and granulite-facies metamorphism. This deformation may have been of a 'thin-skinned' nature; in support of this suggestion, it may be noted that no large scale (>10 km) repetitions of sequence are apparent in the Scourie complex. These early (D_1) repetitions of the sequence have been deformed by large flat-lying F_2 fold structures (Davies 1976; Coward *et al.* 1980). Coward *et al.* (1980) suggest that fresh pyroxene did not grow during this deformation, and that amphibolite facies assemblages developed at this time in the eastern portion of the outcrop of the Scourie complex, although granulite facies assemblages were stable in the western part of the Scourie complex at or after this time. Davies (1976) considers that granulite-facies metamorphism was actively proceeding during and after this folding episode. It is not clear whether these two deformation episodes gave rise to the substantial crustal thickening postulated as causing the main

metamorphism. The exact mechanism and geometry of crustal thickening are in any case not crucial to the model presented here—England & Thompson (1984) have shown that the amount of crustal thickening is more important than the process by which it occurs. It is assumed here that the total crustal thickness during the Scourian metamorphism was of the order of 60 km—the rocks record burial to *c.* 35 km. They are currently underlain by 30–35 km of continental crustal rocks, which may have been, at least in part, placed there by later (Laxfordian) tectonic events subsequent to the processes under examination here. The exact total thickness of the crustal edifice at the time of metamorphism does not seriously affect the conclusions produced here.

The thermal evolution of the model has been approximated using an implicit finite-difference approximation of the 1-D heat-flow equation (see appendix). Heat transfer by conduction and solid-state convection (*ie* erosion) has been included. Energy transfer by melt migration and deep-derived fluids has not been considered. In the former case, the distribution but not the amount of energy will be affected—cooling is likely to be more rapid as energy and heat-producing elements are transferred towards the surface by buoyantly-rising magmas. In any case, H_2O-undersaturated magmas developed by anatexis of Scourian rocks will have been highly viscous and unable to move very rapidly or very far. The effects of deep-derived fluids has already been discussed. The effects of shear heating have not been considered, as they are likely to be localized and short-lived, and anyway at the temperatures of interest will be small owing to the low shear-strength of rocks at high temperatures (England & Thompson 1984). The effects of reactions within the rocks (other than those involving partial melting) have also been ignored as possible dehydration reactions (the only reactions with enthalpy changes large enough to be significant) will have been very limited in extent due to the low potential hydrous mineral content of the rocks, at least at the stage considered here (see also England & Thompson 1984). Partial melting has been approximated in the manner of Wells (1980), who assumed the fraction of crystals to change linearly between solidus and liquidus. A melting interval of 800–1150°C at the surface, increasing to 850–1200°C at 50 km has been used, based on the data of Wyllie (1977) for the melting of hornblende-bearing, vapour-absent tonalite.

For tectonic models as discussed above, there is insufficient geological data to construct a thermal model purporting to be accurate, although the general plausibility of such models may be demonstrable if constraints can be placed on the input parameters required. These input parameters are discussed below, and summarized in the appendix.

Bulk rock properties, such as conductivity, heat capacity and density are readily estimated (eg England & Richardson 1977), those used here follow Wells (1980). A minimum estimate of internal heat-generation during the Archaean can be derived from present-day contents of U, Th and K in the rocks of the Scourie complex by recalculating the abundances of radiogenic isotopes at 2.7 Ga. This gives the very low figure of $0.2 \, \mu W \, m^{-3}$ for internal heat production; this must be an underestimate as there has been strong depletion in the radiogenic element content of these rocks during high-grade metamorphism (indicated by isotope studies, eg Moorbath et al. 1969). Wells (1980) adapted a formula for heat production in the Archaean of west Greenland, based upon the U, Th and K contents of undepleted gneisses from Greenland and Phanerozoic andesitic volcanics, in which heat production decreases exponentially with depth according to the formula:

$$A \text{ (heat production)} = 2.6 \exp(-x/20) \, \mu W \, m^{-3} \quad (1)$$

where x is depth in km.

The heat flowing into the crust from the mantle is impossible to estimate accurately; Bickle (1978) indeed used the metamorphic conditions to constrain it! At the present day, it has a value of about $30 \, mW \, m^{-2}$ in stable continental areas. During the Archaean it must have been higher, but not necessarily greatly so, as convection, plate generation and destruction processes are likely to have been more rapid due to the marked decrease in mantle viscosity with increased temperature. Bickle (1978) suggested a maximum value of $50 \, mW \, m^{-2}$ for west Greenland, and this is the upper limit used by Wells (1980) for the same area. Heat flows of $50 \, mW \, m^{-2}$ give rise to steady-state temperatures at 35 km of $c.$ 710°C with internal heat production due only to the radiogenic elements now present. The upper limit to internal heat production (see above) gives rise to steady state temperatures of 900°C at 35 km in an 60 km crustal pile the same basal heat-flow figure. Higher basal heat flows would lead to temperatures such that partial melting of even dry acid rocks would inevitably have occurred at depths just below the present level of exposure (Huang & Wyllie 1975). England (1979) shows that heat flows as high as $90 \, mW \, m^{-2}$ are plausible, but as they would give rise to even more extensive melting (temperatures of 1250°C are attained at 40 km depth in a 40 km crust, with the lower internal heat generation figures), a value of $50 \, mW \, m^{-2}$ has been adapted here.

Two assumptions are implicit in reaching these conclusions: that thermal equilibrium was attained and that the crust was at least 40 km thick at this time. The two are related, as the thickness of crustal material involved will affect thermal equilibration times. If the crust was about 40 km thick in total, only limited melting at most would occur, and the underlying mantle would remain solid at such temperatures. If the approximate maximum thickness of stable crust can therefore be estimated as 40 km at 2.8 Ga (England & Bickle 1984), the maximum mantle heat flow may be estimated at $c.$ $50 \, mW \, m^{-2}$.

The geochronological data of Humphries & Cliff (1982), combined with other geochronological data, suggests that the early cooling of the complex was slow (> 100 Ma for $c.$ 500°C temperature drop), and this suggests modest erosion rates. An approximate lower limit to the erosion rate may be made by noting the difference in pressure of the granulite-facies metamorphism and the intrusion of the Scourie dykes. The former may be estimated as 10 kb, the later as 6–8 kb (O'Hara 1977), corresponding to a difference in depth of up to $c.$ 15 km. This uplift occurred between about 2.68 Ga and 2.39 Ga (Pidgeon & Bowes 1972; Chapman 1979), corresponding to an averaged uniform uplift rate of 0.05 km Ma^{-1} (= mm yr^{-1}). As this is likely to be a minimum estimate, a value of 0.1 km Ma^{-1} has been used in these calculations.

The effects of partial melting have been included in the models, as it could have occurred both at the depth of interest and at deeper levels. It tends to lengthen the response time of a section of crust to change, and to decrease the maximum temperatures attained by $c.$ 50°C in cases where temperatures greater than the solidus are attained. The effects are not larger because the transfer of latent heat occurs over a 350°C melting range, and the amount of heat involved is small relative to that flowing through the crust from below over the time scale involved.

Initial thermal profiles used were sawtooth profiles with the upper and lower portions in equilibrium with either a constant internal heat generation, or with the distribution of heat generation given by equation 1. Sawtooth profiles were used as the duration of the tectonic event causing thickening is likely to have been considerably shorter than thermal equilibration times. Movement rates of 10 cm yr^{-1} correspond to total translations of 100 km in 10 Myr. The timing and nature of the postulated tectonic thickening cannot be accurately constrained. The timing has been left undefined, as the feasibility of a tectonic model for the metamorphism is to be demonstrated, not its accuracy. The effects of varying the thickness of the overthrust block are considered in the following section. Estimates of geologically constrained parameters such as these are impossible to make accurately due to the unknown effects of later deformation. It has been assumed that erosion commenced immediately after tectonism, as any 'eclogite anchor' (Richardson & England 1979) will have lasted for < 10 Ma due to the relatively high basal heat flow, and would have given rise to only a small additional heating effect.

Results

Two groups of models have been used, one with a heat generation of $0.2\,\mu W\,m^{-3}$, distributed uniformly, and the other with heat generation distributed according to equation 1. The results are presented graphically in Figs 1 and 2. The models with constant internal heat production all reach a peak temperature of $750 \pm 50°C$ at 35 ± 4 km. In the case of the models with internal heat production given by equation 1, peak temperatures of $1075 \pm 30°C$ at $c.$ 35 km are attained. These models are all hotter than those labelled (i) as they have greater internal heat generation. These two estimates of metamorphic conditions compare favourably with the figures presented in Barnicoat (1983) which suggest that the rocks of the Scourie complex record conditions of about 1000°C at $c.$ 35 km (10 kb). The comparison is especially good if account is taken of the fact that heat-producing elements were removed from the rocks, either by partitioning into a CO_2-rich vapour phase (*eg* Tarney & Windley 1977) or by anatexis (*eg* Barnicoat 1983). In both cases, depletion is suggested to have occurred at or close to the peak conditions attained.

It should be noted that when melting occurs at depth, the melt, and hence both heat and incompatible heat-generating elements, will be transported upwards at a comparatively rapid rate, leading to the dispersion of energy faster than indicated by the purely conductive models used here. While maximum temperatures reached are likely to be close to those indicated by the models, cooling rates will probably have been more rapid.

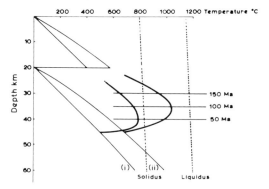

FIG. 1. Thermal profile generated during the relaxation of an overthrust terrain with a 20 km upper thrust sheet. Internal heat production of $0.2\,\mu W\,m^{-3}$ gives rise to initial profile (i), while heat generation given by equation 1 leads to initial profile (ii). The two thermal relaxation profiles are the temperature-depth paths followed by rocks commencing at 45 km and rising at 0.1 mm yr⁻¹ due to erosion.

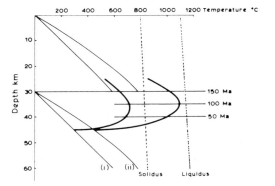

FIG. 2. Thermal profile generated during the relaxation of an overthrust terrain with a 30 km upper thrust sheet. Other details as in Fig. 1.

Some implications

The models show that the rocks of the Scourie complex could readily have remained at temperatures in excess of 900°C for a period of 100 Ma with cooling rates of the order of $1-2°C\,Ma^{-1}$, allowing diffusive re-equilibration to occur on a large scale. This cooling-rate estimate compares

TABLE 1. *Closure temperatures for volume diffusion*

Calculated using equation 1 of Dodson (1976) and the Fe–Mg diffusion data of Elphick *et al.* (1981) for garnet and Brady & McCallister (1983) for clinopyroxene. All temperatures in °C.

Grain radius	10 mm			5 mm			1 mm		
Cooling rate	1	3	10	1	3	10	1	3	10 Cyr-1
gnt	1000	1039	1084	954	990	1032	858	889	924
cpx	1034	1076	1125	984	1023	1069	862	915	954

with a figure of 3°C Ma^{-1} estimated from the data of Humphries (in Cliff 1985). At these cooling rates, closure temperatures estimated for Fe–Mg diffusion in garnet using the formulation of Dodson (1976) range from 1039°C for 10 mm radius crystals to 877°C for 1 mm crystals (see Table 1). Similar temperatures are obtained for clinopyroxene. These estimates use the slowest diffusion coefficients available, and indicate that the closure effect postulated by Barnicoat (1983) where coarse-grained metabasites were suggested to record higher-grade conditions than finer-grained material may be real. The work of Lasaga (1983) has shown that at cooling rates of the order of those estimated here, composition profiles may be very nearly flat although substantially re-equilibrated. These profiles may be extremely difficult to tell from those in which only a small amount of re-equilibration has affected only the rim of crystals. The effect of this is that if peak temperatures were c. 1000°C, diffusive re-equilibration would thoroughly re-set even the core compositions of all but the largest crystals. Obviously, if peak metamorphic temperatures were c. 800°C, only very limited diffusive re-equilibration would occur. Substantial re-equilibration has also affected the Sm–Nd isotope systematics of the rocks of the Scourie complex (Humphries & Cliff 1982) and is also demonstrated by the extensive exsolution visible on all scales within many of the un-retrogressed rocks of the complex.

This paper is not an endeavour to model what did occur in the Scourie complex, but it has attempted to indicate the possibility that tectonic thickening of the crust, coupled with only the heat generated internally by the decay of radio-nuclides and a 'normal' contribution from the mantle would have been sufficient to give rise to the metamorphic conditions observed in the Lewisian complex. Alternative models, based on energy from deep-derived fluids or magmas do not satisfy geochronological and other constraints.

ACKNOWLEDGEMENTS: This work was commenced during the tenure of an NERC studentship; NERC also funded my attendance at the 'Theoretical Petrology' short course in Manchester which provided me with the wherewithal for this work.

Appendix

The one-dimensional heat-flow equation

$$\frac{\rho c \partial T}{\partial t} = K \frac{\partial^2 T}{\partial X^2} + q + \frac{U \partial T}{\partial X} + \frac{L \partial U}{\partial t}$$

was solved using the Crank–Nicholson implicit method with distance steps of 1 km and time steps of 0.1 Ma. A constant temperature upper boundary at 0°C and a moving, constant-flux lower boundary at the base of the crust were used. Other parameters used were a density of 2800 kg m^{-3}, a thermal conductivity of 2.9 W m^{-1} K^{-1} and a temperature dependant heat capacity using the formula of England & Richardson (1977). Two models of internal heat-generation distribution were used: the first assumes a constant value of 0.2 μW m^{-3} throughout the crustal pile, the other uses equation 1 of the main text to model internal heat production decreasing exponentially from the surface. An erosion rate of 0.1 mm yr^{-1} was used for all calculations. The effects of partial melting were modelled with a solidus at 800°C + 1 × depth (km), a liquidus at 1150°C + 1 × depth (km) and a latent heat of fusion of 3.55 × 10^5 J kg^{-1}.

c = heat capacity
ρ = density
q = internal heat production
T = temperature
V = volume fraction of crystals
K = conductivity
L = latent heat of fusion
t = time
U = erosion rate
X = depth

References

BARNICOAT, A. C. 1983. Metamorphism of the Scourian Complex, NW Scotland. *J. Metamorphic Geol.* **1**, 163–182.

BICKLE, M. J. 1978. Heat loss from the Earth: a constraint on Archaean tectonics from the relation between geothermal gradients and the rate of plate production. *Earth planet. Sci. Lett.* **40**, 301–315.

BOTTINGA, Y. & RICHET, P. 1981. High pressure and temperature equation of state and calculation of the thermodynamic properties of gaseous carbon dioxide. *Am. J. Sci.* **281**, 615–660.

BOWES, D. R. 1978. Shield formation in early Precambrian times: the Lewisian complex. *In:* BOWES, D. R. & LEAKE, B. E. (eds.) *Crustal Evolution in NW Britain. Geol. J. Spec. Issue.* **10**, 39–80.

BRADY, J. B. & MCCALLISTER, R. H. 1983. Diffusion data for clinopyroxenes from homogenisation and self-diffusion experiments. *Am. Mineral.* **68**, 95–105.

CARTWRIGHT, I., FITCHES, W. R., O'HARA, M. J., BARNICOAT, A. C. & O'HARA, S. 1985. Archaean supracrustal rocks from the Lewisian near Stoer, Sutherland. *Scott. J. Geol.* **21**, 187–196.

CHAPMAN, H. J. 1979. 2390 myr Rb–Sr whole rock ages for the Scourie dykes of north-west Scotland. *Nature. London*, **277**, 642–643.

—— & MOORBATH, S. 1977. Lead isotope measurements from the oldest recognised Lewisian gneiss of NW Scotland. *Nature. London*, **268**, 41–42.

CLIFF, R. A. 1985. Isotopic dating in metamorphic belts. *J. geol. Soc. Lond.* **142**, 97–110.

COWARD, M. P., KIM, J. H. & PARKE, J. 1980. A correlation of Lewisian structures and their displacements across the lower thrusts of the Moine thrust zone, NW Scotland. *Proc. Geol. Assoc. London.* **91**, 327–337.

DAVIES, F. B. 1976. Early Scourian structures in the Scourie–Laxford region and their bearing on the evolution of the Laxford front. *J. geol. Soc. Lond.* **132**, 543–554.

DODSON, M. H. 1976. Kinetic processes and thermal history of slowly cooling solids. *Nature. London*, **259**, 551–553.

ELPHICK, S. C., GANGULY, J. & LOOMIS, T. P. 1981. Experimental study of Fe–Mg interdiffusion in aluminumsilicate garnet. *EOS Trans. Am. Geophys. Union.* **62**, 411.

ENGLAND, P. C. 1979. Continental geotherms during the Archaean. *Nature. London*, **277**, 556–558.

—— & BICKLE, M. J. 1984. Continental thermal and tectonic regimes during the Archaean. *J. Geol.* **92**, 353–367.

—— & RICHARDSON, S. W. 1977. The influence of erosion upon the mineral facies of rocks from different metamorphic environments. *J. geol. Soc. Lond.* **134**, 201–213.

—— & THOMPSON, A. B. 1984. Pressure–temperature–time paths of regional metamorphism I. Heat transfer during the evolution of regions of thickened continental crust. *J. Petrol.* **25**, 894–928.

HAMILTON, P. J., EVENSEN, N. M., O'NIONS, R. K. & TARNEY, J. 1979. Sm–Nd systematics of Lewisian gneisses: implications for the origin of granulites. *Nature. London*, **277**, 25–28.

HUMPHRIES, F. J. & CLIFF, R. A. 1982. Sm–Nd dating and cooling history of Scourian granulites, Sutherland. *Nature, London*, **295**, 515–517.

HUANG, W. L. & WYLLIE, P. J. 1975. Melting reactions in the system $NaAlSi_3O_8$–$KAlSi_3O_8$–SiO_2 to 35 kilobars, dry and with excess water. *J. Geol.* **83**, 737–748.

LASAGA, A. C. 1983. Geospeedometry: an extension of geothermometry. *In:* SAXENA, S. K. (ed.) *Kinetics and Equilibrium in Mineral Reactions.* Springer-Verlag, New York, 273 pp.

MOORBATH, S., WELKE, H. & GALE, N. H. 1969. The significance of Pb isotope studies in ancient high-grade metamorphic basement, as exemplified by the Lewisian rocks of NW Scotland. *Earth planet. Sci. Lett.* **6**, 245–256.

O'HARA, M. J. 1977. Thermal history of excavation of Archaean gneisses from the base of the continental crust. *J. geol. Soc. Lond.* **134**, 185–200.

OXBURGH, E. R. & TURCOTTE, D. L. 1974. Thermal gradients and regional metamorphism in overthrust terrains with special reference to the eastern Alps. *Schweiz. mineral. petrogr. mitt.* **54**, 641–662.

PIDGEON, R. T. & BOWES, D. R. 1972. Zircon U–Pb ages of granulites from the central region of the Lewisian, north-west Scotland. *Geol. Mag.* **109**, 247–258.

PITCHER, W. S. 1979. The nature, ascent and emplacement of granitic magmas. *J. geol. Soc. Lond.* **136**, 627–662.

RICHARDSON, S. W. & ENGLAND, P. C. 1979. Metamorphic consequences of crustal eclogite production in overthrust orogenic zones. *Earth planet. Sci. Lett.* **41**, 183–190.

SCHUILING, R. D. & KREULEN, R. 1979. Are thermal domes heated by CO_2-rich fluids from the mantle? *Earth planet. Sci. Lett.* **43**, 298–302.

TARNEY, J. & WINDLEY, B. F. 1977. Chemistry, thermal gradients and evolution of the lower crust. *J. geol. Soc. Lond.* **134**, 153–172.

VALLEY, J. W. & O'NEILL, J. R. 1984. Fluid heterogeneity during granulite facies metamorphism in the Adirondacks: stable isotope evidence. *Contrib. Mineral. Petrol.* **85**, 158–173.

WELLS, P. R. A. 1980. Thermal models for the magmatic accretion and subsequent metamorphism of continental crust. *Earth planet. Sci. Lett.* **46**, 253–265.

WYLLIE, P. J. 1977. Crustal anatexis: an experimental review. *Tectonophysics.* **43**, 41–71.

A. C. BARNICOAT, Department of Geology, University College of Wales, Aberystwyth, Dyfed SY23 3DB, UK.

Metamorphic evolution of the mainland Lewisian complex

J. D. Sills & H. R. Rollinson

SUMMARY: The equilibration conditions of early Scourian (Badcallian) granulite-facies metamorphism appear to be similar for the whole mainland Lewisian outcrop. Pyroxene and garnet assemblages equilibrated at about 7–8 kb and 750–800°C. Peak granulite facies conditions may have been slightly higher. An early high-pressure gt-cpx assemblage partially broke down to lower pressure opx + plag ± magt ± sp ± hb symplectites, indicating decompression after the peak of metamorphism. At a later stage, there was growth of a more Fe-rich garnet. Discordant trondhjemite and granite sheets, which were also metamorphosed to granulite facies, indicate very high magmatic temperatures of 890–1030°C from Fe-Ti oxides and 1000°C from hypersolvus feldspars.

The Scourian complex was extensively retrogressed during the Inverian as a result of the influx of hydrous fluids at about 600°C.

Aims of review

In the light of the wide range of P-T estimates for the conditions of granulite-facies metamorphism of the Scourian complex, our aim in this paper is threefold. Firstly we review previous attempts to calculate the conditions of Scourian metamorphism and we revise these estimates in relation to new methods, and to new calibration of previously used methods. Secondly we shall attempt to evaluate these results in order to define geothermometric and geobarometric methods which are appropriate to the bulk compositions in the Scourian complex in the pressure–temperature range of interest. Thirdly, in the light of our revised data, we present a P-T estimate for the granulite-facies event in the Scourian and present a P-T-time path for the subsequent evolution of the central mainland Lewisian complex.

Much of the controversy over the Scourian complex has centred on material collected from Scourie. Detailed mapping in this area (Davies 1975, Rollinson & Windley 1980) has revealed a distinct sequence of magmatic events prior to, and possibly synchronous with, the granulite-facies event. Thus comparisons between different geothermometers and geobarometers and the results of different workers should strictly be made only for rocks of the same age in the gneiss complex. Further, in this paper we review P-T data from Scourie, Drumbeg and Achiltibuie and present new data from Gruinard Bay and, whilst typically granulite-facies terrains show little variability in conditions of metamorphism over large areas, it is possible that there is some variation in P-T conditions between rocks of the same age from different parts of the Lewisian outcrop.

Geological relationships

Detailed geological mapping in the Scourie area (Davies 1975; Rollinson & Windley 1980) shows that the gneiss complex is a deformed meta-igneous complex comprising layered gabbro, tonalite, trondhjemite and granite. Whereas the separate intrusive events have not yet been resolved by geochronology, field mapping in selected low-strain areas suggests the following chronology. Early layered gabbro–ultramafic complexes, with a small amount of associated metasedimentary material, were intruded by large volumes of tonalite. Post-dating the tonalites and the gabbros are acid sheets a few metres wide ranging in composition from trondhjemite to granite. These acid sheets cut early Scourian folds but are themselves deformed by late Scourian folding. All the rocks types show granulite-facies mineral assemblages but it is by no means certain that they were all metamorphosed at the same time, or under exactly the same conditions.

Farther to the south at Gruinard Bay, rocks of Scourian age show some distinct differences from those at the type area, Scourie (Rollinson & Fowler this volume). Scourian rocks at Gruinard Bay form an extensive agmatite complex in which the earliest identifiable components are rafts of amphibolite, layered gabbro and tonalitic gneiss enclosed in later trondhjemitic gneiss. Tonalitic gneisses were deformed prior to the injection of trondhjemite, but trains of enclaves in the trondhjemites are also folded, indicating deformation after the emplacement of trondhjemite. The dominant metamorphic grade at Gruinard Bay is amphibolite facies, although granulite facies relics are found in the gabbros, amphibolite and tonalite. This suggests that the early

From: PARK, R. G. & TARNEY, J. (eds), 1987, *Evolution of the Lewisian and Comparable Precambrian High Grade Terrains*, Geological Society Special Publication No. 27, pp. 81–92.

gneisses were deformed and may have been metamorphosed to granulite grade prior to the emplacement of the trondhjemite. Thus the difference between Scourian rocks from Scourie and Gruinard Bay is in the importance of the trondhjemite event. At Gruinard Bay trondhjemite makes up 75% of the complex, whereas at Scourie, only a small volume of trondhjemite (and associated granite) was emplaced. Thus in this review we pay some attention to the relative ages of the rocks for which we have made some *P-T* measurements. Relict granulite facies assemblages are also found south of Gairloch (Cresswell & Park 1973).

Previous *P-T* estimates

Available *P-T* estimates for the Scourian granulite-facies metamorphism are shown in Table 1. These range from extreme values of 15 ± 3 kb and $1150 \pm 100°C$ (O'Hara & Yarwood 1978) to $820 \pm 50°C$ and 7–8.5 kb (Rollinson 1981; Newton & Perkins 1982). The high temperature estimates of over 1000°C are from: 1) late trondhjemite-granite sheets (O'Hara & Yarwood 1978) and will be discussed in detail later; 2) from complexly exsolved pyroxenes in a meta-ironstone (Barnicoat & O'Hara 1979) but these results can be questioned because the pyroxenes have 2–5 wt% MnO so that Ca–Fe–Mg-phase relations may not be applicable; and 3) from garnet-clinopyroxene geothermometry (Barnicoat 1983). Metagabbros will be discussed in detail later. As pointed out by Savage and Sills (1980) and Barnicoat (1983) the Lewisian complex cooled extremely slowly so that *P-T* estimates are obviously affected by re-equilibration during cooling.

The data used for this review have previously been presented in Savage & Sills (1980); Rollinson (1978, 1980a, 1981, 1982) and Sills (1983) with some additional analyses from Gruinard Bay.

Granulite facies metamorphism

Granulite-facies rocks have been examined from the Scourie, Drumbeg, Achiltibuie and Gruinard Bay areas (Fig. 1). Firstly, we will examine pyroxene-garnet geothermometry and barometry and then ilmenite-magnetite and two-feldspar thermometry from late trondhjemite sheets.

Within the dominant quartzo-feldspathic gneisses, there are a series of mafic and ultramafic gneisses sometimes associated with metasediment. The ultramafic mineral assemblages comprise opx-hb-cpx-ol-sp-magt and have a granoblastic texture. The gabbros contain cpx $+$ gt-opx-plag-magt $\pm$ hb and have a series of garnet breakdown textures which have been described in detail by O'Hara & Yarwood (1978), Savage & Sills (1980) and Barnicoat (1983); the main features of which are summarized below. Metagabbro textures are related to Fe/Mg ratios. Mg-rich gabbros contain amoeboid intergrowths of opx $+$ plag $+$ sp or hb, believed to be pseudomorphing garnet. At Scourie, garnet has sometimes regrown in these symplectites (Barnicoat 1983). Slightly more Fe-rich gabbros contain monomineralic areas of granoblastic cpx and large garnet porphyroblasts rimmed by plag, opx and magt or hb, resulting from gt $+$ cpx breakdown. In the most mafic rocks plagioclase is restricted to these garnet breakdown areas. More plagioclase-rich rocks tend to have a more equigranular texture. All these mafic rocks are

TABLE 1. *Previous estimates of the P-T conditions of Scourian granulite facies metamorphism*

Author	Method	$T°C$	P kb
O'Hara & Yarwood 1978	feldspar and pyroxene parageneses, garnet stability	1150 ± 100	15 ± 3
Barnicoat & O'Hara 1979	pyroxene phase relations	1000	12
Barnicoat 1983	gt-pyx-sp thermometry	1000 peak	12
		800–900 (re-equil)	11
Savage & Sills 1980	gt-pyx thermometry	1000 peak	12–15
		800–900 (re-equil)	10–14
Pride & Muecke 1980	gt-pyx thermometry	900	
Rollinson 1981	gt-pyx-plag-qz	820 ± 50	11 (max)
Newton & Perkins 1981	gt-pyx-plag-qz	840	8.5
Rollinson 1980b	T-scap-plag-cpx P-cpx-plag-qz	915 ± 130	11 (max)
Rollinson 1980a	Fe-Ti oxides	950–830	
Rollinson 1982	two-feldspar	1000	

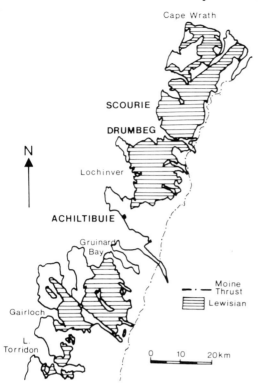

FIG. 1. Simplified sketch map showing mainland Lewisian outcrop.

quartz-free but some metasedimentary granulites near Scourie contain gt-opx-plag-qz (Rollinson 1981).

Two-pyroxene thermometry

Two-pyroxene assemblages occur in ultramafic granulites throughout the area and in rocks of tonalitic composition from Scourie and Gruinard Bay. The commonly used methods of Wood & Banno (1973) and Wells (1977) have recently been criticized by Lindsley (1983); Stephenson (1984) suggested that the Wells method probably overestimates by at least 50°C. We have applied the above three calibrations of the two-pyroxene thermometer to ultramafic granulites from the above four areas studied to assess any difference between them, although the absolute temperature cannot be accurately determined. The calculated temperatures (Table 2) are similar for all areas. The Wood & Banno (1973) temperature is consistently the highest (*c.* 875°C) with Wells (1977) temperatures up to 100°C lower (*c.* 780°C) but Lindsley (1983) temperatures calculated for cpx depend critically on the estimate of the Fe_2O_3

content of the pyroxene. If all the iron is taken as FeO, temperatures of about 700°C are obtained, but if Fe_2O_3 is estimated by charge balance, they increase to 850°C. However, there is about 11% of non-quadrilateral components in these clinopyroxenes, greater than the amount for which the Lindsley (1983) thermometer is strictly valid.

Tonalitic gneisses from Scourie give temperatures of 810 to 840°C by the Wood & Banno (1973) and Wells (1977) methods and about 780°C by the Lindsley (1983) method. Tonalites from Gruinard Bay give slightly lower temperatures by the Wood & Banno and Wells methods, and considerably lower (*c.* 650°C) by the Lindsley method.

Garnet-pyroxene temperatures and pressures

The garnet-clinopyroxene thermometer of Ellis & Green (1979) is thought to be reliable for granulite-facies temperatures (Johnson *et al.* 1983). However, as outlined above, in most gabbros garnet and clinopyroxene have reacted to produce orthopyroxene and plagioclase, so that they are no longer in equilibrium. Where garnet and clinopyroxene are adjacent, temperatures for the Ellis & Green (1979) calibration are between 700 and 800°C with an average of 770°C (with Fe_2O_3 estimated from charge balance). Centres of grains tend to give temperatures up to 50°C higher than grain edges. Barnicoat (1983) showed that very large grains may give temperatures as high as 1000°C.

The temperature of symplectite formation was estimated using the gt-opx thermometer of Harley (1984*a*). Symplectite orthopyroxene grains and the adjacent garnet rims give temperatures of 780–840°C obtained from granoblastic orthopyroxene and garnet grains found in some magnesium-rich gabbros. A low temperature of 610°C is obtained for a gt-opx pair from a symplectite (sample 85; Savage & Sills 1980) where the garnet is believed to have regrown after the initial garnet breakdown (Barnicoat 1983).

Temperatures for the Achiltibuie area, calculated from the gt-hb thermometer of Graham & Powell (1984) range from between 760 and 790°C for large hornblende grains and from 650–730°C for symplectite hornblende and garnet rims, again suggesting that the symplectites equilibrated at a lower temperature than the garnet porphyroblasts and larger hornblende grains.

Pressure is much more difficult to estimate as the most reliable geobarometer, gt-plag-opx-qz (Newton & Perkins 1982; Bohlen *et al.* 1983) is not applicable to the mafic rocks which are qz-free. However, rare metasedimentary granulites

TABLE 2. *Two-pyroxene temperatures for ultramafic granulites from Scourie, Drumbeg Achiltibuie, and Gruinard Bay (°C)*

	Scourie	Drumbeg	Achiltibuie	Gruinard Bay	
Wood & Banno	873	885	800	867	ultramafic
Wells	819	800	800	766	
Lindsley		850 (900)	700 (850)	700 (850)	
Wood & Banno	810			760–810	tonalite
Wells	825			760–810	
Lindsley	780			600–620	

Calculated using the methods of Wood & Banno (1973); Wells (1977) and Lindsley (1983). The figure in brackets for the Lindsley calibrations is that when Fe_2O_3 has been recalculated by charge balance. Two-pyroxene data for tonalites are from Scourie and Gruinard Bay.

do contain this assemblage (*eg* HRR275; Rollinson 1981; Fig. 2) giving pressures of 7–8 kb at temperatures of 700–800°C for the Mg-end member reaction (Bohlen *et al.* 1983; Fig. 2). A garnet-biotite pair from the same sample gives a temperature of 800°C (Ferry & Spear 1978) and garnet-opx pairs give 730°C. It is interesting to compare the data for the Harley & Green (1982) semi-empirical gt-opx geobarometer with that of the Harley (1984*b*) method. At the temperature estimated from the gt-opx thermometer, the pressure is 9.9 kb for the Harley (1984*b*) method and only 3.5 kb for the Harley & Green method.

Pressure estimates for the gabbros are rather variable (Table 3). Samples from Drumbeg and Achiltibuie give very high pressures (11–12 kb). Both areas contain hornblende; the Drumbeg samples containing retrogressive green hornblende and the Achiltibuie samples a granulite-facies pargasite so that, in both cases, Al_2O_3 in orthopyroxene may be re-equilibrated with hornblende. Amphibole-free samples such as J125 (Fig. 2) give more consistent results. Symplectite orthopyroxene and garnet rims give pressures of 7.7 to 8.5 kb using the method of Harley (1984*b*) and 7 to 7.5 kb using Harley & Green (1982) at about 780°C. For amphibole-bearing samples the Harley & Green method gives similar pressures but the Harley method gives much higher values, supporting Harley's (1984*c*) suggestion that the Harley & Green method is more consistent for granulites. Symplectites from Scourie give similar pressures but the gt-opx pair from sample 85 gives a slightly lower pressure of 7.1 kb.

Significance of garnet-pyroxene thermometry

Savage & Sills (1980) presented textural evidence showing that an early assemblage dominated by cpx-gt was partially replaced by opx-plag bearing symplectites, *i.e.* a high-pressure granulite assemblage was being replaced by a low-pressure

granulite assemblage. This suggests that the temperatures calculated from garnet-pyroxene equilibria are unlikely to reflect the peak of metamorphism. The data presented above suggest that equilibria between pyroxenes and

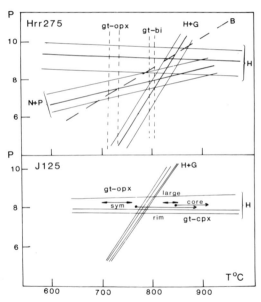

FIG. 2. *P-T* data for sample HRR275 (metasediment from Scourie) and J125 (metagabbro from E. of Stoer). gt-opx: garnet-orthopyroxene temperatures (Harley 1984*a*), gt-bi: garnet-biotite temperatures (Ferry & Spear 1978), N + P: pressure estimated from Newton & Perkins (1982), B from Bohlen *et al.* (1983), H-from Harley (1984*b*) and H + G from Harley & Green (1982), gt-cpx: garnet-clinopyroxene temperatures (Ellis & Green 1979), ●—T calculated using an estimate of Fe_2O_3 from charge balance >—T using all iron as FeO, for core and rim compositions. For gt-opx temperatures, large indicates temperatures calculated from coarse granoblastic grains, sym from symplectite grains and garnet rims.

TABLE 3. *P-T estimates from garnet-pyroxene thermometry and barometry for granulite facies assemblage*

	T°C			P kb			
	gt-cpx E&G	gt-opx Harley	gt-hb G&P	gt-opx H&G	gt-opx Har	gt-opx-plag-qz N&P	gt-opx-plag-qz Bohlen *et al.*
HRR275		720–730		2.8–3.7 (700°)	8.5–10.0 (700°)	6.8–7.8 (700°)	7.0 (700°)
				6.9–7.9 (800°)	8.3–9.9 (800°)	7.3–8.0 (800°)	8.5 (800°)
DS81	882	765 (coarse)		3.8 (700°)	8.1 (700°)		
	814 (sym)	665 (sym)		6.9 (800°)	7.6 (800°)		
DS84	850	729 (coarse)		3.7 (700°)	7.8 (700°)		
		641 (sym)		7.4 (800°)	7.6 (800°)		
DS85		611 (sym)		6.7 (700°)	7.2 (700°)		
				10.7 (800°)	7.2 (800°)		
W4	770 (core)						
W5	790 (core)	714–850		1.8 (700°)	8.8 (700°)		
	720 (rim)			5.3 (800°)	8.6 (800°)		
W6	780 (core)						
	710 (rim)						
W7	870						
J125	770	720–750		4.9 (700°)	9.2 (700°)		
				8.5 (800°)	9.5 (800°)		
W32	830	750–830	775 (coarse)	4.4–4.9 (700°)	9.5–11.5 (700°)		
			690–730 (sym)	8.5–9.2 (800°)	9.0–10.7 (800°)		
W34	760	783 (coarse)	765 (coarse)	4.0 (700°)	9.7–11.2 (700°)		
			700–730 (sym)	7.7 (800°)	9.9–11.5 (800°)		
W35	680	814–866		4.1 (700°)	11.0–12.2 (800°)		
			750 (sym)	8.9 (800°)			
W36	710–860		750 (coarse)	5.7 (700°)	12.2		
		707–750 (sym)	640 (sym)	9.8 (800°)			

P-T estimates from garnet-pyroxene thermometry and barometry for granulite facies assemblages. Samples as follows: HRR275—metasediment from near Scourie (Rollinson 1981); DS81–85—metagabbros from Scouriemore; W4–W7—metagabbros from Drumbeg; W32–W36—metagabbros from Achiltibuie (Savage & Sills 1980). Temperatures and pressures were calculated from the following methods: gt-cpx: garnet-clinopyroxene thermometer (Ellis & Green 1979); gt-opx: garnet-orthopyroxene thermometer (Harley 1984a); gt-hb: garnet-hornblende thermometer (Graham & Powell 1984); gt-opx: garnet-orthopyroxene geobarometer (Harley & Green 1982; H&G) and (Harley 1984b; Har); gt-opx-plag-qz: garnet-orthopyroxene-plagioclase-quartz geobarometer (Newton & Perkins 1982; N&P; Bohlen *et al.* 1983). Where indicated, temperatures were calculated from adjacent cores and rims and from granoblastic (coarse) grains as well as from symplectite grains and adjacent garnet edge compositions. Pressures were calculated at both 600 and 700°C.

garnets were 'frozen in' at about 750–800°C and 7–8 kb, so the peak of metamorphism was probably higher, but how much higher is difficult to quantify. Barnicoat (1983) obtained a temperature of about 1000°C from the centres of adjacent garnet-clinopyroxene grains and Lasaga (1983) showed that garnet could retain evidence of temperatures near the peak of metamorphism so that peak temperatures of the order of 1000°C cannot be ruled out. However, garnet and clinopyroxene did not remain in equilibrium, being replaced by opx + plag + sp + magt + hb assemblages suggesting that the garnet-clinopyroxene thermometer could produce erroneous results.

The gt-opx and gt-hb data suggest that the symplectites formed at slightly lower temperatures of 700–750°C. Garnet-orthopyroxene barometry implies pressures of 7–8 kb and the same range is obtained for symplectites in amphibole-free rocks. These lower temperatures could merely reflect the fact that the rate of volume diffusion during slow cooling allows smaller grains to attain equilibrium at lower temperatures than larger grains (*eg* Lasaga 1983).

These data suggest that the two-pyroxene temperatures of Wood & Banno (1973) and Wells (1977) are too high. Garnet-orthopyroxene and garnet-hornblende temperatures seem to be consistent, but garnet-orthopyroxene barometry produces erratic results for hornblende-bearing assemblages.

Iron-titanium oxides

Iron-titanium oxide oxygen barometry and thermometry have been reported by Rollinson (1979; 1980a) for ilmenite-magnetite intergrowths from late intrusive trondhjemite and granite sheets metamorphosed to granulite grade in the Scourian complex. These studies used the method of Powell & Powell (1977) based on the experimental work of Buddington & Lindsley (1964). More recently Spencer & Lindsley (1981) reformulated the ilmenite-magnetite thermometer and oxybarometer, but the earlier version of Buddington & Lindsley is now preferred (Lindsley, pers comm).

Experimental studies of the ilmenite-magnetite system (Buddington & Lindsley 1964; Spencer & Lindsley 1981) were carried out in the Fe-Ti system; thus their application to naturally occurring oxide pairs requires some treatment of the minor elements. A number of such calculation schemes have been proposed (Anderson 1968; Carmichael 1967; Lindsley & Spencer 1982; Stormer 1983), and the method of Powell & Powell (1977), used here, attempts to combine several of these schemes and calculates maximum and minimum permissible amounts of ülvospinel and hematite in the ilmenite and magnetite solid solutions respectively. In this study, however, Mn in ilmenite is the only minor element of any significance, some ilmenite grains having 8 wt% MnO. Barnicoat (1983) suggested that $MnTiO_3$ does not behave ideally in ilmenite and thus the results may be in error. However, the high Mn-ilmenite results plot within the main array of data points suggesting a tendency towards ideal behaviour. Further, only a few of the results calculated are based on high Mn-ilmenites and thus the conclusions summarized below are not materially affected.

Below, we present a summary of Fe-Ti oxide temperatures and oxygen fugacities calculated from the experimental results of Buddington & Lindsley (1964) for cogenetic trondhjemite and granite sheets near Scourie. These results are compared with temperatures calculated using the calibration of Spencer & Lindsley (1981) using Stormer's (1983) recalculation scheme.

Calculated temperatures and oxygen fugacities fall into three main groups as shown for the Scourie granite sheets (Rollinson 1980a). Ilmenite and magnetite from composite grains show a range of exsolution patterns varying in size from 50–150 mm. There is a group of averaged grains (analyses obtained by scanning composite grains) which show high temperatures (890–1034°C) and oxygen fugacities about the NNO buffer. This group of grains gives exactly the same temperatures on the Spencer & Lindsley calibration. The second group of points is based on analyses made on adjacent ilmenite-magnetite lamellae in composite grains, which show a range of temperatures from 830–660°C, with oxygen fugacity buffered *below* the NNO buffer curve. On the Spencer & Lindsley (1981) calibration some points in this group yield temperatures up to 100°C cooler, although the overall pattern does not change. A third group of points, also determined on adjacent lamellae, show low temperatures, less than 530°C, and oxygen fugacities which define a trend that

cuts across the main buffer curves. In this case temperatures calculated using the Spencer & Lindsley (1981) calibration are up to 100°C higher, although on a $T-fO_2$ plot, the overall pattern does not change.

The highest temperatures are thought to represent the magmatic temperatures at the time of emplacement and crystallization of the granite and trondhjemite magmas, perhaps at depth in the crust. Lower temperatures show subsolidus cooling and re-equilibration of complex ilmenite-magnetite grains under variable fluid conditions. Temperatures for the averaged grains are very high for acid plutonic rocks and are based on grains with low contents of minor elements (max. MnO, 1.5 wt%) and are thus not seriously in error for this reason. Fe-Ti oxide temperatures in excess of 950°C are reported from dacites and rhyolites (Ewart 1979) so although these temperatures are high, we do not regard them as unreasonable.

The second group of points reflects the cooling and re-equilibration under conditions of granulite-facies metamorphism. The fO_2 lies almost entirely below the NNO buffer curve on the QFM (Rollinson 1980a) and may reflect the adjustment of the fluid phase to that of granulite-facies metamorphic conditions (*cf.* Oliver 1978; Lamb & Valley 1984; Sharp & Essene 1985). With both the calibration of Buddington & Lindsley (1964) and Spencer & Lindsley (1981), points fall below the C-CO_2 buffer curve of Lamb & Valley (1984). We have looked carefully again at our samples but find no graphite, thus the argument of Lamb & Valley (1984) stands, that the Scourie granulites may not have been subjected to a massive influx of CO_2. This is in marked contrast to the gneisses of southern India (Hansen *et al.* 1984) and indicates that each granulite terrain must be treated separately.

The third group of points shows a range of temperatures below 630°C, with the oxygen fugacity higher for an equivalent temperature than the previous group, but with rapidly falling fO_2 no longer parallel to any buffer curves. The difference in temperature at about $-\log_{10} fO_2 = 20$ is real and marks a significant change in the ülvospinel content of magnetite solutions. It is outside the error limits quoted for the calibration of Spencer & Lindsley (1981), even allowing for a significant MnO content in ilmenite. These data indicate a marked change in fluid conditions brought about by variation in the controls on the buffering of the fluid phase composition. It is suggested that the data document the introduction of H_2O into the system during retrogression of the granulites. The nature and extent of this change in fluid conditions is indicated from sample 69, a granite from the Shios peninsula, Scourie, which contains separate composite ilmenite-magnetite grains, some of which have equilibrated with group 2 and others with group 3 (Rollinson 1980a, Fig. 1) indicating the localized nature of the fluid. The change in fluid conditions took place between 530 and 630°C.

The new calibration of Anderson & Lindsley (1985) gives the same results as Spencer & Lindsley (1981) tending to slightly lower the higher temperatures and to slightly increase the lower temperatures; however the conclusions are not affected.

Feldspar thermometry

Alkali feldspars with a mesoperthite texture and a high An content (An_{10}) have been described from granite sheets discussed above (O'Hara & Yarwood 1978; Rollinson 1982). The unusual chemistry is indicative of high temperatures and these have been variably interpreted as the original igneous temperatures of the granitic melts (Rollinson 1982) and extremely high temperatures of metamorphism (O'Hara & Yarwood 1978). The granite sheets are discordant with respect to the enclosing gneisses and are therefore clearly intrusive, but also possess a granulite-facies mineralogy. The ambiguity over the meaning of the unusual feldspar compositions may be resolved if the melts were emplaced at depth in the lower crust.

Mesoperthite feldspars are present in both hypersolvus and subsolvus granites. Analyses were made using a scanning electron beam and each mesoperthite analysis plotted in Fig. 3 is the mean of three scanning analyses. In the hypersolvus granites they have the composition

$An_{56-44}Or_{52-44}An_{10-12}$ (Fig. 3). Subsolvus granites show a wider range of compositions, with orthoclase mesoperthites in the compositional range $An_{48-44}Or_{41-35}Ab_{13-16}$, similar to mesoperthites in the hypersolvus granite, but with a slightly higher An-content, and microcline mesoperthites have a lower An-content (Fig. 3). Coexisting plagioclase is in the range $Ab_{77.5-72.5}Or_{1-2}An_{21.5-26}$. The crossing of tie-lines on Fig. 3 is to some extent coincident with the structural change in the alkali feldspar host and suggests that the plagioclase mesoperthite pairs are not in equilibrium. This is further supported when the feldspar compositions are compared with the experimental results of Seck (1971), for plagioclase grains plot inside the 900°C (1 kb) ternary solvus of Seck, whereas mesoperthite grains plot outside the solvus. Whilst there is some doubt about the reliability of Seck's data (Brown & Parsons 1985) the work of Johannes (1979) also suggests that the orthoclase content of the plagioclase should be higher than observed. Mora & Valley (1985) describe similar compositional relationships in feldspar pairs from the Oaxacan granulites, Mexico and suggested that plagioclase loses K by diffusion during slow cooling of the granulites. Thus any attempt to use such feldspars in two-feldspar thermometry will result in a minimum temperature estimate and may be seriously in error. We have used the two-feldspar thermometer of Haselton *et al.* (1983) which circumvents some of the criticisms of Brown & Parsons (1981) and which Mora & Valley (1985) have shown yields reliable results on ternary feldspars. This yields temperatures of 630–730°C at 10 kb, significantly lower than other estimates for the Scourian metamorphism. Mora & Valley calculate the equilibrium temperature for a K-rich plagioclase grain and a mesoperthite alkali feldspar using data reported by O'Hara & Yarwood (1978) and obtained $T = 765 + 65°C$ at 11 kb, using the Haselton *et al.* (1983) thermometer.

Rollinson (1982) argued that mesoperthite feldspars in hypersolvus granites were indicative of temperatures in excess of 1000°C (at 1 bar). The argument is based upon observations (i) that mesoperthite bulk compositions lie within 15 mol % Or of the trace of critical solution curve in the ternary feldspar system and (ii) that the critical temperature of the ternary system at high An contents is considerably higher than for the binary system (Smith 1978). Whereas the feldspar ternary system has not yet been fully investigated, a semi-quantitative estimate of the effect of An on the critical temperature of the ternary solvus may be obtained from Parson's (1978) constant Ab:Or ratio section through the ternary system

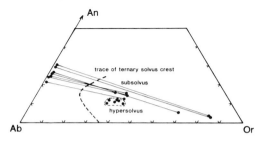

FIG. 3. Feldspar compositions from granite sheets, plotted in an An–Ab–Or triangle. The subsolvus granite mesoperthites may be further subdivided into grains with an orthoclase host and high An-content and those with lower An-contents and a microline host. Data from Rollinson (1978).

from which a value of 30°C/mol % anorthite may be derived. Using a conservative estimate of the critical temperature of the alkali feldspar solvus at 1 bar (625°C) and assuming that the slope of the solvus is such that at high An-contents the bulk compositions within 50°C of the critical temperature for that composition, and that the crest of the ternary solvus behaves in a similar fashion to Parson's (1978) constant Ab:Or section, then mesoperthite grains with 10–12% An crystallized at about 875–935°C. If a further adjustment is made for the emplacement of the granites at depth, then using a pressure correction of 18°C/kb (Brown & Parsons 1981) for an 8 kb pressure, temperatures are in the range 1020–1080°C.

These calculated temperatures are subject to the assumptions outlined above, but are thought to be a conservative estimate, and whilst lower than originally suggested by Rollinson (1982) and O'Hara & Yarwood (1978) they point to unusually high temperatures preserved in the granite sheets. Similar high temperatures are preserved in the Fe-Ti oxides of this suite as discussed above. The intrusive nature of the granite sheets, coupled with feldspar temperatures up to 200°C higher than recorded in the enclosing gneisses suggests that these temperatures are close to magmatic equilibration and thus imply that the magmas were very dry. It does not, however, mean that similar high temperatures necessarily existed in the enclosing gneisses, as the granites and trondhjemites occur at discrete parallel-sided sheets rather than anastomosing veins and were thus able to be self-insulating during crystallization. However, there is some evidence that these high temperatures might represent those of the granulite-facies metamorphism (Barnicoat 1983; Cartwright & Barnicoat, this vol.). If these data are correct, the temperature during the Badcallian (greater than 950°C) was unusually high and would have implications regarding the role of partial melting in the formation of the Scourian complex (Barnicoat 1983). Such high temperatures suggest that a large amount of partial melt would have been generated, a possibility ruled out by Weaver & Tarney (1981). At lower temperatures (eg c. 800°C) the amount of melt would be less and might be streaked out and thus obscured by subsequent deformation.

The data suggest two possibilities: (1) the temperatures recorded by the trondhjemite-granite sheets represent temperatures near the peak of metamorphism and the lower temperatures recorded by garnet-pyroxene thermometry are cooling temperatures or (2) the temperatures of 750–800°C are near the peak of metamorphism and the high temperatures recorded by the intrusive sheets are those of the magmas and are in excess of the metamorphic temperatures.

More data are needed to resolve this controversy.

Retrogression and cooling

Extremely slow cooling of the Lewisian complex (O'Hara 1977) is documented by the mineral assemblages, particularly in the mafic rocks. As outlined above, garnet-clinopyroxene pairs were partially replaced by orthopyroxene and plagioclase with magnetite, spinel or hornblende symplectites, while granulite facies conditions prevailed. At a later stage, a more Fe-rich garnet grew around opaque oxides (Savage & Sills 1980) and in a few spinel bearing symplectites (Barnicoat 1983). This late garnet records lower temperatures (610°C) from the gt-opx thermometer (Harley 1984a) and 570–630°C from the garnet-hornblende thermometer (Graham & Powell 1984).

A Sm-Nd mineral age of 2.49 + 0.12 Ga (Humphries & Cliff 1982) from coexisting garnet and clinopyroxene was interpreted as a cooling age, possibly indicating that temperatures were about 600°C at this time.

The granulite facies gneisses were extensively retrogressed during the Inverian (Sheraton et al. 1973; Evans & Lambert 1974) associated with the development of NW-trending monoclinal folds. This caused the Lewisian to be uplifted in a series of blocks with relative movement occurring along long-lived shear zones such as the Laxford Front (Davies 1978) and the Canisp Shear Zone (Jensen 1984). The initial retrogression clearly preceded the emplacement of the Scourie dykes (at about 2.39 Ga; Chapman 1979). The Scourie dykes are themselves commonly metamorphosed and often have a strong fabric parallel to their margins. This fabric has commonly been considered to be Laxfordian but some of the deformation may have been synchronous with dyke intrusion (Tarney 1963) or occurred shortly afterwards when the dykes were still hot.

The age of the Inverian retrogression is not certain, but Tarney (1963) showed it was only shortly before and overlapped the period of dyke emplacement. It is possible that the 2.49 Ga age of Humphries & Cliff (1982) and the regrowth of garnet in mafic rocks may be in response to the introduction of fluid into the complex.

In the central part of the Lewisian outcrop where Laxfordian effects are minor, the last deformation was the development of narrow, post-dyke WNW-trending shear zones (Sheraton et al. 1973; Sills 1983).

During the Inverian, in the Assynt region, a very uniform hb-plag-qz + bi assemblage developed in all but ultramafic and granitic compositions. The variance of Inverian assemblages is very high, suggesting that the fluid was externally buffered. The few Inverian assemblages which contain good geothermometers generally yield temperatures about 600°C (Sills 1983). Garnet-biotite temperatures are quite variable (Sills 1983) ranging from 480–670°C (using the calibration of Hodges & Spear (1982)) but the majority of samples give temperatures between 550 and 600°C. Garnet-hornblende temperatures (Graham & Powell 1984) range from 560–640°C with one very Fe-rich metasediment from near Stoer giving anomalously high gt-bi and gt-hb temperatures.

In the Scourie area, Inverian shear zones (Beach 1973) contain a wider variety of mineral assemblages which locally contain kyanite, staurolite, corundum and spinel, possibly indicating formation at slightly higher *P-T* conditions than the Inverian assemblages in Assynt. However, garnet-hornblende temperatures (Graham & Powell 1984) and garnet-biotite temperatures (Ferry & Spear 1978) are also in the range 580–640°C (Sills unpublished data).

These data suggest the Inverian retrogression occurred at about 600°C, consistent with the estimate of the change in fluid conditions indicated by Fe-Ti oxides. Pressures during the Inverian are difficult to estimate as there are few reliable geobarometers. One Inverian assemblage from N of Scourie contains qz-plag-sill-gt-bi and gives a pressure of 4.78 kb at 600°C using the gt-sill-plag-qz geobarometer of Newton & Haselton (1981). The garnet has a very low grossular content so this result could be in error, also it is not absolutely certain that the garnet and sillimanite are in equilibrium.

The Scourie dykes, believed to have been emplaced at depth (O'Hara 1961; Tarney 1973) yield metamorphic temperatures of 600°C for the Scourie area using gt-cpx and gt-hb pairs from the data of O'Hara (1961). Scourie dykes in the Assynt area do not contain garnet but contain more amphibole, suggesting they were emplaced at shallower depth, into a more hydrous environment (Tarney 1973). This temperature is similar to that for the Inverian retrogression and is consistent with field evidence which suggests that the dykes were emplaced towards the end of the Inverian.

The composition of post-tectonic muscovite from late WNW-trending shear zones in the Assynt region suggests that temperatures were still in excess of 500°C after the formation of these Laxfordian shear zones (Sills 1983).

Temperature–time paths

Figure 4 shows a temperature–time path for the evolution of the Lewisian complex in the Assynt area. It suggests a fairly rapid drop in temperature immediately after the peak of granulite facies metamorphism followed by a more gradual decrease. The age of formation of the symplectite after garnet is not clear, but it is assumed to be quite soon after the peak of metamorphism. The

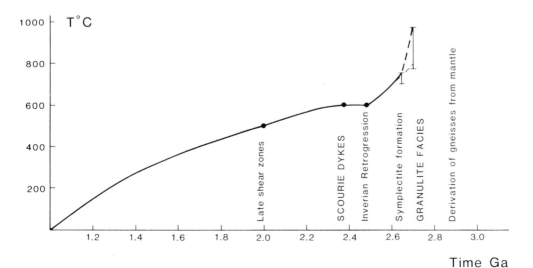

FIG. 4. Temperature–time path for the Assynt block.

formation of opx + plag symplectites replacing gt + cpx assemblages indicates a drop in pressure, rather than temperature, so there was probably a rapid drop in pressure shortly after the peak of the metamorphism. It is not known whether there was any increase in temperature during the Inverian. In the Assynt (and Scourie) areas the Inverian retrogression was followed by very slow uplift until final exhumation before deposition of the Torridonian at *c.* 1000 Ma (Moorbath 1969). The evolution of the Scourie area would be similar except that uplift during the Inverian was probably less. However, pressures are very poorly constrained. Both areas seemed to have experienced similar conditions during the granulite-facies event although this could reflect closure temperatures. The northern and southern parts of the Lewisian complex, which experienced

pervasive amphibolite-facies metamorphism during Laxfordian reworking have obviously experienced a different *P-T-t* path. In the Gairloch area, the Loch Maree and Gairloch schist belts were deposited during the early Proterozoic (O'Nions *et al.* 1983) and were presumably deformed with their basement during the Laxfordian and metamorphosed to amphibolite facies. However, there are no *P-T* data available for the Loch Maree Group to quantify the conditions of Laxfordian metamorphism.

In order to evaluate possible mechanisms for crustal uplift, it is necessary to have a detailed pressure–time path, but unfortunately there are not sufficient data at present.

ACKNOWLEDGMENTS: J. D. Sills gratefully acknowledges the receipt of an NERC research fellowship.

References

ANDERSEN, D. J. & LINDSLEY, D. H. 1985. New (and final!) models for the Ti-magnetite/ilmenite geothermometer and oxygen barometer. *EOS.* **66**, 416.

ANDERSON, A. T. 1968. The oxygen fugacity of alkali basalts and related magmas, Tristan da Cunha. *Am. J. Sci.* **266**, 704–27.

BARNICOAT, A. C. 1983. Metamorphism of the Scourian Complex, NW Scotland. *J. Metamorphic Geol.* **1**, 163–82.

—— & O'HARA, M. J. 1979. High temperature Pyroxenes from an ironstone at Scourie, Sutherland. *Mineralog. Mag.* **43**, 371–5.

BEACH, A. 1973. The mineralogy of high temperature shear zones at Scourie, NW Scotland. *J. Petrol.* **14**, 231–48.

BOHLEN, S. R., WALL, V. J. & BOETTCHER, A. L. 1983. Experimental investigation and application of garnet granulite equilibria. *Contrib. Mineralog. Petrol.* **83**, 52–61.

BROWN, W. L. & PARSONS, I. 1981. Towards a more practical two-feldspar thermometer. *Contrib. Mineralog. Petrol.* **76**, 369–77.

—— & —— 1985. Calorimetric and phase diagram approaches to two-feldspar geothermometry: a critique. *Am. Mineral.* **70**, 356–61.

BUDDINGTON, A. F. & LINDSLEY, D. H. 1964. Iron-titanium oxide minerals and synthetic equivalents. *J. Petrol.* **5**, 310–57.

CARMICHAEL, I. S. E. 1967. Iron-titanium oxides and oxygen fugacity in volcanic rocks. *J. Geophys. Res.* **72**, 4665–87.

CHAPMAN, H. J. 1979. 2390 myr Rb-Sr whole rock age for the Scourie dykes of north-west Scotland. *Nature, London,* **277**, 642–3.

CRESSWELL, D. & PARK, R. G. 1973. The metamorphic history of the Lewisian rocks of the Torridon area in relation to that of the remainder of the southern Laxfordian belt. *In:* PARK, R. G. & TARNEY, J. (eds) *The Early Precambrian of Scotland and Related Rocks of Greenland,* Keele Univ. 77–84.

DAVIES, F. B. 1975. Origin and ancient history of gneisses older than 2800 my in the Lewisian complex. *Nature, London,* **258**, 589–91.

—— 1978. Progressive simple shear deformation in the Laxford shear zone, Sutherland. *Proc. Geol. Assoc.* **289**, 177–296.

ELLIS, D. J. & GREEN, D. H. 1979. An experimental study of the effect of Ca on garnet-clinopyroxene Fe-Mg exchange equilibria. *Contrib. Mineralog. Petrol.* **71**, 13–22.

EVANS, C. R. & LAMBERT, R. ST. J. 1974. The Lewisian of Lochinver: The type area for the Inverian metamorphism. *J. geol. Soc. Lond.* **130**, 125–50.

EWART, A. 1979. A review of the mineralogy and chemistry of Tertiary-Recent dacitic, latitic, rhyolitic and related salic volcanic rocks. *In:* BARKER, F. (ed.) *Trondhjemites, Dacites and Related Rocks* Elsevier. 13–122.

FERRY, J. M. & SPEAR, F. S. 1978. Experimental calibration of the partitioning of Fe and Mg between biotite and garnet. *Contrib. Mineralog. Petrol.* **66**, 113–17.

GRAHAM, C. M. & POWELL, R. 1984. A garnet-hornblende geothermometer: calibration, testing and application to the Pelona schist, Southern California. *J. Metamorphic Geol.* **2**, 13–31.

HANSEN, E. C., NEWTON, R. C. & JANARDHAN, A. S. 1984. Fluid inclusions in rocks from the amphibolite-facies to charnockite progression in southern Karnataka, India: direct evidence concerning the fluids of granulite facies metamorphism. *J. Metamorphic Geol.* **2**, 249–64.

HARLEY, S. L. 1984*a*. An experimental study of the partitioning of Fe and Mg between garnet and orthopyroxene. *Contrib. Mineralog. Petrol.* **86**, 359–73.

—— 1984*b*. The solubility of alumina in orthopyroxene coexisting with garnet in FeO-MgO-Al$_2$O$_3$-SiO$_2$ and CaO-FeO-MgO-Al$_2$O$_3$-SiO$_2$. *J. Petrol.* **25**, 665–96.

—— 1984c. Comparison of the garnet-orthopyroxene geobarometer with recent experimental studies, and applications to natural assemblages. *J. Petrol.* **25**, 697–712.

—— & GREEN, D. H. 1982. Garnet-orthopyroxene barometry for granulites and garnet peridotites. *Nature, London,* **300**, 696–700.

HASELTON, H. T., HOVIS, G. L., HEMINGWAY, B. S. & ROBIE, R. A. 1983. Calorimetric investigation of the excess entropy of mixing in analbite-sanidine solid solutions: lack of evidence for Na, K short-range order and implications for two-feldspar thermometry. *Am. Mineral.* **68**, 398–413.

HODGES, K. V. & SPEAR, F. S. 1982. Geothermometry and geobarometry and the Al_2SiO_5 triple point at Mt. Moosilauke, New Hampshire. *Am. Mineral.* **67**, 1118–34.

HUMPHRIES, F. J. & CLIFF, R. A. 1982. Sm-Nd dating and cooling history of Scourian granulites, Sutherland. *Nature, London,* **295**, 515–17.

JENSEN, L. M. 1984. Quartz microfabric of the Laxfordian Canisp Shear Zone. NW Scotland. *J. Struct. Geol.* **6**, 293–302.

JOHANNES, W. 1979. Ternary feldspars: kinetic and possible equilibrium at 800°C. *Contrib. Min. Pet.* **68**, 221–30.

JOHNSON, C. A., BOHLEN, S. R. & ESSENE, E. J. 1983. An evaluation of garnet-clinopyroxene thermometry in granulites. *Contrib. Min. Pet.* **84**, 191–8.

LAMB, W. & VALLEY, J. W. 1984. Metamorphism of reduced granulites in low CO_2 vapour-free environment. *Nature, London,* **312**, 56–8.

LASAGA, A. C. 1983. Geospeedometry: an extension of geothermometry. *In*: SAXENA, S. A. (ed.) *Kinetics and Equilibrium in Mineral Reactions.* Springer-Verlag, New York, 81–114.

LINDSLEY, D. H. 1983. Pyroxene thermometry. *Am. Mineral.* **68**, 477–93.

—— & SPENCER, K. J. 1982. Ve-Ti oxide geothermometry: reducing analyses of coexisting Ti-magnetite (Mt) and ilmenite (Ilm). *EOS* **63**, 471.

MOORBATH, S. 1969. Evidence of the age of deposition of the Torridonian sediments of northwest Scotland. *Scott. J. Geol.* **5**, 154–70.

MORA, C. I. & VALLEY, J. W. 1985. Ternary feldspar thermometry in granulites from Oaxacan complex, Mexico. *Contrib. Min. Pet.* **89**, 215–25.

NEWTON, R. C. & HASELTON, H. T. 1981. Thermodynamics of the garnet-plagioclase-Al_2SiO_5-quartz geobarometer. *In*: NEWTON, R. C., NAVROSKY, A. & WOOD, B. J. (eds) *Thermodynamics of Minerals and Melts.* Springer-Verlag, New York, 129–45.

—— & PERKINS, D. 1982. Thermodynamic calibration of geobarometers based on the assemblages garnet-plagioclase-orthopyroxene (clinopyroxene)-quartz. *Am. Mineral.* **67**, 203–222.

O'HARA, M. J. 1961. Petrology of the Scourie dyke, Sutherland. *Min. Mag.* **32**, 848–65.

—— 1977. Thermal history of excavation of Archaean gneisses from the base of the continental crust. *J. geol. Soc. Lond.* **134**, 185–200.

—— & YARWOOD, G. 1978. High pressure-temperature point on an Archaean geotherm, implied magma genesis by crustal anatexis, and consequences for garnet-pyroxene thermometry and barometry. *Phil. Trans. R. Soc. Lond.* **A.288**, 441–56.

OLIVER, G. J. M. 1978. Ilmenite-magnetite thermometry and oxygen barometry in granulite and amphibolite facies gneisses from Doubtful Sound, Fjordland, New Zealand. *Lithos.* **11**, 147–54.

O'NIONS, R. K., HAMILTON, P. J. & HOOKER, P. J. 1983. A Nd isotope investigation of sediments related to crustal development in the British Isles. *Earth planet. Sci. Lett.* **63**, 229–40.

PARSONS, I. 1978. Feldspars and fluids in cooling plutons. *Min. Mag.* **42**, 1–17.

POWELL, R. & POWELL, M. 1977. Geothermometry and oxygen barometry using coexisting iron-titanium oxides. *Min. Mag.* **41**, 257–63.

PRIDE, C. & MUECKE, G. K. 1980. Rare earth element geochemistry of the Scourian complex. NW Scotland: evidence for the granite granulite link. *Contrib. Min. Pet.* **73**, 403–12.

ROLLINSON, H. R. 1978. *Geochemical studies on the Scourian complex. NW Scotland.* Unpubl. PhD thesis Univ. Leicester.

—— 1979. Ilmenite-magnetite geothermometry in trondjhemites from the Scourian complex of NW Scotland. *Min. Mag.* **43**, 165–70.

—— 1980a. Iron-titanium oxides as an indicator of the role of the fluid phase during the cooling of granites metamorphosed to granulite grade. *Min. Mag.* **43**, 623–31.

—— 1980b. Mineral reactions in a calc-silicate rock from Scourie. *Scott. J. Geol.* **16**, 153–64.

—— 1981. Garnet-pyroxene thermometry and barometry in the Scourie granulites, NW Scotland. *Lithos* **14**, 225–238.

—— 1982. Evidence from feldspar compositions of high temperatures in granite sheets in the Scourie complex, NW Scotland. *Min. Mag.* **46**, 73–6.

—— & WINDLEY, B. F. 1980. An Archaean granulite grade tonalite-trondhjemite-granite suite from Scourie, NW Scotland: geochemistry and origin. *Contrib. Min. Pet.* **72**, 265–81.

SAVAGE, D. & SILLS, J. D. 1980. High pressure metamorphism in the Scourian of NW Scotland: evidence from garnet granulites. *Contrib. Min. Pet.* **74**, 153–63.

SECK, H. A. 1971. Der Einfluss des Drucks auf die Zusammensetzung koexistierender Alkalifeldspate und Plagioclase in System $NaAlSi_3O_8$-$KAlSi_3O_8$-$CaAl_2Si_2O_8$-H_2O. *Contrib. Min. Pet.* **31**, 67–86.

SHARP, Z. D. & ESSENE, E. J. 1985. Granulite-grade iron formations as sensors of fluid fugacities (*Abs*) *EOS.* **66**, 389.

SHERATON, J. W., TARNEY, J., WHEATLEY, T. J. & WRIGHT, A. E. 1973. The structural history of the Assynt district. *In*: PARK, R. G. & TARNEY, J. (eds) *The Early Precambrian of Scotland and Related Rocks of Greenland.* Keele Univ. 31–45.

SILLS, J. D. 1983. Mineralogical changes occurring during the retrogression of Archaean gneisses from the Lewisian complex of NW Scotland. *Lithos,* **16**, 113–24.

SMITH, P. 1978. The effect of anorthite on the alkali

feldspar solvus at P_{H20} 1 kb. *In: Progress in Experimental Petrology*, 4th Report (NERC), 247–9.

SPENCER, K. J. & LINDSLEY, D. H. 1981. A solution model for coexisting iron-titanium oxides. *Am. Mineral.* **66**, 1189–1201.

STEPHENSON, N. C. N. 1984. Two-pyroxene thermometry of Precambrian granulites from Cape Riche, Albany-Fraser Province, Western Australia. *J. Metamorphic Geol.* **2**, 297–314.

STORMER, J. C. 1983. The effects of recalculation on estimates of temperatures and oxygen fugacity from analyses of multicomponent iron-titanium oxides. *Am. Mineral.* **68**, 586–94.

TARNEY, J. 1963. Assynt dykes and their metamorphism. *Nature, London*, **199**, 672–4.

——— 1973. The Scourie dyke suite and the nature of the Inverian event in Assynt. *In:* PARK, R. G. & TARNEY, J. (eds) *The Early Precambrian of Scotland and Related Rocks of Greenland.* Keele Univ. 105–18.

WEAVER, B. L. & TARNEY, J. 1981. Lewisian gneiss geochemistry and Archaean crustal development models. *Earth planet Sci. Lett.* **55**, 171–80.

WELLS, P. R. A. 1977. Pyroxene thermometry in simple and complex systems. *Contrib. Min. Pet.* **62**, 129–39.

WOOD, B. J. & BANNO, S. 1973. Garnet-orthopyroxene and orthopyroxene-clinopyroxene relationships in simple and complex systems. *Contrib. Min. Pet.* **42**, 109–24.

J. D. SILLS, Department of Geology, Leicester University, Leicester LE1 7RH, UK.

H. R. ROLLINSON, Department of Geography and Geology, College of St. Paul and St. Mary, The Park, Cheltenham, Gloucestershire, UK.

Petrology of Scourian supracrustal rocks and orthogneisses from Stoer, NW Scotland: implications for the geological evolution of the Lewisian complex

I. Cartwright & A. C. Barnicoat

SUMMARY: The Lewisian complex at Stoer comprises a diverse assemblage of paragneisses together with several generations of acid to basic orthogneiss. All lithologies are early-Scourian in age and underwent granulite-facies metamorphism in the Badcallian (c. 2.7 Ga) event. Petrogenetic modelling coupled with geothermometry yields a P-T estimate for the peak of metamorphism of 920–990°C and > 11 kb, as well as estimates of conditions encountered during Inverian (c. 2.6–2.3 Ga) and Laxfordian (< 1.7 Ga) retrogression. Certain lithologies, especially those of supracrustal origin, show evidence of partial melting. It is suggested that anatexis, controlled by the internal buffering of metamorphic fluids, may have been an important process in the evolution of the complex.

Abbreviations

The following abbreviations are used for end member compositions and minerals:

or = $KAlSi_3O_8$, ab = $NaAlSi_3O_8$, an = $CaAl_2Si_2O_8$

qtz = quartz, cpx = clinopyroxene, opx = orthopyroxene, plg = plagioclase, ksp = potassium feldspar, amp = amphibole, gnt = garnet, liq = silicate melt, vap = H_2O vapour, kya = kyanite, sil = sillimanite, and = andalusite, mus = muscovite, bio = biotite

Invariant points and reactions are labelled according to the phases absent at them, so [gnt] is the garnet-absent invariant point and

amp + qtz (gnt, vap) plg + opx + liq

is the vapour-absent reaction emanating from [gnt] which converts amp-qtz to plg-opx-liq.

Introduction

The Lewisian at Stoer (Fig. 1) comprises a diverse assemblage of paragneisses, the Cnoc an t'Sidhean supracrustals, together with two generations of basic orthogneiss, a suite of acid leucogneisses and hornblende-biotite tonalitic 'grey gneisses' (Cartwright et al. 1985). All units are cut by the Scourie dyke swarm and show closely similar

tectonometamorphic histories. The petrology of the main lithologies present in the Stoer area was discussed in Cartwright et al. (1985), and Table 1 summarizes the mineralogy of the various gneiss units.

The structural history of the area can be divided into three broad stages (cf Sheraton et al. 1973b; Jensen 1984; Cartwright et al. 1985). The first phase of deformation (D₁) forms part of the regional Badcallian subhorizontal shear event which affected much of the central Scourian block (Sheraton et al. 1973b). A pervasive flat-lying fabric and intrafolial folds, including major kilometre-scale recumbent folds, were formed in this event. Early D₂ deformation involved the formation of broad, upright, ESE–WNW periclinal F₂ folds. These folds are cut by pre-Scourie dyke, Inverian, shear zones which form an E–W to ESE–WNW anastomosing network of steeply inclined structures, with either N- or S-side-up dip-slip displacements. These shear zones range from a few centimetres to hundreds of metres in width (Beach 1974) and may persist along strike for several kilometres. The last major phase of deformation (D₃) produced major post-Scourie dyke, Laxfordian, strike-slip shear zones and associated structures (Beach 1974; Jensen 1984).

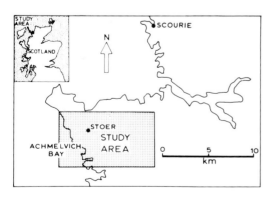

FIG. 1. Location of the study area.

From: PARK, R. G. & TARNEY, J. (eds), 1987, *Evolution of the Lewisian and Comparable Precambrian High Grade Terrains*, Geological Society Special Publication No. 27, pp. 93–107.

TABLE 1. *Petrology of Stoer supracrustals and orthogneisses*

	gnt	cpx	opx	hbl	bt	ep	cz	cum	plg	afp	qtz	mus	ap	sp	dol	zir	scp	kya	sta	cor	sil	chl
Cnoc an t'Sidhean Supracrustals																						
Brown Gneisses	×			×	+	+			s	×	s	×		o		s	o					+
	×				+	+			×		×	×	o		o							+
White mica layer (host)									×		×	o						×	×	×	+	+
(veins)									×	×	×	×				s						+
Plagioclase amphibolite		R		×	+	+	+		×	×	×	s	s	s								
Calcareous gneisses				×	+	×	×		×		×		o	o	s							+
				×	×	×	s		×		×		s		×		×					
				×	s	×	×		×		o		s	o								
Orthogneisses																						
Tonalitic grey gneisses		R		×	+	+			×		×		o			o						+
Early basic orthogneiss	s			×		+			×		o											
Late basic orthogneiss	s	R	R	×	+	+			×		o											+
Acid leucogneisses	s			×	+	+			×	s	×	+	o			o						+

× Major phase (usually > 10%)   o Minor phase (< 10%)
s Present in some samples   + Phase occurs as a late mineral
R Phase occurs only as relict crystals

Additional abbreviations: hbl-hornblende, bt-biotite, ep-epidote, cz-clinozoisite, cum-cummingtonite, afp-alkali feldspar, mus-muscovite, ap-apatite, sp-sphene, dol-dolomite, zir-zircon, scp-scapolite, kya-kyanite, sta-staurolite, cor-corundum, sil-sillimanite, chl-chlorite.

The area preserves mainly amphibolite-facies parageneses, formed during the Inverian (*c.* 2.6–2.3 Ga) phase of retrogression (Evans & Lambert 1974), although relict granulite-facies mineralogies are locally preserved. The aims of this paper are, firstly to use the petrology and mineralogy of the lithologies of the Stoer area to characterize the conditions of metamorphism at various stages in the evolution of the Lewisian complex in this region, and secondly to combine textural and field evidence with petrogenetic modelling to attempt to constrain the processes that occurred during the Badcallian granulite-facies metamorphic episode.

Time relationships within gneiss complex

Cartwright *et al.* (1985; Table 1) demonstrated the relative ages of some of the gneiss units in the Stoer area from field data. Additional data have enabled the sequence of gneiss-forming events to be more closely defined. The modified time relationships are shown in Table 2.

With one exception, all the gneiss units precede the peak of Badcallian metamorphism and deformation; the formation of the acid leucogneisses overlapped the earliest part of the Badcallian (D_1) deformation. The relationships of the

Cnoc an t'Sidhean supracrustals to the regional tonalitic gneisses are still not resolved from field data although isotopic work is in progress to help define their relative ages.

Summary of *P-T* conditions during metamorphism

The study of the lithologies present in the Stoer area has provided estimates of the conditions of metamorphism at various stages in the evolution of the complex (Table 3 and Fig. 2). The peak of Badcallian metamorphism is estimated at 925–990°C from both geothermometry and petrogenetic modelling considerations.

TABLE 2. *Events in the early evolution of the Stoer complex*

*Formation of tonalitic grey gneisses and early basic orthogneisses	2.9 Ga (i)
*Intrusion of late basic orthogneisses Intrusion of acid orthogneisses	
D_1 Deformation	
Peak of Badcallian metamorphism	2.7 Ga (ii)

* – Possible ages of the Cnoc an t'Sidhean supracrustals
Date of (i) from Hamilton *et al.* (1979)
　　　(ii) from Chapman & Moorbath (1977)

TABLE 3. *Summary of P-T estimates for the Scourie complex*

Author	P (kbar)	T (°C)	Number on Fig. 2
i) Estimates of the peak of granulite facies metamorphism, *c.* 2.7 Ga			
Cartwright & Barnicoat 1986	>11	900–925	1
Cartwright & Barnicoat this study	—	910–990	2
Savage & Sills 1980	12–15	1000±100	3
Barnicoat & O'Hara 1979	—	1000	4
Rollinson 1980	>11	915±130	5
ii) Estimates probably recording re-equilibration from peak conditions			
Savage & Sills 1980	8–12	800–900	6
Wood 1975, 1977	10–13	825	7
Rollinson 1981	11	820±50	8
iii) Estimates of Inverian conditions			
Cartwright & Barnicoat 1985	3–6	500–625	9
Sills 1983	5–7	575–625	10
iv) Estimates of conditions at intrusion of Scourie Dykes *c.* 2.39 Ga			
O'Hara 1977	7±2	450±100	11
Tarney 1963	5–6	500	12

Date of i) from Chapman & Moorbath (1977); iv) from Chapman (1979)

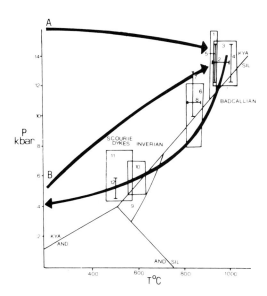

FIG. 2. Summary of the *P-T* conditions at various stages in the metamorphic history of the complex and alternative *P-T*-time paths based on these estimates (data from Table 2). Paths A and B show two possible approaches to the peak of metamorphism: Path A would be followed if the Badcallian metamorphism was caused by overthrusting with subsequent thermal re-equilibration (as proposed by Barnicoat 1982). If the complex attained peak metamorphic conditions by relatively slow burial then the prograde *P-T*-time path would be similar to path B.

The brown gneisses contain several thin (<1 m) layers of a muscovite-rich, aluminous rock (the white mica layers, Table 1). These layers comprise two distinct parageneses: a) a mica-rich, quartz-free assemblage which forms 70–80% of the layer and is composed of centimetre-sized corundum, kyanite and staurolite porphyroblasts in a muscovite and plagioclase matrix; b) millimetre- to centimetre-wide lenses and veins comprising variable quantities of quartz, plagioclase, alkali feldspar and minor muscovite.

Textural and bulk compositional evidence suggests that the quartz-bearing lenses and veins can be interpreted as neosomes generated by local anatexis of the layer leaving a silica-undersaturated, corundum-bearing restite. Petrogenetic modelling of these assemblages in the systems $CaO-KAlO_2-NaAlO_2-Al_2O_3-SiO_2-H_2O$ and $CaO-Na_2O-FeO-Al_2O_3-SiO_2-H_2O$ (Cartwright & Barnicoat 1986) indicates that the formation of such melts and restites is possible and could result from a variety of initial starting compositions and $a(H_2O)$ values. The analysis of the possible reactions in these systems (Cartwright & Barnicoat 1986) yielded estimates for the peak of metamorphism of 900–925°C and >11 kb, with $a(H_2O)$ estimated at >0.3 and internally buffered. The retrogression of the corundum-kyanite-staurolite-plagioclase assemblages to margarite-paragonite-sillimanite-chlorite parageneses was also modelled in these systems and yielded pressure temperature estimates of

500–625°C and 3–6 kb with a(H_2O) estimated as > 0.4.

The late basic orthogneiss (Table 1) locally preserves relict granulite-facies assemblages. The garnet-clinopyroxene Fe-Mg exchange geothermometers of Ganguly (1979), Saxena (1979) and Ellis & Green (1979) have been applied to these assemblages. The cores of coarse grained (c. 5–10 mm) garnet and clinopyroxene crystals in samples showing least retrogression (Table 4) yield temperatures of 940–990°C at 11 kb. These temperatures are considered to represent the thermal peak of the granulite-facies metamorphism although they probably slightly underestimate the conditions, as discussed by Barnicoat (1983). The temperatures calculated using the compositions of mineral rims and the compositions of phases from partially retrogressed samples (Table 4) are in the range 790–850°C. These lower values are probably the result of down-temperature re-equilibration of mineral compositions during the slow cooling of the terrain.

As shown in Table 3 and Fig. 2 these estimates are in close agreement with several other published estimates for the peak of granulite-facies metamorphism and for subsequent conditions encountered during recovery of the complex. The P-T estimates shown in Table 3 combined with geochronology allow the speculative retrograde P-T-time path of Fig. 2 to be constructed. The prograde P-T-time path is less well constrained and Fig. 2 shows two possible paths to the peak of metamorphism. On the basis of numerical thermal modelling, Barnicoat (1982) suggested that crustal thickening and subsequent thermal re-equilibration was the most likely cause of the Badcallian metamorphism which would result in the complex following path A of Fig. 2.

Processes occurring during prograde metamorphism

The prograde metamorphic stage in the evolution of the Lewisian complex is the least well understood as the pervasive Badcallian metamorphism and deformation usually obscures all evidence of any preceding events. The diverse range of lithologies present in the Stoer area and the knowledge of their relative ages provide a good opportunity to assess the possible processes that occurred during the approach to the peak of metamorphism.

Partial melting during metamorphism

At the high temperatures and pressures recorded by these rocks at the peak of metamorphism it is

TABLE 4. *Compositions of garnets and clinopyroxenes from late basic orthogneisses and calculated temperatures*

Mineral analyses (wt%)

	Core compositions				Rim compositions	
	GNTO1	CPXO1	GNTO2	CPXO2	GNTO3	CPXO3
SiO_2	39.43	49.53	39.61	47.83	39.95	49.02
TiO_2	0.11	0.56	0.04	0.87	0.02	0.06
Al_2O_3	21.53	5.63	21.43	6.58	21.95	5.13
FeO	22.76	9.76	22.26	10.07	22.13	8.03
MnO	0.93	0.18	1.03	0.19	0.80	0.60
MgO	7.85	12.05	7.86	12.34	8.24	12.68
CaO	7.73	21.39	7.81	21.56	6.33	22.81
Na_2O	0.00	0.70	0.00	0.83	0.00	0.66
Total	100.34	99.80	100.04	99.83	99.42	99.89

Geothermometry results (°C)

	Mineral Pairs		
Method	GNTO1–CPXO1	GNTO2–CPXO2	GNTO3–CPXO3
Saxena (1979)	939	945	824
Ganguly (1979)	978	990	856
Ellis & Green (1979)	928	931	799

Note: All iron is expressed as FeO. Analyses obtained by WDS on a Cambridge Microscan V instrument.

predicted that many of the lithologies present would have undergone anatexis even with low to moderate $a(H_2O)$ values and even in the absence of a vapour phase. For example, a rock of tonalitic composition which is hydrated (amphibole- and biotite-bearing) but vapour-absent will begin to melt at c. 800°C at 11 kb (Wyllie 1977), *ie* within the range of conditions recorded in the complex. An amphibolite in a similar state of hydration would not melt until c. 1000°C (Wyllie 1977) and so would have to contain a H_2O-bearing vapour phase if it were to undergo anatexis at the recorded conditions of metamorphism. Partial melting in basic granulites has been discussed by Barnicoat (1983) and Powell (1983*b*) who indicate that it is probably an important process at the conditions of metamorphism recorded by the Lewisian complex. Rocks with the composition of the supracrustal lithologies, such as the brown gneisses and the plagioclase amphibolites (Table 1), should also have undergone anatexis at these conditions of metamorphism (Wyllie 1977).

The evidence that partial melting did take place in the rocks of the Stoer area is discussed in the following sections, together with an evaluation of the likely mode of occurrence of the partial melting process and the effects on element distribution.

Partial melting in metabasites

The late basic orthogneisses (Table 1) contain felsic segregations and veins (up to 3 cm wide) which locally truncate layering but are themselves cut by the Badcallian foliation. These veins are trondhjemitic, comprising mainly plagioclase and quartz, and as shown in Fig. 6 and Table 5, are close to the expected composition of melts of basic rocks. The most likely origin of these segregations is that they are the products of local anatexis of the basic orthogneisses formed during the Badcallian metamorphism.

To analyse the petrogenesis of these metabasites, relations between cpx, opx, plg, gnt, amp, qtz, vap, liq have been examined in the model system $CaO-MgO-Al_2O_3-SiO_2-H_2O$ (CMASH) as shown in Fig. 3. The resultant grid is similar to that of Powell (1983*b*, Fig. 2) except that it considers cpx (rather than gnt-plg) saturated assemblages. The liquid used in this study is of broadly trondhjemitic composition, analogous to that of the discordant veins, projecting close to the qtz-plg tie line with a small ferromagnesian (M) component in Fig. 4. Such liquids would be formed at the eutectic minimum melting reactions (1), (3) and (12). All liquids, including those formed at vap-absent reactions, will have a higher $a(H_2O)$ than all coexisting solid phases (Thomp-

son 1982, p. 1575). The suprasolidus evolution of liq has not been depicted, as expansion of the liquid field to intersect compositional planes, such as plg-amp-vap in Fig. 4, will only occur with advanced degrees of partial melting, and, for the purposes of this study, liq can be considered as a single composition.

Melting in metabasites modelled in CMASH

The phase relationships depicted in Fig. 3 can be used to model the partial melting of various initial compositions in this system and to illustrate several important points regarding anatexis of crustal rocks in general. It is convenient to examine the petrogenesis of the assemblages by using $T:a(H_2O)$ diagrams (*cf* Powell 1983*a*, his Fig. 4) as such diagrams may be used to describe evolution under vapour-present (either internally or externally buffered) or vapour-absent conditions. Fig. 4 shows an isobaric $T:a(H_2O)$ diagram for the section X–X′ of Fig. 3; this particular pressure was chosen as assemblages formed during the Badcallian metamorphism fall into the medium-pressure granulite facies as defined by Barnicoat (1983, fig. 4) and reaction (10) of Fig. 3 forms the high pressure limit of this facies.

The subsolidus assemblage of the metabasites in CMASH is considered to have been cpx-opx-plg-amp $\pm$ gnt $\pm$ qtz $\pm$ vap or amp-plg $\pm$ qtz $\pm$ vap and, from textural evidence, the final assemblage was cpx-opx-plg-liq $\pm$ amp $\pm$ gnt $\pm$ vap. Evolution in the model system will be examined firstly for qtz-bearing assemblages and qtz-absent assemblages both with a vapour phase present and under vapour-absent conditions, in both cases any vapour present is assumed to be a H_2O-CO_2 fluid which is internally buffered, as discussed later.

Evolution of initially qtz-bearing, vap-present assemblages

Assemblages which are qtz-bearing and coexist with a H_2O-rich vapour phase will probably show evolution along a path like A–A′ of Fig. 4. The first melting reaction encountered will be (3); assuming that vap is internally buffered, the partitioning of H_2O into liq will buffer vapour-phase compositions to lower $a(H_2O)$ along (3) towards [gnt]. If the quantity of fluid present is small (which is probable in metabasic compositions at this grade of metamorphism) then only a minor amount of reaction at (3) will occur before the assemblage is buffered to the invariant point [gnt]. As H_2O is the only vapour-phase component that takes part in these reactions and as the position of [gnt] is fixed in the $T:a(H_2O)$ section,

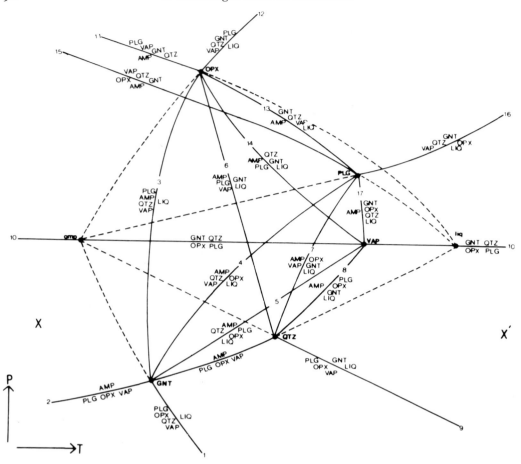

FIG. 3. Schematic phase diagram illustrating relations between cpx-opx-amp-qtz-gnt-plg-vap-liq in the CMASH system. The phases are projected from cpx (CMS_2) into the CA-M-S-H volume, hence all reactions include cpx. Dashed lines are the metastable extensions of reactions which terminate at metastable invariant points. X–X′ is the line of the T:aH_2O section of Fig. 4.

the reaction at [gnt] must conserve H_2O. From the considerations of Greenwood (1975 p. 580) the reaction at [gnt] will be the vapour-absent reaction:

$$\text{amp} + \text{qtz (gnt, vap) plg} + \text{opx} + \text{liq} \quad (5)$$

As the final assemblages are qtz-free, this reaction would consume the remaining qtz and evolution will continue along (2) which is a dehydration reaction buffering assemblages to higher a(H_2O) values towards [qtz]. If [qtz] was reached then the reaction:

$$\text{amp (qtz, vap) liq} + \text{gnt} + \text{opx} + \text{plg} \quad (8)$$

would occur which would consume amp and result in evolution continuing along (9).

Path B–B′ in Fig. 4 illustrates the evolution of a qtz-bearing assemblage which contains a fluid of low a(H_2O). In this case the first reaction that

will be encountered is (2) which will buffer the assemblage to higher values of a(H_2O). An initially vap-bearing assemblage will undergo reaction at this equilibrium producing opx-plg-vap at the expense of amp. At [gnt] vap-absent melting, as discussed above, will occur and further evolution will be as discussed for path A–A′.

Evolution of initially qtz-absent, vap-present assemblages

Path C–C′ of Fig. 4 illustrates the evolution of an assemblage which is initially qtz-absent but contains a H_2O-dominated vapour phase. Melting will not occur until the qtz-absent curve (6) is encountered, which will result in buffering of the assemblage to (qtz) with further evolution as described for path A–A′.

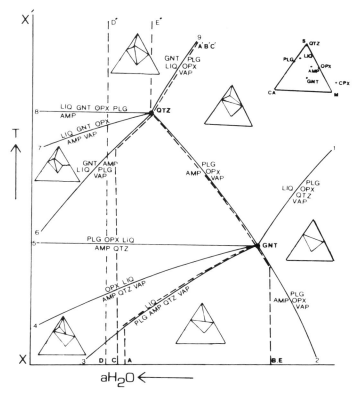

FIG. 4. T:aH_2O section for X–X′ in Fig. 7, constructed on the basis that any fluids present are binary H_2O-CO_2 vapours and only H_2O is soluble in the solid or liquid phases present in this system. For fluid-present conditions a(H_2O) will vary mainly as a function of H_2O:CO_2 in the vapour phase. For fluid-absent conditions a(H_2O) is defined for all compositions that contain hydrous phases (either crystals or liquid). As CO_2 is virtually insoluble in the liquids formed at these reactions and no carbonate minerals are present, reactions that consume vap will buffer assemblages to lower values of a(H_2O) whilst vap-producing reactions will buffer assemblages to higher values of a(H_2O). Compatibility diagrams are projected from vap onto the CA–M–S face from H_2O and all assemblages are also cpx-bearing. A–A′, B–B′, C–C′, D–D′ and E–E′ are reaction paths discussed in the text.

Evolution of vap-absent assemblages

Figure 4 can also be used to describe the evolution of vap-absent lithologies as a(H_2O) is defined for all assemblages which contain hydrous phases. An initially vap-absent, qtz-bearing assemblage with moderate initial a(H_2O) would show evolution along path D–D′ in Fig. 4. Melting will take place at the vap-absent equilibria (5) and (8) which are the same reactions that occur at the invariant points [gnt] and [qtz]. A qtz-bearing, vap-absent assemblage with a lower a(H_2O) will evolve along path E–E′ and the initial reactions will be as described for path B–B′. However, reaction (2) is a dehydration reaction producing vap. If vap were to be produced at this equilibria it would result in a(H_2O) reaching unity. Under conditions of internal buffering this would occur by buffering the assemblage along (2) until it

reached a(H_2O) = 1; Fig. 4 shows that the invariant points [gnt] and [qtz] will be encountered before the assemblage reached a(H_2O) = 1. An infinitesimal amount of reaction at (2) will cause buffering to an invariant point and the assemblage will remain vap-absent throughout. The sequence of melting reactions encountered will be the same as for the vap-absent assemblage with the higher initial a(H_2O).

This study of potential reaction paths in the CMASH model system illustrates the following important general points regarding anatexis in crustal rocks: i) Partial melting can occur in a broad range of starting compositions. ii) If internal buffering of fluid phases prevails, then very similar reactions will occur for a wide range of initial a(H_2O) values, so assemblages that initially contain CO_2- or H_2O-rich fluids will undergo very similar sequences of reactions.

iii) Melting at vap-conserving reactions at invariant points is important, with the bulk of the melting occurring at these reactions (Powell 1983*b*). This means that initially vap-absent assemblages which contain hydrous minerals, whilst remaining vap-absent throughout, will undergo almost identical degrees of partial melting as similar vap-bearing assemblages. iv) The vapour in equilibrium with an assemblage which contains hydrous minerals must always be H_2O-bearing. As CO_2 is relatively insoluble in silicate melts, and no other mechanism to remove CO_2 is likely, a mixed vapour phase must persist in such parageneses until all the hydrous minerals are removed by dehydration or melting reactions. After this has occurred the composition of the fluid phase is no longer buffered by the mineral assemblages. v) As H_2O partitions readily into the melt phase, migration of the melt would result in a general dehydration of the restite assemblages producing either vapour-absent parageneses or assemblages dominated by CO_2-rich fluids.

In the case of the metabasites considered here, liq in equilibrium with the assemblage cpx-opx-plg $\pm$ amp $\pm$ gnt $\pm$ vap is stable over a wide range of *P-T* space (Fig. 3). In reality, no single evolution path discussed in the model system will totally describe the petrogenesis of these lithologies because the initial composition of the metabasites may have varied over distances ranging from centimetres to tens of metres and a vapour phase may not have been present throughout. Such variations would result in different volumes of the rock undergoing slightly different reaction sequences and, as discussed below, partial melting may have occurred mainly in areas which were initially quartz- and vapour-bearing; certainly at the conditions of metamorphism recorded in the complex, partial melting would be unlikely in zones which were originally anhydrous (Wyllie 1983).

Reactions in the model system during cooling

The liquids formed by partial melting in the model system, if aggregated, would complete crystallizing at either (1) or (3) with the final neosome assemblage being plg-qtz-amp-vap $\pm$ cpx or plg-qtz-opx-vap $\pm$ cpx depending on whether reaction (2) was intersected. The restite would initially consist of cpx-opx-plg $\pm$ gnt $\pm$ vap; vap-bearing assemblages, or anhydrous assemblages to which vap is introduced during retrogression (as happened in the Lewisian complex during the Inverian event), would show the formation of amp during cooling at reaction (2). Assemblages remaining anhydrous throughout retrogression undergo no reactions during

cooling in this system, although both anhydrous and vap-bearing assemblages would undergo a series of reactions breaking down cpx-gnt parageneses (Barnicoat 1983, fig. 2) which are not shown in this projection.

Conditions of partial melting

Little direct estimate of *P-T* conditions can be made using the model system depicted in Fig. 3, as the rocks contain significant quantities of additional components (notably Na and Fe). However, as illustrated by Powell (1983*a*) the addition of such components will not significantly alter the model of partial melting discussed above. Reaction (10), however, was used by Barnicoat (1983 Fig. 4) to define the high-pressure boundary of the medium-pressure granulite facies. As discussed by Thompson and Algor (1977), eutectic minimum melting reactions involving a component that is relatively insoluble in the melt will lie a few degrees below melting reaction, involving only the main components of the melt. Thus, reactions (1) and (3) will lie a few degrees below reactions involving the melting of qtz-plg-vap assemblages due to the relative insolubility of the ferromagnesian (M) component in the melts formed at these equilibria. The location of the qtz-plg-vap melting reaction at $a(H_2O) = 1$ involving albite is given by Thompson & Algor (1977 Fig. 3), and from the data of Johannes (1983 Fig. 3) the corresponding reaction involving anorthite will be located *c.* 150°C above this. At a pressure of 10–12 kb quartz-bearing assemblages at $a(H_2O) = 1$ will commence melting at between *c.* 650 and 800°C. From the data of Thompson & Algor (1977) and Johannes (1983) quartz-absent assemblages at the same conditions would not melt until *c.* 700–1200°C. Decreasing $a(H_2O)$ will displace these equilibria to higher temperatures.

These estimates are within the temperatures recorded for the Stoer area, and the predicted assemblages formed after cooling agree with the parageneses observed in the basic orthogneisses and segregations. Thus, partial melting in these rocks is feasible and the system depicted in Figs 3 and 4 provides a reasonable model for the evolution of these lithologies under the recorded conditions of metamorphism.

Partial melting in the tonalitic grey gneisses

At the pressures and temperatures of metamorphism recorded by the Lewisian complex, the regional tonalitic gneisses would have undergone partial melting if they contained hydrous minerals, even in the absence of a vapour phase

(Wyllie 1983 Fig. 7). Sheraton *et al.* (1973*a*) and Pride & Muecke (1982) proposed that the suites of granitic to trondhjemitic gneisses that are commonly associated with the grey gneisses throughout the Lewisian complex were the products of local anatexis of the grey gneisses. However, Rollinson & Windley (1980) interpreted these lithologies as the products of fractional crystallization from the tonalitic precursors to the grey gneisses.

Suites of granitic to trondhjemitic gneisses, termed collectively acid leucogneisses (Cartwright *et al.* 1985), are common in the Stoer area (Table 1). These leucogneisses occur as sheets ranging from centimetres to hundreds of metres in thickness and persisting across strike for up to several hundred metres. The leucogneisses occur mainly interleaved with the grey gneisses, although the late basic orthogneiss and brown gneisses are cut by sheets of leucogneiss near their margins with the grey gneisses. The contacts of the leucogneiss sheets vary from sharp to gradational and are usually concordant. However, in a low-strain zone in the core of a major Badcallian (F_1) fold, a sheet of leucogneiss is seen to cut the layering in the grey gneisses with both units showing axial-planar S_1 fabrics which are discordant to the margins of the sheet (Fig. 5*a*). Accordingly, the acid leucogneisses appear to have been emplaced after the formation of layering in the tonalitic grey gneisses. In fact, as shown in Table 2, the acid leucogneisses cut the late basic orthogneisses which themselves were formed later than the tonalities (Cartwright *et al.* 1985) and are the youngest gneiss unit in the Stoer area.

Major element data

Figure 6 shows the compositions of acid leucogneisses and tonalitic grey gneisses from Stoer (Table 5) and similar lithologies from Scourie (Rollinson & Windley 1980) projected in the qtz-ab-or and or-ab-an systems. In the qtz-ab-or projection the majority of the leucogneiss compositions fall between the 1 and 5 kb cotectics in the H_2O-saturated system and between the 5 and 10 kb cotectics in the anhydrous system. In the or-ab-an system the leucogneisses have distinctly lower normative An contents than the tonalites. The composition of the leucogneisses in both projections is also similar to the compositions of melts from the experiments of Holloway and Burnham (1972) and Helz (1976), as demonstrated by Barnicoat (1983 Fig. 8).

These data are consistent with the acid leucogneisses representing the aggregated products of partial melting of the tonalitic grey gneisses at mid-crustal levels. The formation of these rocks by the fractionation of a tonalitic magma at the same crustal level is not ruled out by these data. However, as field relations imply that the acid leucogneisses postdate the crystallization of the tonalites, the intrusion of a suite of basic rocks and the formation of layering within the tonalites, the derivation of the tonalites by fractional crystallization seems unlikely.

Partial melting in supracrustal lithologies

The white mica layer, as discussed above, preserves evidence of undergoing local anatexis with the formation of quartz-bearing neosomes and corundum-bearing restites (Cartwright & Barnicoat 1986).

The brown gneisses (Table 1) contain no discordant veins or segregations, even though rocks of their composition should have undergone anatexis at the conditions recorded by the complex (Wyllie 1983, Fig. 7). These gneisses, however, are layered and it is possible that partial melting occurred early in their evolution and the D_1 Badcallian deformation has smeared out the felsic neosomes to form the leucocratic layers.

The plagioclase amphibolites (Table 1) also contain irregular veins up to 10 cm in width which truncate layering in low-strain zones (Fig. 5*b*). These veins are broadly granitic in composition, comprising quartz, plagioclase and alkali feldspar, and are again probably the products of partial melting of these gneisses.

Discussion

Partial melting during metamorphism

It has been suggested that partial melting was an important process in the evolution of this part of the Lewisian complex and that several lithologies preserve evidence of anatexis. At the temperatures and pressures recorded by these rocks many of the lithologies would have undergone anatexis even with low to moderate initial $a(H_2O)$ values. Certain lithologies (*e.g.* the tonalitic gneisses) would have commenced melting even in the absence of a vapour phase if they contained hydrous minerals, whereas the metabasites must have contained an H_2O-bearing vapour phase to undergo anatexis.

Crucial to the discussion of partial melting, therefore, is the hydration state of the complex; whether a fluid phase was present; and if so, its composition and behaviour during metamorphism. Powell (1983*b*) proposed that the widespread occurrence of low variance assemblages implied

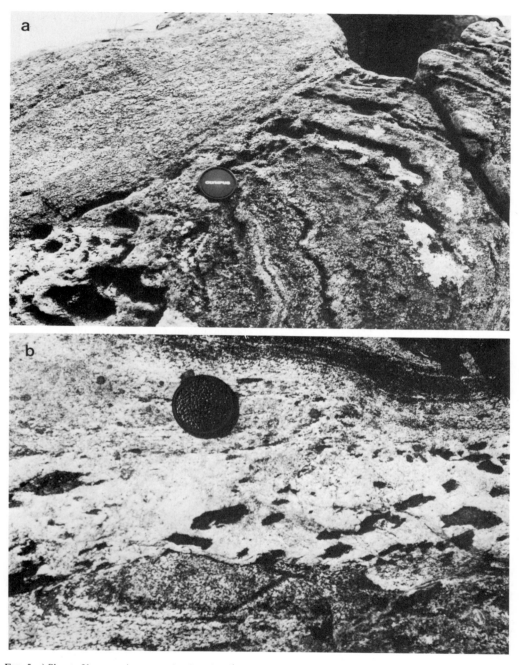

FIG. 5. a) Sheet of leucogneiss truncating layering in tonalitic gneisses in the core of a major F_1 fold. Both units are cross-cut by gently-inclined S_1 fabric. (Lens cap is 49 mm in diameter.) b) 5 cm wide felsic vein cross-cutting layering in plagioclase amphibolite. (Lens cap is 49 mm in diameter.)

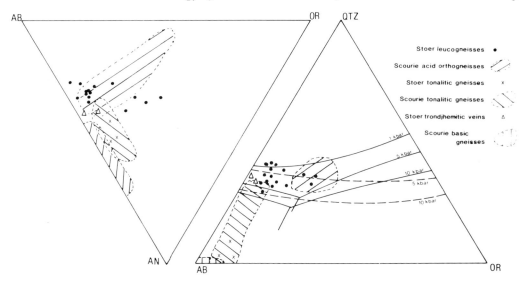

FIG. 6. Probable melts and restites from Stoer and Scourie projected into the qtz-ab-or and or-ab-an systems. The data in both projections are consistent with the acid leucogneisses from Stoer and analogous lithologies from Scourie being the partial melts of the tonalitic gneisses, and the trondhjemitic segregations in the basic gneisses also being formed by local anatexis of those gneisses. Sources of data: cotectic curves in the hydrous (solid lines) and anhydrous (dashed lines) qtz-ab-or systems from Luth (1969) and Huang & Wyllie (1975); Scourian acid orthogneisses and tonalitic gneiss compositions from Rollinson & Windley (1980); Scourian basic gneiss compositions from O'Hara (1961). Composition of Stoer rocks from X.R.F. analyses.

that $a(H_2O)$ in granulite-facies terrains was probably internally buffered within the individual lithologies. Under such conditions, dehydration reactions can rapidly increase the $a(H_2O)$ of the system (as demonstrated in the discussion of the model melting system). The result of such an increase in $a(H_2O)$ would be to promote partial melting in compositions which had initially low

TABLE 5. *Representative analyses of tonalitic gneisses, acid leucogneisses and trondhjemitic veins from late basic orthogneiss*

wt% oxides	Tonal-ite	Acid Leucogneisses		Trondh-jemite
SiO_2	61.94	71.38	71.13	72.12	69.05
TiO_2	0.55	0.27	0.31	0.02	0.37
Al_2O_3	22.81	15.42	15.30	15.93	14.91
Fe_2O_3	0.74	2.08	2.24	0.11	4.91
MnO	0.00	0.01	0.04	0.00	0.07
MgO	0.15	0.87	0.62	0.01	1.24
CaO	4.04	2.57	1.66	1.05	3.96
Na_2O	8.05	5.28	4.15	4.05	4.25
K_2O	0.53	0.87	3.24	5.83	0.66
P_2O_5	0.29	1.23	1.05	0.23	0.51
Total	99.10	99.98	99.74	99.35	99.93

Note: All iron is expressed as Fe_2O_3. Analyses obtained by X.R.F.

values of $a(H_2O)$ and allow certain lithologies, *eg* the tonalitic grey gneisses, to undergo anatexis even if they remained fluid absent.

For these processes to occur, the precursors to the gneisses must have been hydrated. Rollinson & Windley (1980) and Sheraton *et al.* (1973*a*) postulate that amphibole was an important phase in the tonalitic parents to the grey gneisses. The supracrustal lithologies presumably also contained hydrous minerals prior to granulite-facies metamorphism, whilst the basic gneisses, which had amphibole stable at the peak of metamorphism, may also have been originally hydrated.

Previously, a range of geochemical arguments based largely on trace element distributions has been used to discount partial melting as an important process in the evolution of the Lewisian complex; both for the formation of individual lithologies (Rollinson & Windley 1980) and for the formation of anhydrous trace element-depleted granulite-facies assemblages (*eg* Tarney 1976; Weaver & Tarney 1983). However, many of these discussions considered only models of single-stage partial melting. From the modelling of melting reactions in the basic orthogneiss it is apparent that the likely regime of partial melting in high-grade terrains is one where batches of melt are formed at discrete intervals. The behaviour of trace elements under such a scheme of anatexis may vary significantly from their behaviour under single stage melting processes. The behaviour of major elements under these conditions is controlled by the melting reactions and, as illustrated by Fig. 4, melts of similar composition are likely to be formed by successive melting reactions.

To illustrate the effects of this type of melting process, Fig. 7 shows the theoretical concentrations of compatible (rock-melt distribution coefficient, $D = 2$), incompatible ($D = 0.1$), and more highly incompatible ($D = 0.01$) trace elements in successive batches of liquids and restites formed under these conditions of anatexis.

To isolate the effects of the melting process, D values are assumed to have remained constant throughout, and the degree of partial melting considered is between 5 and 10% in each batch up to a maximum of 20% total melting, so the effects of very small or large degrees of melting are not considered. The resultant distributions of elements is shown in Fig. 7, compared with the distribution of the same elements under the same degree of single stage melting and shows the following trends: i) the behaviour of compatible elements ($D > 1$) does not differ significantly from their behaviour under conditions of single stage melting. ii) In the case of incompatible elements

($D < 1$) the initial melts have higher concentrations of these elements than later melts. The decline in concentration in later melts is more marked for highly incompatible elements ($D = 0.01$) and later melts can have lower concentrations of these elements than the initial rock. iii) Small variations in the number and size of the batches of melt may produce significant variations in the trace element content of later melts. In this simple model, Fig. 7 shows that the highly incompatible elements can vary by over an order of magnitude in the later melts. In the discussion of the possible melting reactions in the basic orthogneiss it was indicated that the degree of partial melting could have varied throughout the rock, which may have produced batches of melt with variable trace element concentrations.

These results predict that even under these simplified conditions of partial melting it is possible to produce batches of melt of virtually identical whole rock compositions but variable concentrations of incompatible trace elements, and that the ratios of individual trace elements within the melt may vary significantly.

Another important mechanism in producing variations in trace element concentrations results from the changes in the restite assemblage during the melting process. Fig. 4 demonstrates that

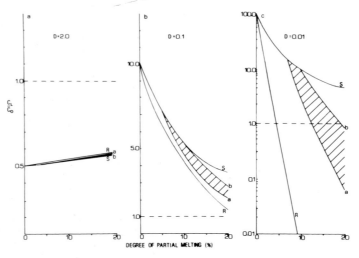

FIG. 7. Behaviour of compatible and incompatible trace elements under conditions of batch melting. The concentration of each element (from the equations of Wood & Fraser 1977 p. 220) in the liquid (C_L) is plotted relative to its concentration in the original rock (C_O) for elements with distribution coefficients of a) $D = 2$, b) $D = 0.1$, c) $D = 0.01$. The hatched area represents the range of trace element content in the melt when successive batches of between 5 and 10% melt are formed, up to a maximum of 20% total melting. The lines a and b which limit this area are the trace element concentrations in the melts formed by successive batches of 5 and 10% melting respectively. If smaller batches of melt are able to form then a) will approach the Raleigh melting curve (R). The formation of larger batches will cause b) to approach the single stage melting curve (S). The dashed line represents the concentration of trace elements in the original rock; values plotting below this line are depleted in that element relative to the source rock.

early melts may have been in equilibrium with amphibole but later melts of similar composition were in equilibrium with clino- and orthopyroxene. Hanson (1978) indicates that these phases have different distribution coefficients for most trace elements, which would itself result in a different trace element concentration in early and later melts. Minor phases such as zircon and apatite are common in Lewisian gneisses and as shown by Hanson (1978) they have extremely high distribution coefficients for certain trace elements, and so small variations in the concentration of these minerals in the restites would also cause variations in the trace element content of the melt.

Such mechanisms could probably account for much of the variation in trace element content in suites of gneisses such as the acid leucogneisses (Rollinson & Windley 1980) and it is apparent that the trace element data need further analysis to take into account the effects discussed above.

Elemental depletion during granulite-facies metamorphism

With partial melting apparently an important process in the evolution of the Lewisian complex, it is tempting to ascribe the more intermediate average chemistry of granulite-facies terrains and the depletion of U, Th, Rb and K compared with comparable amphibolite-facies rocks to the removal of a melt during metamorphism (Fyfe 1973; Pride & Muecke 1980). The removal of a melt is also an extremely efficient way of removing H_2O from the terrain. As discussed by Pride & Muecke (1982), the potential products of partial melting still visible in the complex are themselves depleted in many of these elements, and so an earlier melt phase must have been removed to account for the observed depletions. Kennah & Hollister (1983) describe a series of melting reactions from the Tertiary granulite-facies terrain of British Columbia where, from mass balance considerations, they infer that the earliest melts escaped from the complex. Removal of early formed melts is possible as they would almost certainly be more hydrated, and hence more mobile, than later melts.

Because of the difficulty in accounting for the distribution of rare earth elements by partial melting processes Weaver & Tarney (1983) discuss an alternative model in which granulite-facies metamorphism and elemental depletions are the result of the passage of CO_2-rich fluids through the crust. In this model the Lewisian would represent the deeper levels of terrains, such as southern India (Newton *et al.* 1980), where CO_2-dominated fluids are responsible for trace element enrichment. In this model anatexis in the Lewisian complex would have taken place prior to the formation of granulite-facies assemblages (Weaver 1980).

However, as the mineral-CO_2 partition coefficients are not well known, and none of the textural evidence of CO_2 flushing that is present in southern India (such as cross-cutting veins of charnockite) is observed in the Lewisian terrain, the model is not readily evaluated. Furthermore, Lamb & Valley (1984) show that, at the oxygen fugacities reported for the Lewisian and other comparable granulite-facies terrains, the passage of large quantities of CO_2 would cause the precipitation of significant quantities of graphite, which is not observed in the Lewisian.

It is obvious that both models have their drawbacks and that more data are required to evaluate them fully. The interpretation of the major and trace element data must take into account the likely mode of occurrence of the processes (such as partial melting) that affect granulite-facies terrains.

The use of petrogenetic modelling combined with geothermometry has proved a useful approach to the investigation of the Lewisian complex in this area. The analysis of model systems has allowed not only *P–T* conditions to be estimated but has also provided an insight into the possible processes that occurred during metamorphism.

ACKNOWLEDGEMENTS We are grateful to Professor M. J. O'Hara for initiating this work and both he and Dr W. R. Fitches have provided much useful discussion. We wish to thank Drs P. G. Hill and D. G. Russell of the Edinburgh microprobe unit for their help with the mineral analyses and Drs P. K. Harvey and B. P. Atkin of Nottingham for their help with the X.R.F. analyses. Mr A. Thawley and Mr W. Edwards helped to produce the figures. I.C. acknowledges a U.C.W. studentship.

References

BARNICOAT, A. C. 1982. *Thermal history of parts of the Lewisian gneiss complex, NW Scotland.* Unpubl. Ph.D. Thesis Univ. Edinburgh.

—— 1983. Metamorphism of the Scourian Complex, NW Scotland. *J. metamorphic Geol.* **1**, 163–82.

—— & O'HARA, M. J. 1979. High temperature pyroxenes from an ironstone at Scourie, Sutherland. *Mineralog. Mag.* **43**, 371–5.

BEACH, A. 1974. The measurement and significance of displacements on Laxfordian shear zones. NW Scotland. *Proc. Geol. Ass.* **85**, 13–21.

CARTWRIGHT, I. & BARNICOAT, A. C. 1986. The

generation of silica-saturated melts and corundum-bearing restites by crustal anatexis: Petrogenetic modelling based on an example from the Lewisian of NW Scotland. *J. metamorphic Geol.* **4**, 77–79.

——, FITCHES, W. R., O'HARA, M. J., BARNICOAT, A. C. & O'HARA, S. 1985. Archaean supracrustals from the Lewisian near Stoer, Sutherland. *Scott. J. Geol.* **21**, 187–96.

CHAPMAN, H. J. 1979. 2390 myr Rb-Sr whole rock age for the Scourie Dykes of north-west Scotland. *Nature, London* **277**, 642–3.

—— & MOORBATH, S. 1977. Lead isotope measurements from the oldest recognised Lewisian gneiss of NW Scotland. *Nature, London* **268**, 41–2.

ELLIS, D. J. & GREEN, D. H. 1979. An experimental study of the effect of Ca upon garnet-clinopyroxene Fe-Mg exchange equilibria. *Contrib. Mineral. Petrol.* **71**, 13–22.

EVANS, C. R. & LAMBERT, R. ST. J. 1974. The Lewisian of Lochinver Sutherland: The type area for the Inverian metamorphism. *J. geol. Soc. Lond.* **130**, 125–50.

FYFE, W. S. 1973. The granulite facies, partial melting and the Archaean crust. *Phil. Trans. R. Soc. London.* **A273**, 457–62.

GANGULY, J. 1979. Garnet and clinopyroxene solid solutions and geothermometry based on Fe-Mg distribution coefficients. *Geochim. Cosmochim. Acta.* **43**, 1021–9.

GREENWOOD, H. J. 1975. Buffering of pore fluids by metamorphic reactions. *Am. J. Sci.* **275**, 573–93.

HAMILTON, P. J., EVENSEN, N. M., O'NIONS, R. K. & TARNEY, J. 1979. Sm-Nd systematics of Lewisian gneisses: implications for the origin of granulites. *Nature, London* **277**, 25–8.

HANSON, G. N. 1978 The application of trace elements to the petrogenesis of igneous rocks of granitic composition. *Earth planet. Sci. Lett.* **38**, 26–43.

HELZ, R. T. 1976. Phase relations of basalts in their melting range at $P_{H_2O} = 5$ kb. Part II. Melt compositions. *J. Petrology* **17**, 139–93.

HOLLOWAY, J. R. & BURNHAM, C. W. 1972. Melting relations of basalts with equilibrium water pressure less than total pressure. *J. Petrology* **13**, 1–29.

HUANG, W. L. & WYLLIE, P. J. 1975. Melting reactions in the system $NaAlSi_3O_8$-$KAlSi_3O_8$-SiO_2 to 35 kilobars, dry and with excess water. *J. Geol.* **83**, 737–48.

JENSEN, L. N. 1984. Quartz microfabric of the Laxfordian Canisp Shear Zone, NW Scotland. *J. Struct. Geol.* **6**, 239–302.

JOHANNES, W. 1983. Metastable melting in the granite system. *In*: ATHERTON, M. P. & GRIBBLE, C. D. (eds) *Migmatites, Melting and Metamorphism.* Shiva, Nantwich. 27–36.

KENNAH, C. & HOLLISTER, L. S. 1983. Anatexis in the Central Gneiss Complex, British Columbia. *In*: ATHERTON, M. P. & GRIBBLE, C. D. (eds) *Migmatites, Melting and Metamorphism.* Shiva, Nantwich. 142–62.

LAMB, W. & VALLEY, J. W. 1984. Metamorphism of reduced granulites in low CO_2 vapour-free environment. *Nature, London* **312**, 56–8.

LUTH, W. C. 1969. The systems $NaAlSi_3O_8$-SiO_2 and

$KAlSi_3O_8$-SiO_2 to 20 kb and the relationship between H_2O content, P_{H_2O} and P_{total} in granitic magmas. *Am. J. Sci.* **267-A**, 325–41.

NEWTON, R. C., SMITH, J. V. & WINDLEY, B. F. 1980. Carbonic metamorphism, granulites and crustal growth. *Nature, London* **288**, 45–50.

O'HARA M. J. 1961. Zoned ultrabasic and basic gneiss masses in the early Lewisian metamorphic complex at Scourie, Sutherland. *J. Petrology* **2**, 248–76.

—— 1977. Thermal history of excavation of Archaean gneisses from the base of the continental crust. *J. geol. Soc. Lond.* **134**, 185–200.

POWELL, R. 1983a. Fluids and melting under upper amphibolite facies conditions. *J. geol. Soc. Lond.* **140**, 629–34.

—— 1983b. Processes in granulite facies metamorphism. *In*: ATHERTON, M. P. & GRIBBLE, C. D. (eds) *Migmatites, Melting and Metamorphism.* Shiva, Nantwich. 127–39.

PRIDE, C. & MUECKE, G. K. 1980. Rare earth element geochemistry of the Scourian complex NW Scotland—evidence for the granite granulite link. *Contrib. Mineral. Petrol.* **73**, 403–12.

—— & —— 1982. Geochemistry and origin of granitic rocks, Scourian complex, NW Scotland. *Contrib. Mineral. Petrol.* **80**, 379–85.

ROLLINSON, H. R. 1980. Mineral reactions in a granulite facies calc-silicate rock from Scourie. *Scott. J. Geol.* **16**, 153–64.

—— 1981. Garnet-clinopyroxene thermometry and barometry in the Scourian complex, NW Scotland. *Lithos* **14**, 225–38.

—— & WINDLEY, B. F. 1980. An Archaean granulite-grade tonalite-trondhjemite-granite suite from Scourie, NW Scotland. *Contrib. Mineral. Petrol.* **72**, 265–81.

SAVAGE, D. & SILLS, J. D. 1980. High pressure metamorphism in the Scourian of NW Scotland: Evidence from garnet granulites. *Contrib. Mineral. Petrol.* **74**, 153–63.

SAXENA, S. K. 1979. Garnet-clinopyroxene geothermometer. *Contrib. Mineral. Petrol.* **70**, 229–35.

SHERATON, J. W., SKINNER, A. C. & TARNEY, J. 1973a. The geochemistry of the Scourian gneisses of the Assynt district. *In*: PARK, R. G. & TARNEY, J. (eds) *The Early Precambrian of Scotland and Related Rocks in Greenland.* Univ. Keele. 13–30.

——, TARNEY, J., WHEATLEY, T. J. & WRIGHT, A. E. 1973b. The structural history of the Assynt District. *In*: PARK, R. G. & TARNEY, J. (eds) *The Early Precambrian of Scotland and Related Rocks in Greenland.* Univ. Keele. 31–45.

SILLS, J. D. 1983. Mineralogical changes occurring during the retrogression of Archaean gneisses from the Lewisian complex of NW Scotland. *Lithos* **16**, 113–24.

TARNEY, J. 1963. Assynt dykes and their metamorphism. *Nature, London* **199**, 672–4.

—— 1976. Geochemistry of high-grade Archaean gneisses. *In*: WINDLEY, B. F. (ed) *The Early History of the Earth.* Wiley, Chichester. 405–18.

THOMPSON, A. B. 1982. Dehydration of pelitic rocks and the generation of H_2O–undersaturated granitic liquids. *Am. J. Sci.* **282**, 1576–95.

—— & ALGOR, J. D. 1977. Model systems for the anatexis of pelitic rocks. I. Theory of melting in the system $KAlO_2$-$NaAlO_2$-SiO_2-H_2O. *Contrib. Mineral. Petrol.* **63**, 247–69.

WEAVER, B. L. 1980. Rare earth element geochemistry of Madras granulites. *Contrib. Mineral. Petrol.* **71**, 271–9.

—— & TARNEY, J. 1983. Elemental depletion in Archaean granulite facies rocks. *In:* ATHERTON, M. P. & GRIBBLE, C. D. (eds) *Migmatites, Melting and Metamorphism.* Shiva, Nantwich. 250–63.

WOOD, B. J. 1975. The influence of pressure, temperature and bulk composition on the appearance of garnet in orthogneiss—an example from South Harris. *Earth planet. Sci. Lett.* **26**, 299–311.

—— 1977. The activities of components in the clinopyroxene and garnet solid solutions and their applications to rocks. *Phil. Trans. R. Soc. London.* **A286**, 331–42.

—— & FRAZER, D. G. 1977. *Elementary Thermodynamics for Geologists.* Oxford University Press. Oxford.

WYLLIE, P. J. 1977. Crustal anatexis: An experimental review. *Tectonophysics,* **43**, 41–71.

—— 1983. Experimental studies on biotite- and muscovite-bearing granites and some crustal magmatic sources. *In:* ATHERTON, M. P. & GRIBBLE, C. D. (eds) *Migmatites, Melting and Metamorphism.* Shiva, Nantwich. 12–26.

I. CARTWRIGHT, Department of Geology, University College of Wales, Aberystwyth, Dyfed SY23 3DB, UK.

A. C. BARNICOAT, Department of Geology, University College of Wales, Aberystwyth, Dyfed SY23 3DB, UK.

The geochemistry of Lewisian marbles

N. M. S. Rock

with analytical data by
A. E. Davis, D. Hutchison, M. Joseph & T. K. Smith

SUMMARY: To rectify the dearth of published petrographical and analytical data for Lewisian marbles, 307 samples, from nearly all outcrops known, have been examined in thin section, and 114 samples analysed for 35 elements. Lewisian marbles can be divided texturally into: 1) *macrocrystalline* (generally white, pure to silicate-rich) *eg* from Glenelg; 2) *microcrystalline* (often coloured, ornamental, pure to silicate-rich), *eg* from Iona; 3) *microbrecciated* (grey, crushed, fine-grained, silicate–opaque-rich), *eg* from the Loch Maree Group (LMG). Lewisian marbles are geochemically typical of ancient carbonates, tending to have lower contents of trace elements (notably Sr) than younger (*eg* Scottish Dalradian) marbles. Whereas all analyzed marbles from the South Harris and Coll foreland outcrops and from the Glenelg and Kintail inliers are *dolostones* (%MgO 15–20, %SiO_2 5–15), those of the eastern inliers (Glen Strathfarrar, Shinness) are pure *limestones* (%MgO < 10, %SiO_2 < 10). Elsewhere, limestones and dolostones are intimately associated or interbanded (*eg* Scardroy inlier). Microbrecciated LMG marbles (Flowerdale belt of Gairloch; Furnace belt of Loch Maree) have notably higher chalcophile and siderophile element contents than macrocrystalline marbles in adjacent belts (Cloiche of Gairloch; Gleann Tulacha of Loch Maree). Aside from such local differences, however, limestones and dolostones of the inliers, LMG and remaining foreland reveal few non-trivial differences in composition. Moreover, Lewisian marbles collectively show strong Pearson and Spearman correlations between elements concentrated in accessory phases (*eg* Y–La–Ce, K–Rb–Al, Fe–Co–V). Given established secular variations in the chemistry of global carbonate rocks, these relationships between both marble groups and chemical variables are difficult to explain if some Lewisian marbles (*eg* S. Harris) represent late Scourian, and others (*eg* LMG) early Proterozoic sediments. They may provide a tentative hint that most Lewisian marbles were deposited contemporaneously.

Marbles have been recognized for over 150 years as a major metasedimentary component within the Lewisian complex. However, they remain exceptionally poorly documented, having received little more than passing mention in local, often unpublished studies. Lewisian marbles are not as old as, say 3600–3700 Ma marbles from Russia or Greenland (Salop 1983, p. 24), but may include the oldest Lewisian rocks (Watson 1983, table 1). They are in any case important examples of globally rare sediments—carbonates deposited at a time of inhibitingly high atmospheric CO_2 and oceanic HCO_3^- concentrations (Maissoneuve 1982), well before the onset of global carbonate sedimentation some 2000 Ma ago (Cameron & Baumann 1972). Moreover, the association of many Lewisian marbles with euxinic pelites (Rock *et al.* 1986) is important, as characteristic of Archaean (supposed shelf-type) sediments (McCall 1977; Windley 1978); this paper presents among the first regional data for such associations anywhere, and certainly for the Lewisian itself.

Distribution and stratigraphy

Marbles are present both in restricted areas of the Lewisian foreland and in inliers of the 'Scardroy sheet', E of the Moine Thrust (Fig. 1; Rock 1983). A few isolated marbles are known within the Moine outcrop, well away from the Scardroy sheet (Fig. 1). The Shinness marble-gneiss succession was once attributed to the Moine (*eg* BGS sheet 102), but Winchester & Lambert (1970) and Rock & Waterhouse (1986) revealed its Lewisian affinities. By contrast, the Armadale, Glen Dessarry, Glen Urquhart and Rosemarkie marbles (Fig. 1) are geochemically dissimilar to *bona fide* Lewisian (Rock *et al.* 1984; Rock & Waterhouse 1986). Because conflicting ages (Lewisian, Moinian, Dalradian, Cambro-Ordovician) have been assigned to them by different authors, they are not considered further here.

The mainly geographical terms *occurrence*, *belt* and *locality* (Rock 1985a) here proxy for 'Group', 'Subgroup' and 'Formation' in formal lithostratig-

From: PARK, R. G. & TARNEY, J. (eds), 1987, *Evolution of the Lewisian and Comparable Precambrian High Grade Terrains*, Geological Society Special Publication No. 27, pp. 109–126.

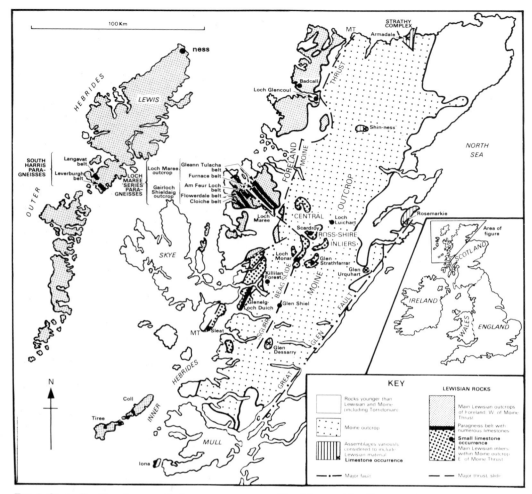

Fig. 1. Generalized location map for known occurrences of Lewisian marbles. For geological details of each occurrence, including outcrop listings and 1:75,000 sketch-maps, see table 1 of Rock (1985a). The unassigned marbles at Armadale, Glen Urquhart, Rosemarkie, and Glen Dessarry are considered elsewhere (Rock *et al.* 1984; Rock & Waterhouse 1986). Examples of Lewisian localities for non-metasedimentary carbonate-rich rocks (Badcall, Loch Glencoul, Sleat) are also shown (see text for explanation).

raphy. A 'locality' is a cluster of marble outcrops separated from the next cluster by a wider tract of carbonate-free terrain. A 'belt' is an elongated cluster of localities. An 'occurrence' comprises one or more belts, or several localities.

Non-metasedimentary, tectono-metamorphic carbonate rocks in the Lewisian

The following are included on Fig. 1, but not considered further: *a*) A thick ferriferous dolomite body near Badcall Bay [NC 186 399] (Peach & Horne 1907, p. 148). This is almost certainly a fault rock. *b*) A small mass at Loch Glencoul [NC 2486 3334], recorded on unpublished BGS maps as 'calcareous rock weathering like limestone'. This is in fact a magnesite-talc rock—probably a carbonated ultramafite (Table 5). *c*) A severely cataclased succession near Aird of Sleat, Skye [NG 5982 0020], adjacent to the Moine Thrust, including interbanded blastomylonitic, pelitic and quartz-carbonate schists. This succession was considered by Peach & Horne (1907, p. 265) as Lewisian, but the petrography and geochemistry of the various rock-types (Table 5) do not confirm them even as unmodified sediments.

Just because these few examples occur, does not mean that *all* Lewisian marbles are tectono-metamorphic. For although many others are pod-like, or associated with zones of high strain (*eg* along shears at Gairloch, and the Sgurr Beag Slide (Tanner 1970) at Glen Shiel), a metasedimentary origin is supported by the following arguments: 1) The structural setting could equally be due to the plasticity of carbonates, which represent zones of weakness. 2) Most Lewisian marbles are associated with unequivocally metasedimentary pelites, quartzites, and/or banded iron formations. Marbles may carry silicate 'lumps', commonly interpreted as metamorphosed chert nodules (*eg* Sanders 1972). 3) Some have argued that high CO_2 fluxes required for prograde amphibolite to granulite facies transition (as in the Scourian) might arise by decarbonation of buried, pre-existing marbles (discussion in Newton *et al.* 1980). Tectono-metamorphic Lewisian marbles, on the other hand, could probably only form by fixation of CO_2 released during granulite to amphibolite facies retrogression. A circular argument is thereby threatened, in which marbles are both product and cause of metamorphism. 4) Limestone/dolostone interbanding (see below) is unlikely to be tectonic. 5) Lewisian marbles are mineralogically and chemically typical of carbonate metasediments (Fig. 4 and see below). By contrast, the above nonsedimentary carbonate rocks bear little resemblance to 'typical' Lewisian marbles (Table 5).

Date of sedimentation and metamorphic history of Lewisian marbles

Lewisian marbles could theoretically have been metamorphosed up to 5 times (Scourian, *c.* 2800 Ma; ?Inverian, *c.* 2400 Ma; Laxfordian, *c.* 1900 Ma; and in the inliers, Grenvillian, *c.* 1000 Ma; and Caledonian, *c.* 500 Ma). No isotopic method is thus likely to identify sedimentation ages—least of all the K-Ar method, which gave the only date so far for a Lewisian marble (a 1510 Ma phlogopite age from S. Harris—Giletti *et al.* 1961). The Rb-Sr method is similarly precluded by vanishingly low Rb levels, the La-Ce method (Tanaka & Masuda 1983) by lack of negative Ce anomalies (A. Masuda, pers. comm.), and the Nd-Sm method possibly by the chondritic levels of both elements (though pilot Nd-Sm studies are warranted).

Assuming that Lewisian marbles are sedimentary, the following are among few age constraints; each is problematical in itself, reflecting wide controversies over Lewisian metamorphic history in general (this vol. and Watson 1983): 1) The granulite-facies metamorphism suffered by the Coll/Tiree, Glenelg and S. Harris marbles has long been taken to imply their Scourian age (*eg* Watson 1983). If granulite conditions were locally attained in the Laxfordian (Cliff *et al.* 1983) or even Grenvillian (Sanders *et al.* 1984), however, this needs reappraisal. 2) The oldest dates from rocks intimately associated with Lewisian marbles are for the Scardroy gneisses (2700 Ma; Moorbath & Taylor 1974); however, there is as yet no direct proof that the marbles are older still (*ie* Scourian). 3) The S. Harris metasediments predate the 2060 Ma S. Harris igneous complex and the possible early Laxfordian granulite-facies event (Cliff *et al.* 1983), but their relationship to the Scourian granulite-facies event is equivocal. 4) The Gairloch metasediments have yielded Rb-Sr isochrons of 1500 Ma and 1980 Ma (Bickerman *et al.* 1975), and 2 single Sm–Nd *model ages* of 2200 and 2500 Ma (O'Nions *et al.* 1983); unfortunately, both are equivocal, the isochrons because they incorporate rocks now regarded as basement (A. E. Wright, pers. comm.), and the model ages because they are *not* isochrons. 5) Lewisian marbles could be correlated either with the Nagssugtoqidian supracrustals (*ie* post-Scourian; Myers, this vol.), or the Malene supracrustals (2800–3750 Ma; Beach & Chadwick 1980) of Greenland.

Present data still seem to allow two broad interpretations: *a*) Most or all Lewisian marbles represent (late) Scourian sediments; younger dates reflect subsequent metamorphic history (*eg* Watson 1983, p. 34–35). *b*) The Loch Maree Group (LMG) marbles represent post-Scourian, pre-Laxfordian (*c.* 2200 Ma) cover (*eg* Bowes 1978); whereas marbles intimately associated with unequivocally Scourian rocks (*eg* S. Harris and Scardroy) represent Scourian sediments (*eg* Fettes *et al.* 1986).

Sampling and analytical methods

Nearly all localities for Lewisian marbles known to BGS (>70) were revisited, and 114 new analyses made. Samples were carefully selected to cover both local and regional *ranges* of composition (much more exhaustive sampling would be needed to cover *bulk* compositions in each locality—*cf* Lamar & Thompson 1956). Exact procedures, including checks from 307 thin sections in the BGS collections, and 223 specific gravity measurements, were detailed in Rock (1985*a*, *b*) and Rock *et al.* (1984). Numbers of analyses were adjusted in relation to outcrop sizes: small, homogeneous outcrops (*eg* Killilan Forest) were represented by 1–2 analyses, whereas

TABLE 1. *Summary of lithological association and mineralogy of the various Lewisian marble occurrences.*

Occurrence (in alphabetical order)	Silicate lithologies intimately associated with the marbles *†									Non-carbonate minerals recorded in thin sections from the marbles † (in alphabetical order)																							Number of thin sections examined	Number of analyses available (definitions of Fig. 2)			
	Paragneisses							Igneous origin		Apatite	Alkali feldspar	Baryte	Biotite/phlogopite	Chlorite	Diopside/augite	Epidote group	Graphite	Hornblende/tremolite	Humite group	Magnetite, haematite, ilmenite	Muscovite	Olivine/serpentine	Plagioclase	Pyrite	Quartz	Rutile	Scapolite	Sphene	Spinel	Talc	Tourmaline	Zircon		Limestone	Dolostones	Skarns	Total
	Biotite-rich schists & gneisses	Kyanite-bearing pelites	Graphitic pelites	Garnetiferous pelites	Psammites	Quartzites	'Skarns' (Ca-Mg-Fe-silicates)	Amphibolites & hornblende-schists	Pegmatites																												
Lewisian Foreland																																					
Coll	2			2		3	2	2	4	1	2		3	3	2	3	1	3			2	3	3	2	2						2		17	0	3	3	6
Gairloch-Shieldaig	3		2	2	3	3	2	3	2		2		3	1	3	2		3		1	2		2	1	3	1		1		2	2	1	39	6	10	2	18
Iona	3		2	2	2	3	3	2	2	1			2	2	2	3		3	2				2		2				1	1	1		23	5	9	0	14
Langavat	3		3	3		3	3	3	2				3	3	3		1	3	2	2		3	1				2		1	2			16	0	4	0	4
Leverburgh	2	2	2	4	2	2	3	3	2	1			3	2	3		1	2	2	1		3	1	1	2			1	2				40	0	9	0	9
Lewis (Ness)	4	1			2													2				1											1	1	0	0	1
Loch Maree	3		3	3	4	2	3	3	3		2	1	4		2			3			3			1	3	2		2		2	2	1	41	3	7	2	12
Tiree	2		2	2	2	2	4	3	3		2		2	2	3	2		2				3			2				2	2	1	1	43	3	1	1	5
																																	Totals 219	18	43	8	69
Lewisian Inliers																																					
Glenelg-Loch Duich	3	3	3				3	3			2		3		3	1	1	3	2		4							1	2				33	0	15	0	15
Glen Shiel							4							3				4	1		4												2	0	2	0	2
Glen Strathfarrar			2				2	2					3		3		4	2					3					3					7	0	3	0	3
Killian Forest							2										Silicate-free																1	0	1	0	1
Loch Luichart							2						3	2			3																4	1	2	0	3
Loch Monar			3				3						3		3	3	3	3					3		3								4	7	1	0	2
Scardroy	2		2				3	2		1			3	2	2	2	4		2		2				2	2		1				1	19	0	0	2	8
Shinness			2				3	3		2			2	2	3	3	3	3			2		1		2	2		1			1		18	15	0	6	21
																																	Totals 88	27	22	8	57

For details of National Grid references, limestone bed thicknesses, relative abundance of pure to impure carbonate rocks, BGS registered specimen numbers, and published references, see table 1 of Rock (1985a). Other occurrences of carbonate-bearing rocks in the Lewisian are regarded as non-metasediment (see text) and hence not included here.

No other Lewisian marble occurrences are known to BGS.

* Most marbles are closely associated with typical Lewisian 'grey' hornblende-biotite-orthogneisses.

† *Approximate abundances* of associated lithologies/constituent minerals are indicated by numbers as follows:
1 = rare/accessory; 2 = present/minor; 3 = common/essential; 4 = dominant metasediment/silicate mineral.

Accessory minerals are given as '1' only where specifically noted in at least one thin section; they are probably represented more widely.

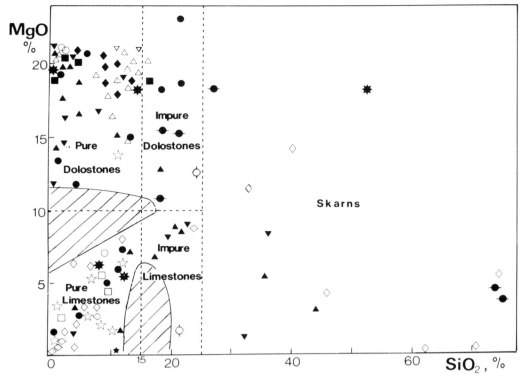

FIG. 2. MgO–SiO₂ plot for 126 Lewisian marbles, illustrating compositional gaps (diagonally ruled) used to divide them. 114 analyses from the present study, others from Moorhouse & Moorhouse (1983) and various BGS publications (see Rock 1985*b*). For justification of the term 'skarn', see Rock (1985*a*). Some symbols represent more than one overlapping sample. The compositional gaps are believed to be real, as they are also present in Dalradian marbles (Rock 1986), and are based on comprehensive sampling of the purer marbles. The limestone/dolostone gap can be explained by the miscibility gap between calcite and dolomite (Deer *et al.* 1962), the pure/impure limestone gap by the readier dolomitization of limestones with higher silicate impurities (*cf* Hickman & Wright 1983). Sampling of the skarns was, however, by no means comprehensive, and they probably cover much of the right-hand part of the diagram.

Foreland marbles (closed symbols)
- ●— Coll
- ▲ Gairloch-Shieldaig
- ● Iona
- ■ Langavat (S. Harris)
- ♦ Leverburgh (S. Harris)
- ▼ Loch Maree
- ★ Ness (Lewis)
- * Tiree

Inlier marbles (open symbols)
- △ Glenelg-Loch Duich
- ▽ Glen Shiel
- ◇ Glen Strathfarrar
- □ Killilan Forest
- ◓ Loch Luichart
- ○ Loch Monar
- ☆ Scardroy
- ◇ Shinness

larger or more inhomogeneous outcrops were analysed more exhaustively.

Major elements (14) were determined by Betaprobe (Roberts & Davis 1977), and trace elements (21) by conventional XRF techniques. Rock (1985*b*) details machine parameters, precision, accuracy, and inter-laboratory comparability of the results.

In what follows, 'marble' is used for all Lewisian carbonate metasediments, irrespective of Mg/Ca ratio or SiO₂ content. Chemical subdivisions are defined in Fig. 2. Tables 4 and 5 summarize data for limestones, dolostones and

skarns. Skarns were not sampled comprehensively, and are not considered further, because: i) they are extremely inhomogeneous and mineralogically variable; ii) many are monomineralic or bimineralic, tracing metasomatic marble–country-rock interactions (as in Thompson 1975; Fraser 1977; Lazell 1977); their compositions differ greatly from original sediments; iii) by restricting consideration to purer marbles, element distributions between carbonate and silicate phases can be largely ignored for the purposes of the present, preliminary account.

TABLE 2. *Sections through continuously exposed Lewisian marble bands apparently uncomplicated by tectonism, and probably representing original stratigraphy*

	Allt Coire Dubh (Scardroy inlier) [NH 2240 5224]		Gleann Meinich (Scardroy inlier) [NH 2346 5430]		Bay Steingie (Langavat belt, S Harris)† [NG 0199 9390]	
	Epidote-biotite-chlorite-gneiss with carbonate veins (S70980)		Acidic hornblendic gneiss		Laminated biotite-epidote-hornblende*-quartz-plagioclase rock with lenticles of hornblende-schist	
25 cm	Laminated hornblende-biotite-epidote gneiss (S70981)		Mafic hornblende-rich gneiss			
20–25 cm	Tremolite-diopside rock (S70983) sheathed in tremolite-biotite-carbonate-schist (S70982) layers	1 m	Biotite-diopside-tremolite-quartz-plagioclase-sphene skarn (S70992)	1 m	Pale to dark grey impure forsterite-dolostone split into several crumpled bands (S72649–50), and interbanded with hornblende-biotite-schist and tremolite-biotite-microcline-plagioclase skarn	
30 cm	Pure limestone with minor tremolite (S70984) sandwiched between 10 cm layers of Ca-Mg-silicate rock	50 cm	Phlogopite-tremolite limestone (S70993) with interbanded biotite-clinozoisite-diopside-tremolite skarn (S70994)	2 m	Rib of hornblende-diopside-chlorite-pyrite-carbonate rock	
5 cm	Ca-Mg-silicate rock	10–15 cm	Very pure white limestone (S70995)	5–0 cm	Pure white tremolite-diopside dolostone (S72644)	⎫ All separated by bands of hornblende-biotite-schists
10 cm	Graphitic mica-schist (S70985)			10–20 cm	Coarse banded olivine-chondrodite dolostone (S72645–6)	
10–15 cm	Chlorite-phlogopite-tremolite-dolostone (S70986) passing into carbonate-tremolite-phlogopite schist (S70987)	7 m	Limestone band varying from fairly pure to fairly rich in phlogopite and tremolite (S70996–9). Lenticles and impersistent layers of biotite-tremolite-diopside-epidote-carbonate schist towards base (S71000)	20–30 cm	Pale grey phlogopite-tremolite dolostone (S72647)	
20 cm				10–20 cm	Pure white phlogopite-bearing dolostone (S72648)	
				0.5–1 m	Coarse banded ophicalcite dolostone (S72651)	
>15 cm	Tremolite limestone with quartzose patches (S70988)	50 cm	Poikiloblastic diopside-biotite clinozoisite-plagioclase-sphene skarn (S71001)	2.5 m	Coarse to fine-grained and banded forsterite-phlogopite graphitic dolostone with diopside nodules (S72652–4), enclosing lenticles of red biotite-schist and traversed by veins of crumpled hornblende-biotite rock; partly ophicalcite	⎭
	Mafic hornblende-epidote gneiss (S70989)		Mafic hornblende-rich gneiss		Hornblende-biotite-schist with 4 m band of quartz-garnet-biotite-schist.	

NB. Successions are listed in structural sequence. Way-up criteria are not present. Dashed lines mark limits of calcareous rocks. All thicknesses are approximate due to variability along strike.

* 'Tremolite' and 'hornblende' are used loosely to differentiate between feebly and strongly coloured green amphiboles.

† Information partly after Jehu & Craig (1927).

'S' numbers refer to British Geological Survey (BGS) registered specimens. 'NH' numbers are UK National Grid coordinates.

TABLE 3. *Lithological and chemical variations within the spectacular folded marble body of Cobhain Cuildich, Iona [NM 2656 2512]*

BGS Sample	S71090	S71091	S71092	S71093	S71094	S71095
Sr, ppm*	290	153	—	121	82	—
%SiO$_2$	0.8	4.0	—	4.3	1.6	—
%MgO	1.6	2.9	—	11.7	13.4	—
%CaO	52.6	50.0	—	39.8	38.3	—
Grain-size	Medium-fine	Medium	Medium-fine	Variable	Coarse	'Pegmatitic'
Colour	White	Pinkish	Blue-grey/pink	Grey	Blue-grey/white	Grey
Fabric	Massive	Massive	Banded	Massive	Banded	Massive
Texture	Crushed	Subgrano-blastic	Crushed	Lepido-blastic	Mortar	Crushed
Non-carbonate minerals present	Accessory apatite, biotite	Biotite, diopside, magnetite, tremolite	Accessory apatite, quartz, streaks of magnetite	Diopside, olivine (with coronas), spinel, (tremolite)	Accessory phlogopite, quartz, tourmaline	Diopside, tremolite, carbonate
Lithology	Limestone	Limestone	Limestone	Dolostone	Dolostone	Skarn nodule

* 'Major' and trace elements not listed are at levels near or below detection limits.

Lithological and mineralogical variations in Lewisian marbles (Table 1)

Lewisian marbles are petrographically variable rocks, but may be divided into three broad textural groups: *a) Macrocrystalline:* generally massive, pink, white or grey, homogeneous rocks formed of subgranoblastic, isotropic carbonate aggregates, usually with equally coarse silicate grains (*eg* most inlier marbles, plus those of S. Harris). *b) Microcrystalline:* fine-grained, white, pink or green ornamental marbles, often with irregularly distributed veins, flakes or lumps of silicate minerals (*eg* the well-known examples on Tiree and Iona). *c) Microbrecciated:* grey or black, inhomogeneous, cherty-looking rocks, rich in opaques, relict carbonated silicate minerals and mortar-textured quartzose patches. These often require acid treatment to be recognized in the field (*eg* 'Flowerdale' and 'Furnace' belts, LMG).

Lithological variations within single marble localities are often considerable, but poor exposure, intense folding or high strain complicate interpretation. Table 2 compares the only Lewisian marble-rich successions which are likely to approach original stratigraphy, and Table 3 compares multiple samples from one intensely folded mass which *cannot* be interpreted stratigraphically. Limestone–dolostone interbanding, as in Tables 2–3, has not been recorded before (probably because such bands are macroscopically indistinguishable); it was noted also at

Gairloch, Tiree and Loch Luichart. In addition, most Lewisian marbles are interbanded with, grade into, or contain nodules or lenses of skarns (*eg* Tables 3 & 4).

Among aspects warranting further study are the following: 1) *P-T* estimates from coexisting calcite–dolomite (as in Sanders 1972), or from calc-silicate minerals. 2) Genetic comparisons of olivine–humite–diopside–scapolite-bearing parageneses from S. Harris, Glenelg and Coll–Tiree with epidote–tremolite–phlogopite parageneses in most other Lewisian marbles. 3) Explanations for the origin of matrix quartz in some dolostones (*eg* BGS sample S72672, LMG); quartz should have reacted out during the amphibolite-facies metamorphism reached, and it may thus (despite its texture) be coeval with secondary quartz veins (*eg* S72629, LMG).

Overall geochemical characteristics of Lewisian marbles

Significance of general trace element levels and outlying values

Of 35 elements analysed, H, F, S, Ga, Nb, Mo, Ag, Sn, Sb, Th and U are not considered further, as >80% of values lie near detection limits (*c.* 1 ppm; Table 4). Pilot Li, Be, B, Cd and Bi determinations (by direct reading emission spectrometry) showed very low tenures, apart from single values of 45 (Li) and 32 ppm (B). Pilot

LREE determinations by A. Masuda revealed chondrite-normalized enrichments of 2–12 for La, falling monotonically to 0.3–4 for Eu.

Cu, Zn, Y, Sr, Ba and Ce show one or two outlying values (Fig. 3), usually due to elevated amounts of appropriate accessory minerals. The most extreme case is LMG dolostone S35264, carrying 10,620 ppm Ba in modal baryte. LMG limestone S72609, with thin epidote-magnetite-sphene seams, shows the highest Co, Sr, La, Ce (Fig. 5) and second highest Cu values. Such values have been confirmed as real by 3 analytical techniques (XRF, optical and direct reading

spectrometry), and are by no means unusual for large limestone data-sets (cf. Carlson 1984).

Mean tenures of nearly all elements lie within a factor of 5 of Wedepohl's (1978) mean global carbonate sediment, and overall patterns are quite similar to Scottish Dalradian marbles (Fig. 4). REE patterns, too, are comparable with those published for pure marbles (eg Haskin et al. 1966; Loubet & Allegre 1970). Even relatively elevated Lewisian values are within ranges for silicate-rich, but still metasedimentary, Archaean marbles (Fig. 4c). Such comparisons thus confirm Lewisian marbles as metasediments.

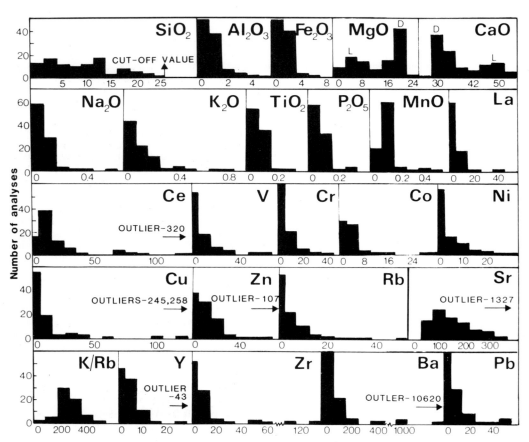

FIG. 3. Histograms of major and trace element contents in 110 purer Lewisian marbles ($< 25\%$ SiO_2). Thin bars at 0 levels include values below detection limits, which are treated as *real values of zero*. For CaO and MgO, 'L' and 'D' peaks correspond to limestones and dolostones (Fig. 2). Histograms are not supplied for Ga, Nb, Mo, Ag, Sb, or Th (which lie below 5 ppm for all samples); for Sn (which lies below 2 ppm except for one value of 20 ppm; S31697); or for U (which lies below 4 ppm except for two values of 11 and 23 ppm). At these levels, La, Ce, V, Cr, Ba are quoted to the nearest 10 ppm, 20 indicating a value between 15 and 24 ppm. Note that although only alkalis tend to be lost during chlorite to sillimanite grade marble metamorphism (eg Ferry 1982), decarbonation at least of dolostones (potentially losing up to 25 wt%), will have increased metamorphic element contents above levels in precursor sediments; only pure limestone values are likely to approximate original sediments.

Methods of statistical interpretation

Unfortunately, several features just outlined cause severe problems in statistical interpretation (*cf* Merriam & Pena Daza 1978). For example: 1) Missing data (due to different element-sets in 13 analyses from the literature), necessitate unsatisfactory casewise exclusion of samples or elements, when multivariate techniques are applied to the various marble groups. 2) Numerous real values of zero (*ie* below detection limits) lead to instability in matrix manipulations (especially inversion). 3) Outlying values have excessive influence on means and test results. 4) Many distributions are evidently non-Gaussian (Fig. 3), as is typical of carbonate sediments (*eg* Ianovici & Dimitriu 1965); note the often gross inequality of means and medians (Table 4). CaO and MgO distributions are bimodal; others (*eg* MnO, Ce, Sr, K/Rb) are positively skewed, approximately log-normal; some low level elements may approximate binomial distributions, reflecting the probability of 1, 2, 3 . . . concentrating mineral grains occurring within a given analysed sample. Unfortunately, power transformations nowadays used to 'improve' normality (*eg* Howarth & Earle 1979) are unsuccessful with distributions showing features 1)–3). Many parametric (especially multivariate) techniques are thus inapplicable. 5) Multivariate techniques such as discriminant and factor analysis cannot properly be used to compare whole-rock compositions of groups which are already defined (Fig. 2) by whole-rock chemistry (LeMaitre 1982, p. 141). 6) Because of the low levels of many trace elements, error variances may approach sample variances, and sample variances frequently exceed means (Table 4).

Succeeding sections include a necessarily preliminary statistical analysis, covering relationships both between marble groups (Q-mode; Table 6) and chemical variables (R-mode; Table 7). Non-parametric methods are mostly employed, to minimize problems caused by irregular distributions, low and outlying values.

Lewisian marbles versus other ancient carbonate rocks and Lewisian silicate rocks

Most features accord with generalized secular variations in carbonate rocks globally. For example, increasing Mg/Ca with age (Veizer 1978; Veizer & Garrett 1978) is seen in greater dolostone/limestone abundances for Lewisian than Dalradian marbles (Rock 1985*b*); it possibly reflects the longer time available for dolomitization (Chilingar 1953, 1956; Maissoneuve 1982). Nevertheless, Lewisian marbles are still rare examples of *mixed* ancient limestone + dolostone assemblages (as in Toens 1966; Bond *et al.* 1973; Hoffman 1973; Young 1973; Garde 1979).

Low Lewisian Sr (Table 4; Fig. 3) is especially typical of ancient carbonates. As in other stratigraphically related dolostones and limestones (*eg* Fig. 4*b*; Mogharabi 1968; Garde 1979), Sr is lower in Lewisian dolostones. However, it is also much lower in Lewisian limestones than in Dalradian limestones (Fig. 4; Table 6), and this could reflect: *a*) lower Sr/Ca in 'Lewisian seawater'; *b*) greater cumulative Sr loss after more numerous recrystallizations (as in Kinsman 1969).

Lewisian marbles also have significantly lower contents of many other elements than Dalradian marbles (Fig. 4; Table 6; Rock *et al.* 1984, Figs 4–5)—especially Cr, Zn, Rb, Sr, Zr, Nb, Ba, Th, Al, Na and K, where the Mann-Whitney U statistic (Table 6) has >99.9% significance for both limestone and dolostone comparisons. By contrast, K/Rb in Lewisian marbles (despite unusual consistency, especially between dolostones, Table 4), is statistically indistinguishable from K/Rb in Dalradian marbles (Dalradian dolostones mean and median: 220, 197; limestones: 308, 249). K/Rb in Lewisian marbles is low relative to most Lewisian silicate rocks, but comparable to some associated gneisses (*eg* Coll/Tiree gneisses, with modal K/Rb 200–300; Sheraton *et al.* 1973).

Significance of limestone/dolostone relationships (Tables 2–3)

Possible models include the following: 1) Lewisian dolostones were deposited as primary dolomitic sediments (as in Maissoneuve 1982; Tucker 1982), and Lewisian limestones as calcitic sediments; local Mg/Ca variations reflect changes in Precambrian depositional conditions. 2) All Lewisian marbles were deposited as limestones; local Mg/Ca variations reflect selective later dolomitization (as in Garde 1979). 3) All Lewisian marbles were deposited as, or later converted into, dolostones; local limestones represent *de*-dolomites (as in Shearman & Shirmohammadi 1969).

Model (3) is felt to be highly unlikely, for the Sr contents of Lewisian limestones greatly exceed the few ppm typical of calcite replacing dolomite; on model 3, limestones could not have higher Sr than dolostones (as in Table 4). Detailed assessment of models 1 and 2 is beyond the present scope—not least because established geochemical

TABLE 4. *Mean and median compositions of purer Lewisian limestones and dolostones (<25% SiO_2)*

	Dolostones (> 10% MgO)				
	Foreland + inliers (all samples)	All of Foreland	Foreland excluding Loch Maree Group	Loch Maree Group only	Inliers only
N^1	65	43	26	17	22
SiO_2,%	9.0 ±6.8 [10.4]	8.7 ±7.2 [7.0]	11.3 ±7.2 [12.5]	4.5 ±5.1 [2.5]	9.6 ±6.1 [10.9]
Al_2O_3	0.81±0.93 [0.56]	0.81±1.0 [0.5]	1.1 ±1.1 [0.66]	0.36±0.38 [0.18]	0.82±0.79 [0.74]
FeO_t	1.2 ±1.0 [1.0]	1.2 ±1.1 [0.9]	0.93±0.63 [0.82]	1.6 ±1.6 [1.2]	1.2 ±0.6 [1.1]
MgO	18.2 ±2.8 [19.1]	17.8 ±2.9 [18.7]	18.3 ±3.0 [18.8]	17.2 ±2.9 [16.7]	19.0 ±2.4 [19.9]
CaO	31.6 ±2.8 [31.1]	31.8 ±3.1 [31.4]	31.8 ±3.1 [31.4]	31.8 ±3.1 [30.7]	31.3 ±2.0 [31.0]
Na_2O	0.03±0.04 [0.02]	0.04±0.05 [0.02]	0.04±0.04 [0.03]	0.03±0.06 [0.01]	0.02±0.03 [0.01]
K_2O	0.22±0.40 [0.07]	0.23±0.47 [0.02]	0.33±0.56 [0.05]	0.05±0.09 [0.02]	0.19±0.26 [0.11]
TiO_2	0.06±0.04 [0.04]	0.06±0.06 [0.05]	0.08±0.04 [0.07]	0.04±0.02 [0.03]	0.05±0.04 [0.04]
P_2O_5	0.07±0.11 [0.03]	0.09±0.12 [0.04]	0.11±0.14 [0.03]	0.04±0.01 [0.44]	0.03±0.06 [0.01]
MnO	0.12±0.12 [0.09]	0.14±0.14 [0.09]	0.10±0.07 [0.08]	0.25±0.19 [0.17]	0.09±0.06 [0.08]
F	0.07±0.05 [0.05]	0.06±0.03 [0.07]	0.08±0.05 [0.08]	0.04±0.02 [0.04]	0.08±0.04 [0.07]
S	0.07±0.04 [0.06]	0.10±0.05 [0.11]	0.12±0.06 [0.11]	0.04±0.02 [0.04]	0.04±0.02 [0.04]

Trace elements (ppm), in order of atomic number

V	7±12 [0]	8±14 [0]	10±12 [10]	6±16 [0]	5±9 [0]
Cr	7±10 [0]	6±9 [0]	7±7 [10]	5±11 [0]	9±13 [0]
Co	2±3 [2]	2±3 [2]	2±2 [2]	3±4 [2]	2±2 [2]
Ni	5±7 [2]	6±8 [3]	7±9 [4]	4±6 [2]	4±6 [2]
Cu	12±36 [0]	6±10 [0]	5±8 [0]	8±13 [0]	24±57 [4]
Zn	13±18 [8]	16±22 [9]	17±25 [11]	14±15 [8]	8±7 [7]
Ga	3±2 [2.5]	5±2 [5]	—	5±1 [5]	3±2 [2]
Rb	6±9 [2]	5±10 [1]	8±12 [2]	2±3 [1]	6±8 [5]
Sr	141±101 [104]	157±114 [111]	123±74 [96]	212±145 [175]	113±68 [98]
Y	3±3 [2]	3±4 [2]	4±4 [2]	2±2 [2]	3±2 [2]
Zr	12±25 [3]	11±23 [2]	15±28 [3]	4±5 [2]	13±28 [6]
Nb	<1 [0]	<1 [0]	<1 [0]	<1 [0]	<1 [0]
Mo	1±1 [0]	1±1 [0]	1±1 [0]	1±1 [1]	<1 [0]
Ag	1±1 [1]	1±1 [0]	1±1 [0]	1±1 [1]	1±1 [0]
Sn	<1 [0]	<1 [0]	<1 [0]	<1 [0]	<1 [0]
Sb	2±2 [0]	2±1 [1]	2±1 [1]	2±1 [2]	1±1 [0]
Ba	308±1406 [37]	464±1775 [30]	153±302 [30]	898±2721 [30]	53±44 [50]
La	3±8 [0]	3±10 [0]	3±9 [0]	4±12 [0]	2±4 [0]
Ce	21±27 [10]	14±20 [10]	17±25 [10]	9±9 [10]	32±34 [20]
Pb	6±12 [2]	6±11 [3]	2±2 [2]	10±16 [4]	6±14 [1]
Th	<1 [0]	<1 [0]	<1 [0]	<1 [0]	<1 [0]
U	1±3 [0]	1±4 [0]	2±5 [1]	<1 [0]	1±1 [1]

Molecular ratios

Ca/Mg	1.3±0.3	1.3±0.4	1.3±0.4	1.4±0.3	1.2±0.3
Ca/Sr	2236±1122	2071±1093	2346±1028	1630±1081	2530±1138
K/Rb	241±127	239±156	241±172	237±126	244±83

Notes:
1. Total number of samples analysed. Numbers of individual values for some elements are slightly less, due to missing data in literature. Values below detection limits are included in calculations as real values of zero.
2. Averages are given in the form $X \pm Y$ [Z] where X=arithmetic mean, Y=standard deviation $(N-1)$, Z=median. Means of 0 and <1 indicate all and nearly all values below detection limits respectively: standard deviations are not then quoted.

and textural criteria (*eg* Grems 1973; Eriksson 1979) are inapplicable to Lewisian marbles, but also because the dolomite problem is intrinsically so complex (*eg* Zenger *et al.* 1980). Possible constraints include the following: i) Sr contents of Lewisian limestones on average are 1.5–2 times those of dolostones (Table 4); the appropriate Sr distribution coefficient for calcite is similarly about twice that of dolomite (Jacobsen & Usdowski 1976). ii) Both within- and between-group variations for Lewisian dolostones seem on the whole less than those for limestones (Table

	Limestones (< 10% MgO)								
	Foreland + inliers (all samples)		All of Foreland		Foreland excluding Loch Maree Group		Loch Maree Group only		Inliers only
N[1]	45		18		9		9		27
SiO$_2$,%	8.9 ±6.4	[8.2]	11.7 ±6.6	[11.5]	8.7 ±4.0	[9.6]	14.8 ±7.4	[17.3]	7.0 ±5.7 [6.9]
Al$_2$O$_3$	1.0 ±1.1	[0.5]	1.7 ±1.5	[1.4]	1.6 ±1.4	[1.3]	1.8 ±1.7	[1.9]	0.54±0.49 [0.40]
FeO$_t$	1.1 ±1.6	[0.7]	2.1 ±2.2	[1.0]	0.75±0.32	[0.77]	3.7 ±2.6	[3.4]	0.47±0.32 [0.35]
MgO	4.3 ±2.7	[3.7]	5.1 ±2.9	[5.7]	4.1 ±2.4	[5.0]	6.1 ±3.1	[7.1]	3.7 ±2.5 [3.5]
CaO	46.1 ±5.5	[46.4]	42.8 ±6.1	[42.8]	45.7 ±4.4	[45.4]	40.0 ±6.4	[39.8]	48.2 ±3.9 [48.2]
Na$_2$O	0.17±0.37	[0.06]	0.31±0.55	[0.08]	0.43±0.72	[0.06]	0.16±0.19	[0.08]	0.07±0.10 [0.05]
K$_2$O	0.20±0.44	[0.05]	0.32±0.65	[0.08]	0.45±0.84	[0.11]	0.15±0.24	[0.03]	0.11±0.18 [0.04]
TiO$_2$	0.06±0.08	[0.03]	0.13±0.09	[0.10]	0.10±0.09	[0.08]	0.15±0.09	[0.17]	0.02±0.02 [0.01]
P$_2$O$_5$	0.06±0.03	[0.07]	0.06±0.04	[0.05]	0.05±0.05	[0.04]	0.06±0.03	[0.07]	0.06±0.03 [0.07]
MnO	0.06±0.09	[0.04]	0.11±0.14	[0.07]	0.14±0.19	[0.06]	0.09±0.04	[0.10]	0.03±0.02 [0.02]
F	0.05±0.03	[0.05]	0.10±0.07	[0.10]	0.10±0.06	[0.10]	0.10±0.05	[0.10]	0.01±0.01 [0.01]
S	0.06±0.04	[0.06]	0.09±0.06	[0.09]	0.09±0.05	[0.09]	0.10±0.06	[0.10]	0.03±0.02 [0.03]

Trace elements (ppm), in order of atomic number

V	7±12	[0]	16±16	[10]	3±5	[0]	28±13	[30]	2±3 [0]
Cr	5±10	[0]	11±14	[10]	10±13	[5]	12±16	[10]	1±4 [0]
Co	5±6	[2]	7±7	[4]	5±8	[1]	9±7	[7]	1±1 [1]
Ni	6±9	[1]	13±11	[12]	13±13	[11]	13±10	[12]	1±2 [1]
Cu	17±44	[3]	33±68	[7]	41±89	[4]	25±37	[10]	6±12 [3]
Zn	9±12	[3]	15±14	[18]	7±8	[3]	23±14	[21]	6±10 [3]
Ga	5±3	[4]	6±2	[6]	8±1	[8]	4±1	[4]	4±1 [4]
Rb	6±6	[3]	6±8	[2]	7±10	[3]	4±6	[1]	6±6 [4]
Sr	223±204	[190]	237±311	[157]	178±84	[153]	305±456	[176]	222±99 [207]
Y	6±8	[4]	9±10	[6]	5±3	[5]	13±15	[6]	5±5 [4]
Zr	10±16	[5]	17±23	[7]	13±20	[7]	21±28	[7]	6±7 [3]
Nb	<1	[0]	<1	[0]	0	[0]	<1	[0]	<1 [0]
Mo	1±1	[1]	1±1	[1]	1±1	[1]	1±1	[1]	1±1 [1]
Ag	3±1	[2]	3±1	[2]	3±1	[2]	3±1	[2]	3±1 [2]
Sn	<1	[0]	2±5	[0]	3±7	[0]	0	[0]	0 [0]
Sb	<1	[0]	1±1	[0]	1±1	[0]	1±1	[0]	<1 [0]
Ba	52±98	[20]	98±145	[36]	95±151	[30]	102±155	[42]	25±33 [20]
La	8±16	[0]	11±23	[0]	12±29	[0]	9±18	[0]	6±7 [0]
Ce	27±55	[10]	38±90	[10]	13±14	[10]	62±127	[10]	22±26 [10]
Pb	8±20	[3]	13±32	[3]	4±6	[12]	22±44	[6]	6±9 [4]
Th	<1	[0]	<1	[0]	<1	[0]	0	[0]	<1 [0]
U	1±2	[1]	2±3	[1]	1±1	[0]	3±4	[2]	<1 [0]

Molecular ratios

Ca/Mg	39±161	69±254	129±360	8±8	19±22
Ca/Sr	2225±1775	2659±2363	2293±1307	3078±3264	1953±1267
K/Rb	284±317	405±438	566±596	243±62	212±196

4). iii) Overall, Ca/Sr ratios of Lewisian limestones and dolostones are indistinguishable (using Mann-Whitney U), and there is relatively little between- or within-group Ca/Sr variation in Table 4, for either limestones or dolostones, compared with that for Ca, Mg or Sr individually. Such relationships might be seen as more consistent with model 1) than 2), but no rigorous interpretation is possible on present data (or theory). Moreover, any interpretation depends on how many carbonate sedimentation events

are represented by Lewisian marbles; it is to this problem we therefore finally turn.

Number of Lewisian marble stratigraphical units (sedimentation events)

As argued by Rock *et al.* (1984), stratigraphical affinities are better tested using chemical varia-

TABLE 5. Representative analyses of Lewisian skarns and non-sedimentary carbonate-rich rocks

Rock-type	Magnesite-talc rock (carbonated ultramafite)	Siliceous biotite-garnet-skarn	Tremolite-rich skarn	Microbrecciated quartzose skarns with biotite, epidote, hornblende etc	quartzose skarns	Crushed carbonate-chlorite-epidote-schist	Crushed muscovite-(carbonate)-schist	Diopside-tremolite-microcline-quartz-calcite skarn	Quartz-microcline-tremolite-epidote-calcite skarn
Locality (Fig. 1)	Loch Glencoul	Loch Maree	Loch Maree	Gairloch-Shieldaig	Gairloch-Shieldaig	Moine Thrust Zone, Sleat, Skye (tectonic)	Moine Thrust Zone, Sleat, Skye (tectonic)	Coll	Coll
NGR	NG [2486 3334]	NG [995 710]	NG [9873 6790]	NG [8467 7160]	NG [8429 7210]	NG [5982 0020]	NG [5982 0020]	NG [131 529]	NM [143 551]
BGS Sample	S2953	S4795	S72594†	S72627	S72628	S72673	S72672	S21385	S72701
SiO_2	30.9	31.9	35.9	35.3	43.7	42.6	64.6	73.2	75.0
Al_2O_3	1.05	2.47	0.36	8.57	8.41	14.34	16.3	6.79	7.51
Fe_2O_3	9.86	2.12	11.8	10.2	9.17	7.97	2.89	1.18	0.91
MgO	29.6	1.23	8.43	5.57	3.07	9.65	0.99	4.28	3.62
CaO	2.70	34.1	26.39	20.7	18.9	10.3	2.64	7.67	5.54
Na_2O	0.08	0.46	0.07	1.36	1.52	3.91	5.67	0.47	0.50
K_2O	0.24	0.33	0.01	0.41	0.60	0.30	2.73	4.29	5.33
LOI	24.47	26.2	16.6	17.8	14.2	9.20	2.58	2.85	2.73
TiO_2	0.08	0.20	0.06	0.72	0.67	0.22	0.42	0.10	0.14
P_2O_5	bdl	0.03	0.28	0.15	0.20	0.04	0.11	0.07	0.05
MnO	—	—	—	0.16	0.20	0.12	0.01	0.03	bdl
Total	99.32*	99.04	99.90	100.94	100.64	98.65	98.93	100.93	101.33
Trace elements (ppm), in order of atomic number									
V	30	30	20	210	—	80	30	20	10
Cr	1200	10	bdl	310	10	60	bdl	10	10
Co	131	9	13	29	—	47	5	2	2
Ni	2385	13	29	110	30	63	bdl	7	3
Cu	bdl	bdl	3	51	81	1	7	2	bdl
Zn	108	17	17	38	41	73	33	7	3
Rb	3	14	1	12	16	6	34	76	76
Sr	33	175	45	88	91	324	172	131	260
Y	2	6	16	16	34	6	11	7	5
Zr	9	10	10	46	50	13	491	180	593
Nb	bdl	bdl	bdl	bdl	bdl	bdl	2	1	2
Sn	bdl	bdl	bdl	bdl	2	bdl	bdl	bdl	1
Ba	20	100	10	880	921	70	950	1250	850
La	bdl	bdl	bdl	bdl	3	bdl	30	20	10
Ce	10	10	bdl	20	4	10	60	50	20
Pb	1	72	2	1	4	3	6	7	bdl
Th	bdl	bdl	bdl	bdl	—	bdl	1	bdl	2
U	1	2	4	5	—	bdl	bdl	2	1

bdl = below detection limit.   * Includes F 0.34%.

† Possibly a crushed and carbonated amphibolite (S72592) via S72594 to carbonate-tremolite skarn

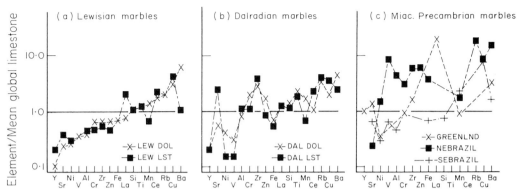

FIG. 4. Comparative mean geochemistry of Lewisian, Scottish Dalradian (Vendian–Cambrian) and miscellaneous Precambrian marbles. Element order chosen to yield monotonically increasing plots for Lewisian dolostones, from left to right. Elements are normalized to mean global carbonate sediment values of Wedepohl (1978), which are mostly similar to those of Graf (1960): Y 30; Sr 610; Ni 20; V 20 ppm; Al_2O_3 2.2%; Cr 11; Zr 19; Zn 20 ppm; Fe_2O_3 1.8%; La 4 ppm; SiO_2 8.2; TiO_2 0.05; MnO 0.09%; Ce 12; Rb 20; Cu 4 ppm. Ba is normalized to 50 ppm, a more reasonable value than Wedepohl's (1978) 10 ppm. Mean values are plotted despite non-Gaussian distributions (see text) owing to lack of published median values for global carbonates (Wedepohl 1978) and for other available marble data-sets. (*a*) Lewisian dolostones and limestones (data from Table 4). (*b*) Scottish Dalradian dolostones and limestones (data from Rock 1985*b*, 1986). (*c*) Miscellaneous Precambrian marbles as follows—GREENLND = 6 Archaean marbles, Greenland (Bollinberg *et al.* 1976). NE BRAZIL = 7 silicate-rich Archaean marbles (Sighinolfi 1974; Sighinolfi *et al.* 1980). SE BRAZIL = 131 Late Precambrian marbles (Bettencourt & Landim 1974).

bles (R-mode) than marble groups (Q-mode). To take an igneous analogy, coeval basalt and trachyte lavas are chemically distinct, but may reveal consanguinity in *element* covariance behaviour (*eg* constant incompatible element ratios). We nevertheless briefly compare the chemistry of LMG, foreland and inlier marble groups (Q-mode) first because, in the special case of carbonate rocks, global secular variations (mentioned above) mean that Lewisian marbles of different ages are likely to have different compositions.

Stratigraphical affinities revealed by Q-mode marble group comparisons (Tables 4 & 6)

Foreland versus inlier marbles: No limestones have been found in the S. Harris or Coll foreland, nor in the Glenelg or Kintail inliers. By contrast, few or no dolostones have been found on Tiree, or in the Strathfarrar, Scardroy or Shinness inliers. Overall, rather more inlier (52%) than foreland (30%) analyses are limestones (Table 1). Specific gravity determinations (Rock 1985*a*) imply the same pattern: means (223 determinations) differ significantly in the order dolomite (2.87) > foreland marbles (2.79 ± 0.03) > inlier marbles (2.76 ± 0.03) > calcite (2.72). However, these differences apply mainly to marble *distribution*, less to composition: few elements differ significantly between foreland and inlier limestones (or dolostones; Tables 4 & 6).

Loch Maree group versus other Lewisian marbles: Tables 4 & 6 also show that any differences here are swamped by those within LMG marbles themselves: 10 elements (plus Mg, Ca) differ significantly between LMG limestones and dolostones, but only 4 differ between LMG and other foreland dolostones–limestones.

Relationships between marble belts within the Loch Maree Group: The Flowerdale belt of Gairloch shows not only higher metallic trace element contents and more brecciated textures than the adjacent Cloiche belt, presumably reflecting mineralization (Rice, pers. comm.), but also higher contents of Rb, Sr, Y, Zr and Ba. As both the Flowerdale (Gairloch) and Furnace (L. Maree) belts comprise microbrecciated marbles, associated with banded iron formations, quartzites and amphibolites, but both the Cloiche (Gairloch) and Gleann Tulacha (L. Maree) belts comprise macrocrystalline marbles with much lower trace element contents, correlation seems more likely across the L. Maree Fault, than between adjacent belts (*cf* Park 1964).

Stratigraphical affinities revealed by R-mode element covariances (Table 7)

Table 7 compiles and Fig. 5 illustrates highly significant correlations from a matrix of coefficients for the 24 consistently detectable elements. These correlations are considered geologically

TABLE 6. *'Q-mode' non-parametric element-by-element comparison of purer Lewisian and Dalradian marble groups (< 25% SiO$_2$), using the Mann-Whitney statistic*

	(a) LEWISIAN versus LEWISIAN*					(b) DALRADIAN versus LEWISIAN†
	Overall	Foreland excluding Loch Maree Group	Loch Maree Group only	Inliers		
Overall	Zn, Sr, Y, Fe, Na, Ti, P, Mn, (Mg, Ca) ‡	—	—	—	L I M E S T O N E S	**Limestones Versus Limestones** > Cr, Cu, Zn, Rb, Sr, Y, Zr, Nb, Ba, Th, Al, Na, K, Ti, < Mg
Foreland excluding Loch Maree Group	—	Sr, (Mg, Ca)	V, Zn, Fe, Ca	Ni, Al, Fe, Ti, Mn		
Loch Maree Group only	—	Sr, Si, Ti, Mn	V, Co, Ni, Zn, Y, Si, Al, Fe, Na, Ti (Mg, Ca)	V, Co. Ni, Zn, Ba, Si, Fe, Mg, Ca, Ti, Mn		**Dolostones Versus Dolostones** > Cr, Co, Ni, Zn, Rb, Sr, Y, Zr, Nb, Ba, La, Th, Na, K, Al, < Mg, Ca
Inliers	—	Fe, Na, Ti, P	Ce, Rb, Sr, Si, Fe, Mg, K, P, Mn	Ce, Zn, Rb, Fe, P, (Mg, Ca)		

DOLOSTONES

Notes:

* Upper half of Lewisian Table (a) refers to limestone/limestone, lower half to dolostone/dolostone, and diagonal to limestone/dolostone comparisons.

† > indicates listed elements are higher in Dalradian marbles, for Dalradian/Lewisian comparisons.
 < indicates listed elements are higher in Lewisian marbles, for Dalradian/Lewisian comparisons.

‡ Listed elements are the only ones out of 30 elements tested which show significant differences in central tendency at >95% significance. Other element distributions are indistinguishable at this level. Ca, Mg, bracketed in limestone/dolostone comparisons (along diagonal) since these differ by definition. F, S, Mo, Ag & Sb not tested owing to lack of values above detection limits.

— means comparison not meaningful, and not therefore executed.

All computations performed using the MINITAB statistical package (Ryan *et al.* 1976).

Example: Loch Maree Group dolostones differ from other Foreland dolostones in Sr, Si, Ti, Mn distributions, but not in 26 other element distributions.

meaningful, not only because both Pearson and Spearman coefficients have >99.9% significance, but also because correlations follow a clear geological pattern: for example, highest correlations are between groups of elements concentrated in a single accessory mineral (*eg* Table 7*a, b, c*). Correlations between elements concentrated in different minerals (*eg* Table 7*d*) can also be significant, though weaker. Such correlations imply that many Lewisian marbles carry similar assemblages of accessory minerals, in approximately similar proportions: for example, the Ce–Zr and Rb–Al correlations, which pass very near the origin, could reflect increasing modal amounts of zircon and K-feldspar, respectively, whereas the Zr–Rb correlation would imply a constant proportion of these two minerals.

As argued by Rock *et al.* (1984), such patterns are unlikely to reflect metamorphic control, even for 'mobile' elements such as K–Rb, when foreland and inlier Lewisian marbles have such different metamorphic histories. Indeed, *all* the 'immobile' elements (relatively unaffected by metamorphism, and carried by 'inert' accessory minerals) show strong correlations, and these seem especially likely to have pre-metamorphic, *ie* stratigraphical significance. (Such correlations have only been reported before in stratigraphically related ancient carbonate rocks—*eg* Bettencourt & Landim 1974). Whether accessory minerals are of detrital or authigenic origin, similar accessory assemblages may in fact imply that many Lewisian marbles were originally deposited in a similar setting.

In conclusion, Garson & Plant's (1972) stratigraphical correlation of the Leverburgh and Coll/Tiree paragneisses is not only supported, but may perhaps be taken further. For Lewisian marbles show much stronger regional R- and Q-mode affinities than their scattered present-day distri-

TABLE 7. *'R-mode' covariance analysis of element relationships in purer Lewisian marbles (<25% SiO₂)*

(a) *Elements concentrated mainly in alkali feldspars*

		Al	Na	K	Rb	Ba
			SPEARMAN			
Al		—	0.57	0.67	0.65	0.46
	P		(0.57)	(0.77)	(0.78)	(*)
Na	E	0.57	—	0.39	0.52	0.37
	A	(0.70)		(*)	(*)	(*)
K	R	0.74	0.68	—	0.77	0.58
	S	(0.60)	(0.77)		(0.93)	(*)
Rb	O	0.67	0.40	0.86	—	0.49
	N	(0.62)	(0.73)	(0.99)		(*)
Ba		0.32	*	0.55	0.43	—
		(*)	(*)	(*)	(*)	

(b) *Elements concentrated mainly in zircon, apatite*

		Zr	Y	La‡	Ce‡
			SPEARMAN		
Zr	P	—	0.35	0.53	0.41
	E		(0.59)	(*)	(*)
Y	A	0.33	—	0.44	*
	R	(0.83)		(0.60)	(*)
La	S	0.44	0.48	—	0.65†
	O	(0.51)	(0.68)		(*)
Ce	N	0.35	0.70	0.83	—
		(0.95)	(0.97)	(0.96)	

(c) *Elements concentrated mainly in opaques*

		Al	Fe	Ti	V‡	Cr	Co	Ni
				SPEARMAN				
Al		—	0.49	0.69	0.54	0.56	0.60	0.70
			(0.48)	(0.78)	(0.58)	(0.66)	(0.67)	(0.80)
Fe		0.32	—	0.69	0.54	0.38	0.77	0.62
	P	(*)		(0.63)	(0.74)	(*)	(0.82)	(0.55)
Ti	E	0.75	0.65	—	0.59	0.49	0.60	0.73
	A	(0.80)	(*)		(0.78)	(0.59)	(0.76)	(0.84)
V	R	0.47	0.76	0.66	—	0.61	0.75	0.64
	S	(0.51)	(0.92)	(0.78)		(0.51)	(0.91)	(0.78)
Cr	O	0.54	0.43	0.50	0.66	—	0.62	0.56
	N	(0.78)	(0.52)	(0.51)	(0.69)		(0.51)	(0.68)
Co		0.45	0.70	0.62	0.78	0.77	—	0.76
		(0.67)	(0.80)	(0.76)	(0.93)	(0.75)		(0.80)
Ni		0.69	0.56	0.70	0.70	0.76	0.76	—
		(0.85)	(0.68)	(0.72)	(0.87)	(0.93)	(0.87)	

(d) *Correlations mainly between elements in groups (a), (b), (c)*

	PEARSON	SPEARMAN
Fe-Y	0.59 (0.73)	0.32 (*)
Ti-Y	0.51 (0.71)	0.39 (0.74)
Ze-Al	0.61 (0.60)	0.64 (0.68)
Al-Ni	0.69 (0.85)	0.70 (0.80)
P-Zr	0.56 (0.49)	0.40 (0.60)
Nb-Ce†	0.54 (0.90)	* (*)
Cu-Ce†	* (0.87)	* (*)
Sr-Y†	0.59 (0.78)	* (*)
Sr-La†	0.47 (0.81)	* (*)
Sr-Ce†	0.62 (0.91)	* (*)

Notes:
In each sub-table, lower half gives Pearson and upper half Spearman rank correlation coefficients. For each element pair, the upper figure refers to all 110 purer Lewisian marbles, the lower (bracketed) figure to 26 Loch Maree Group purer marbles only. Calculations based on pairwise omission of missing data, but as almost all analyses have the same determined element-set, this approximates casewise omission. All quoted correlations are >99% significant against a null value of zero; most are ≫99.9% significant.
* Indicates insignificant correlation at 99% level.
† Indicates correlations which are probably *not* geologically significant, being strongly influenced by one or two outlying values; note insignificant values of Spearman coefficients. Eg. Pearson coefficient for Sr-Ce (110 marbles) falls from 0.62 to 0.05 when S 72609 is omitted.
‡ Correlations involving these elements should be treated with special caution, as most values are rather near detection limits.

bution (Fig. 1) might imply. In particular, LMG marbles are generally indistinguishable in both average composition and element covariance relationships from other Lewisian marbles (Tables 4, 6, 7; Fig. 5). Very consistent K–Rb ratios (Fig. 5; Table 4) are particularly difficult to explain if LMG marbles represent a much younger sedimentary unit than other Lewisian marbles, with a different history. They may provide a tentative hint that most Lewisian marbles in fact represent a single sedimentation event, either of late Scourian or earliest Proterozoic age.

ACKNOWLEDGEMENTS: We thank Prof. A. Masuda for preliminary REE plots, J. G. Holland, J. R. Mendum, F. May and a referee for comments on earlier drafts. The late Prof. Janet Watson provided valuable encouragement in the early stages.

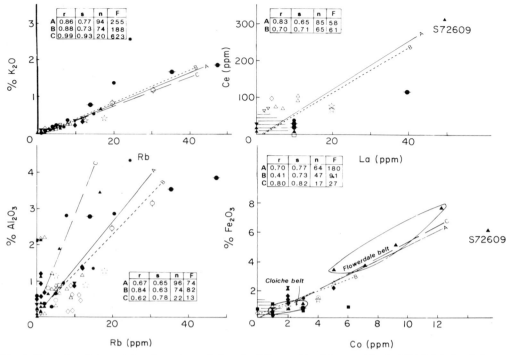

FIG. 5. Examples of strong inter-element correlations for 110 purer Lewisian marbles ($<25\%$ SiO_2). Symbols as in Fig. 2. On La–Ce and Fe–Co, many analyses plot within the horizontally-ruled fields, at low element levels, but are not individually symbolized, to avoid clutter. The table within each figure contains the following information: Group A = all Lewisian marbles (110 total samples); Group B = Lewisian marbles excluding Loch Maree group (83 total samples); Group C = Loch Maree group only (26 total samples); r = Pearson linear correlation coefficient (outlying values omitted); s = Spearman rank correlation coefficient; n = number of pairs of values available (variations reflect missing data); F = F ratio for testing overall significance of regression (i.e. that slope >0); associated degrees of freedom = [1, n–2]. All illustrated r, s, and F values are $>99.9\%$ significant. The La–Ce regression for Group C alone is omitted, as nearly all determined values are below detection limits. Principal axis 'structural' regression lines (LeMaitre 1982) are also shown for all groups, assuming analytical errors for each plotted element pair are approximately equal (i.e. $\lambda = 1$). Relative line positions are not greatly changed for reduced major axis or other structural regressions.

References

BEACH, E. M. & CHADWICK, B. 1980. The Malene supracrustal gneisses of NW Buksefjorden, their origin and significance in the Archaean evolution of southern west Greenland. *Precambrian Res.* **11**, 329–55.

BETTENCOURT, J. S. & LANDIM, P. M. B. 1974. Estudo geoquímico de óxidos e elementos traços de rochas calcários do grupo acungi pela analise fatorial. *28th Congr. Bras. Geol.* **7**, 153–160.

BICKERMAN, M., BOWES, D. R. & VAN BREEMEN, O. 1975. Rb-Sr whole-rock isotopic studies of Lewisian metasediments and gneisses in the Loch Maree region, Ross-shire. *J. geol. Soc. Lond.* **131**, 237–254.

BOLLINBERG, H., HOPGOOD, A. M. & KALSBECK, F. 1976. Some minor and trace elements in Archaean marbles and metamorphosed silico-carbonatites from the Fiskanaesset region. *Rapp. Gronlands geol. Unders.* **73**, 86–90.

BOND, G., WILSON, J. F. & WINNALL, N. J. 1973. Age of the Huntsman limestone (Bulawayan) stromatolites. *Nature, London* **244**, 275–276.

BOWES, D. R. 1978. Application of U-Pb zircon and other isotopic studies to the identification of Archaean rocks in thermally and tectonically overprinted terranes, Lewisian complex of Scotland. *In*: WINDLEY, B. F. & NAQVI, S. M. (eds.) *Archaean Geochemistry*, Elsevier, 25–40.

CAMERON, E. M. & BAUMANN, A. 1972. Carbonate sedimentation during the Archaean. *Chem. Geol.* **10**, 17–30.

CARLSON, E. H. 1984. High strontium dolostones from

northwestern Ohio. *Abstr. Progr. (Boulder)* **16/3**, p. 127.

CHILINGAR, G. V. 1953. Use of a Ca/Mg ratio in limestones as a geologic tool. *Compass* **30**, 202–209.

—— 1956. Relationship between Ca/Mg ratio and geologic age. *Bull. Am. Assoc. Petrol Geol.* **40**, 2256–2266.

CLIFF, R. A., GRAY, C. M. & HUHMA, H. 1983. An Sm–Nd isotopic study of the South Harris igneous complex, Outer Hebrides. *Contrib. Mineral. Petrol.* **82**, 91–98.

DEER, W. A., HOWIE, R. A. & ZUSSMAN, J. 1962. *Rock-forming minerals.* Longmans, London.

ERIKSSON, K. A. 1979. Dolomitisation models from an early Precambrian sequence in South Africa. *Bull. Am. Assoc. Pet. Geol.* **63**, 446.

FERRY, J. M. 1982. A comparative geochemical study of the pelitic schists and metamorphosed carbonate rocks from south-central Maine. *Contrib. Mineral. Petrol.* **80**, 59–72.

FETTES, D. J., MENDUM, J. R., WATSON, J. V., MYKURA, W., MACDONALD, R. & ROCK, N. M. S. 1985. Geology of the Outer Hebrides. *Br. geol. Surv. Rep.* (in press).

FRASER, F. M. 1977. *The Lewisian and Torridonian geology of Iona.* Unpubl. PhD. thesis, St. Andrews Univ.

GARDE, A. A. 1979. Strontium geochemistry and carbon and oxygen isotopic compositions of lower Proterozoic dolomite and calcite marbles from the Marmorilik formation, west Greenland. *Precambrian Res.* **8**, 183–199.

GARSON, M. S. & PLANT, J. 1972. Possible dextral movements on the Great Glen and Minch Faults in Scotland. *Nature, London* **240**, 31–5.

GILETTI, B. J., MOORBATH, S. & LAMBERT, R. St. J. 1961. A geochronological study of the metamorphic complexes of the Scottish Highlands. *Q. J. geol. Soc. Lond.* **117**, 233–272.

GRAF, D. L. 1960. Geochemistry of carbonate sediments and sedimentary carbonate rocks. *Illinois geol. Surv. Circs.* **297, 298, 301, 308, 309**.

GREMS, G. J. B. 1973. Geochemistry of some carbonate members of the Nama group, South West Africa. *South Afr. J. Sci.* **69**, 14–17.

HASKIN, L. A., WILDEMAN, T., FREY, F. A., COLLINS, K., KEEDY, C. & HASKIN, M. 1966. Rare earths in sediments. *J. Geophys. Res.* **71**, 6091–6106.

HICKMAN, A. E. & WRIGHT, A. E. 1983. Geochemistry and chemostratigraphical correlation of slates, marbles and quartzites of the Appin Group, Argyll. *Trans. R. Soc. Edinburgh Earth-Sci.* **73**, 251–78.

HOFFMAN, P. 1973. Evolution of an early Proterozoic continental margin, the Coronation geosyncline and associated aulacogens of the northwestern Canadian Shield. *Phils. Trans. R. Soc. Lond.* **A273**, 547–581.

HOWARTH, R. J. & EARLE, S. A. M. 1979. Application of a generalized power transformation to geochemical data. *J. Int. Assoc. Math. Geol.* **11**, 45–62.

IANOVICI, V. & DIMITRIU, A. L. 1965. Lois de distribution de la concentration des éléments

chimiques dans les roches carbonatées. *Rev. Roum. Geol. Géophys. Géogr. géol. Ser.* **9(2)**, 197–227.

JACOBSEN, R. L. & USDOWSKI, H. E. 1976. Partitioning of strontium between calcite, dolomite and liquids: an experimental study under high temperature diagenetic conditions, and a model for the prediction of mineral pairs for geochemistry. *Contrib. Mineral. Petrol.* **59**, 171–85.

JEHU, T. J. & ORME, R. M. 1927. Geology of the Outer Hebrides Part IV. *Trans. R. Soc. Edinburgh* **55**, 457–488.

KINSMAN, D. J. J. 1969. Interpretation of Sr concentrations in carbonate minerals and rocks. *J. Sed. Petrol.* **39**, 486–508.

LAMAR, J. E. & THOMSON, K. B. 1956. Sampling limestone and dolomite deposits for trace and minor elements. *Illinois geol. Surv. Circ.* **221**, 18 pp.

LAZELL, B. H. 1977. *The geochemistry and metamorphic history of the Moine and Lewisian rocks in the area around Strathconon, Ross-shire.* Unpubl. Ph.D. thesis, Birmingham Univ.

LE MAITRE, R. W. 1982. *Numerical Petrology.* Elsevier Developments in Petrology **8**.

LOUBET, M. & ALEGRE, C. J. 1970. Analyse des terres rares dans les échantillons géologiques par dilution isotopique et spectrometre de masse. Application à la distinction entre carbonatites et calcaires. *C. r. Acad. Sci. Paris* **270** (ser. D), 912–915.

MAISSONEUVE, J. 1982. The composition of the Precambrian ocean waters. *Sediment. Geol.* **31**, 1–11.

McCALL, G. J. H. 1977. *The Archaean.* Dowden, Hutchison and Ross. 505 pp.

MERRIAM, D. F. & PENA DAZA, M. 1978. Influence on the chemical composition of Pennsylvanian limestones in Kansas. *In*: MERRIAM, D. F. (ed.), *Recent Advances in Geomathematics.* Pergamon, 51–60.

MOGHARABI, A. 1968. Trace elements in carbonates of the Fora Formation (Lower Permian) in north-central Oklahoma. *Oklahoma geol. Notes*, **28**, 14–20.

MOORBATH, S. & TAYLOR, P. N. 1974. Lewisian age for the Scardroy mass. *Nature, London* **250**, 41–43.

MOORHOUSE, V. E. & MOORHOUSE, S. J. 1983. The geology and geochemistry of the Strathy Complex of north-east Sutherland, Scotland. *Mineralog. Mag.* **47**, 123–137.

NEWTON, R. C., SMITH, J. V. & WINDLEY, B. F. 1980. Carbonic metamorphism and crustal growth. *Nature, London* **288**, 45–50.

O'NIONS, R. K., HAMILTON, P. J. & HOOKER, P. J. 1983. A Nd isotope investigations of sediments related to crustal development in the British Isles. *Earth planet Sci. Lett.* **63**, 229–40.

PARK, R. G. 1964. The structural history of the Lewisian rocks of Gairloch, Wester Ross. *Q. J. geol. Soc. Lond.* **120**, 397–433.

—— & TARNEY, J. 1973. *The Early Precambrian rocks of Scotland and related rocks of Greenland.* Keele Univ. 200 pp.

PEACH, B. N. & HORNE, J. 1907. Geological structure of the north-west Highlands of Scotland. *Mem. geol. Surv. Scotland.*

ROBERTS, J. L. & DAVIS, A. E. 1977. Analysis of limestone survey samples by direct electron excitation X-ray spectrometry. *Rep. Inst. geol. Sci.* 77/3.

ROCK, N. M. S. 1983. A note on the distribution and significance of metamorphic limestones in the Moine and Lewisian of the Scottish Highlands and Islands. *Geol. Mag.* **120**, 639–641.

—— 1985a. Contributions on the limestones of Scotland. *Br. geol. Surv. Rep.* Vol. **16**, no. 5.

—— 1985b. Compilation of analytical data for Scottish metamorphic limestones, with comments on the accuracy and reproducibility of data. *Br. geol. Surv. Petrol. Mineral. Rept.* 85/5 (unpubl.)

—— (in press). Chemistry of the Dalradian (Vendian–Cambrian) metalimestones, British Isles. *Chem. Geol.* **56**.

—— JEFFREYS, L. A. & MACDONALD, R. 1984. The problem of anomalous local limestone-pelite successions within the Moine outcrop; I, metamorphic limestones of the Great Glen area, from Ardgour to Nigg. *Scott. J. Geol.* **20**, 383–406.

—— DREWERY, S. E. & MACDONALD, R. 1986. The problem of anomalous local limestone-pelite successions within the Moine outcrop; II: comparative geochemistry of some Lewisian, Moinian, Dalradian and anomalous pelites. *Scott. J. Geol.* **22**, 107–126.

—— & WATERHOUSE, K. 1986. The value of whole-rock geochemistry in stratigraphical correlations: an illustration from the Shinness and Armadale marbles, Sutherland, Scotland. *Proc. Geol. Assoc.* **97**(4), (in press).

RYAN, T. A., JOINER, B. L. & RYAN, B. F. 1976. *MINITAB student handbook.* Duxbury Press, Massachusetts, USA.

SALOP, L. J. 1983. *Geological evolution of the Earth during the Precambrian.* Springer-Verlag, 459 pp.

SANDERS, I. S. 1972. *The petrology of eclogites and related rocks at Glenelg, Inverness-shire.* Unpubl. Ph.D. thesis, Cambridge Univ.

SANDERS I. S., CALSTEREN, P. W. C. VAN, & HAWKESWORTH, C. J. 1984. A Grenville Sm-Nd age for the Glenelg eclogite in north-west Scotland. *Nature* **312**, 439–440.

SHEARMAN, D. J. & SHIRMOHAMMADI, N. H. 1969. Distribution of strontium in dedolomites from the French Jura. *Nature, London* **223**, 606–608.

SHERATON, J. W., SKINNER, A. C. & TARNEY, J. 1973. The geochemistry of the Scourian gneisses of the Assynt district. *In*: PARK, R. G. & TARNEY, J. (eds) *The early Precambrian rocks of Scotland and related rocks of Greenland.* Univ. Keele, pp. 13–30.

SIGHINOLFI, G. P. 1974. Geochemistry of early Precambrian carbonate rocks from the Brazilian shield, implications for Archaean carbonate sedimentation. *Contrib. Mineral. Petrol.* **46**, 189–200.

SIGHINOLFI, G. P., KRONBERG, B. I., GORGONI, C. & FYFE, W. S. 1980. Geochemistry and genesis of sulphide-anhydrite-bearing Archaean carbonate rocks from Bahia (Brazil). *Chem. Geol.* **29**, 323–331.

TANAKA, T. & MASUDA, A. 1983. The La-Ce geochronometer, a new dating method. *Nature, London* **300**, 515–518.

TANNER, P. W. G. 1970. The Sgurr Beag Slide—a major tectonic break with the Moinian of the Western Highlands of Scotland. *Q. J. geol. Soc. Lond.* **126**, 435–63.

THOMPSON, A. B. 1975. Calc.-silicate diffusion zones between marble and pelitic schist. *J. Petrol.* **16**, 314–346.

TOENS, P. D. 1966. Precambrian dolomite and limestone of the northern Cape Province. *Mem. geol. Surv. South Afr.* **57**, 109 pp.

TUCKER, M. E. 1982. Precambrian dolomites, petrographic and isotopic evidence that they differ from Phanerozoic dolomites. *Geology* **10**, 7–12.

VEIZER, J. 1978. Secular variations in the composition of sedimentary carbonate rocks, 2. Fe, Mn, Ca, Mg, Si and minor constituents. *Precambrian Res.* **6**, 381–413.

—— & GARRETT, D. E. 1978. Secular variations in the composition of sedimentary carbonate rocks, I. Alkali metals. *Precambrian Res.* **6**, 367–380.

WATSON, J. V. 1983. Lewisian. *In*: CRAIG, G. Y. (ed.) *The Geology of Scotland.* Scottish Academic Press, 23–48.

WEDEPOHL, K. 1978. *Handbook of Geochemistry.* Springer, Berlin.

WINCHESTER, J. A. & LAMBERT, R. St. J. 1970. Geochemical distinctions between the Lewisian of Cassley, Durcha and Loch Shin, and the surrounding Moinian. *Proc. Geol. Assoc.* **81**, 275–301.

WINDLEY, B. F. 1978. *The Evolving Continents.* Wiley, London.

YOUNG, G. M. 1973. Origin of the carbonate-rich Early Proterozoic Espanola Formation, Ontario, Canada. *Bull. geol. Soc. Am.* **84**, 135–160.

ZENGER, D. H., DUNHAM, J. B. & ETHINGTON, R. L. 1980. Concepts and models of dolomitization. *Soc. Econ. Palaeontol. Min. Spec. Publ.* **28**, 320 pp.

N. M. S. ROCK, Department of Geology, University of Western Australia, Nedlands 6009, WA, Australia.

A. E. DAVIES, D. HUTCHINSON, M. JOSEPH & T. K. SMITH, British Geological Survey, 64 Grays Inn Road, London WC1X 8NG, UK.

The role of mid-crustal shear zones in the Early Proterozoic evolution of the Lewisian

M. P. Coward & R. G. Park

SUMMARY: The major shear zones in the Lewisian complex are either steep NW–SE zones, with a generally dextral strike-slip component, or were subhorizontal before subsequent deformation. They appear to share the same NW–SE movement direction. The Outer Hebrides lie mostly within a major mid-crustal 'flat' which on the mainland, at a higher structural level, is seen only north of Loch Laxford and south of Loch Torridon. Inclined NW–SE-striking shear zones at Diabaig, Carnmore and Loch Laxford are interpreted as ramps by which this zone descends below the central region.

Movements on these major zones record a long period of probably intermittent activity from c. 2600 Ma to c. 1400 Ma. Early movements (Inverian) were widespread on the mainland, and indicate a generally overthrust regime with a small dextral component. A major change in kinematic regime occurred during dyke emplacement and in the early Laxfordian (D_1–D_2) where relative movements appear to have been dominantly strike-slip and extensional (transtensional). In the later Laxfordian (D_3) major upright folds and steep dextral shear zones indicate a return to a dextral transpressional regime.

This sequence, together with evidence from Greenland, can be interpreted in the context of a reconstructed N. Atlantic, as the result of relative movements between two Archaean 'plates' to N and S of the combined Nagssugtoqidian–Lewisian belt.

The Inverian–Nag I structure indicates a dominantly N–S convergence. A change to a NW–SE convergence direction in the Early Laxfordian explains a dextral strike-slip regime in the Lewisian and convergence in W Greenland. A further change to NNW–SSE convergence in the later Laxfordian would explain the D_3 transpressional regime in Scotland.

Introduction

Since the classic shear zone work of Ramsay & Graham (1970) based on examples of small shear zones from the Lewisian complex, there have been many studies of individual Lewisian shear zones (eg Beach 1974; Beach et al. 1974; Graham 1980; Davies 1976; Odling 1984), but no previous attempt has been made to integrate the observations on individual shear zones to produce a structural and kinematic model for the Lewisian as a whole. All Early Proterozoic deformation in the Lewisian complex may be attributed to displacements on a set of major shear zones which must form a coherent inter-connecting network in order to transfer the displacements through the crust between the various unde-formed blocks. These shear zones were formed at mid-crustal levels of around 15–20 km depth as indicated by the high metamorphic grade of the associated fabrics. There is increasing evidence from deep seismic reflection surveys (eg Brewer & Smythe 1984) and from theoretical considera-tions of crustal rheology (Kusznir & Park in press) that major detachment horizons of this kind exist within the middle and lower crust.

Individually, shear zones, like faults, may be compressional (thrust), extensional (normal or lag), strike-slip or oblique-slip and the determi-nation of the movement direction, not always obvious, is critical to the kinematic interpreta-tion. The most useful guide to the movement direction is the orientation of elongation linea-tions (parallel to the axis of greatest extension) in zones of high strain (see Coward 1984). At a shear strain of $\gamma = 10$ (a value commonly reached in highly deformed Lewisian zones) the lineation would lie very close to the movement direction (cf Ramsay 1980).

Measurable shape fabrics or strain indicators are uncommon in the Lewisian gneisses but deformed felsic aggregates of the Scourie dykes are extremely useful in providing estimates of the Laxfordian (post-dyke) finite strain (eg see Cow-ard 1973). In the dykes therefore, the elongation lineation produced by these felsic aggregates gives the movement direction. In small shear zones the movement sense may be deduced by the sense of curvature of the syn-shear planar fabric into the centre of the shear zone. However, in large shear zones the movement sense is sometimes not immediately obvious.

One problem with the kinematic interpretation of Lewisian shear zones is the length and complexity of the deformation history leading to interference between structures of different age and re-orientation of earlier fabrics (particularly lineations) by later movements.

From: PARK, R. G. & TARNEY, J. (eds), 1987, *Evolution of the Lewisian and Comparable Precambrian High Grade Terrains*, Geological Society Special Publication No. 27, pp. 127–138.

Structural chronology

The principles underlying the use of the Scourie dyke suite in Lewisian chronology are now well understood and generally accepted (*eg* Peach *et al.* 1907; Sutton & Watson 1951; Park 1970, 1973; Coward 1973).

Bowes (1969) has highlighted the possibility that the Scourie dyke suite may be the product of two or more periods of emplacement separated by deformations. Although the evidence for this is disputed, the length of time available for the intrusion of the suites (*c.* 400 Ma) and the likelihood that the dykes were emplaced during active tectonic shearing, suggest that caution should be exercised against simple assumptions of synchroneity of either dyke emplacement or tectonic phase.

Early Proterozoic deformation chronology commences with the Inverian episode (Table 1) dated at 2600–2400 Ma. During this period a large proportion of the mainland Lewisian was re-worked. Granulite-facies Archaean gneisses were retrogressed to amphibolite facies and a uniform steep NW–SE fabric was established over wide areas.

The oldest Scourie dykes are dated at 2400 Ma

TABLE 1. *Outline of Lewisian chronology*

Ma	
2900	Formation of early Scourian plutonic complex with associated strong sub-horizontal thrusting and deformation.
2700	Main Badcallian high-grade granulite facies metamorphism affecting deeper parts of Lewisian crust.
2600?	Initiation of Inverian shear zones associated with uplift and segmentation of Archaean blocks.
2500	Late Badcallian (post-Badcallian) biotite pegmatites.
2400–	Emplacement of Scourie dyke suite.
?2200	Continuing retrogression of the granulites and intermittent movement on shear zones.
2000	Crustal extension with extrusion of lavas and sediments of the Loch Maree Group. Emplacement of late Scourie dykes? Formation of S. Harris igneous complex?
1900?	Early Laxfordian deformation and high-grade metamorphism.
1800	Early Laxfordian migmatization and emplacement of granites and muscovite pegmatites.
1600–	Late Laxfordian deformation and
1400	retrogressive metamorphism.
1400–	Late- or post-Laxfordian brittle folds
1000?	and crush-belts.

From PARK & TARNEY (this vol.).

(Chapman 1979) and this event corresponds to a major kinematic change. The dyke emplacement spanned a period possibly until 1900 Ma and may have overlapped the first Laxfordian deformation, D_1 (see Park & Tarney, this vol.). The formation of the Loch Maree Group (Early Proterozoic metasediments and metavolcanics) falls in the latter half of this period (a likely age of 2000 Ma is proposed by O'Nions *et al.* 1983). Both D_1 and D_2 structures are associated with amphibolite-facies fabrics (Coward 1973; Park 1980) and D_1 cannot be separated chronologically from D_2—indeed they may represent a single episode of protracted deformation in which earlier formed fabrics are refolded by continued deformation. The early Laxfordian metamorphism, during which D_{1-2} took place, culminated in the local injection of granite and pegmatite sheets and veins which provide a convenient chronological marker for the end of this period of deformation (*c.* 1900–1800 Ma).

The third Laxfordian deformation phase, D_3, post-dates the granite and pegmatite sheets and is associated with retrogression to greenschist facies in the southern mainland region (see Park *et al.* this vol.). A date of *c.* 1600 Ma is assigned to the event on the basis of K-Ar mineral and whole-rock ages (Moorbath & Park 1971).

The fourth Laxfordian deformation phase, D_4, includes localized low-temperature brittle folding and crush belts which, in the southern region, may correspond to a concentration of K-Ar whole rock ages at *c.* 1400 Ma or possibly to Grenvillian (Middle Proterozoic) reworking at 1000 Ma (Moorbath & Park 1971), or both periods may even be represented. This phase is discussed further by Park *et al.* (this vol.).

The use of the Scourie dykes to identify the different deformation phases is illustrated in Fig. 1. Inverian structures are cut by the dykes. D_1 produces the first fabric to form in the dykes; folds are uncommon. D_2 refolds the S_1 fabric but shares the same lineation and, like D_1, formed at high grade. Most F_2 folds are recumbent. D_3 involves retrogression of D_1–D_2 high-grade fabrics and F_3 folds are generally upright. It cannot be assumed that these phases are synchronous throughout the Lewisian; indeed it is likely that the Inverian deformation, the sequence D_1–D_2 and D_3 are all diachronous, as is the Scourie dyke emplacement, since it is to be expected that deformation will progress laterally through the complex with time, and commence in different shear zones at different times. However the major kinematic changes (between Inverian and D_1, and between D_2 and D_3) can probably be correlated in a broad sense throughout the complex.

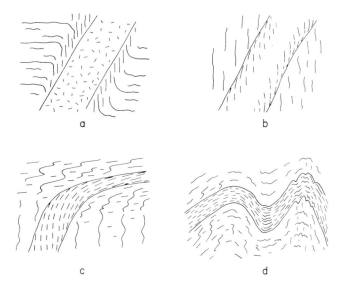

FIG. 1. Diagrammatic profiles illustrating the Early Proterozoic deformation sequence using Scourie dykes as markers: a) steep Inverian shear zone affecting sub-horizontal Archaean banding and cut by undeformed Scourie dyke; b) first Laxfordian deformation D_1 produced by shears at dyke margins eventually spreading through the dykes; c) second Laxfordian deformation D_2 caused by sub-horizontal shear which rotates the dykes into a sub-horizontal attitude and causes recumbent folds in the gneisses; d) third Laxfordian deformation D_3 producing upright folds and localized steep crenulation cleavages.

The major shear zones

The most important tectonic elements of the complex are shown in Fig. 2. The shear zones can be described in terms of 'ramps' or 'flats' using thrust zone terminology (Dahlstrom 1970). Flats are zones which formed horizontally or sub-horizontally in the crust whereas ramps were formed as inclined zones. On the mainland, steep NW–SE shear zones occur at Canisp and Gairloch, and inclined ramp-type NW–SE zones form the northern and southern boundaries of the Archaean central region (central block) at Laxford and Carnmore respectively, both dipping below the central block. A major NE-inclined ramp occurs at Diabaig, Loch Torridon. These are all major shear zones, several km in width. North of the Laxford zone and south of the Diabaig zone, major sub-horizontal shear zone flats are refolded by upright folds. In the Outer Hebrides, major steep NW–SE shear zones are located in South Harris and at Ness at the NE end of Lewis. The remaining outcrop area of the Outer Hebrides (*ie* between these two zones in North Harris and Lewis, and south of South Harris, in the Uists and Barra) is interpreted as a major refolded shear zone flat (Coward 1984).

The Laxford shear zone

This classic shear zone (Fig. 3) described by Sutton & Watson (1951, 1962), Beach *et al.* (1974) and Davis (1976) strikes NW–SE (130°), is about 8 km wide, and is inclined at 50–60° to the SW. The southern half shows mainly Inverian deformation, and the northern half shows Laxfordian. Archaean granulite-facies gneisses of the central block to the SW thus overlie the amphibolite-facies Early Proterozoic gneisses to the NE. The arrangement of Inverian fabrics in relation to the shear zone boundary and to the orientation of the most intensely deformed central part of the shear zone (occupied by the belt of granites) suggests a component of dextral shear (*cf* Davies 1976). The Inverian elongation lineations plunge uniformly to the SSE indicating a south-up dextral overthrust sense of movement. The outcrop pattern of folded early basic igneous sheets and metasediments suggests the presence of sheath folds with steeply-plunging axes (see Coward 1984).

The early Laxfordian deformation is preserved in the southern part of the shear zone as first fabrics formed in the Scourie dykes. Here, discrete small SW-dipping shear zones dip roughly parallel to the Inverian foliation but strike anticlockwise of the main intensely de-

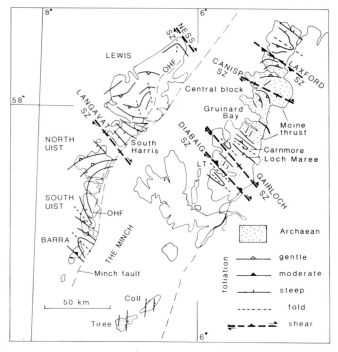

FIG. 2. Location of the principal Lewisian shear zones. Steep shear zones occur at Langavat (South Harris) and Ness in the Outer Hebrides, and Gairloch and Canisp on the mainland. Inclined shear zones occur at Laxford and Diabaig. Most of outcrop area of the Outer Hebrides, and of the mainland NE of Laxford and SW of Diabaig are interpreted as refolded shear zone flats. Note the areas of unmodified or little modified Archaean in the central block, the Ruadh Mheallan block (between the Gairloch and Diabaig shear zones) and the island of Tiree. See Park & Tarney (this vol.) for a more detailed geological map of the Lewisian.

formed part of the shear zone, giving a sinistral north-up sense of movement, with elongation lineations plunging at around 30° SE (see Beach 1974). Thus the sense of movement across this inclined belt has changed to give a component of down-dip extension indicating that the central block has moved down to the SW. The movement sense on the central intensely deformed part of the shear zone is not obvious. There are no dykes in the critical belt and the early structures are obscured by pervasive granite injection. North of this belt, early fabrics are again preserved in Scourie dykes but are affected by later Laxfordian refolding. There are two alternative possibilities for the main shear sense in the horizontal plane during the early Laxfordian: (1) that it is sinistral as suggested by Beach (1974) and that the oblique sinistral shears on its southern flank are shear band structures with the same sense of shear; (2) that it is dextral (see Davies 1976) continuing the Inverian sense of movement and that the oblique sinistral shears represent discrete antithetic accommodation shears in the flanking region brought about by dextral movement on the main

shear (see Park et al. this vol. Fig. 7; Wheeler et al. this vol.). It is also possible that both sinistral and dextral movements occurred (at different times) during this phase.

In the later Laxfordian, after the granite emplacement, the sense of movement is again clear; overfolds consistently verge NE and elongation lineations plunge SE at low angles, indicating a south-up dextral movement.

The Canisp Shear Zone

This zone is described by Attfield (this vol.) and previously by Sheraton et al. (1973) and Jensen (1984). It is WNW–ESE in trend, dips steeply to the SW and is approximately 2 km wide. The main movement is Inverian and is dominantly SW-up with a small dextral component; lineations plunge steeply S. The Laxfordian movements, which are concentrated in narrow belts, are again SW-up but with a much larger dextral component; this lineation shows low to moderate plunges to the SE.

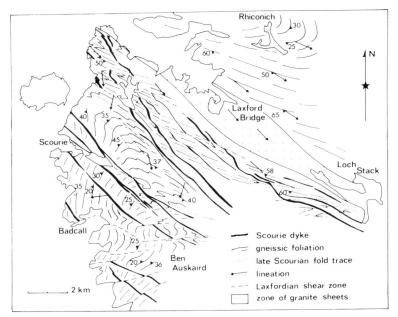

FIG. 3. The Laxford shear zone at the northern margin of the central Archaean block. Note that the Scourie dykes cut late Scourian (Inverian) folds which become more intensely developed to the northeast. The central, most intensely deformed, part of the shear zone is marked by a zone of granite sheets. After Beach *et al.* (1974), from Coward (1984).

Major shear zones of the southern region

The structures of the southern mainland region, between Gruinard Bay and Loch Torridon (Fig. 2) are described in more detail by Park *et al.* (this vol.) and in the case of the Diabaig shear zone by Wheeler *et al.* (this vol.). The whole belt can be regarded as a single NW–SE Inverian shear zone inclined to the NE but including a large undeformed enclave (the Ruadh Mheallan block). The central most highly deformed part of this shear zone probably corresponds quite closely with the site of the later Gairloch shear zone. A NE-up sense of movement with a small dextral component is interpreted from the lineations which, in areas least affected by subsequent deformation, generally plunge steeply northwest.

During the early Laxfordian, deformation (D_1) appears to have been concentrated in three separate major shear zones within the broad Inverian belt as well as in innumerable small-scale shear zones of the order of cm to m in width. Abundant evidence of the sense of movement in the small shear zones is given by the fabric of the Scourie dykes, but the sense is not consistent. The major shear zones at Carnmore, Gairloch and Diabaig appear to indicate a S-up sense of movement (down-dip extension) with a large dextral strike-slip component (Park *et al.* this

vol.). South of Loch Torridon on the major shear zone 'flat', elongation lineations exhibiting very high strain are NW–SE and sub-horizontal, similar to those north of the Loch Laxford Zone. D_2 deformation in this region is restricted to certain belts of high D_1 strain (the Tollie antiform, Gairloch and Kenmore) and appears to demonstrate the same movement sense as D_1.

In the late Laxfordian, D_3 deformation produced the obvious major NW–SE upright folds and the major Gairloch shear zone, which has a NE-up, dextral sense of movement with moderately NW-plunging lineations (Odling 1984).

A crustal model for the mainland

The movements on the Inverian shear zones suggest an overall dextral transpressional regime with a roughly N–S convergence direction. During Scourie dyke emplacement and the Laxfordian D_1 deformation of the dykes, there appears to have been a major change in kinematic regime to transtensional across the major northern and southern ramps. The principal movement direction is NW–SE as given by the orientation of the high-strain elongation lineations on the shear zone flats. Fig. 4 shows the mainland D_1 as a combination of NW–SE horizontal movement

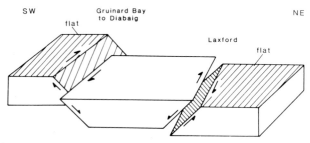

FIG. 4. Block diagram illustrating the effects of oblique-slip extensional movements on the Laxford and Diabaig shear zones, with an overall dextral component, coupled with NW–SE movement on the flats to the NE and SW.

on the flats and dextral oblique-normal slip on the ramps. If the Laxford shear zone is sinistral in D_1, the sense of movement of the northern block would be up to the N instead of up to the E.

In the D_3 Laxfordian phase, another significant kinematic change must have occurred to produce effectively dextral transpressional regimes in the north and south which refold the previously flat-lying D_1 structures. The overall convergence direction presumably then had returned to a roughly N–S orientation. In simple terms therefore, the kinematic history of the Early Protero-zoic can be visualized as compression followed by extension then a return to compression across the NW–SE strike of the belt but possibly with a continued dextral strike slip component, resulting in the central block being first uplifted, then depressed and finally uplifted again. The D_3 uplift resulted in extensive retrogression of previously higher-grade assemblages.

Two possible ways of linking these shear zone movements into a crustal-scale network are shown in Fig. 5. In both models the ramps are shown to link up at depth on a lower detachment shear zone beneath the central block; and also

above, as an upper detachment zone represented by the presently exposed shear zone flats which probably extended across the top of the central block (Beach *et al.* 1974). Model (A) is a basically symmetrical type with NW–SE convergence (perpendicular to the page); model (B) is an asymmetrical (strike-slip) model based on an analogy with the NE-dipping East Greenland Nagssugtoqidian belt, assuming that the structure results from a primary southwest over-riding of a northern block in the Inverian. The Laxford ramp on this model would represent a 'back thrust'. In this model also, of course, a large component of the movement is perpendicular to the page. Fig. 5 shows the shear zone pattern before substantial movements have taken place. Fig. 6 illustrates both models as 3D cartoons. Dip-slip movements are ignored for simplicity. Note that the sense of strike-slip displacement on the Laxford shear zone is a major distinguishing feature between the two models.

The Outer Hebrides

The major NW–SE dextral shear zone in South Harris (Fig. 7) dips steeply southwest and is

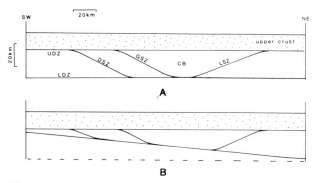

FIG. 5. Crustal profiles illustrating two alternative models of the shear-zone network. UDZ-upper detachment zone; LDZ—lower detachment zone (base of crust?); DSZ, GSZ, LSZ—Diabaig, Gairloch and Laxford shear zones; CB—central block. The lower profile differs in having the LDZ inclined to the NE.

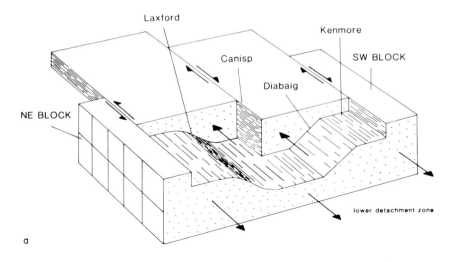

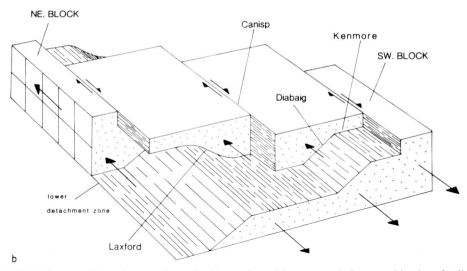

FIG. 6. Block diagrams illustrating two alternative kinematic models accommodating a combination of strike-slip and thrust movements on flat, ramp, and transfer type shear zones. a) is a basically overthrust model; b) is a basically strike-slip model. Dip-slip movements on the ramps are ignored for convenience.

approximately 10 km wide with a weakly de-formed central lensoid enclave (Graham 1980; Coward 1984). However, the steep dextral zone is a late Laxfordian structure which deforms an early Laxfordian high-strain fabric. Coward (1984) suggests that in the early Laxfordian (D_1–D_2) the Langavat shear zone (on the northeast side of the South Harris belt) was a low-angle lateral ramp up which the South Harris granulites were thrust towards the NW (Fig. 8b). Thus the

South Harris belt appears to record dextral transpressional movements in both early and late Laxfordian times, although the dip-slip sense changes from southwest-up to northeast-up. The latter movement is directly comparable with that of the Gairloch shear zone.

The major shear zone flats north and south of the South Harris belt record high early Laxfordian strains with a NW–SE movement direction. F_2 folds appear to show northward vergence

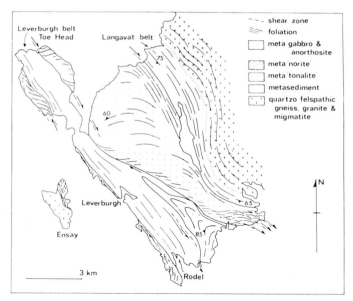

FIG. 7. Simplified map of the Langavat or South Harris shear zone, from Coward (1984) after Graham (1980).

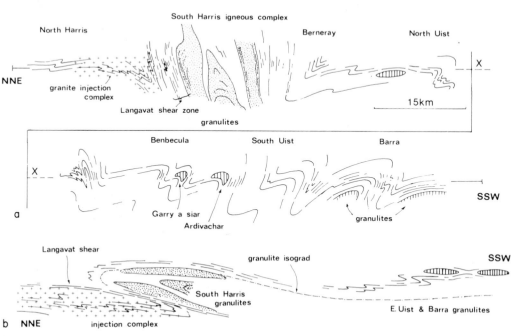

FIG. 8. a) A cross-section through the Early Proterozoic structure of the Outer Hebrides showing NE-facing early folds refolded by major SW-facing D_3 folds in the Uists and Barra. b) Schematic section prior to D_3 folding showing the Langavat shear zone as a low-angle lateral ramp upthrusting the South Harris granulites. After Coward (1984).

(Coward 1984 Fig. 8*b*). These flat-lying fabrics are refolded by more upright, southwestwards verging F_3 folds (Fig. 8*a*).

Synthesis

Very little information is available from the Outer Hebrides concerning the earlier part of the sequence of events (Inverian to Laxfordian D_1) recognized on the mainland, due to the destructive effects of subsequent deformations. However, there is no reason to suppose that the Outer Hebrides did not exhibit a similar kinematic history to that of the mainland during these events, and there are obvious similarities in the later part of the sequence (D_2–D_3).

The early Laxfordian metamorphic assemblages in the Outer Hebrides (the South Harris granulite-facies rocks in particular) reflect generally deeper crustal levels than the mainland. The Outer Hebrides is regarded as the outcrop of

a major shear zone flat, and it is convenient to correlate this structure with the lower detachment zone on which the major ramps of the mainland 'bottom out' (*cf* Figs 5 and 6). However, the possibility must be borne in mind that multiple detachment horizons may exist, and that the true picture may be much more complicated than is envisaged here. There can therefore be no precise match of the major shear zones across the Minch since the major displacements can be transferred from the ramps above onto the flats below. The only major structure that might perhaps be expected in both terrains is the South Harris belt. Three possible matches across the Minch are considered. The actual displacement involved is of course unknown, although there is no seismic evidence for a strike-slip displacement on the Minch fault. Dip-slip displacements on the Outer Hebrides fault are large, and are both extensional and compressional (see White & Glasser, this vol.) but appear to be perpendicular to the strike, so that large offsets of NW–SE trending structures seem unlikely.

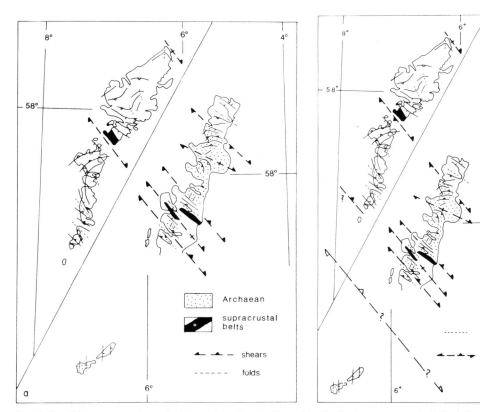

FIG. 9. Possible reconstructions of the Lewisian allowing for strike-slip displacements on the Minch fault. a) Alignment of the South Harris and Gairloch shear zones. b) Alignment of the South Harris and Laxford shear zones. Compare with Fig. 2 and see text for discussion.

Fig. 2 shows the present relative position. It can be seen that the South Harris shear zone would project southwest of the southern end of the mainland outcrop and the Ness shear zone would project through unexposed ground around Loch Broom. Fig. 9a shows perhaps the most obvious correlation across the Minch, suggested originally by Park (in discussion of Dearnley 1962). It correlates the two major steep dextral shear zones—South Harris and Gairloch, as well

as the large early Proterozoic basic masses. Unfortunately the flanking regions do not correspond well. Fig. 9b shows the match suggested by Dearnley (1962) which correlates the two major southwest-inclined ramps—South Harris and Laxford. This match has superficial attractions but demands much too great a strike-slip displacement along the Minch. The Fig. 2 match is probably to be preferred since it poses fewest problems.

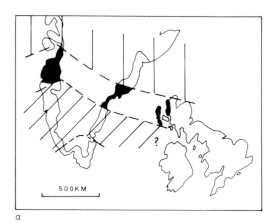

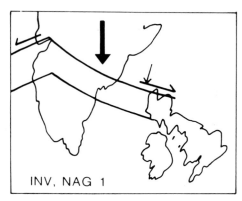

INV, NAG 1

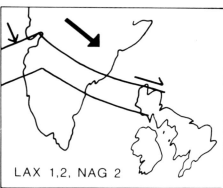

LAX 1,2, NAG 2

FIG. 10. a) Reconstruction of the Early Proterozoic belts of Greenland and Scotland after removing the effects of the North Atlantic opening. The restoration is based on the removal of oceanic crust and on the assumption of an average 50% thinning of continental crust on the continental shelves. The N belt comprises the Nagssugtoqidian of W and E Greenland and the Lewisian, and appears to be between two more stable Archaean 'plates' to N and S. b) The kinematic history of the Lewisian can be interpreted in terms of a change in movement direction of the N plate with reference to the S plate between the Inverian and Laxfordian 1, and between Laxfordian 2 and Laxfordian 3, with resulting changes between dominantly convergent, and dominantly strike-slip tectonics (see text).

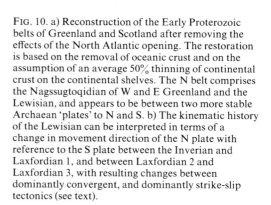

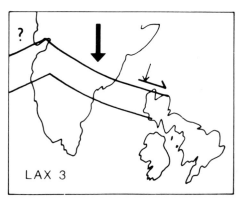

LAX 3

b

Kinematic model for the North Atlantic region

Fig. 10 shows a reconstruction of the relative positions of Scotland and Greenland prior to the opening of the North Atlantic. The distance between Scotland and Greenland has been reduced to allow for a presumed 50% crustal thinning and extension in the spreading direction prior to ocean formation. The Lewisian lies directly along strike of the Nagssugtoqidian belt of E. Greenland (see also Myers this vol.). This belt forms part of a regional system of Early Proterozoic shear zones established at around 2.7–2.6 Ga (Watterson 1978; Park 1982) in the North Atlantic region indicating N–S compression and convergence. Such a regional kinematic control fits well with the Inverian shear regime in Scotland and explains both the Inverian and the Nagssugtoqidian I of West Greenland as dominantly transpressional regimes, dextral in the former case and sinistral in the latter. A change to a NW–SE convergence direction is necessary

to explain the NW–SE movement directions in the early Laxfordian which corresponds with a change to a dominantly overthrust region in the Nagssugtoqidian II of West Greenland (see Korstgård 1979). An essentially strike-slip movement during this period in the Lewisian could produce either transtensional or transpressional regimes depending on the orientation of the shear zone in relation to the movement direction. Thus Laxfordian D_1 transpression in the Canisp Shear Zone (a trend of 115°) and transtension in Diabaig (trend 140°) suggest a movement vector of about 120°–130°.

A further change in regional convergence direction back to approximately NNW–SSE in the late Laxfordian is indicated by the widespread evidence of dextral transpressional regimes overthrusting to the south (southern Outer Hebrides and southern mainland region) and to the north (Laxford). These changes are summarized in cartoon form in Fig. 10*b*.

References

BEACH, A. 1974. The measurement and significance of displacements on Laxfordian shear zones, North-West Scotland. *Proc. Geol. Ass.* **85**, 13–21.

——, COWARD, M. P. & GRAHAM, R. H. 1974. An interpretation of the structural evolution of the Laxford front, north-west Scotland. *Scott. J. Geol.* **9**, 297–308.

BOWES, D. R. 1969. The Lewisian of Northwest Highlands of Scotland. *In:* KAY, M. (ed). *North Atlantic-geology and continental drift—a symposium. Mem. Am. Assoc. Petrol. Geol.* **12**, 575–594.

BLUNDELL, D. J., HURICK, C. A. & SMITHSON, S. B. 1985. A model for the MOIST seismic reflection profile, N. Scotland. *J. geol. Soc. London,* **142**, 245–258.

BREWER, J. A. & SMYTHE, D. K. 1984. MOIST and the continuity of crustal reflector geometry along the Caledonian–Appalachian orogen. *J. geol. Soc. London,* **141**, 105–120.

CHAPMAN, H. J. 1979. 2,390 Myr Rb-Sr whole-rock age for the Scourie dykes of north-west Scotland. *Nature, London* **277**, 642–3.

COWARD, M. P. 1973. Heterogeneous deformation in the development of the Laxfordian complex of South Uist, Outer Hebrides. *J. geol. Soc. Lond.* **129**, 137–160.

——, 1974. Flat lying structures within the Lewisian basement gneiss complex of N.W. Scotland. *Proc. Geol. Assoc.* **85**, 459–72.

——, 1984. Major shear zones in the Precambrian crust; examples from NW Scotland and southern Africa and their significance. *In:* KRONER, A. & GREILING, S. R. (eds) *Precambrian Tectonics Illustrated,* Stuttgart, 207–235.

DAHLSTROM, C. D. 1970. Structural geology of the

eastern margin of the Canadian Rocky Mountains. *Bull. Can. Pet. Geol.* **18**, 332–406.

DAVIES, F. B. 1976. Early Scourian structures in the Scourie–Laxford region and their bearing on the evolution of the Laxford Front. *J. geol. Soc. Lond.* **132**, 543–54.

DEARNLEY, R. 1962. An outline of the Lewisian complex of the Outer Hebrides in relation to that of the Scottish mainland. *Quart. J. geol. Soc. Lond.* **118**, 143–76.

GRAHAM, R. H. 1980. The role of shear belts in the structural evolution of the South Harris igneous complex. *J. struct. Geol.* **2**, 29–37.

JENSEN, L. N. 1984. Quartz microfabric of the Laxfordian Canisp shear zone, N.W. Scotland. *J. struct. Geol.* **6**, 293–302.

KORSTGÅRD, J. A. 1979. Metamorphism of the Kagamiut dykes and the metamorphic and structural evolution of the southern Nagssugtoqidian boundary in the Itivdleq–Iqertoq region, West Greenland. *In:* KORSTGÅRD, J. A. (ed) *Nagssugtoqidian geology* Grønlands Geologiske Unders. Rapp. **89**, 63–75.

KUSZNIR, N. J. & PARK, R. G. in press. The extensional strength of the continental lithosphere: its dependence on geothermal gradient, crustal composition and crustal thickness. *In:* COWARD, M. P. *et al.* (eds) *Continental Extensional Tectonics.* Special Publication, Geological Society of London.

MOORBATH, S. & PARK, R. G. 1971. The Lewisian chronology of the southern region of the Scottish Mainland. *Scott. J. Geol.* **8**, 51–74.

ODLING, N. E. 1984. Strain analysis and strain path modelling in the Loch Tollie gneisses, Gairloch, N.W. Scotland. *J. struct. Geol.* **6**, 543–62.

O'NIONS, R. K., HAMILTON, P. J. & HOOKER, P. J. 1983. A Nd-isotope investigation of sediments related to crustal development in the British Isles. *Earth planet. Sci. Lett,* **63**, 229–40.

PARK, R. G. (1970). Observations on Lewisian chronology. *Scott. J. Geol.* **6**, 379–99.

——, 1973. The Laxfordian belts of the Scottish mainland. *In:* PARK, R. G. & TARNEY, J. (eds) *The early Precambrian of Scotland and Related Rocks of Greenland.* Univ. Keele, 65–76.

——, 1980. The Lewisian of NW Britain. *In:* OWEN, T. R. (ed) *United Kingdom: Introduction to general geology and guides to excursions 002, 055, 093 and 151.* 26th Int. Geol. Congr. Paris, 8–13.

——, 1982. Archaean tectonics. *Geol. Rundsch.* **71**, 22–37.

PEACH, B. N., HORNE, J., GUNN, W., CLOUGH, C. T. & HINXMAN, L. W. 1907. The geological structure of the North-West Highlands of Scotland. *Mem. geol. Surv. Gt. Britain.*

RAMSAY, J. G. 1980. Shear zone geometry: a review. *J. struct. Geol.* **2**, 83–99.

—— & GRAHAM, R. H. 1970. Strain variation in shear belts. *Can. J. Earth Sci.* **7**, 786–813.

SHERATON, J. W., SKINNER, A. C. & TARNEY, J. 1973. The structural history of the Assynt district. *In:* PARK, R. G. & TARNEY, J. (eds) *The early Precambrian of Scotland and Related Rocks of Greenland.* Univ. Keele, 31–43.

SUTTON, J. & WATSON, J. V. 1951. The pre-Torridonian metamorphic history of the Loch Torridon and Scourie areas in the North-West Highlands, and its bearing on the chronological history of the Lewisian. *Quart. J. geol. Soc. Lond.* **106**, 241–308.

—— & ——, 1962. Further observations on the margin of the Laxfordian complex of the Lewisian near Loch Laxford, Sutherland. *Trans. R. Soc. Edinb.* **65**, 89–106.

WATTERSON, J. 1978. Proterozoic intraplate deformation in the light of South-east Asian neotectonics. *Nature, London* **273**, 636–40.

M. P. COWARD, Department of Geology, Imperial College, London, SW7 2BP, UK.

R. G. PARK, Department of Geology, Keele University, Newcastle, Staffordshire, ST5 5BG, UK.

Early Proterozoic structure and kinematic evolution of the southern mainland Lewisian

R. G. Park, A. Crane & M. Niamatullah

SUMMARY: The southern mainland region of the Lewisian is a belt of intense Early Proterozoic deformation with a minimum width of 55 km, in which all the main structures trend NW–SE. Archaean structures are dominant in the central block to the northeast, and in a small enclave (the Ruadh Mheallan block) between Gairloch and Loch Torridon. Major structures within the belt include upright NW–SE folds (the Carnmore antiform, the Letterewe synform, and the Tollie and Torridon antiforms) and the Gairloch and Diabaig shear zones. The structural history is divided into six phases: (1) Inverian (2600–2400 Ma)—the whole belt represents a major steep Inverian shear zone. Structures in areas little affected by subsequent deformation indicate a N–up overthrust movement with a small dextral component (dextral transpressional), (2) Emplacement of dykes and Loch Maree Group (2400–1900 Ma)—evidence of dextral shear during dyke emplacement indicates a change to a dextral transtensional regime, (3) Laxfordian D_1 and, (4) D_2 deformation (1900–1800 Ma)—oblique dip-slip shears and asymmetric shear folds suggest a continuation of the previous dextral transtensional movements on inclined lateral ramps, connected with major gently-inclined shear zone 'flats', (5) Laxfordian D_3 deformation (c. 1600 Ma)—upright folding of previously sub-horizontal fabrics and a reversal of movement to N–up on the Gairloch shear zone indicate a change to a dextral transpressional regime, which is accompanied by retrogressive metamorphism, (6) Laxfordian D_4 deformation (c. 1400 or c. 1000 Ma)—steeply plunging large and small-scale asymmetric folds and crush belts indicate a change to a sinistral strike-slip regime. We suggest that these phases of movement represent major changes in relative plate movement direction probably separated by relatively long periods of comparative stability.

Introduction

The southern region of the mainland Lewisian extends from Gruinard Bay in the north to Loch Torridon in the south, including the islands of Rona and Raasay (Fig. 1). It is part of a belt of Early Proterozoic tectonic activity with a minimum width of 55 km separated from a northern belt between Laxford and Durness (the 'northern region') by a central block of Archaean rocks (the 'central region') little affected by Proterozoic activity.

Extensive research has taken place in the region commencing with the Geological Survey mapping of Peach *et al.* (1907) and the work of Sutton in Torridon (Sutton & Watson 1951). Detailed structural mapping of parts of the region took place in the period 1958–1973 by a number of workers (Park 1964; 1970a; Elliott 1964; Ghaly 1966; Keppie 1967; Bhattacharjee 1968; Cresswell 1972; and Crane 1978). The usefulness of much of the earlier work however is limited by a lack of general agreement over correlation and nomenclature. Alternative overviews of the chronology of the region are found in Bowes (1969) and Park (1970b, 1973, 1980).

More recent structural work in the southern region by two of the authors (RGP and AC) has concentrated on detailed examination of individual shear zones and on documenting variations in strain distribution across the area. The third author (MN) has recently completed the first detailed structural analysis of the critical Kenmore inlier in the SW part of the region (Niamatullah 1984). Other relevant recent work includes studies of strain variation across the Gairloch shear zone (Odling 1984) and the Diabaig shear zone (Wheeler *et al.*, this vol.).

Chronology

For the purposes of this paper, the Early Proterozoic deformation chronology can be summarized as follows—see Park & Tarney (this vol.) and other references quoted below for further discussion:

c. 2600 Ma[1]	. pre-Inverian pegmatites
	Inverian deformation
c. 2400–2000 Ma[2,3]	Scourie dyke emplacement
	Laxfordian D_1 deformation
	Laxfordian D_2 deformation
c. 1800 Ma[4,5]	. granite and pegmatite
	emplacement
c. 1600 Ma[6]	. Laxfordian D_3 deformation
c. 1400 Ma[6]	. Laxfordian D_4 deformation
(or c. 1150 Ma?[6])	

[1]Giletti *et al.* (1961); [2]Evans (1965); [3]Chapman (1979); [4]Lyon *et al.* (1973); [5]Pidgeon (1973); [6]Moorbath & Park (1971).

From: PARK, R. G. & TARNEY, J. (eds), 1987, *Evolution of the Lewisian and Comparable Precambrian High Grade Terrains*, Geological Society Special Publication No. 27, pp. 139–151.

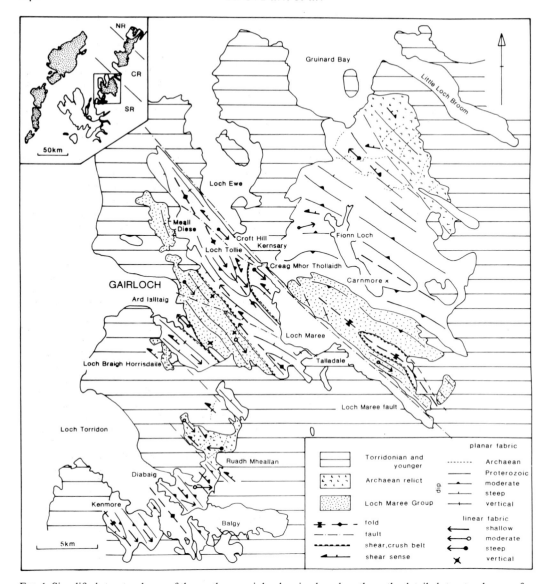

FIG. 1. Simplified structural map of the southern mainland region based partly on the detailed structural maps of
Park (1964, 1970a), Cresswell (1972), Crane (1978), Niamatullah (1984) and on published Geological Survey 6 in.
sheets. Insert shows location within the Lewisian outcrop of NW Scotland (dotted). NR—northern region, CR—
central region, SR—southern region.

Although each of the deformational phases
recognized was probably diachronous, we believe
that in general (with the possible exception of
D_2) each new phase commenced after the
previous phase had ceased, and that the 4–5
phases cited reflect genuine regional tectonic
changes of a profound nature—rather than
aspects of a continuous and progressive defor-

mation. The sequence can be divided into two
high-temperament phases (Inverian and Laxfordian D_1–D_2) associated with amphibolite-facies
metamorphism, and two low-temperature phases
associated with retrogression to low greenschist
facies or even lower grade (Laxfordian D_3 and
D_4). A marked change can thus be distinguished
in the Laxfordian from essentially mid-crustal to

upper-crustal deformation in the period 1700–1600 Ma.

The distinction between Inverian and Laxfordian deformation is made primarily by reference to the relationships of the structures to the Scourie dykes (*eg* see Park & Cresswell 1972, 1973; Cresswell 1972 and Crane 1978). However, the long time period (2400–*c.* 2000 Ma) during which dyke emplacement may have occurred, and the uncertainty over the precise age of individual dykes within the region, render it impossible to fix accurately either the end of Inverian deformation or the beginning of Laxfordian as originally defined. It is likely that both events are diachronous and that deformation continued throughout the period of emplacement; this assumption underlies our kinematic reconstruction.

If a time is to be selected for the commencement of 'Laxfordian' activity (post-Scourie dyke by the original Sutton & Watson definition) we would suggest the beginning of dyke emplacement at 2400 Ma. This event may mark a fundamental change in regional tectonic conditions, as argued below. The implication that later dykes may cut 'Laxfordian' structures is of course contrary to previous usage, but the solution is less unwieldy than the alternative one of inventing a new name for deformation occupying the 2400–2000 Ma interval that is in practice indistinguishable.

The emplacement of the supracrustal formations of the Loch Maree Group also occurred during this time interval. The sediments have yielded a maximum Sm/Nd depositional age of *c.* 2000 Ma (O'Nions *et al.* 1983), are cut by minor sills of Scourie dyke type, and are affected by all the Laxfordian deformations.

Main structural elements

The main elements of the structure of the region are shown in Figs 1 and 2. Archaean structures are dominant in the central block to the northeast, and in a small enclave (the Ruadh Mheallan block) between Gairloch and Loch Torridon. The predominant structure in the remainder of the region is a NW–SE-trending foliation with variable dip, to which all lithological boundaries are sub-parallel. Two major supracrustal belts occur; at Gairloch, and northeast of Loch Maree.

There are five major NW–SE upright folds in the region. These are, from NE to SW: the Carnmore antiform, the Letterewe synform, the Tollie antiform, the Torridon antiform, and an un-named synform near the SW edge of the Kenmore inlier. The Letterewe and Tollie folds

are separated by the large, post-Lewisian, Loch Maree fault. There are two major shear zones in the region, separated by the Ruadh Mheallan block: the steep Gairloch shear zone northeast of the block, and the NE-dipping Diabaig shear zone SW of the block. The belt of most intense deformation in the Gairloch shear zone lies on the SW side of the Tollie antiform and includes the whole of the Gairloch supracrustal belt. The Daibaig shear zone is bounded on its SW side by the hinge of the Torridon antiform.

The major NW–SE upright folds and the related Gairloch shear zone are of D_3 age and refold a sub-horizontal to moderately-inclined foliation which is itself produced by high Laxfordian strain and contains a strong linear fabric oriented NW–SE. This fabric is associated with recumbent folding (F_2) of dykes and gneissose banding in the hinge areas of the Tollie and Torridon antiforms and in the Kenmore area. These F_2 folds affect S_1, the first Laxfordian fabric seen in the Scourie dykes. F_1 folds are rare. In areas of strong D_2 deformation, there is a composite D_1–D_2 fabric.

In areas of low Laxfordian strain, the deformation is markedly heterogeneous and D_1 structures are represented by narrow shear zones associated with the Scourie dykes. These shear zones first occur mainly at the margins but sometimes within the dykes, and gradually spread through the whole dyke as the strain increases. The sense of movement on the shears can be estimated from the orientation of the oblique dyke fabrics, and is often consistent over large areas. The results of a study of 135 such shears by two of the authors (RGP & AC) are summarized in Table 1, and are discussed later.

The dominant strong linear fabric, which is typically of D_1–D_2 age, shows considerable plunge variation across the area, but this variation is mostly due to refolding by F_3 major folds.

TABLE 1. *Analysis of movement sense on small shear zones*

1. All shear zones* (135)
   63% SIN; 63% SW up
2. Shear zones in low-strain areas (Gruinard and Ruadh Mheallan) (34)
   No preferred shear sense: 57% SIN, 62% SW up
3. Shear zones in moderately D_1-strained 'border zones' (40)
   90% SIN; 71% SIN, SW up
4. Shear sense in D_1 high-strain areas (13)
   100% SW up; 82% DEX; 71% DEX, SW up
5. Shear sense in $D_{2\cdot 3}$ high-strain areas (31)
   83% NE up; 56% SIN

* Only shear zones with orientations in the range NNW–SSE to WNW–ESE are included.

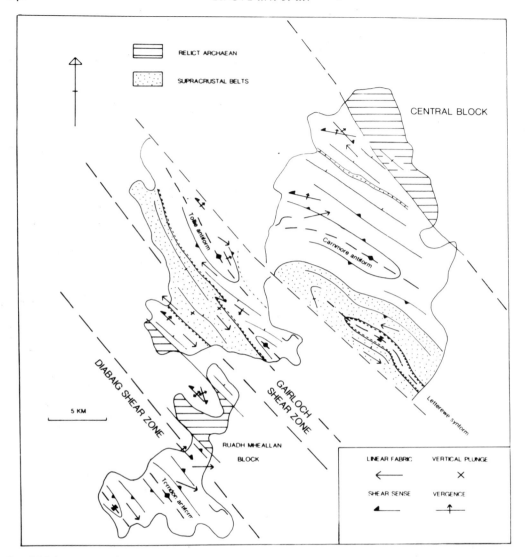

FIG. 2. Major structural features of the southern mainland region (simplified from Fig. 1). Structural symbols as for Fig. 1.

When the effect of the folds is removed, the lineations show a more consistent pattern, with a generally WNW–ESE to W–E trend N of Loch Torridon, and NW–SE in the high-strain Kenmore area.

Kinematic reconstruction

The general principles governing the interpretation of structure in terms of shear zone displacements is discussed in Coward & Park (this vol.). In this paper, these principles are applied to the southern mainland region by attempting to establish movement criteria for the six main stages of the tectonic history of the region: the Inverian, the emplacement of the Scourie dykes and Loch Maree Group, and the Laxfordian deformations D_1 to D_4. Each of these stages is examined in turn.

The Inverian

Figure 3a summarizes the essential elements of the Inverian structure (compare Figs 1 and 2). Over much of the region, Inverian structures have been almost totally obliterated by strong Laxfordian deformation. There are only three areas where the Inverian structure is sufficiently well preserved to be interpretable: in the northeast, from the margin of the central Archaean block to the northeast side of Fionn Loch, where strong Laxfordian deformation commences; in the Ruadh Mheallan block in the south, and in several small enclaves in the Gairloch area isolated by Laxfordian shearing. In each case, the Inverian foliation is steep and the elongation lineations, in zones of high strain, plunge consistently steeply NW or W (*eg* see Cresswell 1972; Crane 1978). The sense of movement indicated by the obliquity of the Inverian fabric to the margins of the shear zone, and by the asymmetry of some of the Inverian major folds, is dextral but with a large NE-up overthrust component.

Most areas exhibiting moderately strong Laxfordian deformation also appear to have suffered previous Inverian deformation, although the evidence for this becomes progressively harder to find as Laxfordian deformation increases. Both in the north, and in the Ruadh Mheallan block, the margins of Laxfordian deformation appear

to lie within a zone of previous Inverian deformation, suggesting that the whole region south of the central block consisted of a single wide Inverian shear zone with only a small undeformed enclave at Ruadh Mheallan. The later Laxfordian shear zones are thus probably localized within this broad Inverian zone.

The orientation of this Inverian shear zone must have been NW–SE dipping steeply NE, as indicated on the NE side of the Carnmore antiform and on the SW side of the Ruadh Mheallan block. The central most highly deformed part of the shear zone probably lay in the position presently occupied by the later Gairloch shear zone. The evidence for this is the intense Inverian deformation seen in the enclaves near Gairloch: Ard Ialltaig (Park 1964), Creag Mhor Thollaidh (Park 1970a) and Croft Hill (Crane 1978). An asymmetric late Inverian fold is mapped by Cresswell (1972) in the Diabaig area around Loch na Beiste. This fold verges SW and has a variable plunge suggesting a sheath-like shear fold and corroborates the NE-up movement sense on the main shear zone.

In the tectonic model proposed by Coward and

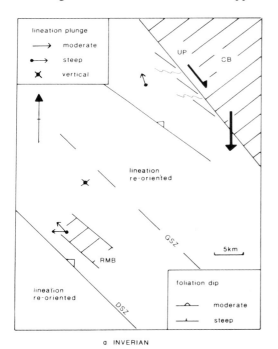

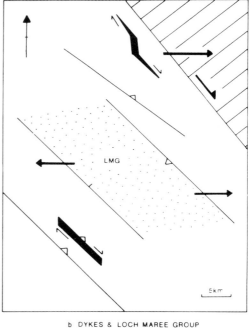

a INVERIAN   b DYKES & LOCH MAREE GROUP

FIG. 3. a) Kinematic interpretation of Inverian structure in the southern mainland region of dextral transpression with overthrust movement to the south. b) Kinematic interpretation of the region during emplacement of Scourie dykes and Loch Maree Group by a change to dextral transtension. CB—central block; GSZ—Gairloch Shear Zone; RMB—Ruadh Mheallan block; DSZ—Diabaig shear zone; LMG—Loch Maree Group (dotted). Generalized dykes in solid black; heavy arrows represent movement direction. Based on Fig. 2. Compare profiles (Fig. 4).

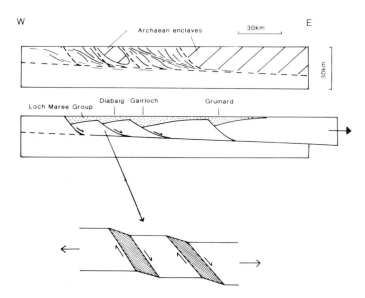

FIG. 4. Kinematic profiles illustrating the Inverian structure (upper) and the emplacement of the Loch Maree Group (dotted ornament). W–E extension is accomplished by movements on normal (growth?) faults detaching on a major low-angle shear zone. Emplacement and first deformation of dykes within the fault blocks fits the same movement pattern. Compare with Fig. 3.

Park (this vol.) the steep Inverian shear zones are interpreted as ramps detaching on a major low-angle shear zone at depth (see Fig. 4).

Emplacement of Scourie dykes and Loch Maree Group

Figure 3*b* summarizes our interpretation of the essential kinematic pattern during this period. Evidence from the shape of the dykes in areas of little or no Laxfordian deformation in the north (see Fig. 5) suggests that the dykes were emplaced in a dextral transtensional regime. Criteria which may be used to indicate shear sense during emplacement are discussed by Escher *et al.* (1976) and by Nicholson & Pollard (1985), and include orientation of apophyses and *en-echelon* arrangement (see Fig. 5*b* for diagrammatic summary).

The emplacement of the Loch Maree Group also indicates a degree of crustal extension in order to allow a thickness of probably several kilometres of supracrustal material to be deposited. Figure 4 suggests that this may have been achieved by movements on a set of extensional normal faults–shear zones detaching on the major low-angle shear zone resulting from the previous Inverian movements.

The emplacement of the dykes, the extrusion of the Loch Maree volcanics and the first deformation of the dykes may all be related to the same tectonic framework. Thus movements

on high-angle faults near the surface may be expressed at depth by shearing on already emplaced dykes (see Fig. 4 inset). Deformation occurring within this period which affects the dykes is of course indistinguishable from Laxfordian D_1 *sensu stricto* as discussed previously.

Laxfordian D_1 deformation

The regional pattern of the Laxfordian D_1 deformation is summarized in Fig. 6*a*. Our knowledge of the D_1 structure is derived by examining the first-formed fabric in the Scourie dykes throughout the region and in the supracrustal rocks of the Loch Maree Group. This fabric is only significantly affected by later deformation in the Gairloch shear zone, and in the Kenmore area, south of Loch Torridon. However even in these areas D_1 fabric can still be detected in F_2 fold hinges.

Analysis of the sense of shear at dyke margins across the region yields conflicting results. 135 small shear zones were studied (Table 1); of those showing a clear strike-slip component, two-thirds were sinistral, and of those showing a clear dip-slip component, two-thirds were south-up. The distribution of these data is interesting: areas of very low Laxfordian strain, near the margin of the central block, and in the Ruadh Mheallan block, display variable movement senses which depend partly on the orientation of the dykes. As

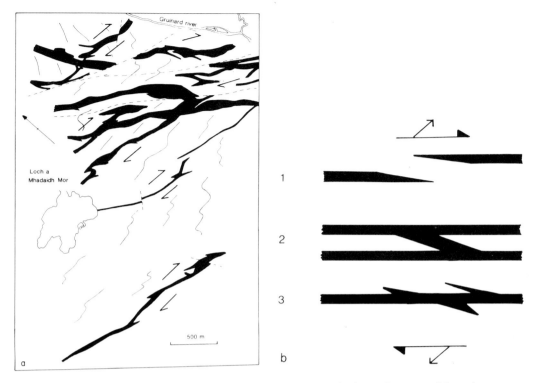

FIG. 5. a) Selected dyke outcrop patterns in the Creag-mheall Beag area, in the northern part of the region southwest of Gruinard River, showing evidence of dextral shear during emplacement. b) Three geometric criteria indicating dextral shear during emplacement (see text): 1—en-echelon arrangement; 2—inclined bridges; 3—inclined apophyses.

the Laxfordian strain increases towards the margins of the main shear zones however, the dykes become near-parallel to each other and show typically a sinistral S-up sense of movement (*eg* the N side of the Carnmore antiform, the S Sithean Mor belt at Gairloch, and the SW margin of the Ruadh Mheallan block at Diabaig). Within the main shear zones themselves, the evidence for sense of shear is often obscured by the high strain, but when it can be determined is typically dextral and S-up (*eg* Diabaig, Gairloch).

The explanation for this apparently rather paradoxical distribution of movement sense probably lies in the changing behaviour of the dykes under increasing Laxfordian strain. The margins of the dykes, and subsequently the dykes as a whole, appear to behave as more ductile layers in a heterogeneous medium. In the early stages of deformation the shear sense will be determined by the orientation of the principal stress axes in relation to that of the dyke walls (see Davidson & Park 1978). With increasing strain, shear sense is determined by the kinematic behaviour of the complex and specifically by the

sense of rotation of the dykes as they rotate towards the shear plane (see Fig. 8, Hageskov 1985; Wheeler *et al.* this vol.). At high strains, the sense of shear in the dykes should correspond to that of the main shear zone.

The orientation of the main shear zone at Diabaig, deduced from the highest-strain parts of the complex, strikes around 150° with a dip of about 45° NE, and the shear direction, given by elongation lineations, plunges around 30° E. In dykes oriented more steeply than the shear plane and with a strike anticlockwise of it, minor shears may form along the dyke margins as the dykes rotate towards the shear plane. Such shears would have a sinistral S-up shear sense and a NW-plunging shear direction. This would explain the majority of the measured shears in the intermediate-strain zones.

Dykes oriented clockwise from, or dipping less steeply than, the shear plane would tend to form dextral or N-up shears respectively. Such shears may be regarded as shear-band structures.

It is not possible to reconstruct the geometry of the major D_1 shear zones accurately because of

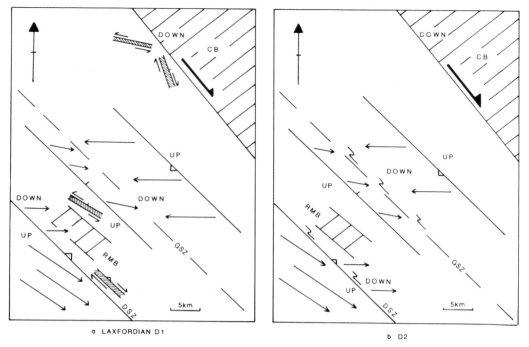

a LAXFORDIAN D1   b D2

FIG. 6. Kinematic models for the Laxfordian D_1 and D_2 deformations, simplified from Fig. 2. a) Sense of shear and lineation arrangement (arrows) suggests dextral transtension in D_1 (see text). Stylized dykes are hachured . Compare Fig. 7a. b) Fold asymmetry and lineation arrangement suggest a continuation of dextral transtension in D_2. Key as for Fig. 3.

uncertainties about the effects of D_2 and D_3. Figures 6a and 7b give an interpretation of the possible D_{1-2} shear zone arrangement. The Diabaig shear zone is considered to have been little affected by subsequent rotation, and the Kenmore shear zone to have been sub-horizontal. The change in orientation of L_1 and S_1 across the Torridon antiform is interpreted as an original feature—the transition from Kenmore flat to Diabaig ramp.

Both the Gairloch shear zone and the Letterewe synform have clearly been steepened by D_3 movements. The Gairloch shear zone in D_1 was probably inclined at a moderate angle to the northeast, sub-parallel to the Diabaig shear zone; the sense of movement appears to be the same. North of Loch Maree, a major D_1 shear zone may be inferred from the moderately strained zone on the NE limb of the Carnmore antiform with a dip of around 50° NE. Between here and Loch Maree, the D_1 structures have been modified by later deformation.

Generally, elongation lineations in zones of high strain plunge SE to E on steep or NE-dipping foliations (eg at Diabaig and Gairloch) and NW to W on SW-dipping foliations (eg at Letterewe) (see Fig. 6a). Southwest of Loch Torridon, the lineation is uniformly NW–SE and sub-horizontal. This distribution is consistent with dextral oblique-slip movements on inclined NW–SE shear zones under overall E–W extension.

Laxfordian D_2 deformation

F2 folds have only been recognized in the hinge zone of the Tollie antiform (F_3 of Park 1970a), within the Gairloch schist belt (Park 1978) and in the Kenmore inlier, where they are abundant (Niamatullah 1984). These minor folds (no major folds are identified) are colinear with the D_1 lineation, and in the Gairloch area were initially assigned to D_1 (Park 1964). The distinction is most clearly seen in the Kenmore inlier. Here the fabrics resulting from the combined D_1–D_2 deformations indicate very high but variable strains with X:Z ratios typically between 50 and 100 (Niamatullah 1984). Belts of higher strain are folded around major F_3 fold hinges and are thus clearly pre-D_3 in origin. When the effects of these major folds are removed, the D_1–D_2 fabric is sub-horizontal or gently inclined, with a strong NW–SE elongation lineation. This fabric is related to a major low-angle shear zone 'flat' (cf

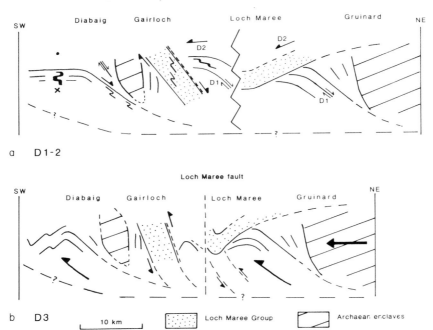

FIG. 7. a) Diagrammatic profile across the southern region to illustrate the main effects of the D_1–D_2 deformation. Note that the steep D_1 shear zones have a normal dip-slip (extensional) component. There is also a major strike-parallel component perpendicular to the section plane. b) Diagrammatic profile to illustrate the D_3 deformation. Note that extension in the NE–SW plane has changed to compression resulting in overthrust movements on the steep shear zones. Ornament as on Fig. 6.

Coward & Park this vol.) which has rotated the dykes and gneissose banding into a sub-horizontal attitude. This structure probably existed in D_1 as well as in D_2 (see Fig. 7*a*).

It seems probable, in view of the colinearity of D_1 and D_2, and of the continuity of amphibolite-facies conditions, that these two phases represent a progressive deformation where earlier formed

fabrics are refolded during the evolution of the shear zone.

The suggested arrangement of D_1–D_2 shear zones is shown diagrammatically in Fig. 7*a*. Inclined oblique-slip ramps at Diabaig, Gairloch and Carnmore link at depth to a major detachment horizon. North of Loch Maree, the main D_2 shear zone may have been inclined SW. This

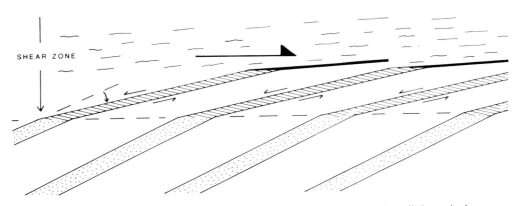

FIG. 8. Model to explain the formation of antithetic sinistral shears by the rotation of ductile layers in the marginal region of a dextral shear zone (see text).

would explain the lack of correspondence of the structure across the Carnmore antiform. The D_2 high-strain zone which is represented on the SW limb of the antiform, and in the Letterewe synform, must pass across the top of the central Archaean block to the northeast as suggested by Coward (1974) and must intersect the Gairloch shear zone to the SW. It is represented in the hinge zone of the Tollie antiform (D_3 of Park 1970) but is folded and truncated by later movements associated with the D_3 Gairloch shear zone.

The asymmetry of F_2 minor folds in the south (Diabaig and Gairloch) appears to indicate a continuation of dextral SW-up movements during D_2 there, whereas at Carnmore and Tollie there appears to be a component of NE-up movement (or top towards the SE—see Park 1970a, 1973; Coward 1974). Taken together, these indications suggest a continuation of the combination of normal dip-slip and dextral movements on inclined shear zones under overall E–W extension seen in D_1 (see Fig. 6b).

One problem with this interpretation is the difficulty of explaining the emplacement of the Letterewe gneisses above the supracrustal rocks of the Loch Maree Group. The relatively high metamorphic grade of the latter is most conveniently explained by the presence of a thick overthrust sheet of basement gneiss during D_2 (the mylonites at the base of the Letterewe gneisses are clearly folded by F_3). A possible explanation is suggested in Fig. 9. Under a strike-slip regime, it is possible that basement gneisses from up-faulted blocks along-strike of the supracrustal outcrops were slid laterally over them. Overthrusting (emplacement of older over younger rocks) is compatible with a strike-slip regime, as is extension (see Reading 1980).

Laxfordian D_3 deformation

Since D_3 is the last major regional deformation to affect the Lewisian it is comparatively easy to reconstruct its effects. Major F_3 folds are identified in Fig. 2. These folds are rather variable in geometry. The Carnmore antiform is broad and open, but to the southwest, F_3 folds become tighter and the associated minor structures more intensely developed towards the Gairloch shear zone, which is the most prominent D_3 structure in the region. This shear zone has been steepened to near-vertical in D_3 and the direction of movement has changed from SW-up (in D_2) to NE-up, although still with a dextral strike-slip component as shown by Odling (1984). In the most intensely deformed belts within this shear zone, a new fabric associated with retrogressive

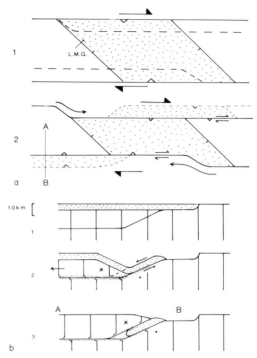

FIG. 9. Hypothetical model to explain the emplacement of the Letterewe gneiss in a dextral strike-slip regime. Upper diagram (plan view) shows lateral displacement of parts of a LMG graben along inclined branch faults. Lower diagram shows successive stages in this process represented in profile along line AB Loch Maree Group (LMG)—dotted; basement gneisses—blank or vertical ruling.

metamorphism to greenschist facies is developed with a NW-plunging linear element (Fig. 10a). This D_3 shear zone is about 6 km wide from the crest of the Tollie antiform to the SW margin of D_3 deformation 1 km northeast of Loch Braigh Horrisdaile.

Between the Gairloch shear zone and Loch Torridon, D_3 deformation is weak or absent. At Diabaig, occasional minor folds occur (F_8 of Cresswell, 1972) probably associated with small shears. SW of the axis of the Torridon antiform however, in the Kenmore inlier, D_3 deformation is again prevalent, forming a number of zones of tight upright satellite folds, sometimes with associated crenulation cleavage in the hinge regions of the major folds (Niamatullah 1984).

The regional picture is best understood in profile (Fig. 7b) where it can be seen that the major zones of D_3 deformation occupy the SW limbs of antiforms which were initiated during previous deformation (the Carnmore, Tollie and

Torridon antiforms). The deformation pattern indicates an overall south-westwards overthrusting with a strong dextral strike-slip component. Thus the tectonic regime appears to have changed from dextral transtension in D_1–D_2 to dextral transpression in D_3 across the southern region.

Laxfordian D_4 deformation

The existence of late localized folds of various styles and orientations, together with late crush zones, often containing pseudotachylite, has been recognized by most authors of detailed structural work in the region (see *eg* the 'late-phase' folds of Park 1964 and Bhattacharjee 1968 and D_9 of Cresswell 1972). The folds are typically steeply plunging and many have sinistral asymmetry, including all the larger, mappable folds at Meall Deise, north of Gairloch (Bhattacharjee 1963), Kernsary, north of Loch Maree (Crane 1978), Talladale on the west shore of Loch Maree (see Geological Survey 1 in. sheet 92) and Balgy, on Loch Torridon (Sutton & Watson 1951).

It would therefore appear that the D_4 deformation was associated with a major kinematic change in the southern region to a sinistral strike-slip regime (Fig. 10*b*). The age of this deformation is uncertain. A significant concentration of K-Ar ages around 1400 Ma was noted by Moorbath & Park (1971) who suggested a correlation with the retrogressive Laxfordian M_3 metamorphism which accompanied the D_4 structures in Gairloch and Torridon. However the possibility cannot be excluded that some or all of the late deformation is of Grenville age (*c.* 1000 Ma).

Conclusions

The structural interpretation which we have presented of the southern region of the mainland Lewisian gives a series of kinematic 'snapshots' (Figs 3, 6 & 10) which cover a very long period of time (*c.* 2600–*c.* 1400 Ma). Coward & Park (this vol.) attempt to explain the Early Proterozoic deformation over the whole Lewisian outcrop in terms of movements on a network of major midcrustal shear zones of which the zones in this region form an important component.

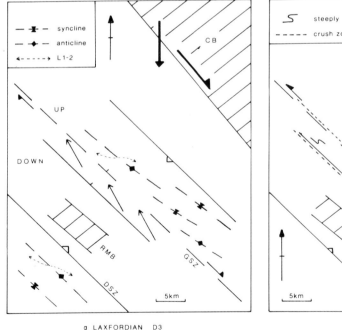

a LAXFORDIAN D3

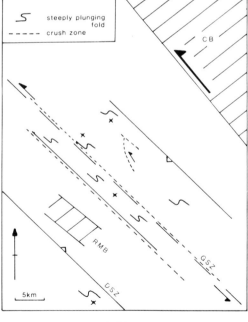

b D4

FIG. 10. Kinematic models for Laxfordian D_3 and D_4 deformation. a) D_3: Sense of shear on the major Gairloch shear zone is N-up and dextral. Major F_3 upright folding indicates a strong compressional component, suggesting a dextral transpressional regime overall. Refolded D_1–D_2 lineation are shown. Arrows represent D_3 lineations in the Gairloch shear zone. Compare Fig. 8*b*. b) D_4: Sense of asymmetry on major and minor steeply plunging F_4 folds indicates sinistral strike-slip movements. Based on Fig. 2; Key as for Fig. 3.

The changes in tectonic regime noted between Inverian and dyke emplacement, between D_2 and D_3, and between D_3 and D_4 seem to correspond to fundamental changes in the direction of relative movement between the major blocks of the Lewisian. These changes can be summarized in terms of the sequence: dextral transpressional–dextral transtensional–dextral transpressional–sinistral strike-slip. Each of these changes is responsible, we believe, for an important change in tectonic style and orientation, and for a new deformation phase.

The age of each period of movement can be assessed with varying degrees of precision in terms of the date of the associated peak of metamorphic activity, but the length of time occupied by the deformation is unknown. It is extremely unlikely, however, that the Inverian–Laxfordian activity represents a period of continuous deformation.

Modern plate movements undergo significant changes in direction after periods of the order of 100 Ma. Although the early Proterozoic plate configuration may have been more stable (cf Piper 1982) it seems unlikely that such a long period (c. 1200 Ma) elapsed without several significant changes in movement direction taking place. We envisage a scenario where periods of relative movement lasting perhaps 100 Ma or so were separated by rather longer periods of stability when relative plate movements were transferred to another part of the system. Each time activity was renewed, an appreciable change in movement direction occurred.

References

BHATTACHARJEE, C. C. 1963. The late structural and petrological history of the Lewisian rocks of the Meall Deise area, north of Gairloch, Ross-shire. *Trans. geol. Soc. Glasgow.* **25**, 31–60.

—— 1968. The structural history of the Lewisian rocks north-west of Loch Tollie, Ross-shire, Scotland. *Scott. J. Geol.* **4**, 235–64.

BOWES, D. R. 1969. The Lewisian of Northwest Highlands of Scotland. *In*: KAY, M. (Ed.). *North Atlantic geology and continental drift—a symposium.* Mem. Am. Assoc. Petrol. Geol. **12**, 575–594.

CHAPMAN, H. J. 1979. 2,390 Myr Rb-Sr whole-rock age for the Scourie dykes of north-west Scotland. *Nature, London* **277**, 642–3.

COWARD, M. P. 1974. Flat lying structures within the Lewisian basement gneiss complex of N.W. Scotland. *Proc. Geol. Assoc. London* **85**, 459–72.

—— 1984. Major shear zones in the Precambrian crust; examples from NW Scotland and southern Africa and their significance. *In*: KRONER, A. & GREILING, S. R. (eds) *Precambrian tectonics illustrated*, Stuttgart, 207–235.

CRANE, A. 1978. Correlation of metamorphic fabrics and the age of Lewisian metasediments near Loch Maree. *Scott. J. Geol.* **14**, 225–46.

CRESSWELL, D. 1972. The structural development of the Lewisian rocks on the north shore of Loch Torridon, Ross-shire. *Scott. J. Geol.* **8**, 293–308.

DAVIDSON, L. M. & PARK, R. G. 1978. Late Nagssugtoqidian stress orientation derived from deformed granodiorite dykes north of Holsteinsborg, West Greenland. *J. geol. Soc. Lond.* **135**, 283–9.

ELLIOTT, D. W. 1964. *Geology of the Lewisian complex of the Slattadale area, south of Loch Maree, Ross-shire.* Unpubl. Ph.D. thesis, Univ. Glasgow.

ESCHER, A., JACK, S. & WATTERSON, J. 1976. Tectonics of the North Atlantic Proterozoic dyke swarm. *Phil. Trans. R. Soc. Lond. A.* **280**, 529–39.

EVANS, C. R. 1965. Geochronology of the Lewisian basement near Lochinver, Sutherland. *Nature, London* **207**, 54–6.

GHALY, T. S. 1966. The Lewisian geology of the area between Loch Shieldaig and Loch Braigh Horrisdaile, Gairloch, Ross-shire. *Scott. J. Geol.* **2**, 282–305.

GILETTI, B. J., MOORBATH, S. & LAMBERT, R. St. J. 1961. A geochronological study of the metamorphic complexes of the Scottish Highlands. *Quart. J. geol. Soc. Lond.* **117**, 233–72.

HAGESKOV, B. 1985. Constriction deformation of the Koster dyke swarm. *Bull. geol. Soc. Denmark*, **34**, 151–197.

KEPPIE, J. D. 1967. *Geology of the Lewisian complex around Furnace, north-east of Loch Maree, Ross-shire.* Unpubl. Ph.D. thesis, Univ. Glasgow.

LYON, T. D. B., PIDGEON, R. T., BOWES, D. R. B. & HOPGOOD, A. M. 1973. Geochronological investigation of the quartzofeldspathic rocks of the Lewisian of Rona, Inner Hebrides. *J. geol. Soc. Lond.* **129**, 389–402.

MOORBATH, S. & PARK, R. G. 1971. The Lewisian chronology of the southern region of the Scottish Mainland. *Scott. J. Geol.* **8**, 51–74.

NIAMATULLAH, M. 1984. *The Laxfordian structure of the Kenmore inlier, Loch Torridon, Ross-shire.* Unpubl. Ph.D. thesis, Univ. Keele.

NICHOLSON, R. & POLLARD, D. D. 1985. Dilation and linkage of echelon cracks. *J. struct. Geol.* **7**, 583–90.

ODLING, N. E. 1984. Strain analysis and strain path modelling in the Loch Tollie gneisses, Gairloch, N.W. Scotland. *J. struct. Geol.* **6**, 543–62.

O'NIONS, R. K., HAMILTON, P. J. & HOOKER, P. J. 1983. A Nd-isotope investigation of sediments related to crustal development in the British Isles. *Earth planet. Sci. Lett.* **63**, 229–40.

PARK, R. G. 1964. The structural history of the Lewisian rocks of Gairloch, Western Ross. *Quart. J. geol. Soc. Lond.* **120**, 397–434.

—— 1970a. The structural evolution of the Tollie antiform—a geometrically complex fold in the

Lewisian north-east of Gairloch, Ross-shire. *Quart. J. geol. Soc. Lond.* **125**, 319–50.

—— 1970*b*. Observations on Lewisian chronology. *Scott. J. Geol.* **6**, 379–99.

—— 1973. The Laxfordian belts of the Scottish Mainland. *In:* PARK, R. G. & TARNEY, J. (eds). *The early Precambrian of Scotland and related rocks of Greenland.* Univ. Keele, 65–76.

—— 1978. The Tollie and Gairloch districts (Lewisian). *In:* BARBER, A. J. *et al.* (eds) *The Lewisian and Torridonian rocks of North-West Scotland.* Geol. Ass. Guide, **21**, 59–72.

—— 1980. The Lewisian of NW Britain. *In:* OWEN, T. R. (ed.) *United Kingdom: Introduction to general geology and guides to excursions 002, 055, 093 and 151.* 26th Int. Geol. Congr. Paris, 8–13.

—— & CRESSWELL, D. 1972. Basic dykes in the early Precambrian (Lewisian) of NW Scotland: their structural relations, conditions of emplacement and orogenic significance. *Proc. 24th Int. geol. Congr. 1972*, **1**, 238–45.

—— & —— 1973. The dykes of the Laxfordian belts. *In:* PARK, R. G. & TARNEY, J. (eds). *The early Precambrian of Scotland and related rocks of Greenland.* Univ. Keele, 119–130.

PEACH, B. N., HORNE, J., GUNN, W., CLOUGH, C. T. & HINXMAN, L. W. 1907. The geological structure of the North-West Highlands of Scotland. *Mem geol. Surv. Gt. Britain.*

PIDGEON, R. T. 1973. Rb-Sr, K-Ar and U-Pb age studies in the Lewisian of Scotland. *In:* PIDGEON, R. T. *et al.* (eds) *Geochronology and isotope geology of Scotland*, 3rd European Congress of Geochronologists, Univ. Oxford, D1–12.

PIPER, J. D. A. 1982. The Precambrian palaeomagnetic record: the case for the Proterozoic supercontinent. *Earth planet. Sci. Lett.* **59**, 61–89.

RAMSAY, J. G. 1980. Shear zone geometry: a review. J. struct. Geol. 2, 83–99.

READING, H. G. 1980. Characteristics and recognition of strike-slip fault systems. *Spec. Publ. Int. Ass. Sediment.* **4**, 7–26.

SUTTON, J. & WATSON, J. V. 1951. The pre-Torridonian metamorphic history of the Loch Torridon and Scourie areas in the North-West Highlands, and its bearing on the chronological history of the Lewisian. *Quart. J. geol. Soc. Lond.* **106**, 241–308.

R. G. PARK, A. CRANE & M. NIAMATULLAH, Department of Geology, University of Keele, Keele, Staffs ST5 5BG, UK.

Internal evolution of the major Precambrian shear belt at Torridon, NW Scotland

J. Wheeler, B. F. Windley & F. B. Davies

SUMMARY: The Torridon shear belt is a NW-striking region of heterogeneous reworking within the Lewisian complex. Mapping of the deformation fabric intensity reveals a geometry of low-strain, lozenge-shaped blocks surrounded by an anastomosing set of shear zones which form a linked system of flats and lateral ramps. These various orientations of shear zones share a common movement direction but show both sinistral–reverse and dextral–normal shear sense. This is true both in the Inverian, when the linked system was established, and in the Laxfordian, when shearing followed the established network but was localized along the ductile Scourie dykes. Possible explanations for the occurrence of opposed shear senses include local differential shear, and a modification of the Lister & Williams model of deformation. In the latter, shear zones generally show a sense of shear opposite to the overall displacement on the belt, and this underlines the need for a comprehensive analysis of the geometry of such shear belts.

The Inverian structure controlled emplacement of the Scourie dyke swarm, which in turn controlled the localization and orientation of the Laxfordian structures. Given the ductility of the dykes, this leads to a simple explanation for the coaxiality of Inverian and Laxfordian structures. A tentative model for the evolution of the Torridon shear belt is given, in which emphasis is placed on the importance of dykes as easy-slip horizons.

Deformation in the continental middle crust is commonly concentrated in major shear belts, best seen in Precambrian terrains (Sutton & Watson 1974; Davies & Windley 1976; Coward 1984). Examples include those of West Greenland (Bak et al. 1975; Sorensen 1983) and NW Scotland (Beach 1974; Davies 1978; Graham 1980; Coward 1984). Typically these shear belts produce gneisses with a strong shape fabric derived from tonalites and tonalitic migmatites, and have lateral and vertical displacements of several tens of kilometres (Escher et al. 1975). Determination of the displacement on these shear belts is important in elucidating the large-scale tectonics of orogenic belts. In the Lewisian complex shear belts have long been recognized but, due to limited outcrop, there is often dispute as to the overall shear sense which operated in these belts (eg Coward et al. 1980; Davies 1978; Beach 1976; Odling 1984; Jensen 1984).

The internal structure of few major shear belts has been studied in detail. The aim of this paper is to present an analysis of the internal geometry of the major shear belt at Torridon, NW Scotland. Emphasis will be made of the importance of understanding the local processes operating within such a shear belt before extrapolating observations to deduce the relative displacement of the wall rocks.

Form of the major shear belt

The Torridon shear belt lies to the south of the largest preserved Scourian block in the Lewisian, in an area of Inverian and Laxfordian reworking. It is bounded on its NE side by the Ruadh Mheallan block, which preserves Badcallian structures. NE of this block, which we take as the NE wall to the Torridon shear belt, is the Gairloch shear belt (Park et al., this vol.). In this paper we will describe two sets of Scourian rocks: an amphibolite-facies migmatite complex, and flaggy gneisses produced by subsequent deformation of the migmatites. Following Park & Cresswell (1973) it is convenient to describe the migmatites as Badcallian, and the reworking with NW trend as Inverian. This does not necessarily imply an absolute age correlation with structures elsewhere that have been described as Inverian.

There is a broad succession of structural zones moving SW across the exposure at Loch Torridon (Fig. 1). Park et al. (this vol.) consider the rocks in the Kenmore inlier to belong to a separate (Kenmore) shear zone, distinct in orientation from the Diabaig shear zone. We prefer to assign all the Torridon inliers to parts of the Torridon shear zone; this may have crustal-scale ramp–flat geometry as suggested by Park et al., but alternative explanations for the structure will be explored in this paper. In the least-deformed areas in the NE, there is a migmatite complex (Region A, Fig. 2) that consists of banded tonalitic migmatites which are intruded by more homogeneous migmatites (nebulites, Mehnert 1968) containing ghosts of folds, and true igneous plutonic rocks with tonalitic, trondhjemitic and granitic compositions. Both sets of rocks contain

From: PARK, R. G. & TARNEY, J. (eds), 1987, *Evolution of the Lewisian and Comparable Precambrian High Grade Terrains*, Geological Society Special Publication No. 27, pp. 153–163.

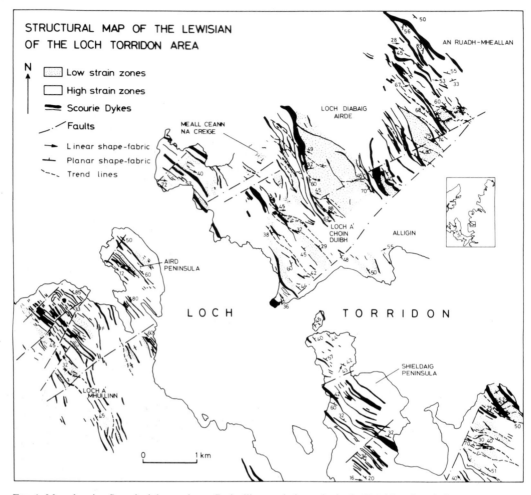

FIG. 1. Map showing Scourie dykes and post-Badcallian strain intensity in the Torridon shear belt.

xenoliths of banded amphibole gneisses. This migmatite complex is Badcallian, and the banding has an overall NE strike.

Passing to the SW there are zones of heterogeneous reworking characterized by amphibolite-facies gneisses of flaggy appearance with strong shape fabrics. These contain deformed Badcallian mafic xenoliths similar to those in the NE wall of the shear belt. Badcallian structures defined by agmatite trains, banding, intrafolial folds and boudins are deflected into these shear zones. Often the deflection in strike of these features is dextral but, as discussed below, this may not reflect the true movement on the shear zones. The shear zones anastomose around lozenge-shaped areas of low strain. In Region B

(Fig. 2), these low-strain lacunae are large (up to 1 km by 3 km) and few in number. To the SW, in Region C, an increase in overall strain intensity is marked by a decrease in size of the lacunae and an increase in their number. The highest overall strain is in Region D where very few low-strain lacunae are preserved.

In the NE of the Torridon shear belt the shear zones dip NE at 50°–70°. This dip decreases towards the loch where, in Region C and the part of Region D on the Shieldaig peninsula, dips are 30°–50°. In the Kenmore inlier upright folds affect the foliation but the enveloping surface is subhorizontal. So the increase in overall strain correlates with a decrease in dip of the local shear planes.

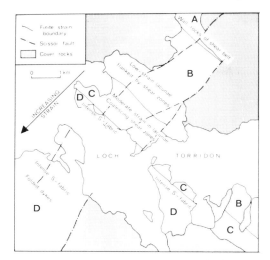

FIG. 2. Qualitative large-scale distribution in the Torridon shear belt.

Sutton & Watson (1951) recognized that in the shear zones, Scourie dykes often show parallelism between their internal fabrics, their boundaries and the flaggy fabric in the adjacent gneisses. Thus they date the hereogeneous deformation and production of flaggy gneisses as Laxfordian. Cresswell (1972) used several criteria to show that in many shear zones (his 'monoclines') the flaggy fabric was in existence prior to dyke emplacement, and is therefore Inverian (Fig. 3). It is difficult to assess how much of the tonalitic gneisses were affected by Laxfordian deformation; however definite post-dyke shears in the tonalitic gneisses are rare. Figure 4 shows structures which suggest the ductility of the dykes was much greater than that of the gneisses. It may be that, at least in Region B and parts of Region C, high Laxfordian strains are restricted to the dykes (*cf* Park 1973). The pattern of high- and low-strain zones in the tonalitic gneisses is therefore essentially Inverian.

The intrusion density of the dykes was higher in the zones of flaggy gneiss than in the low-strain lacunae. There is therefore a consistent positive correlation between the flaggy gneisses and the dykes, and between the high dyke densities and the high Laxfordian strains. This is a strong indication that the dykes were emplaced into Inverian shear zones that continued to deform during the Laxfordian.

The mean shear plane in the NE of the shear belt dips NE on 324/60, and the mean shear direction is 40/110. The shear plane and direction remained unchanged through the Inverian and Laxfordian. This 'coaxiality' was noted by Park & Cresswell (1973) and will be returned to later.

FIG. 3. Scourie dyke cross-cutting pronounced NW-striking Inverian foliation, from the NE corner of the Diabaig inlier.

FIG. 4. Evidence for the relatively high ductility of dykes in the Laxfordian: a) Wall-rock gneisses highly strained at contact with an intensely sheared dyke. The bulk of the deformation is concentrated in the dyke. b) Mullion structure with cusps pointing into competent gneisses.

Geometry of the anastomosing shear zones

Figure 1 shows that the shear zones bounding the low-strain lacunae vary in orientation. For instance, many shears strike NW–SE whereas the one south of Meall Ceann na Creige strikes E–W. It is tempting to postulate that these represent a conjugate set of shears. To confirm or negate this it is necessary to determine movement directions and senses in each set of shears. If we take the foliation and lineation in the high-strain zones to approximate to the shear plane and direction, then Cresswell's (1972) stereonets of Inverian foliation and lineation can be used to deduce the relation between shear directions and shear planes (Fig. 6c). Lineations define a cluster; poles to foliation define a girdle with the lineation cluster as the pole to that girdle. This implies that all the various orientations of shear zone contain a common movement direction (Fig. 5). This shows that the shear planes which deviate from the common NW-striking set can be thought of as 'lateral ramps' relative to the mean shear plane 'flat' (*cf* Coward 1984). They are not parts of a conjugate set.

Sorensen (1983) describes 'augen' within the Nordre Stromfjord shear zone, which resemble the low-strain lacunae of the Torridon shear zone. When seen in the profile (*XZ*) plane of the shear belt, the surrounding high-strain zones are bent around the augen. This reflects a true change in shear direction as deforming rocks flow around

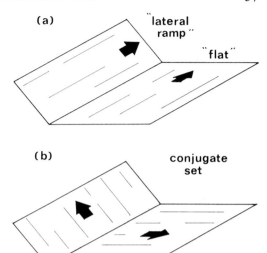

FIG. 5. a) The geometry of shear planes and shear directions as seen in Regions B and C of the Torridon shear belt. b) The geometry to be expected if two shear planes form a conjugate set.

the augen (Sorensen 1983). This situation would give rise to a pattern of foliations and lineations as shown in Fig. 6b. In contrast, the foliation/lineation distribution in much of the Diabaig inlier is what would result from movement around a set of augen elongate parallel to the overall transport direction (Fig. 6a). If this is the case then the tapered edges of low-strain lacunae as

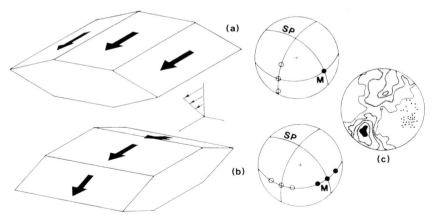

FIG. 6. Flow regimes around low-strain lacunae of idealised shapes. a) Lacuna elongate parallel to transport direction, but with tapered lateral edges, and stereographic projection showing local shear orientations. b) Lacuna with varying thickness along transport direction but long in a direction perpendicular to the profile plane. Stereographic projection shows predicted scatter in local shear directions (filled circles) and poles to local shear planes (open circles), when lacuna lies within a shear belt of the orientation seen in Regions B and C, SP: shear plane, M: movement direction. Note that strain may be plane in either situation. c) Stereographic projection showing Inverian foliations (contoured plot of poles, highest density in black) and lineations (dots) from part of the Diabaig inlier (after Cresswell 1972).

seen on the map (Fig. 1) are, to a first approximation, expressions of the lateral shape change of long, thin lacunae. They are of finite length in the X-direction, but sufficiently long that the flow regime, expressed by the anastomosing shear zones, was not affected.

The general geometry of the shear zones has been defined above; we now address the problem of determining true shear senses of individual shears. As remarked above, the strike of Badcallian banding is often seen to bend dextrally into shear zones. This does not necessarily imply that movement on such a shear zone was dextral, since they are oblique-slip. To determine the true shear sense, the deflection method described in Wheeler (1987) has been applied to selected regions. Examination of an example from the Balgy area (Fig. 7) shows that the locus of poles to banding describes a clockwise path towards the pole to the shear plane, in accord with the dextral bending-in of the strike of banding; the arrow on the XZ (profile) plane indicates the true movement sense, and it is dextral-normal.

Figure 8 gives another example, from Meall

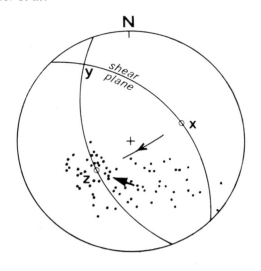

FIG. 7. Stereographic projection showing locus of poles (filled circles) to Badcallian banding in the Balgy area, bending into the local shear plane (xy). Movement direction is indicated by x.

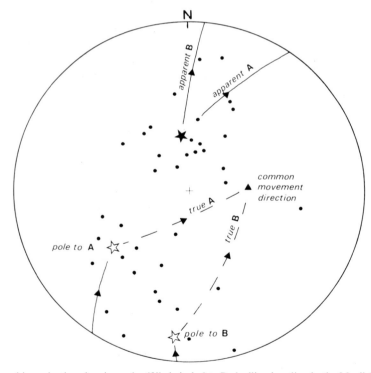

FIG. 8. Stereographic projection showing poles (filled circles) to Badcallian banding in the Meall Ceann na Creige area. The area is bounded by two shear planes (poles marked by open stars). These share a common movement direction. The strike of banding bends dextrally into both shears, as shown by the clockwise path of poles; but for both shear zones the true movement sense is sinistral–reverse, as shown by arrows on their respective profile planes.

Ceann na Creige, where a low-strain lacuna is bounded by two non-parallel shear zones, sharing the same shear direction. The Badcallian banding bends dextrally into both shear zones; but the true movement sense on both shear zones is sinistral–reverse. This confirms Sutton & Watson's (1951) observation of reverse–sense shear zones on Meall Ceann na Creige. The occurrence of both dextral and sinistral shear zones is confirmed by observations of minor (outcrop scale) shear zones. It is not clear which shear sense predominates, thus it is not easy to infer the overall movement sense. First, the genesis of individual shear zones must be understood. This problem is also apparent in the dykes, where both senses of shear are found.

Possible explanations for the occurrence of opposing shear senses

There are three possible explanations considered here. (1) The first explanation is that the shear zones of different senses are of different ages. However, there is no evidence that the deformation in the tonalitic gneisses of Regions B and C was partly of Laxfordian age; in addition minor shears in dykes are both dextral and sinistral. It would be an oversimplification to assign one sense of shear to the Inverian, and the other to the Laxfordian, and this idea is not pursued further. (2) In the previous section it was noted that the low-strain lacunae are bounded by flats and lateral ramps and so can move freely past one another without geometrical constraint. Figure 9 illustrates a possible consequence of this. During an overall consistent sense of shear, the blocks within the shear belt will shuffle past one another, the regions of differential movement giving rise to the anastomosing shear zones in the interior of the shear belt. Often the relative movement of two blocks will comply with the

overall shear sense; but there is no reason why, in principle, a local zone of differential movement should not have the opposite sense to the overall shear regime. (3) The third possible explanation relates to the occurrence of a shape fabric within the low-strain lacunae. This is a weak foliation subparallel to the regional shear plane (Fig. 10). The occurrence of deformation within the wall rocks of the shear zones means that they depart from the geometry described by Ramsay & Graham (1970). In the Appendix it is shown that, if the shear plane–parallel extension produces a strain ellipse with axial ratio R_{min} outside the shear zones, than the maximum angle which the fabric will make with the shear plane is given by

$$\theta'_{max} = \tfrac{1}{2} \arcsin \frac{1}{R_{min}}.$$

As Fig. 11 shows, the angle between the new, shear-related fabric and the shear plane is never as great as 45°, the angle it would have if the wall rocks were undeformed. For instance, if $R_{min} = 2$ then $\theta'_{max} = 15°$. Thus a small plane–parallel extension markedly reduces the maximum angle the foliation will make with the shear plane. This lower angle might be difficult to separate from statistical scatter in measurements of the shape fabric orientation. This correlates with the observation that significant bending-in to the shear zones of the shape foliation is not often observed. Only the Badcallian banding shows large rotations near shear zones. Note that this argument applies whether or not the extension was coeval with, or distinct from, the Inverian shearing.

The occurrence of overall shear plane–parallel extension in a shear zone gives rise to a strain compatibility problem (Coward 1984), if the wall of the major shear belt (Region A) is undeformed. This problem can be circumvented by considering a generalization of the model of deformation proposed by Lister & Williams (1979). This model applies to a situation in which the rocks within a

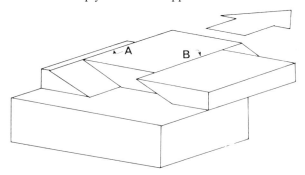

FIG. 9. Possible mode of deformation of a set of low-strain lacunae separated by shear zones. Some shear zones (*eg* A) show the same shear sense as the overall movement. Others such as B show an opposite shear sense.

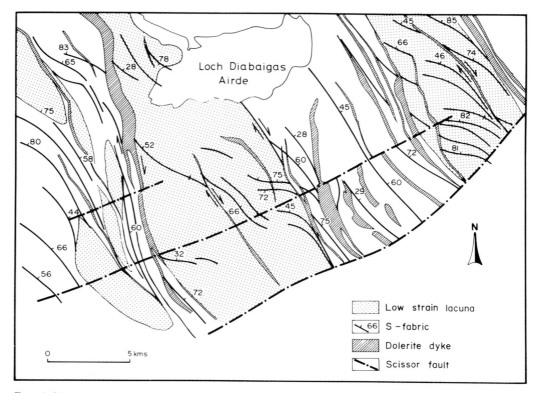

FIG. 10. Sketch map across low strain lacunae flanked by shear zones with apparently dextral offsets. Note approximate parallelism of shape fabric and general shear zone strike in places within the low-strain lacunae.

shear zone contain a strong mechanical aniso-tropy oblique to the shear plane. Potts (1983), discussing the inverted limb of the Lochalsh fold, presents evidence that the weak bedding planes in the Torridonian Sandstone may allow slip, whereas the interiors of the beds deform along a coaxial path to produce a bedding–parallel fabric (Fig. 12a). As strain increases, bedding makes a smaller and smaller angle with the shear plane. Nevertheless the slip along the bedding planes remains opposite to the overall sense of shear.

For such a model to be viable, the cause of the strong anisotropy should be identified. As noted

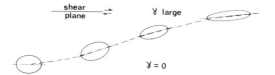

FIG. 11. Qualitative finite strain intensity and foliation orientation produced when simple shear is coeval with shear plane–parallel extension in the wall rocks. Note the maximum angle the fabric makes with the shear plane.

above the Scourie dykes appear to have been much more ductile than the country rocks during Laxfordian deformation. They may be thought of as easy-slip horizons, similar in their behaviour to bedding in a sedimentary sequence. In this scenario (Fig. 12b), intensely sheared dykes would separate blocks of country-rock containing dyke-parallel Laxfordian fabrics. Many of the shear zones would display a consistent sense of move-ment opposite to the overall displacement. The strain pattern in this model is similar to that seen in the Torridon shear belt. Thus it is conceivable that, even if shear zones of one sense are demonstrably dominant in the area, the overall movement sense would be opposite to this.

The coaxiality of Inverian and Laxfordian structures

Coaxiality of successive generations of fold axes and lineations is a commonly observed feature of deformation in high-grade terrains. For instance Park & Cresswell (1973) recognize two Inverian and three Laxfordian deformation episodes in

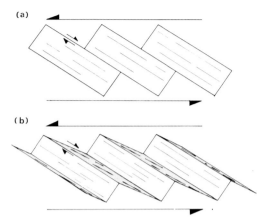

FIG. 12. a) Deformation model after Lister & Williams (1979) in which overall simple shear is accomplished by coaxial, layer-parallel extension within slab-shaped regimes coeval with slip along discontinuities between these regimes. Note slip on the discontinuities is opoosite to the overall shear sense. b) A modification of this model in which the 'slip' is accomplished along shear zones of finite width. Thin lines show fabric orientations.

the Torridon area, all coaxial. This observation can be partly explained by the realization that, in progressive deformation of a large area, it is inadvisable to correlate folds on the basis of style and orientation. During, for example, simple shear, perturbations continually arise in the deforming system, and these can give rise to one or more generations of folds whose relative ages have purely local significance (Coward 1980). In this scheme, coaxiality is simply a consequence of many styles and generations of fold being produced within a single deformation regime. It is clear at Torridon that Laxfordian deformation was often coaxial with the Inverian structures. The Inverian predated Scourie dyke intrusion at 2.39 Ga (Chapman 1979), whereas Laxfordian deformation has been dated down to *c.* 1.7 Ga (Park 1973). If all these events are coaxial due to being the results of a single deformation regime, then that regime was consistent for over 700 Ma. Such long-lived regimes may have been a feature of Proterozoic tectonics (Coward 1984); but a simpler explanation can be proposed for parts of the Torridon shear belt.

The idea of dykes as easy-slip surfaces has already been presented. The Scourie dyke swarm intruded parallel to Inverian fabrics, thus they vary in orientation with these fabrics (Fig. 1). In particular, their common intersection direction is parallel to the common intersection of Inverian shear planes, in turn parallel to the Inverian lineation. Whatever subsequent stress system is imposed on this geometry, if large strains are restricted to the dykes then deformation must be simple shear with local shear plane parallel to local dyke margin, and shear direction parallel to the common dyke intersection direction. Therefore (Fig. 13) the Inverian foliation and lineation are parallel to the Laxfordian foliation and lineation, and the coaxiality is explained. It is not therefore essential to propose mechanical anisotropy induced by fold axes in the gneisses (Park 1973); it is sufficient to note that the Inverian structure controlled the emplacement of the dyke swarm, whose geometry subsequently controlled the orientation of Laxfordian deformation.

Discussion

The Torridon shear belt consists of low-strain lacunae bounded by shear zones with a flat–lateral ramp geometry and a common shear direction. These were established in the Inverian and operated in modified form during the Laxfordian. Both dextral–normal and sinistral–reverse shear zones are found related to both ages of movement. We have proposed some possible explanations for this geometry, and these show the difficulty of determining the overall displacement sense or magnitude in this shear belt. The concept of dykes as easy-slip horizons has been used to explain the occurrence of two opposing shear senses, and also the coaxiality of Inverian and Laxfordian structures.

A tentative model is proposed here for the evolution of the Torridon area during the Laxfordian. Park *et al.* (this vol.) note the predominance of dextral shears in dykes from the Diabaig inlier.

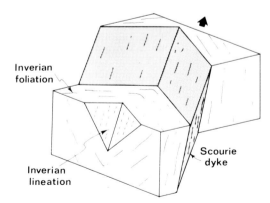

FIG. 13. Block diagram illustrating how coaxiality of Inverian and Laxfordian structures can be produced. It is a result of (i) control of dyke emplacement by Inverian structure and (ii) control of Laxfordian deformation by dyke intrusion geometry.

If the modification of the Lister & Williams (1979) model applies to the Laxfordian evolution of this area, then a top-to-West movement sense would be indicated. This crustal scale movement, affecting a complex with initially NW-striking subvertical dykes, would create NE-dipping structures which, with increasing strain, would become shallow and then subhorizontal. In regions A to D it has been noted that the increasing strain to the SW is associated with a change from subvertical dykes in the Ruadh Mheallan belt, through NE-dipping dykes in the Diabaig inlier, to subhorizontal in the Kenmore inlier. This pattern accords with the model, and suggests that the dip changes across the Torridon belt may be due, at least in part, to a strain gradient, and not necessarily to a transition from a crustal-scale ramp to a flat. The two models are not mutually exclusive; indeed the highly-strained rocks of the Shieldaig peninsula dip gently NE to pass beneath the Diabaig inlier,

although they are of comparable strain intensity to those of the Kenmore inlier. This accords with the model of Park *et al.* (this vol.) in which a flat shear zone at Kenmore is linked to a NE-dipping ramp to the NE. The importance of the model proposed here is that it shows that shear senses in zones of intermediate strain (such as Region B), may not always be used to deduce the overall movement sense, and the possibility remains that the Torridon belt expresses a top-to-West shear regime. This shows how it is important to synthesize all available information on a shear belt before assessing the crustal-scale displacement which it accommodates.

ACKNOWLEDGEMENTS: J.W. thanks N.E.R.C. for a Research Studentship, and B.F.W. acknowledges Leicester University for a research grant. F.B.D. was supported by an I.L.E.A. Research Fellowship at the City of London Polytechnic.

References

BAK, J., SORENSEN, K., GROCOTT, J., KORSTGAARD, J. A., NASH, D. & WATTERSON, J. 1975. Tectonic implications of Precambrian shear belts in western Greenland. *Nature, London* **254**, 566–569.

BEACH, A. 1974. The measurement and significance of displacements on Laxfordian shear zones, NW Scotland. *Proc. Geol. Ass.* **85**, 13–21.

—— 1976. The interrelations of fluid transport, deformation, geochemistry and heat flow in early Proterozoic shear zones in the Lewisian complex. *Phil. Trans. R. Soc. Lond.* **A280**, 569–604.

CHAPMAN, H. J. 1979. 2,390 M.y. Rb-Sr whole rock age for the Scourie dykes of north-west Scotland. *Nature, London* **277**, 642–643.

COWARD, M. P. 1980. Shear zones in the Precambrian crust of Southern Africa. *J. struct. Geol.* **2**, 19–27.

—— 1984. Major shear zones in the Precambrian crust; examples from NW Scotland and southern Africa and their significance. *In:* KRONER, A. & GREILING, R. (eds). *Precambrian Tectonics Illustrated.* E. Schweizerbart'sche Verlagsbuchhandlung, Stuttgart.

——, KIM, J. H. & PARKE, J. 1980. A correlation of Lewisian structures and their displacements across the lower thrusts of the Moine Thrust zone, NW Scotland. *Proc. Geol. Ass.* **91**, 327–337.

CRESSWELL, D. 1972. The structural development of the Lewisian rocks on the north shore of Loch Torridon, Ross-shire. *Scott. J. Geol.* **8**, 293–308.

DAVIES, F. B. 1978. Progressive simple shear deformation on the Laxford shear zone, Sutherland. *Proc. Geol. Ass.* **89**, 177–196.

—— & WINDLEY, B. F. 1976. The significance of major Proterozoic high-grade linear belts in continental evolution. *Nature, London* **263**, 383–385.

ESCHER, A., ESCHER, J. C. & WATTERSON, J. 1975. The reorientation of the Kangâmiut dyke swarm, West Greenland. *Can. J. Earth Sci.* **12**, 158–173.

GRAHAM, R. H. 1980. The role of shear belts in the structural evolution of the South Harris igneous complex. *J. struct. Geol.* **2**, 29–37.

JENSEN, L. N. 1984. Quartz microfabric of the Laxfordian Canisp Shear Zone, NW Scotland. *J. struct. Geol.* **6**, 293–302.

LISTER, G. & WILLIAMS, P. F. 1979. Fabric development in shear zones: theoretical controls and observed phenomena. *J. struct. Geol.* **1**, 283–297.

MEHNERT, K. R. 1968. *Migmatites and the Origin of Granitic Rocks.* Elsevier, Amsterdam.

ODLING, N. E. 1984. Strain analysis and strain path modelling in the Loch Tollie gneisses, Gairloch, NW Scotland. *J. struct. Geol.* **6**, 543–562.

PARK, R. G. 1973. The Laxfordian belts of the Scottish mainland. *In:* PARK, R. G. & TARNEY, J. (eds.), 1973, *The Early Precambrian of Scotland and related rocks of Greenland.* Univ. Keele, pp. 65–76.

—— & CRESSWELL, D. 1973. The dykes of the Laxfordian belts. *In:* PARK, R. G. & TARNEY, J. (eds.), 1973, *The Early Precambrian of Scotland and related rocks of Greenland.* Univ. Keele, pp. 119–130.

POTTS, G. 1983. *The origin of recumbent fold nappes: the Lochalsh Fold as the main example.* Unpubl. PhD thesis, Univ. Leeds.

RAMSAY, J. G. & GRAHAM, R. H. 1970. Strain variations in shear belts. *Can. J. Earth Sci.* **7**, 786–813.

—— & HUBER, M. 1983. *The techniques of modern structural geology. Vol. 1: Strain Analysis.* Academic Press, London.

SORENSEN, K. 1983. Growth and dynamics of the

Nordre Stromfjord shear zone. *J. Geophys. Res.* **88**, 3419–3437.

SUTTON, J. & WATSON, J. V. 1951. The pre-Torridonian metamorphic history of the Loch Torridon and Scourie areas in the NW Highlands and its bearing on the chronological classification of the Lewisian. *Q. J. geol. Soc. London*, **106**, 241–308.

—— & WATSON, J. V. 1974. Tectonic evolution of continents in early Proterozoic times. *Nature, London* **247**, 433–435.

WHEELER, J. 1987. The determination of true shear senses from the deflection of passive markers in shear zones. *J. geol. Soc. London* **144**, (in press).

J. WHEELER, Department of Earth Sciences, University of Leeds, Leeds LS2 9JT, UK.

B. F. WINDLEY, Department of Geology, University of Leicester, Leicester LE1 7RH, UK.

F. B. DAVIES, Department of Geology, Central Michigan University, Mount Pleasant, Michigan 48859, USA.

Appendix

The deformation in the high- and low-strain zones will be modelled by factorizing it into a simple shear γ followed by a shear plane–parallel extension α. This factorization of the finite deformation is still valid if extension and shear evolved simultaneously. Let the shear plane be parallel to the x-axis of the coordinate frame, so that the finite deformation tensor is

$$\mathbf{D} = \begin{bmatrix} \alpha & 0 \\ 0 & 1/\alpha \end{bmatrix} \begin{bmatrix} 1 & \alpha \\ 0 & 1 \end{bmatrix} = \begin{bmatrix} \alpha & \alpha\gamma \\ 0 & 1/\alpha \end{bmatrix}. \quad \text{(A1)}$$

Let θ' be the angle between the fabric and the shear plane, then using eqn. B.14 of Ramsay & Huber (1983) we find

$$\tan 2\theta' = \frac{2\alpha^2\gamma}{\alpha^4 - 1 + \alpha^4\gamma^2}. \quad \text{(A2)}$$

If $\gamma = 0$, $\theta' = 0$ and as $\gamma \to \infty$, $\theta' \to 0$, so there must be a maximum value of θ' for some value γ. By differentiating the R.H.S. of (A2) we find that the maximum occurs when

$$\gamma^2 = 1 - \frac{1}{\alpha^4} \quad \text{(A3)}$$

which substituting in (A2) gives

$$\tan 2\theta'_{\max} = \frac{1}{\sqrt{\alpha^4 - 1}}. \quad \text{(A4)}$$

Now the strain ellipse axial ratio in the wall rocks unaffected by shear ($\gamma = 0$) is given by

$$R_{\min} = \alpha^2.$$

Substituting this in (A4) and rearranging using standard trigonometric relations gives

$$\sin 2\theta'_{\max} = \frac{1}{R_{\min}}.$$

The structural history of the Canisp Shear Zone

P. Attfield

SUMMARY: The Canisp Shear Zone is a major structure in the central region of the mainland Lewisian. Evidence is presented to show that there have been two major phases of movement. In the first phase, during the Inverian, a broad belt of steeply-inclined foliation was formed bounded to the south by the north limb of the Lochinver antiform. The associated lineation plunges steeply to the SE, indicating a dip-slip movement with downthrow to the north, and a small dextral strike-slip component.

Quartz-epidiorite and ultrabasic dykes were then emplaced sub-parallel to the shear plane, their emplacement was controlled by pre-existing planes of weakness.

The second, Laxfordian, phase of movement reactivated the Inverian structure. Deformation was concentrated in narrow zones of high strain, with an associated strong, penetrative lineation plunging shallowly ESE. The shear sense is dominantly dextral strike-slip with a small downthrow to the north.

This change from dominantly dip-slip to dominantly strike-slip movement agrees with models for other areas of the Lewisian (Coward & Park, this vol.) and appears to be associated with a change in style towards more localized zones of deformation.

Introduction

The Lewisian of the Assynt region was first mapped by Peach *et al.* (1907), who noted the major shear structure to the north of Lochinver and followed it inland to Glen Canisp (Fig. 1).

Work in the Lochinver area by Tarney (1963) and Evans (1965) led to the recognition of the Inverian metamorphic event. This is a pre-Scourie dyke, amphibolite-facies event of higher grade than the later Laxfordian, and post-dating the intrusion of a suite of pegmatites, which were emplaced after the Scourian granulite-facies metamorphism.

In this study the terminology of Park (1970) is used, the first event being the Badcallian granulite-facies metamorphism at *c.* 2700 Ma. This

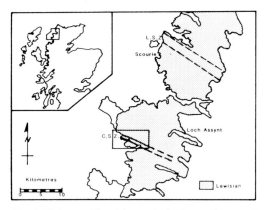

FIG. 1. Outcrop of Lewisian rocks in the northern part of the mainland outcrop showing major shear zones. C.S.Z.—Canisp Shear Zone, L.S.Z.—Laxford Shear Zone.

was followed by intrusion of potassium-rich pegmatites between 2540 and 2310 Ma (Evans & Lambert 1974). The Inverian deformation and metamorphism occurred between the pegmatite intrusion and the emplacement of the Scourie dykes into hot country rock (Tarney 1963), between 2400 and 1900 Ma (Chapman 1979, Evans & Tarney 1964). The boundary between the Inverian and the Laxfordian is not well defined. Evans & Lambert (1974) considered that the dyke emplacement was associated with the end of the Inverian, rather than with a period of quiescence between two separate tectono-metamorphic episodes. The time of peak Laxfordian metamorphism was around 1850 Ma (Lambert & Holland 1972).

A major study of the Assynt region was made by Sheraton *et al.* (1973*a*, *b*). On the evidence of the folding they postulated a N-side-up movement for the Canisp Shear Zone during the Laxfordian, following the N-side-down sense of movement implied by the Lochinver monoform.

Beach (1974), in a paper dealing primarily with the Laxford shear zones, suggested a dextral N-side-up sense of movement, perpendicular to the principal lineation. He was however, unable to calculate a displacement across this zone, due to the absence of well-exposed dykes oblique to the zone, such as those at Tarbet.

A sinistral S-side-up sense of movement was adduced by Evans & Lambert (1974) for the Laxfordian shearing on the Canisp Shear Zone. They also referred to the 'intensely deformed gneiss of the major Inverian structures' but did not specifically mention a period of Inverian shearing.

In the most recent work on the Lochinver area,

From: PARK, R. G. & TARNEY, J. (eds), 1987, *Evolution of the Lewisian and Comparable Precambrian High Grade Terrains*, Geological Society Special Publication No. 27, pp. 165–173.

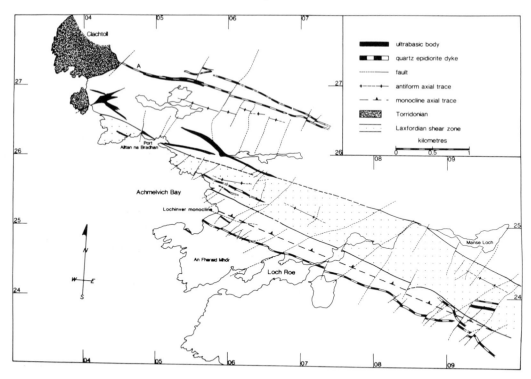

FIG. 2. General geological map of the western end of the Canisp Shear Zone. The dyke 'A' is the later metadolerite dyke, see text.

Jensen (1984) used the quartz microstructures to obtain a dextral, S-side-up sense for the Laxfordian movements, but did not consider the earlier Inverian movements.

It is more than twelve years since the publication of a detailed map (Sheraton *et al.* 1973*b*), that includes both the important coastal exposure south of Clachtoll, and that extends inland to north of Lochinver. Advances in the understanding of shear zones in the past decade have made re-examination of this area desirable, in order that the sense of displacement during the Laxfordian shearing episode can be clarified, and also to establish the nature of the Inverian deformation.

The account that follows is based on detailed mapping of that area (Figs 2 and 3); it attempts to separate the Inverian and Laxfordian deformations, and to assess their relative significance. It is suggested that the Inverian deformation is more important than previous workers have thought, and that a major shear zone existed at this time.

Rock types and structural setting

The petrology and geochemistry of the gneisses in the Lochinver area have been described in detail by Peach *et al.* (1907), Khoury (1968), Sheraton *et al.* (1973*a*) and, most recently, by Jensen (1984), who also described the textures and microstructures. Consequently these aspects will not be discussed in any detail here.

The dominant rock type in the area is banded grey gneiss of broadly tonalitic composition. The stable paragenesis is plagioclase–quartz–hornblende–biotite–epidote (Jensen 1980), with later, local, post-tectonic, poikiloblastic growth of chlorite, hornblende and muscovite. Included within the gneisses are ultramafic pods (Sheraton *et al.* 1973*b*). These are composed almost entirely of hornblende, and vary in shape from near spherical to lensoid.

The foliation within the gneisses is variably developed; in the highest-strain rocks there is a good shape fabric to the grains, and a strong alignment of hornblende and biotite. In the less-

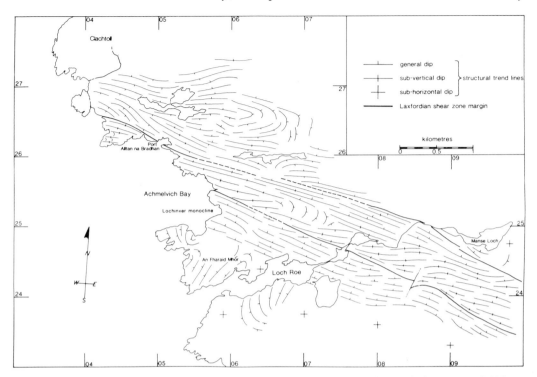

FIG. 3. Structural trend map of the western end of the Canisp Shear Zone, including details from Jensen (1984) for areas not mapped by the author.

deformed gneisses, the quartz grains only exhibit a weak shape fabric, and this is absent outside the shear zone. The hornblende and biotite, however, still show a degree of preferred orientation (Jensen 1984).

To the south of the Canisp Shear Zone, the foliation in the gneisses is flat-lying. These flat-lying gneisses are folded by the Lochinver monocline, the foliation in the north limb being sub-vertical.

The southern margin of the Laxfordian Canisp Shear Zone dips steeply to the south, cutting the Lochinver monocline slightly obliquely to the axial plane. The gneisses along the southern boundary are strongly deformed and locally mylonitic.

Within the Canisp Shear Zone the deformation is extremely heterogeneous. Lenses of low-strain gneiss, similar in character to those south of the zone, are enclosed between anastomosing bands of highly deformed, sheared gneiss. These high-strain zones are variable in character and range from a few cm to several tens of m in width.

The northern margin of the shear zone is less well defined. The northward extent of the Laxfordian shearing can be clearly demonstrated on the coast to the south of Clachtoll, and inland south of Manse Loch. The northern margin of the earlier Inverian zone is however unclear, as there are smaller E–W Inverian shears to the north which obscure the edge of the main zone.

The gneisses to the north of the shear zone dip gently east around Manse Loch, but at the western end of the area, near Clachtoll, they are affected by a series of folds, trending ESE–WNW, often with discrete shear zones along the limbs. These folds vary both in size and style, and are of pre-Laxfordian age, as they are cut by the later shearing.

The two main types of intrusive body in the area are quartz-epidiorite dykes, and ultramafic dykes. These are equivalent to the early dolerites and picrites respectively, as described by Tarney (1973). The quartz-epidiorite dykes contain a high proportion of hornblende with plagioclase, some quartz, and often epidote. The deformation within the quartz-epidiorites is very heterogeneous and will be described below. The ultrabasic dykes are extremely altered and are composed of talc, actinolite, and some dolomite.

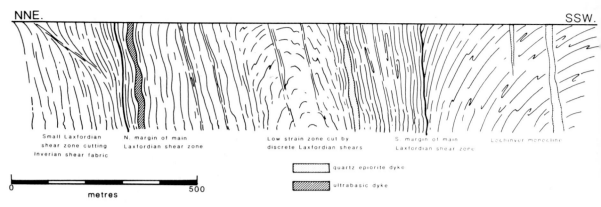

NNE.   SSW.

Small Laxfordian	N. margin of main	Low strain zone cut by	S. margin of main	Lochinver monocline
shear zone cutting	Laxfordian shear zone	discrete Laxfordian shears	Laxfordian shear zone	
Inverian shear fabric				

quartz epidorite dyke

ultrabasic dyke

0   500
            metres

FIG. 4. Diagrammatic cross-section of the extreme western end of the Canisp Shear Zone.

Structural and metamorphic history

The early history of the Assynt area, including the Canisp Shear Zone, has been discussed in detail by Sheraton et al. (1973a, b). They proposed that the early flat-lying foliation, as seen in the south of the area, is the result of the transposition of a previous layering at the crust–mantle interface, possibly due to a degree of de-coupling at the base of the crust. The abundance of early intrafolial folds and the truncation of banding within certain basic gneiss bodies are used to support this suggestion. At this time extreme boudinage of original ultramafic layers led to the formation of the ultramafic pods within the gneiss, and partially flattened them in the plane of the foliation.

The early foliation has been locally folded by NE–SW trending folds. This is well demonstrated on the An Fharaid Mhór peninsula (Fig. 3) where an ultramafic–mafic body has been folded in a synform which plunges gently to the SW (Tarney 1978). Sheraton et al. (1973b) also recognized a series of early monoclinal folds with axes trending approximately 230° and plunging gently to the SW. The earlier events took place during Badcallian granulite-facies conditions.

The beginning of the Inverian episode is marked by the onset of retrogressive amphibolite-facies metamorphism. This was followed by the formation of a major shear zone trending ESE–WNW, up to 1.5 km in width. This formed a belt of subvertical foliation and a weak, steeply SE-plunging lineation. The Lochinver monocline (Figs 2 and 3) represents the southern margin of this zone, the horizontal foliation to the south being folded around an approximately horizontal axis. On the subvertical northern limb of the monocline, there has been a slight attenuation of the fabric within the gneiss (Fig. 4).

In the north of the zone the gneisses are more strongly sheared, as on the coast south of Clachtoll. These also show the weak, steeply SE-plunging lineation and a strong subvertical foliation. Within the shear zone the intensity of deformation is variable, and the Badcallian banding has been strongly modified with intensification of the foliation parallel to the banding. Intrafolial folds are uncommon, and the ultrabasic pods are often more strongly flattened. Many of the Inverian structures have been partly obscured by later Laxfordian movements.

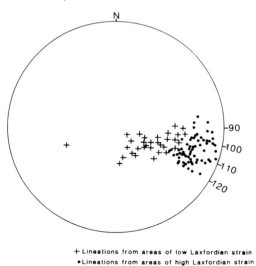

+ Lineations from areas of low Laxfordian strain
• Lineations from areas of high Laxfordian strain

FIG. 5. Stereoplot of lineations from the mapped area showing variation in plunge of Inverian and Laxfordian lineations.

FIG. 6. An early amphibolite dyke cutting an Inverian shear foliation is later folded during the Laxfordian shearing with formation of a weak axial planar fabric.

The Lochinver monocline is taken to indicate a downward movement of the northern block relative to the flat-lying gneisses in the south. As it is assumed that the lineation is parallel to the transport direction, a dextral S-side-up sense of movement is obtained for the Inverian shearing (Fig. 9). The movement was dominantly dip-slip with only a small horizontal component. It is probable that the smaller E–W shears to the east of Clachtoll were also formed at this time, and represent splays from the main zone.

Following the shearing was a period of dyke emplacement. Probably the earliest intrusion in the area is a fine-grained amphibolite dyke (Fig. 6). This has been intruded into an Inverian shear fabric; the dyke itself has only a weak foliation parallel to the axial plane of the later folding. No cross-cutting relationships with other dykes are visible, and so no direct evidence for the relative age of this dyke is presented. Field relations and the degree of alteration however, suggest it is early in the sequence.

The quartz-epidiorite dykes in the area were emplaced along fracture planes associated with the Inverian shearing. Outside the main shear zone the dykes are parallel to the shear plane— see for example the large dyke on the limb of the

Lochinver monocline (Fig. 2). The dykes of the second phase of emplacement are ultrabasic in composition. Some unaltered examples have been described by Tarney (1973) from elsewhere in the Assynt region, but all show a metamorphic mineralogy within the present study area. They form either large irregular bodies, such as the one to the south of Clachtoll, or dyke-like intrusions. No cross-cutting relationships are visible between these ultrabasic bodies and the earlier quartz-epidiorites, and evidence for their relative age is taken from Tarney (1973) and Sheraton *et al.* (1973*b*).

To the east of Clachtoll a metadolerite dyke is intruded along the centre of an ultrabasic dyke (Fig. 2) and is therefore younger. There are petrological features, such as the presence of plagioclase phenocrysts, that suggest that this dyke may have had a different original composition to the earlier quartz-epidiorites.

The first major deformation in the Laxfordian was the re-activation of the main Inverian shear zone, with formation of a new, more intense shear fabric concentrated in discrete planes. The margins to the zone showing this second phase of movement are well defined, especially in the south. Here the steeply south-dipping Laxfordian

FIG. 7. Refolded folds at Port Alltan na Bradhan. The original Badcallian banding was heavily modified and folded in the Inverian shearing and has been refolded and rotated during the Laxfordian shearing. Both fold axes plunge parallel to the Laxfordian lineation.

mylonites cut the steeply north-dipping gneisses of the Lochinver monocline (Fig. 4). The highest-strain rocks of the Laxfordian shear zone are concentrated at the margins, and in discrete planes within the zone. These form an anastomosing pattern surrounding blocks of relatively low-strain gneiss. In places these undeformed blocks show little evidence of either Inverian or Laxfordian deformation, since the Laxfordian shearing has recurred along localized planes of weakness formed during the Inverian.

The Laxfordian deformation is generally associated with the formation of a new shear fabric, and not a modification of the earlier Inverian foliation or the Badcallian banding. In places however, there has been modification and re-folding of Inverian structures. Folds within the zone have small interlimb angles and strongly attenuated limbs, some showing a transition to shear zones along the fold limbs. Refolding of folds is quite common, especially at Port Alltan na Bradhan (Fig. 7) where Inverian folding of a strongly modified Badcallian banding has been refolded during the Laxfordian, on axial planes parallel to the shear plane.

The Laxfordian shearing also affected the dykes in the area, both inside and outside the shear zone. However, as the dykes were emplaced parallel to the Inverian shear plane, and the Laxfordian shearing was a reactivation of the Inverian zone, the dykes have not been rotated. This means that the deflection on the dykes cannot be used for strain estimates using the Ramsay & Graham (1970) method, as attempted in the past (Jensen 1980).

Within the shear zone the dykes deform in a characteristic way. The strain is accommodated in discrete shear zones which form an anastomosing network within the dykes and along the margins, enclosing blocks of undeformed dyke material. This is analogous to the style of deformation across the main Laxfordian shear zone, and has been described from other areas (Coward 1976). Outside the shear zone the dykes have only sheared along the margins, the deformation being between a few cm and a m wide. The sheared margins of the dykes and the shear zones within the dykes, all show a consistent overall dextral displacement, with very little movement in the vertical plane.

FIG. 8. Strong, penetrative lineation from a zone of high Laxfordian strain at the south margin of the Canisp Shear Zone. Lineation plunges 32° towards 119°.

The areas of high Laxfordian strain show a very strong lineation (Fig. 8) plunging between 10° and 30° to ESE (Fig. 5). Using this in conjunction with evidence from the dykes, a dextral S-side-up sense of movement is indicated (Fig. 9). This is in agreement with Jensen (1984) who used the symmetry of the quartz *C*-axis fabrics to indicate the same sense of movement, sub-parallel to the principal lineation. The displacement across the Laxfordian zone is dominantly strike-slip as indicated by the shallow plunge of the lineation, and the lack of significant vertical displacement at the dyke margins.

Post-dating the shearing there was brittle reactivation at both the shear zone margins and some dyke margins. This has locally brecciated the mylonites along the southern margin of the Laxfordian shear zone. In a dyke on the southern side of Achmelvich Bay, the margin has been brecciated with formation of pseudotachylite pods within the breccia.

Late, pre-Torridonian NE–SW faulting has locally displaced both dykes and the shear zone margins, but the movement on these faults is small.

Discussion

Several workers have described pre-Laxfordian features in and around the Canisp Shear Zone. Sheraton *et al.* (1973*b*), used the term 'steep belt' to describe the zone of sub-vertical Inverian rocks from the Lochinver monocline northwards and attributed the formation of this belt to the large-scale monoclinal folding in the area. Also Evans & Lambert (1974) noted a zone of intensely deformed Inverian gneisses. However, neither group of workers recognize that this is a major Inverian shear zone, nor discuss the movement on this zone prior to the Laxfordian shearing. The intensity of the deformation to the N of the Laxfordian shear zone, and the attenuation of the foliation across the Lochinver monocline, indicate that considerable movement has taken place, probably sub-parallel to the weak, steeply SE-plunging lineation. Certain other features within the zone, such as the refolded folds and the parallel emplacement of the dykes, are more easily explained by two separate phases of movement.

The change from dominantly dip-slip to domi-

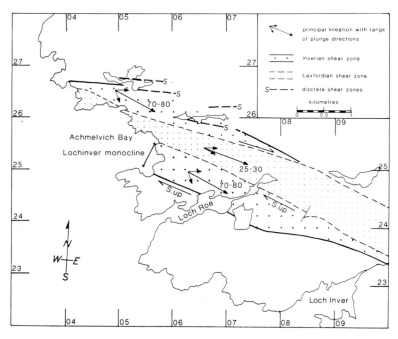

FIG. 9. Movement direction summary diagram for the Inverian and Laxfordian shear zones.

nantly strike-slip movement, but still with a dextral S-side-up sense, concurs with models for the structural history of the southern Lewisian (Coward & Park, this vol.).

Estimates for the total displacement on the Laxfordian shear zone vary between 2 km and 14 km (Jensen 1980) using the re-orientation of the dykes in the area. However, as these dykes were emplaced sub-parallel to the shear zone, re-orientation is minimal and these estimates are therefore unreliable.

ACKNOWLEDGEMENTS: The author would like to thank Dr R. G. Park for supervising the project, and Mr J. L. Constable for help preparing this paper. The work was carried out during tenure of a NERC Research Studentship.

References

BEACH, A. 1974. The measurement and significance of displacements on Laxfordian shear zones, North West Scotland. *Proc. Geol. Ass.* **85**, 13–21.

CHAPMAN, H. J. 1979. 2390 Myr Rb–Sr whole-rock age for the Scourie dykes of north-west Scotland. *Nature, London* **277**, 642–3.

COWARD, M. P. 1976. Strain within ductile shear zones. *Tectonophysics*, **34**, 181–197.

EVANS, C. R. 1965. Geochronology of the Lewisian basement near Lochinver, Sutherland. *Nature, London* **297**, 54–56.

—— & TARNEY, J. 1964. Isotopic ages of Assynt dykes. *Nature, London* **204**, 638–41.

—— & LAMBERT, R. St-J. 1974. The Lewisian of Lochinver Sutherland; the type area for the Inverian metamorphism. *J. Geol. Soc. Lond.* **130**, 125–150.

JENSEN, L. N. 1980. *Grundfjeldsgeologien of de Lewisiske gnejser i Lochinver omradet, NV Skotland. En strukturel, mikrostrukturel og koarks-fabric undersogelse.* Unpublished thesis, Aarhus University.

—— 1984. Quartz microfabric of the Laxfordian Canisp Shear Zone, NW Scotland. *J. struct. Geol.* **6**, 293–302.

KHOURY, S. G. 1968. The structural geology and geological history of the Lewisian rocks between Kylesku and Geisgeil, Sutherland, Scotland. *Krystalinikum*, **6**, 41–78.

LAMBERT, R. St-J. & HOLLAND, G. 1972. A geochronological study of the Lewisian from Loch Laxford to Durness, Sutherland, N.W. Scotland. *J. Geol. Soc. Lond.* **128**, 3–19.

PARK, R. G. 1970. Observations on Lewisian chronology. *Scott. J. Geol.* **6**, 379–399.

PEACH, B. N., HORNE, J., CLOUGH, C. T. & HINXMAN, L. W. 1907. The geological structure of the North-West Highlands of Scotland. *Mem. Geol. Surv. Gt. Britain.*

RAMSAY, J. G. & GRAHAM, R. H. 1970. Strain variation in shear belts. *Can. J. Earth Sci.* **7**, 786–813.

SHERATON, J. W., SKINNER, A. C. & TARNEY, J. 1973a. The geochemistry of the Scourian gneisses of the Assynt district. *In:* PARK, R. G. & TARNEY, J. (eds) *The Early Precambrian of Scotland and Related Rocks of Greenland.* University of Keele, 13–30.

——, TARNEY, J., WHEATLEY, T. J. & WRIGHT, A. E. 1973b. The structural history of the Assynt district. *In:* PARK, R. G. & TARNEY, J. (eds) *The early Precambrian of Scotland and related rocks of Greenland.* University of Keele, 31–44.

SUTTON, J. & WATSON, J. 1951. The pre-Torridonian metamorphic history of the Loch Torridon and Scourie areas in the North West Highlands, and its bearing on the chronological history of the Lewisian. *Quart. J. Geol. Soc. Lond.* **106**, 241–308.

TARNEY, J. 1963. Assynt dykes and their metamorphism. *Nature, London* **199**, 672–674.

—— 1973. The Scourie dyke suite and the nature of the Inverian event in Assynt. *In:* PARK, R. G. & TARNEY, J. (eds) *The Early Precambrian of Scotland and Related Rocks of Greenland.* University of Keele, 105–118.

—— 1978. Achmelvich Bay, Assynt (Lewisian). *In: The Lewisian and Torridonian rocks of North West Scotland. Geol. Assoc. guide no.* **21**, 35–50.

P. ATTFIELD, Department of Geology, University of Keele, Newcastle, Staffordshire ST5 5BG, UK.

The Outer Hebrides Fault Zone: evidence for normal movements

S. H. White & J. Glasser

SUMMARY: The Outer Hebrides Fault Zone is a major structural feature within the Lewisian of the Outer Hebrides. It is well exposed in the Uists where it consists of high-strain strands of ultracataclasite, cataclasite and phyllonite in a crush melange. Microstructural studies of the fault rocks indicate that the sequence crush melange–cataclasite–phyllonite is typical of that for c-type mylonite development and reflects increasing retrogression. This, plus the anastomosing pattern of the high-strain zones, suggests that the fault rocks in the Uists mark the edge of a major fault zone. Fold and shear band asymmetries indicate a major phase of normal movement. It is not possible to assign definite ages to either, but it is clear that the formation of the crush melange preceded that of the high-strain strands, which appear to be immediately post-Caledonian.

The Outer Hebrides Fault Zone penetrates Lewisian gneiss for over 200 km along the eastern margin of the Hebrides, from Tolsta Head on Lewis to Sandray, south of Barra (see Fig. 1). For much of this length, exposure of the fault zone is poor due to submergence or drift cover. Trending NNE for most of its length, it dips on average 20–30° ESE under the Minch (Fig. 1). Many workers have investigated the islands since MacCulloch (1819) first noted the presence of pseudotachylite and ultracataclasite (or 'flinty crush rock' using the field terminology of Jehu and Craig (1923)). He described these fault rock products amongst the otherwise ubiquitous gneisses as 'trap' and 'basaltic paste', but it was not until fairly recently that the importance of the fault zone was recognized.

Several other early investigators recorded outcrops of extensively crushed gneiss (Heddle 1888, Peach & Horne 1930, Dougal 1928) but Jehu and Craig (1923, 1925, 1926, 1927, 1934) were the first to recognize that this crushing was related to a major fault, although they did not assign it a name. Kursten (1957), mapping near Lochboisdale on South Uist, refers to the 'Hebridean Thrust', thus establishing a precedent in terminology—all subsequent workers in this area have used the adjective 'thrust' in conjunction with a geographical qualifier (eg 'Outer Hebrides Thrust Plane' (Dearnley 1962), 'Hebridean Thrust' (Hopgood 1971), 'Outer Hebrides Thrust' (Francis 1969, 1973; Sibson 1977a, b), 'Outer Isles Thrust' (Coward 1969, 1972, 1973)).

However, it is debatable whether the term 'thrust' should be used to describe the feature under consideration. The fault was originally identified as a thrust by the existence on South Uist of supposedly deeper-level granulites cropping out at a higher structural level than amphibolite-facies rocks (Fig. 1). McQuillin and Watson (1973) suggest that this may not necessarily be so, and that a pre-existing line of density

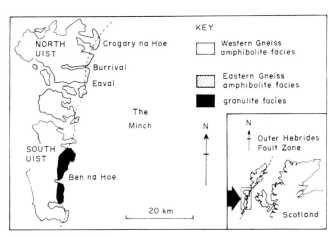

FIG. 1. Map of the Uists, showing their location and the principal lithologies. Areas where sampling traverses were undertaken are indicated.

From: PARK, R. G. & TARNEY, J. (eds), 1987, Evolution of the Lewisian and Comparable Precambrian High Grade Terrains, Geological Society Special Publication No. 27, pp. 175–183.

contrast (dating back to the Scourian) was present within the Lewisian, separating granulite-rich assemblages in the east from generally less dense, hydrated gneisses in the west. They argued that the presence of this zone of transition probably exerted control over the localization of dislocation during later deformation, so that the granulites were not necessarily brought up from depth over the amphibolite-facies gneisses.

Furthermore, it has been shown that there has been at least an element of normal reactivation; seismic (Smythe 1982, Smythe *et al.* 1982) and field evidence (Sibson 1977*a*) both support this. Although Sibson recorded a number of structural criteria suggesting normal movement (*eg* eastward-verging asymmetric folding of phyllonites and late-stage quartz veins; rotated marginal schistosity; sigmoidal tension gashes; asymmetric crenulations) he concluded that this normal movement was largely insignificant compared with earlier thrusting. He interpreted the metamorphic grade of fault rocks along individual faults as increasing to the east, as would be expected if this were a thrust terrain. From this, he formulated his now widely-accepted model of a fault zone transecting the continental crust. He applied this to infer uplifts of greater than 15 km for the eastern faults and less than 5 km for those to the west. In this article, we report a microstructural study of the fault rocks from the Uists and conclude from the resulting data that the fault

rocks do not represent a depth sequence. Rather, they reflect increasing strain and retrogression to the east as marked by increasing phyllonitization; this sequence does not support thrusting. Consequently, we shall refer to the fault structure as the Outer Hebrides Fault Zone.

Fault and fault rock distribution

The best exposures of the Outer Hebrides Fault Zone occur along the eastern coast of the Uists. It is a zone of crushing, referred to as a crush melange by Sibson (1977*a*, *b*) in which zones of more intense crushing and/or retrogression (cataclasites and phyllonites) have developed (Fig. 2—see also Sibson 1977*a*, fig. 1). In the Eaval–Burrival and Crogary na Hoe areas on North Uist, and at Ben na Hoe on South Uist (Fig. 1), these zones weather to produce topographic notches allowing great accuracy when mapping (Sibson 1977*b*).

The country rocks are mainly amphibolite-grade acid gneisses with pods of metabasite, apart from the Corodale Gneisses which are basic granulites (Fig. 1). The crushing and retrogression within the melange is variable, with broken blocks of country rock ranging between a few centimetres and a metre. There is an overall tendency for the block size to decrease and the degree of retrogression to increase towards the

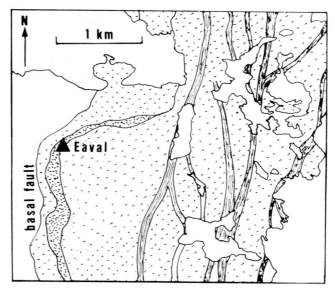

FIG. 2. Map of fault rock distribution in the Eaval area of North Uist. The distribution is typical of that found throughout the Uists. Stipple represents crush melange; heavy stipple represents flinty crush rock (ultracataclasite). Phyllonite bands have an ornament of lines representing the strike of the foliation, with denser lines indicating better foliation.

east. Individual blocks may be slickensided or separated by black to green ultracataclasite with a grain size of <15 μm (locally referred to as 'flinty crush rock'). Ultracataclasites have also been injected into the blocks and superficially resemble pseudotachylite in hand specimen although not in microstructure. The larger blocks of country rock, especially on the southern slopes of Burrival, contain parallel vertical quartz veins with a mean strike of 350° (true). These have horizontal fabrics with their long axes striking at 280°, indicative of an E–W extension. Where these veins cut the high-strain zones, they are reworked.

The widths of the high-strain zones within the crush melange generally increase to the east, from less than one metre in the west to twenty or more in the east. The exceptions are the pronounced crush zones, up to 30 metres thick, on the western sides of Eaval and Ben na Hoe. These consist of ultracataclastic flinty crush rock intruded by pseudotachylite veins, which in turn have been cataclased. Both crush zones are associated with metabasites (of granulite facies in the latter area) (see Fig. 1); they also contain recognizable pods of crushed, predominantly metabasic, gneiss. The conclusion is that these ultracataclasites are derived from the crush melange. The crush zones remain black at Ben na Hoe indicating little retrogression but appear green at Eaval. Below these zones, in both localities, the country rock appears less broken up and only slightly retrogressed. Black pseudotachylite veins are common, whereas in the overlying crush melange blocks they are green and often impossible to differentiate in the field from ultracataclasite injection veins.

The lithology of the high-strain strands varies systematically from west to east. Cataclasites pass progressively into phyllonites, developing a weak and laterally localized foliation. The phyllonites contain pods of cataclasite whose size and frequency decrease to the east, where the isolated pods measure only 5 to 10 cm wide by 20 to 50 cm long. These observations indicate that the phyllonites are derived from the cataclasites.

Fault rock microstructures

Microstructural studies of the fault rock types across traverses in the Ben na Hoe, Eaval–Burrival and Crogary na Hoe areas have been undertaken and the results are summarized below. As the results were similar for the three traverses, they will be described as a single composite traverse with emphasis on any differences that were recorded. Whilst there are gradations between fault rock types, it is convenient to discuss them under separate headings.

The fault rocks along the high-strain zones in the crush melange are characterized by a fine grain size, especially the matrix of the cataclasites and flinty crush rock. Optical microscopy is of limited use; individual grains in both of the above cannot be easily resolved. Consequently, most of our microstructural observations were performed using a Jeol 733 Superprobe with back-scattered electron imaging. In this mode, the relative brightness of a phase reflects its relative mean atomic weight—the higher this is, the brighter the mineral appears in the image. The identification of each mineral phase was based on qualitative element analysis using an energy dispersive spectrometer. The back-scattered technique, which employs standard carbon-coated polished probe slides, has been described by Hall & Lloyd (1981) and White *et al.* (1984).

Ultracataclasite—flinty crush rock

Both types of ultracataclasite have been examined, namely, those associated with the thick crush zones and those occurring as green injection veins within the crush melange. Both types are basically similar, especially the vein material and that from the Eaval crush zone. Consequently, the microstructures of both will be described together. We shall emphasize differences between different localities.

The optical microstructure of the ultracataclasites is depicted in Fig. 3a. It consists of a low percentage area of clasts, both rounded and angular, in an opaque matrix. The clasts reflect the composition of the protoliths; in the Ben na Hoe and Eaval material they consist of amphibole, plagioclase and minor quartz, with pyroxene also present in the Ben na Hoe samples. Retrogression is slight in samples from Ben na Hoe and pronounced in those from Eaval. The clast mineralogy is consistent with derivation from a metabasite. The clasts from injection veins in the crush melange are typically of quartz and highly retrogressed plagioclase. In all cases, the quartz clasts are composed not only of fragments of individual grains but also of quartz cataclasite. The quartz grains all show well-developed undulatory extinction and grain boundary recrystallization. The clasts of cataclasite are criss-crossed by fractures along which small fragments of quartz grains occur. These are more common in the cataclasite zones and will be treated more fully later on. The feldspar, pyroxene and amphibole clasts in the Ben na Hoe samples also display undulatory extinction and fine-scale shattering

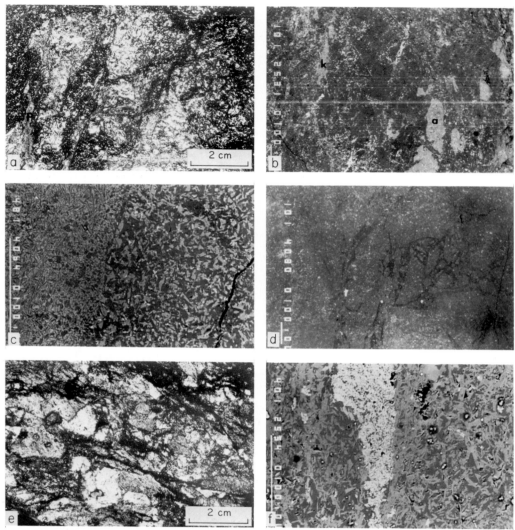

FIG. 3. Back-scattered electron and optical micrographs of the cataclasites and ultracataclasites. Scale bars are on the micrographs. (a) Optical micrograph showing typical microstructures of the ultracataclasite. A fractured vein of pseudotachylite (p) is set in a structureless matrix. Plane polarized light. Eaval, GR 9019 5840. (b) BSEM view of the matrix of Fig. 3a. Fragments of amphibole (a) and potassium feldspar (k) are set in a finer matrix. (c) BSEM view of a pseudotachylite vein in relatively undeformed gneiss. There are fine-grained chilled margins on both sides of the vein, consisting of radiating plagioclase grains in a potassium feldspar and amphibole matrix. The central portion of the vein shows the reverse—potassium feldspar and amphibole in a plagioclase matrix. Ben na Hoe, GR 8011 2910. (d) BSEM view of the fractured matrix of an ultracataclasite from Ben na Hoe. The fragments are surrounded by quartz. GR 8136 2760. (e) Optical micrograph of a cataclasite. The microstructure consists of fractured clasts in a structureless matrix which appears to be similar to that of the ultracataclasite (Fig. 3a). Plane polarized light. Burrival area, GR 9103 6163. (f) BSEM micrograph of the matrix of Fig. 3e. A patch of fine-grained epidote (bright phase) in an albite matrix, surrounded by albite and phengite (intermediate colour).

with retrogression and development of opaques along the fractures. In some cases, the shattering is so intense as to make mineral identification difficult. In the samples from Eaval and the injection veins, shattering and retrogression was so advanced that little information could be gained regarding the internal strain features prior to the retrogression, nor could the retrogressed products themselves be identified owing to their fine grain size.

The aphanitic matrix of all specimens has a similar microstructure when viewed in the BSEM (Fig. 3b–d). It consists of very fine grains (<10 μm) of quartz, plagioclase, potassium feldspar, iron and titanium oxides, and apatite. The iron and titanium oxides occur mainly as grain boundary phases in the matrix. Small (less than 20 μm) angular clast fragments (Fig. 3d) occur within the matrix and are mainly plagioclase, with lesser amounts of amphibole, potassium feldspar, and pyroxene. The Eaval material also contains biotite, with quartz as a dominant phase in the injection veins. The potassium feldspars are partially altered (especially along microfractures) to phengite, and the plagioclase and amphibole to scapolite and biotite respectively. The large clasts (*ie* those visible optically) are intensely fractured; these fractures are infilled with iron and titanium oxides, quartz, apatite and calcite. The pyroxene, amphibole, plagioclase and potassium feldspar clasts have all undergone retrogression or alteration to some degree; this retrogression increases with the green coloration of the hand specimen. Veins of pseudotachylite, some with chilled margins, are encountered within the matrix of the Ben na Hoe specimens (Fig. 3c). They show typical devitrification microstructures, especially in the chilled margins, consisting of plagioclase with some euhedral pyrite in a matrix of plagioclase, amphibole and potassium feldspar. The centres of the veins have a texture with amphibole and potassium feldspar in a plagioclase matrix. These microstructures are very different from those of the specimen matrix (compare Figs 3a and c).

Evidence exists for later fracturing of the matrix and the Ben na Hoe specimens show evidence of later cataclasis with fragments of matrix set in a further matrix of quartz (Fig. 3d). There is no evidence for a second phase of retrogression associated with this phase of cataclasis, although late stage veins of quartz, potassium feldspar, biotite, calcite and apatite are common in all specimens.

Cataclasite

The main textural difference between the cataclasite and the ultracataclasite (flinty crush rock) is an increase in the percentage of clasts which, with the exception of quartz, show greater retrogression (Fig. 3e). The products of retrogression pseudomorph the clasts, making identification of the original mineralogy difficult. In addition, the identification of the retrogressive products is difficult because of their fine grain size. Potassium feldspar is replaced by sericite; hornblende is replaced by epidote and chlorite; plagioclase by epidote and sericite. Epidote is ubiquitous and can also be recognized in the matrix (Fig. 3f).

The quartz clasts consist either of coarse-grained fragments or are of fine-grained cataclasite. In both, individual grains show a marked undulatory extinction with evidence of intergranular recrystallization. The large quartz grains are fractured and along these are opaque oxides or small quartz grains which, although they appear recrystallized, are also similar to those produced by pressure solution of quartz gouges (Rutter & White 1979). Similar fine grains form the matrix of the cataclasite clasts.

The matrix of the cataclasite consists of albite, quartz, epidote, chlorite and phengite. The epidote, chlorite and phengite occur as patches, often angular, and are thought to represent former clasts (Fig. 3f). The new minerals have a random texture consistent with post-tectonic grain growth. Patches of iron and titanium oxides, sphene and euhedral grains of pyrite are also present.

Phyllonites

The phyllonites exhibit a range of microstructures (Fig. 4) and, although referred to as phyllonites, the foliated matrix is fine grained and the minerals are difficult to recognize optically. The first phyllonites that appear in the west-to-east traverses occur as foliated patches in cataclasites and have a weak foliation marked by a banding of cataclased clasts and retrogression products, particularly epidotes and micas (Fig. 4a). The BSEM micrographs reveal trails of orientated micas, chlorites and pulled-apart epidotes (Fig. 4e). Quartz and albite grains are elongate and have beards of quartz, mica and chlorite. A better foliated matrix develops with increasing phyllonitization (Fig. 4b) and the amount of epidote and cataclasite decreases.

The main eastern phyllonite zones have a well-developed shear-band foliation (Figs 4d & f). Back-scattered micrographs show that the microstructure consists mainly of quartz and mica with minor amounts of chlorite and albite. Epidote is absent. Pyrite and iron oxides are common, and tend to concentrate along the shear bands (Fig. 4f). There has been a loss of epidote and albite, with any remaining albite becoming sericitized. Fibrous quartz veins are common in the phyllonites and have been folded (Fig. 4c). Both these and the shear bands indicate normal movement.

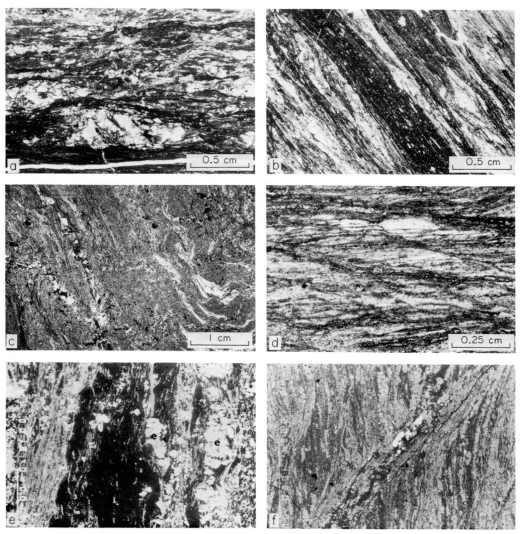

FIG. 4. Back-scattered electron and optical micrographs of the phyllonites. Scale bars are on the micrographs.
(a) Optical microstructure of a weakly-foliated phyllonite. It consists of clasts (feldspar and quartz) in a weakly-foliated, fine-grained matrix. Plane polarized light. Crogary na Hoe area, GR 9637 7061. (b) Optical micrograph of an intermediate stage phyllonite. The foliation is more marked but patches of clasts remain. Plane polarized light. Crogary na Hoe area, GR 9733 7272. (c) Optical microstructure of a well-foliated phyllonite typical of the eastern zones. Folded fine grained quartz–mica bands. Clasts of cataclasite are now rare. Crossed polars. Burrival, GR 9207 6158. (d) Optical micrograph of a well-developed phyllonite, showing a shear band foliation (oblique) in mica rich areas. Crossed polars. Crogary na Hoe, GR 9793 7246. (e) BSEM view of the matrix from Fig. 4a. It consists of epidote (bright clusters, e), small mica grains and quartz/albite (dark phase). (f) BSEM micrograph of the shear band structure from Fig. 4d. The microstructure consists of bands of quartz with subsidiary albite. Pyrite grains (brightest phase) are concentrated along the shear bands.

Discussion

The fault rocks within the Outer Hebrides Fault Zone show a microstructural progression from coarsely brecciated country rock (the crush melange) to cataclasite and, finally, phyllonite. This is identical to the sequence proposed by White (1982) for the development of a c-type mylonite with increasing strain and is similar to that recorded along faults in other gneiss terrains

(White *et al.* 1982). It reflects a strain-dependent increase in retrogression *ie* the higher the strain, the greater the degree of comminution, allowing a larger influx of fluid to finally convert a quartzo-feldspathic ($+$hornblende) gneiss to a quartz-mica-chlorite phyllonite. The passage of fluid into the high-strain strands has brought about changes in bulk rock composition, as well as affecting the mechanism of deformation. A detailed study of these changes is under preparation.

There has been a change from brittle (cataclastic) to ductile (crystal plastic) deformation with increasing fluid component. This change in deformation mechanism does not reflect a temperature difference between the cataclasites and the phyllonites, as postulated by Sibson (1977*a* & *b*), as the phyllonites contain pods of a cataclastic protolith. The brittle to ductile transition is seldom as sharp in the continental crust (White 1984; White *et al.* 1985) as Sibson (1977*a* & *b*) depicts.

The fault rock that does not fit comfortably into the above sequence is the ultracataclasite (flinty crush rock) that forms the crush zone towards the footwall of the crush melange in the Ben na Hoe and Burrival–Eaval areas. In this, the degree of comminution is greater than in the cataclasites but the degree of retrogression is less. This corresponds to an overall partial retrogression which characterizes the gneisses within the crush melange, suggesting that the two may be contemporaneous.

The overall increasing degree of retrogression in the high-strain zones away from the footwall (*ie* eastwards) is the opposite to that encountered in thrust terrains. For example, in the Moine Thrust Zone there is a progressive increase in the metamorphic grade both of the fault rocks and of the intervening thrust slices away from the foreland thrusts into the Slide Zones (Evans & White 1984). Nor is the distribution of fault rock types consistent with a thrust terrain, which would require slices of relatively undeformed country rock, each enveloped by a single, discrete fault zone. The fault rock distribution is consistent with a single major zone of crushing now represented by the crush melange in which subsequent deformation is concentrated. In outcrop, this further deformation is represented by the higher-strain strands which become more retrogressed to the east. This in turn indicates a greater concentration of deformation in this direction due to increased strain softening.

The increasing phyllonitization of the strands towards the hanging wall, together with their tendency to display an increase in width and a greater degree of coalescence, is characteristic of the edge of a major mylonite zone (cf Sibson *et*

al. 1979, Bell 1978, Obee & White 1985). In the Uists, this zone would be out to sea. The consistent indication of normal, or extensional, movement (the fibrous quartz veins in the crush melange, the asymmetry of folds and orientation of shear bands in the phyllonites) all imply normal (down dip) movement to the east. It is concluded that the cataclasite and phyllonite strands mark the low-strain edge of a major normal fault zone. This interpretation is consistent with recent seismic reflection studies (Brewer & Smythe 1984). No clear movement sense can be deduced from the rotation of the gneissic foliation at the edges of the high-strain zones. We can find no evidence to indicate that these zones had a thrust movement.

It is not clear without additional studies whether all the fault rocks belong to a single episode of faulting. There are clearly two phases in the fault rock development seen in the Uists. Firstly there is the formation of the crush melange along with the crush zones containing the ultracataclasites (flinty crush rocks) and the pseudotachylites and, secondly, the subsequent concentration of deformation into the more retrogressed cataclasite and phyllonite strands. Central to this issue are the granulitic Corodale Gneisses. Were these thrust over the amphibolite facies Western Gneisses (Fig. 1) or are they a less retrogressed area within the amphibolites as suggested by McQuillin & Watson (1973)? This is a matter for further research, as is the timing of the normal movements. Sibson (1977*b*) in his PhD studies presents the results of a pilot K–Ar whole rock dating programme of the fault rocks from the Outer Hebrides Fault Zone. They show scattered dates from the pseudotachylites (442–2056 Ma) and the flinty crush rocks (1000–1926 Ma) but a more concentrated range (394–471 Ma) for the phyllonites. The scattered ages most likely reflect the protolith content of the fault rocks. The narrow age range for the phyllonites suggest a late- to immediately post-Caledonian age for initiation of the normal movement.

Conclusions

A study of the fault rocks associated with the Outer Hebrides Fault Zone indicates two phases in their development—an initial development of a major crush zone followed by formation of higher-strain strands of more retrogressed cataclasite and phyllonite as a result of normal faulting. The presence of extensional quartz veins within the crush melange suggests that it may also have developed during normal-sense faulting. The distribution of the higher-strain strands is consistent with the low-strain edge of a major normal fault zone which must lie offshore. The relative ages of the two phases (*ie* if they are the result of two distinct events or phases of a single event) are unknown but the normal motion appears to have commenced immediately post-Caledonian.

There is no unequivocal evidence for thrust-sense movements in the Uists and the term 'Outer Hebrides Fault Zone' is preferred to 'Outer Hebrides Thrust Zone'.

ACKNOWLEDGMENTS: S. H. W and J. G. acknowledge support by NERC through research grant GR3/3848, and a postgraduate studentship, respectively.

References

BREWER, J. A. & SMYTHE, D. K. 1984. MOIST and the continuity of crustal reflector geometry along the Caledonian–Appalachian Orogen. *J. Geol. Soc. London*, **141**, 105–120.

BELL, T. H. 1978. Progressive deformation and reorientation of fold axes in a ductile mylonite zone: the Woodruffe Thrust. *Tectonophysics*, **44**, 285–320.

COWARD, M. P. 1969. *The structural and metamorphic geology of South Uist, Outer Hebrides*. Unpubl. PhD thesis, University of London.

—— 1972. The eastern gneisses of South Uist. *Scott. J. Geol.* **8**, 1–12.

—— 1973. Heterogeneous deformation in the development of the Laxfordian complex of South Uist, Outer Hebrides. *J. Geol. Soc. London*, **129**, 139–160.

DEARNLEY, R. 1962. An outline of the Lewisian complex of the Outer Hebrides in relation to that of the Scottish mainland. *Q. J. Geol. Soc. London*, **118**, 143–176.

DOUGAL, J. W. 1928. Observations on the geology of Lewis (Outer Hebrides). *Trans. Edinburgh Geol. Soc.* **12**, 12–18.

EVANS, D. J. & WHITE, S. H. 1984. Microstructural and fabric studies from the rocks of the Moine Nappe, Eriboll, NW Scotland. *J. Struct. Geol.* **6**, 369–389.

FRANCIS, P. W. 1969. *Some aspects of the Lewisian geology of the Isle of Barra and adjacent small islands*. Unpubl. PhD thesis, University of London.

—— 1973. Scourian-Laxfordian relationships in the Barra Isles. *J. Geol. Soc. London*, **129**, 161–189.

HALL, M. G. & LLOYD, G. E. 1981. The SEM examination of geological samples with a semiconductor back-scattered electron detector. *Am. Mineral.* **66**, 362–368.

HEDDLE, M. F. 1888. Notes in 'A Vertebrate Fauna of the Outer Hebrides' by J. A. Harvie-Brown and T. E. Buckley. David Douglas, Edinburgh.

HOPGOOD, A. M. 1971. Structure and tectonic history of Lewisian gneiss, Isle of Barra, Scotland. *Kristalinikum*, **7**, 27–60.

JEHU, T. J. & CRAIG, R. M. 1923. Geology of the Outer Hebrides, part I, the Barra Isles. *Trans. R. Soc. Edinburgh*, **53**, 419–441.

—— & —— 1925. Geology of the Outer Hebrides, part II, South Uist and Eriskay. *Trans. R. Soc. Edinburgh*, **53**, 615–641.

—— & —— 1926. Geology of the Outer Hebrides, part III, North Uist and Benbecula. *Trans. R. Soc. Edinburgh*, **54**, 467–489.

—— & —— 1927. Geology of the Outer Hebrides, part

IV, South Harris. *Trans. R. Soc. Edinburgh*, **55**, 457–488.

—— & —— 1934. Geology of the Outer Hebrides, part V, North Harris and Lewis. *Trans. R. Soc. Edinburgh*, **57**, 839–874.

KURSTEN, M. 1957. The metamorphic and tectonic history of parts of the Outer Hebrides. *Trans. Edinburgh geol. Soc.* **17**, 1–31.

MacCULLOCH, J. 1819. *A description of the Western Isles of Scotland, including the Isle of Man*. 3 volumes. Hurst, Robinson & Co., London.

McQUILLIN, R. & WATSON, J. 1973. Large scale basement structures of the Outer Hebrides in the light of geophysical evidence. *Nature, Physical Science*, **245**, 1–3.

OBEE, H. K. & WHITE, S. H. 1986. Microstructural and fabric heterogeneities in fault rocks associated with a fundamental fault. *Phil. Trans. R. Soc. London*, **317**, 99–109.

PEACH, B. N. & HORNE, J. 1930. *Chapters on the Geology of Scotland*. Oxford University Press, London.

RUTTER, E. H. & WHITE, S. H. 1979. The microstructures and rheology of fault gouge produced experimentally under wet and dry conditions at temperatures up to 400°C. *Bull. Mineralogy*, **102**, 101–109.

SIBSON, R. H. 1977a. Fault rocks and fault mechanisms. *J. Geol. Soc. London*, **133**, 191–213.

—— 1977b. *The Outer Hebrides Thrust: its structure, mechanism and deformation environment*. Unpubl. PhD thesis, University of London.

——, WHITE, S. H. & ATKINSON, B. K. 1979. Fault rock distribution and structure within the Alpine Fault Zone: a preliminary account *In*: WALCOTT, R. I. & CRESWELL, M. M. (eds). *The Origin of the Southern Alps*. Bull. R. Soc. New Zealand, **18**, 55–65.

SMYTHE, D. K. 1982. Results of the Moine and Outer Isles Seismic Traverse (MOIST) (abs) *Newsletter Geol. Soc. London*, **11**, 11.

——, DOBINSON, A., McQUILLIN, R., BREWER, J. A., MATTHEWS, D. H., BLUNDELL, D. J. & KELK, B. 1982. Deep structure of the Scottish Caledonides revealed by the MOIST reflection profile. *Nature, London*, **299**, 338–340.

WHITE, S. H. 1982. Fault rocks of the Moine Thrust Zone: a guide to their nomenclature. *Textures and Microstructures*, **5**, 211–221.

—— 1984. Brittle deformation in ductile fault zones. *Proc. 27th International Geol. Congress, Moscow*, **2**, 327–350.

——, Evans, D. J. & Zhong, D-L. 1982. Fault rocks of the Moine Thrust Zone: microstructures and textures of selected mylonites. *Textures and Microstructures*, **5**, 33–61.

——, Shaw, H. F. & Huggett, J. M. 1984. The use of back scattered electron imaging for the petrographic study of sandstones and shales. *J. Sed. Pet.* **54**, 487–494.

——, Bretan, P. G. & Rutter, E. H. 1986. Fault zone reactivation: kinematics and mechanisms. *Phil. Trans. R. Soc. London*, **A317**, 81–97.

S. H. White & J. Glasser, Geology Department, Royal School of Mines, Imperial College of Science and Technology, Prince Consort Road, London SW7 2BP, UK.

Physical properties of Lewisian rocks: implications for deep crustal structure

J. Hall

SUMMARY: Data on the densities, seismic velocities, magnetization, and permeability of Lewisian rocks are summarized. These properties have been used to estimate the shallow-depth extension of exposed boundaries within the Lewisian, and between the Lewisian and other rocks; and also to predict downward changes in porosity and electrical conductivity. Geophysical surveys of the deep crust can be interpreted in terms of subsurface distributions of Lewisian, or Lewisian-like, rocks.

Among the more significant conclusions relevant to the interpretation of surface structure of the Lewisian is that the Kylesku Group rocks of the central belt in Sutherland may be isolated from deeper crustal rocks of similar composition which are characterized by P-wave velocities of 6.4 km s^{-1} and over. Such rocks may form the mid crust below NW Scotland, shallowing north of the mainland possibly with a sharp discontinuity upwards into more acid basement rocks. West of the mainland direct evidence of the 6.4 km s^{-1} rocks is missing; they appear to be absent from the upper crust and buried rather deeply, perhaps with a transitional top, in the middle or lower crust.

Granulite-facies rocks occurring in the upper crust west of the mainland are likely to be more acid than average Kylesku Group rocks. The layered basic rocks of the central belt provide an analogue of the deepest crust in NW Britain.

Permeability/porosity studies allow estimates of electrical conductivity to be made in an attempt to explain the high conductivity of the lower crust in terms of trapped saline fluids. Porosities in the deep crust may be high enough to account for deep crustal seismic reflections in areas where porous layers are sub-horizontal.

In most surveys of continental basement, geophysical signatures are ascribed to large blocks of crust, and interpreted in terms of laboratory measurements on very much smaller samples, often hand specimens. A major problem in interpreting the signature of the large block is in the estimation of what mix of hand specimens represents the bulk composition of the block, and furthermore, whether the mix stays sufficiently constant within each of two independent blocks to define a meaningful contrast between them. In the Lewisian, for example, is it meaningful to define a density contrast between the Kylesku Group rocks of the central belt of the mainlaind and the Rhiconich Group rocks of the northern belt (see eg Hall 1978a)? If so, then the gravity anomaly separating the belts is interpretable (see Bott et al. 1972). It is usually supposed that estimated block-scale contrasts are significant, i.e. real, but in the summaries which follow it should be remembered that the contrasts are often estimated from hand specimen measurements and guesses of regional composition with rather poor control.

The density and seismic velocity of a rock are estimated from properties of minerals present, weighted according to their proportional volume. Both properties are affected somewhat by porosity, seismic velocity much more so than density.

Magnetization, on the other hand, is dependent on the presence of magnetite, ilmenite and hematite, usually accessory minerals. In the Lewisian, magnetite appears to be the principal determinant of the intensity of magnetization.

Permeability and electrical conductivity are only dependent on porosity, how it is distributed and the fluids filling the rock.

The greater the number of physical properties which can be estimated from geophysical surveys, the better may composition and porosity of buried rocks be constrained.

In what follows, the main controls on each of the physical properties of Lewisian rocks are described. Then usage of these physical properties in establishing shallow Lewisian structure is illustrated. Finally, the possible distribution of exposed Lewisian rock types at greater depth in northern Britain is discussed, in conjunction with possible porosity variations controlling fluids and transport properties.

Physical properties of Lewisian rocks

A summary of physical properties is given in Table 1. The effects of variation in the properties of various minerals are most readily seen in

From: PARK, R. G. & TARNEY, J. (eds), 1987, *Evolution of the Lewisian and Comparable Precambrian High Grade Terrains*, Geological Society Special Publication No. 27, pp. 185–192.

TABLE 1. *Physical properties of Lewisian rocks*

Property (units)	Range	Control	References
Density (kg m^{-3})	2600 (pegmatites) – 3100 (serpentinized olivine pyroxenites)	Controlled by minerals: quartz (2650), K-feldspar (2600), plagioclase (2600–2750), amphibole (3000–3200), pyroxene (3100–3400), olivine (3200–3400), garnet (3500–4300); porosity is usually small (less than 0.5%), and reduces density by about 20 kg m^{-3} per 1% change in porosity (assumed water saturated)	McQuillin & Watson (1973); Bott *et al.* (1972); Durrance (1976); Hall & Al-Haddad (1979); Hipkin & Hussain (1983)
Intensity of magnetization (A m^{-1})	negligible (most) – 5 (pyroxene granulites and some amphibolites)	Predominantly induced, depends largely on magnetite content and metamorphic grade (eg in granulites intensity increases as 0.8 A m^{-1} per 1% increase in Fe$_2$O$_3$; in amphibolites increase is 0.02–0.4 A m^{-1} per 1% increase in Fe$_2$O$_3$)	Powell (1970)
Seismic velocities (km s^{-1})	V_P $\begin{cases} 5 - 6.0 \text{ (granite sheet)} \\ 6.5 \text{ (open, saturated cracks)} - 7.5 \text{ (closed cracks) (mafic amphibolites)} \end{cases}$ V_S $\begin{cases} 2.8 - 3.6 \\ 3.9 \text{ (open saturated cracks)} - 4.1 \text{ (closed cracks)} \end{cases}$	Porosity has bigger effect than on density, but tends to decrease rapidly with depth in top 2 km. Crack-free velocities dependent on mineral velocities: for isotropic aggregates V_P varies as follows: quartz (6.1), K-feldspar (6.2), plagioclase (6.4–7.2), amphibole (7.0–7.5), pyroxene (7.6–8.1), olivine (8.0–8.6), garnet (8.0–9.2)	Hall & Al-Haddad (1976, 1979); Hall & Simmons (1979)
Permeability (m^2)	<10^{-22} (mafic rocks with cracks sealed) – 10^{-15} (at grain scale) (rocks with transgranular cracks)	Dependent on porosity, and strongly dependent on width of fractures. As cracks close downwards, permeability decreases rapidly. May be more abundant cracks at grain scale in quartz-rich rocks	Hall (new data)
Electrical conductivity (S m^{-1})	10^{-4} – 10^{-6}	Field measurements, main control from saline solutions in connected pores	Mbipom & Hutton (1983)

variations of density and seismic velocity. These properties can be estimated fairly well by summing the values for the minerals weighted by their fractional volume. There are three problems with this approach. Firstly, there are rocks which may contain minerals for which velocities or densities are not available or not readily interpolated (in the case of complex mineral groups). Secondly, the rock aggregate may itself be anisotropic (in velocity) because of preferred crystallographic orientation of minerals. Thirdly, both properties are affected by porosity. Even though porosities in the Lewisian are usually less than 1%, the effects are not negligible. 1% water-saturated porosity would reduce density by about 0.7%, but may reduce seismic velocity by a considerable amount (tens of per cent) depending on the shape of the pores. Usually in crystalline rocks there are flat cracks along grain boundaries and cleavages, and these reduce the stiffness (and hence the velocities) much more so than do circular pores of the same volume. The effect usually decreases as cracks close with confining pressure (see *eg* Hall & Simmons 1979) but at the surface, velocities are often only 80% of those in the same rocks at high pressure.

Density and seismic velocity are of particular value when regional rock units have modest internal variation in these properties but contrast with one another. Then gravity and seismological surveys can be interpreted to locate hidden boundaries between the units. The contrast between Kylesku Group rocks of the mainland central belt and the Rhiconich Group rocks of the northern belt has been used in this way (Hall 1978*a*).

The magnetization of Lewisian rocks has been examined by Powell (1970), who found that magnetite content exerted the primary control. Pyroxene-granulites tend to have more magnetite possibly because of its release during metamorphism to this grade. The magnetite content in the granulites generates greater intensities of magnetization than similar amounts in amphibolites, which are variably but usually more weakly magnetized. This makes it difficult to generalize about amphibolites so that the identification of granulite terrains from strong magnetic field variation may be only locally valid.

Permeability depends solely on porosity, its magnitude and distribution. It tells nothing of lithology. Its importance is in work on fluid flow through the Lewisian—now, in the permeable, open-crack zone near surface and possible deep porous zones; and past, in the metamorphic and uplift history of the rocks. Electromagnetic surveys reveal crustal layers of contrasted electrical conductivity which may imply variations in porosity in the crust, the interpretation of which must involve permeability variation.

Gravity and magnetic surveys of structures involving Lewisian rocks

Regional gravity (Hipkin & Hussain 1983) and BGS aeromagnetic maps provide a background data base on which a number of gravimetric, magnetometric, seismological and electromagnetic surveys have been based to indicate the structure of the Lewisian surface and its internal boundaries. The results are summarized in Fig. 1.

Powell (1970) compared the observed magnetic fields over the central belt of the mainland, and over Barra, Tiree and Coll, to suggest that similar dispositions of variably magnetized rocks would need to be buried by at least 10 km of weakly magnetized cover in both the Minch and Sea of Hebrides basins to give the resultant low field variation in the basins. He also preferred that the magnetic high in the mainland northern belt be produced by a shallow granitic source, rather than by buried granulites (*cf* Bott *et al.* 1972). Powell recognized that strong magnetic anomalies along the eastern edge of the Outer Isles are associated with granulite facies rocks. This was upheld by McQuillin & Watson (1973) who pointed out that the variably retrogressed granulites and upper amphibolite facies rocks of eastern S. Uist and Harris are not all structurally above the Outer Isles Fault, but that the fault zone may have been partly controlled by a pre-existing boundary between the high-grade rocks and lower-grade migmatitic complexes to the west.

Westbrook (1974) showed that metagabbros in the South Harris igneous complex are responsible for strong magnetic anomalies and are likely therefore to account for the continuation of the anomalies 22 km NW of South Harris.

Bott *et al.* (1972) combined gravity and magnetic surveys to suggest that the granulites of the central belt continue at shallow depth below the lower grade rocks of the northern belt of the mainland. Hall (1978*a*) found no seismological evidence of the existence of buried granulites in the top 2–4 km of the northern belt, and pointed out that the gravity interpretation of Bott depended strongly on the choice of regional gradient—the anomaly could be satisfactorily explained by the seismic model (see below for further comment). An alternative explanation, that the magnetic anomaly in the northern belt is caused by a granite, has been suggested by Powell (1970).

In the southern Inner Hebrides, Durrance (1976) and Westbrook & Borradaile (1978) showed from gravity and magnetic profiles that the shallow Lewisian of Islay and Colonsay is downthrown to the SE across the Loch Gruinart Fault but may continue below the Loch Skerrols Thrust (the likely equivalent of the Moine Thrust) on which the Dalradian of the Caledonides rides.

Gravity and magnetic surveys to the north (Watts 1971) and SW (Riddihough & Young 1971) of the area in Fig. 1 have been used to suggest offshore outcrops of Lewisian rocks extending NNE through the West Shetland continental shelf and between Islay and exposed Lewisian on Inishtrahull, north of Ireland.

Distribution of Lewisian and Lewisian-like rocks in northern Britain from seismic surveys

Hall (1978a), Hall & Al-Haddad (1976, 1979) and Hall & Simmons (1979) have shown that the seismic velocities of Lewisian rocks increase with depth due to crack closure, but that at depths of more than 1 km, amphibolite grade gneisses like those of the mainland northern belt have P-wave velocities of 5.9–6.1 km s^{-1}, whereas granulite facies rocks like those of the central belt have P-wave velocities of 6.4 km s^{-1} and greater. Given this guide line and the distribution of velocities indicated on Fig. 1, some broad indications of the lateral and depth distribution of these rocks may be given. (a) There is no other area in Fig. 1 covered by refraction seismics where rocks like those of the central belt occur at surface. (b) Nearly the whole of the basement surface in the area of Fig. 1 has a P-wave velocity like that of the northern belt. Thus the quartzo-feldspathic amphibole gneisses of that belt are a satisfactory analogue of the upper crust for virtually the whole area. East of the Moine Thrust, other rock groups are also present but appear to give the same velocity. (c) The only exceptions to (b) are the central belt and areas west of the Outer Isles where there is local evidence (Jones 1981, Hughes et al. 1984) of near surface velocities around 6.3 km s^{-1} in one or two areas (Fig. 1, lines W. et al. 5, JM 11, 17). These are likely to be granulite terrains perhaps akin to those of the eastern parts of the Outer Isles, which lack the abundant layered basic complexes of the central belt granulites. This would account for the P-wave velocity being somewhat lower. Poisson's Ratio of 0.27 observed by Hughes et al. (1984) is lower than that of the central belt but higher than that

of the northern belt (Hall & Ali 1985), and is compatible with the interpretation offered here that the rocks are more acid granulites than those of the central belt.

In the deeper crust, a mid-crustal layer with P-wave velocity about 6.4 km s^{-1} occurs both on the Archaean foreland north of Scotland (Smith & Bott 1975) and below the Caledonides (Bamford et al. 1978). The Central Belt granulites are a satisfactory analogue of this layer (Hall & Simmons 1979), though in the southern Highlands a similar granulite facies mid-crust would result from Caledonide metamorphism of rocks other than Lewisian (Hall 1978b).

West of the mainland there is no evidence of a discrete 6.4 km s^{-1} layer, though velocities do appear to increase downwards in both HMSP (Bott et al. 1979) and WISE (Summers 1982) to values approaching those of the central belt.

In interpreting the LUST refraction data and the local gravity, Hall (1978a) showed that the gravity low north of the boundary between central and northern Belts is accounted for by the velocity contrast in the top 2 km, assuming a reasonable velocity–density conversion. This yields a gravity anomaly of opposite sense once the 2 km-thick seismic model is stripped off. The uncertainties of the regional gravity and of the velocity–density equivalence make it inappropriate to quantify this in detail, but the obvious conclusion is that the central belt rocks are a thin layer (a few kilometres thick?) above a less dense basement.

Thus it is concluded that the central belt granulite complex may be exotic, a structural outlier from a mid-crustal granulite layer seen to the north of the mainland and below the northern Highlands. To the west, no such discrete layer is seen, though more acid granulite complexes like the remnants in the Outer Isles may be present both at depth in this area and in some areas of shallow basement, particularly west of the Outer Isles. Powell (1978) has shown that a division of the LISPB mid-crustal layer into amphibolitized and pyroxene granulites can provided a satisfactory fit to the regional magnetic field.

The deepest crustal layer in northern Britain has P-wave velocity of around 7 km s^{-1} (Bamford 1978) and Poisson's ratio of 0.24–0.25 (Assumpcao & Bamford 1978). The basic complexes in the central belt could be an analogue of this layer (Hall & Simmons 1979) but the retrogression to amphibolites would require the basic rocks to have a very strong regional amphibole fabric to produce the observed Poisson's ratio. An alternative explanation, that the lower crust is basic and 'dry' (Hall 1978b) appears to be at odds with evidence from electrical conductivity estimates (Mbipom & Hutton 1983) which suggest that the

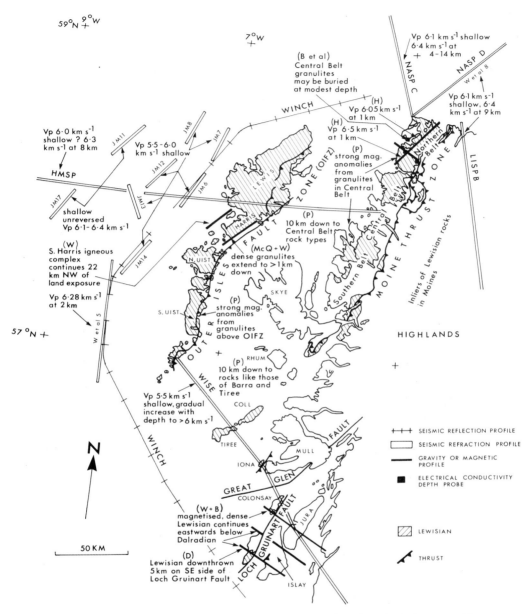

FIG. 1. Map of NW Britain showing outcrop of Lewisian rocks and location of geophysical surveys with notes on their interpretation. For seismic surveys, references are as follows. NASP C, D: Smith & Bott (1975). LISPB: Bamford *et al.* (1978). W. *et al.* 5, 8: White *et al.* (1982), Hughes *et al.* (1984). JM: Jones (1981). HMSP: Bott *et al.* (1979). LUST: Hall (1978), Hall & Ali (1985). WISE: Summers (1982). WINCH: Brewer *et al.* (1983). For gravity and magnetic profiles, references are as follows. B *et al.*: Bott *et al.* (1972). P: Powell (1970). McQ + W: McQuillin & Watson (1973). W: Westbrook (1974). W + B: Westbrook & Borradaile (1978). D: Durrance (1976). For electrical conductivity work, see Mbipom & Hutton (1983).

lower crust contains free or, at least, combined water (Hall 1985).

Porosity, permeability and electrical conductivity

Lewisian rocks have low porosities, usually less than 1%. From *P*- and *S*-wave velocities it is possible to estimate porosity, and from the LUST refraction profile (Hall & Ali 1985), crack densities decrease downwards from the surface as cracks close up under the lithostatic load. Near surface porosity may be regionally about 0.5% decreasing to comparatively negligible amounts at 2 km. This is in agreement with what would be expected from differential strain analysis on Lewisian samples which indicate that most microcracks in surface examples of the Lewisian close under a few hundred bars of effective pressure.

Given the downward decrease in porosity indicated by the field seismic data, it is possible to estimate permeability and electrical conductivity, after making assumptions about crack width and electrolyte conductivity (Table 2).

From scanning electron microscopy, the most abundant microcracks are grain boundary cracks especially around quartz grains, and these are about one micron wide. If permeation in the Lewisian were along such cracks, permeabilities would be as high as 10^{-18} m^2 (1 microdarcy) at the surface reducing to values less than 10^{-21} m^2, below a kilometre or so. Such changes in permeability as a function of confining pressure have been observed by the author in measurements on Lewisian gneisses; though the range of permeabilities is very much wider (high in wider transgranular cracks; low in sealed crack rocks). Thus the exposed Lewisian appears to have a potential ground-water flow zone several hundred metres deep below which very little flow is likely (at least at grain scale).

Estimates of electrical conductivity, assuming the porosities indicated and a sea-water brine (0.6 N NaCl), give values which decrease with depth (Table 2) and concur with measured values (Mbipom & Hutton 1983).

Allowing for temperature rise through the crust, the high electrical conductivity of the deep crust would appear to require that the porosity be as high as that in surface Lewisian rocks. It is difficult to see how this can be sustained unless the deep crustal fluid is at high pressure, near lithostatic. If the porosity is so high in the deep crust and the crack shapes are like those in surface rocks, then the seismic velocities would be like those in surface rocks. Variation between porous and non-porous rocks would be like that between surface Lewisian and Lewisian at depths of a few kilometres. Velocity contrasts would thus be 20%, enough to provide the observed reflectivity of the deep crust in northern Britain seen in WINCH (Brewer *et al.* 1983; Hall *et al.* 1984).

Lewisian analogues of the deep crust of NW Britain

From the summary given above it is clear that a variety of Lewisian rocks could be satisfactory analogues of various parts of the deep crust in NW Britain. A cartoon summarizing the likenesses is given in Fig. 2. It should be emphasized that these likenesses do not imply that the middle or deep crust is of Lewisian derivation.

TABLE 2. *Estimates of effect of cracks in shallow Lewisian as observed in LUST on transport properties (Hall & Ali 1985)*

Depth (m)	Crack Density (ε)	Aspect Ratio (α)	Porosity ($\frac{4}{3}\pi\varepsilon\alpha$)	Permeability (10^{-21} m^2)	Electrical Conductivity 10^{-3} S m^{-1}		
0	0.36	0.3×10^{-3}	0.45%	460	0.062 [5°C]	0.62 [300°C]	6.2 [300°C]
250	0.20	0.27×10^{-3}	0.23%	61	0.019 [8°C]	0.15 [300°C]	1.5 [300°C]
1000	0.09	0.15×10^{-3}	0.07%	2	0.003 [17°C]	0.016 [300°C]	0.16 [300°C]
2000‡	0.04	0.03×10^{-3}	0.005%	10^{-4}	10^{-5} [30°C]	0.001 [300°C]	0.01 [300°C]
						*	*†

Crack density from Hall & Ali (1985). Aspect ratio estimated from differential strain analysis.
Permeability = (crack width)^2 (porosity)^3/5, assuming crack width is 5 micron.
Electrical conductivity = (porosity)^2 (conductivity of fluid), assuming fluid is 0.6 N NaCl at temperatures given in brackets.
* Estimates for deep crust conductivity († for 6N NaCl).
‡ Values at 2000 m are strongly dependent on estimates of closed crack properties of rock and transport properties may be under-estimated.

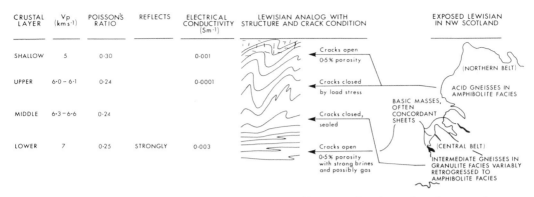

CRUSTAL LAYER	Vp (km s⁻¹)	POISSON'S RATIO	REFLECTS	ELECTRICAL CONDUCTIVITY (Sm⁻¹)	LEWISIAN ANALOG WITH STRUCTURE AND CRACK CONDITION	EXPOSED LEWISIAN IN NW SCOTLAND
SHALLOW	5	0·30		0·001	Cracks open 0·5% porosity	(NORTHERN BELT)
UPPER	6·0 – 6·1	0·24		0·0001	Cracks closed by load stress	ACID GNEISSES IN AMPHIBOLITE FACIES
MIDDLE	6·3 – 6·6	0·24			Cracks closed, sealed	BASIC MASSES, OFTEN CONCORDANT SHEETS
LOWER	7	0·25	STRONGLY	0·003	Cracks open 0·5% porosity with strong brines and possibly gas	(CENTRAL BELT) INTERMEDIATE GNEISSES IN GRANULITE FACIES VARIABLY RETROGRESSED TO AMPHIBOLITE FACIES

FIG. 2. Characteristics of the continental crust of NW Britain, with suggested analogues from the exposed Lewisian in Sutherland.

References

ASSUMPCAO, M. & BAMFORD, D. 1978. LISPB V. Studies of crustal shear waves. *Geophys. J. R. astr. Soc.* **54**, 61–73.

BAMFORD, D., NUNN, K., PRODEHL, C. & JACOB, B. 1978. LISPB IV. Crustal structure of Northern Britain. *Geophys. J. R. astr. Soc.* **54**, 43–60.

BOTT, M. H. P., HOLLAND, J. G., STORRY, P. G. & WATTS, A. B. 1972. Geophysical evidence concerning the structure of the Lewisian of Sutherland, NW Scotland. *J. geol. Soc. London* **128**, 599–612.

——, ARMOUR, A. R., HIMSWORTH, E. M., MURPHY, T. & WYLIE, G. 1979. An explosion seismology investigation of the continental margin west of the Hebrides, Scotland, at 58°N. *Tectonophysics* **59**, 217–231.

BREWER, J. A., MATTHEWS, D. H., WARNER, M. R., HALL, J., SMYTHE, D. K. & WHITTINGTON, R. J. 1983. BIRPS deep seismic reflection studies of the British Caledonides. *Nature*, **305**, 206–210.

DURRANCE, E. M. 1976. A gravity survey of Islay, Scotland. *Geol. Mag.* **113**, 251–261.

HALL, J. 1978a. LUST—a seismic refraction survey of the Lewisian basement complex in NW Scotland. *J. geol. Soc. London*, **135**, 555–563.

—— 1978b. Crustal structure of the eastern North Atlantic seaboard. *In*: BOWES, D. R. & LEAKE, B. E. (eds) *Crustal evolution in northwestern Britain and adjacent regions. Spec. Issue Geol. J.* No. **10**, 23–38.

—— 1985. The physical properties of layered rocks in deep continental crust. *In*: DAWSON, J. B., CARSWELL, D. A., HALL, J. & WEDEPOHL, H. (eds). *Nature of the Lower Continental Crust. Spec. Vol. geol. Soc. London*, (in press).

—— & AL-HADDAD, F. M. 1976. Seismic velocities in the Lewisian metamorphic complex, northwest Britain—'in-situ' measurements. *Scott. J. Geol.* **12**, 305–314.

—— & —— 1979. Variation of effective seismic velocities of minerals with pressure and its use in velocity prediction. *Geophys. J. R. astr. Soc.* **57**, 107–118.

—— & ALI, M. 1985. Shear waves in a seismic survey of Lewisian basement: an extra control on lithological variation and porosity. *J. geol. Soc. London*, **142**, 677–688.

——, BREWER, J. A., MATTHEWS, D. H. & WARNER, M. R. 1984. Crustal structure across the Caledonides from the WINCH seismic reflection profile: influences on the evolution of the Midland Valley of Scotland. *Trans. R. Soc. Edinb.: Earth Sci.* **75**, 97–109.

—— & SIMMONS, G. 1979. Seismic velocities of Lewisian metamorphic rocks at pressures to 8 kbar: relationship to crustal layering in North Britain. *Geophys. J. R. astr. Soc.* **58**, 337–347.

HIPKIN, R. G. & HUSSAIN, A. 1983. Regional gravity anomalies. 1 Northern Britain. *Rep. Inst. geol. Sci.* No. 82/10.

HUGHES, V. J., WHITE, R. S. & JONES, E. J. W. 1984. Seismic velocity structure of the northwest Scottish continental margin: some constraints imposed by amplitude studies. *Ann. Geophys.* **2**, 669–678.

JONES, E. J. W. 1981. Seismic refraction shooting on the continental margin west of the Outer Hebrides, northwest Scotland. *J. geophys. Res.* **86**, 11553–11574.

MBIPOM, E. W. & HUTTON, V. R. S. 1983. Geoelectromagnetic measurements across the Moine Thrust and the Great Glen in northern Scotland. *Geophys. J. R. astr. Soc.* **74**, 507–524.

MCQUILLIN, R. & WATSON, J. 1973. Large scale basement structures of the Outer Hebrides in the light of geophysical evidence. *Nature (Phys. Sci).* **245**, 1–3.

POWELL, D. W. 1970. Magnetised rocks within the Lewisian of western Scotland and under the Southern Uplands. *Scott. J. Geol.* **6**, 353–369.

—— 1978. Gravity and magnetic anomalies attributable to basement sources under northern Britain. *In*: BOWES, D. R. & LEAKE, B. E. (eds) *Crustal evolution in northwestern Britain and adjacent regions.* Geol. J. Spec. Issue No. **10**, 107–14.

RIDDIHOUGH, R. P. & YOUNG, D. G. G. 1971. Gravity and magnetic surveys of Inishowen and adjoining sea areas off the north coast of Ireland. *Proc. geol. Soc. London*, **1664**, 215–220.

SMITH, P. J. & BOTT, M. H. P. 1975. Structure of the crust beneath the Caledonian foreland and Caledonian belt of the North Scottish shelf region. *Geophys. J. R. astr. Soc.* **40**, 187–205.

SUMMERS, T. P. 1982. *A seismic study of crustal structure in the region of the Western Isles of Scotland.* Unpubl. PhD thesis Univ. Durham.

WATTS, A. B. 1971. Geophysical investigations on the continental shelf and slope north of Scotland. *Scott. J. Geol.* **7**, 189–218.

WESTBROOK, G. K. 1974. The South Harris magnetic anomaly. *Proc. Geol. Ass.* **85**, 1–12.

—— & BORRADAILE, G. J. 1978. The geological significance of magnetic anomalies in the region of Islay. *Scott. J. Geol.* **14**, 213–224.

WHITE, R. S., JONES, E. J. W., HUGHES, V. J. & MATTHEWS, D. H. 1982. Crustal structure from two-ship multichannel seismic profiles on the continental shelf off northwest Scotland. *Tectonophysics*, **90**, 167–178.

J. HALL, Department of Geology, University of Glasgow, Glasgow G12 8QQ, UK.

Deep seismic reflection profiling of the Lewisian foreland

D. K. Smythe

SUMMARY: A number of marine deep seismic reflection profiles cross the Hebridean shelf, the Lewisian foreland to the Caledonian orogen. They include the BIRPS MOIST, WINCH and DRUM profiles, several recent commercial deep lines, and many old and new conventional commercial exploration profiles. Basement, comprising the upper crust, is largely devoid of coherent seismic reflections. In contrast, the mid-crust contains many reflectors which may be relics of early Palaeozoic, Caledonian (or earlier Grenvillian) eastward-dipping thrust zones, which pass into an acoustically strongly layered lower crust.

The Outer Isles Thrust is mapped from the surface to the mid-crust, and tied into its land outcrop on north Lewis. Reactivation of this thrust as a normal fault caused the formation of the Sea of the Hebrides, Minch and North Lewis Basins. The Moho is defined by a strong band of reflections at a rather uniform 27 km depth. The eastward-dipping Flannan Thrust can be mapped into the upper mantle from about 15 to 45 km depth.

The Moine Thrust, which carries rocks of the orogen over Lewisian foreland, dips at 20–25° to the east on MOIST, and is either the westernmost of a series of easterly-dipping reflections (thrusts) which flatten or terminate at 17–20 km depth, or a more easterly thrust which structurally overlies these easterly-dipping reflectors. In neither case are the easterly-dipping reflectors themselves likely to be simply 'Caledonised' Lewisian foreland.

The NW margin of the Caledonian orogen and its Proterozoic foreland to the west have been the subject of many crustal-scale geophysical surveys in the last decade. It is here that, in the last five years, marine deep seismic reflection profiling has demonstrated its ability to relate major crustal structure to near-surface geology. It has also revealed new lithosphere-scale structures such as the Flannan Thrust, which extends from the lower crust of the foreland to about 90 km depth beneath the margin of the orogen, that is, nearly to the base of the lithosphere.

The NW Scottish shelf was the focus of much of the first two years of marine deep seismic reflection research by the newly-set up British Institutions' Reflection Profiling Syndicate (BIRPS). The arguments in favour of acquiring seismic reflection data offshore, as a departure from the established American COCORP practice of working onshore, are firstly, that offshore data acquisition is an order of magnitude cheaper than onshore (processing costs being similar), and secondly, that offshore data are also of better quality than their onshore equivalent. The grave disadvantage, of course, is that marine reflection data cannot be as directly linked to land exposure as an onshore survey.

This review draws extensively on two papers, one dealing with the seismic reflection structure of the western margin of the orogen (Brewer & Smythe 1984), the other with the foreland itself (Brewer & Smythe 1986). The present paper summarizes this earlier work, but also refers to very recent work and new data not covered before.

Deep seismic reflection profiles

MOIST and WINCH

The first BIRPS line, the Moine and Outer Isles Seismic Traverse (MOIST), was recorded at sea just north of the coast of Scotland for the Institute of Geological Sciences in 1981 (Smythe *et al.* 1982). It crosses the northern margin of the Caledonian orogen (Fig. 1), in an analogous position to COCORP profiles in the Appalachians (Brewer & Smythe 1984).

The Western Isles–North Channel (WINCH) reflection profile was recorded for BIRPS in 1982 at sea along the west coast of Britain (Brewer *et al.* 1983). Its purpose was to study crustal and upper mantle structure of the Caledonian foreland and orogen. The WINCH profile was designed to extend the results of the highly successful MOIST traverse (Figs 1 and 2).

DRUM, SHET and other data

The DRUM line (Deep Reflections from the Upper Mantle) was shot in 1984 for BIRPS by GECO, and processing, which is still in progress at the time of writing, is being carried out by Seismograph Services Ltd (SSL). However, a preliminary report has been published (McGeary & Warner 1985). DRUM is an ultra-deep reflection line, sub-parallel to MOIST (Fig. 1), but shot and processed to 30 s TWT, that is, potentially 110 km penetration of the lithosphere.

The SHET lines north and south of Shetland

From: PARK, R. G. & TARNEY, J. (eds), 1987, *Evolution of the Lewisian and Comparable Precambrian High Grade Terrains*, Geological Society Special Publication No. 27, pp. 193–203.

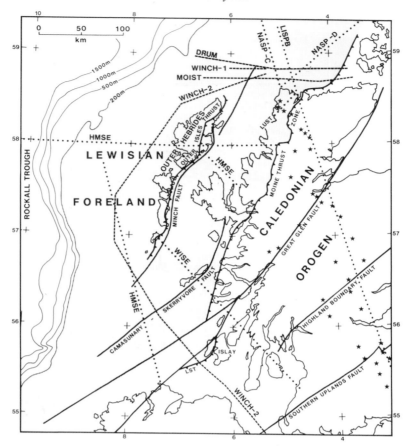

FIG. 1. Location of deep seismic profiles MOIST, WINCH and DRUM (dashed lines) in relation to the Caledonian orogen, foreland, and the passive continental margin of Rockall Trough to the west. Major faults are shown as solid lines. Dotted lines show locations of explosion crustal refraction profiles NASP, LUST, LISPB, HMSE (discussed in text) and WISE (unpublished). Stars show sites of the conductivity traverse parallel to LISPB (Hutton *et al.* 1980). LST—Loch Skerrols thrust.

have also been obtained for BIRPS, under the same arrangements as for DRUM, but are 'conventional' 15 s deep reflection lines. Like MOIST and DRUM, two of these lines cross the margin of the orogen. However, as processing and interpretation of these lines is at an earlier stage than DRUM they will not be discussed further.

Commercial speculative survey profiles, generally of pre-1973 vintage, are abundant in the foreland area west of the Hebrides. These data provide three-dimensional control on some basement reflectors, but in general are of limited value, because they are only recorded to 5 or 6 seconds (15–18 km depth) and, as discussed below, the upper crust down to these depths is generally rather transparent. Since 1981 there has been a revival of interest in exploration reflection

profiling west of Scotland, although this has naturally been concentrated in the basin areas of the Minches, Sea of the Hebrides, and west of Orkney. Several of these lines have been shot to 15 s, and one, shot by Merlin Profilers in collaboration with BGS, has been recorded and processed, like DRUM, to 30 s. The result of all this activity is that one crucial area of the foreland (in deep reflection terms) NE of Lewis now has no less than six 15 or 30 s profiles crossing it.

Regional geology

WINCH and MOIST describe a complete traverse running from the western margin of the Caledonian orogen along the north coast of Scotland into the foreland west of the Outer

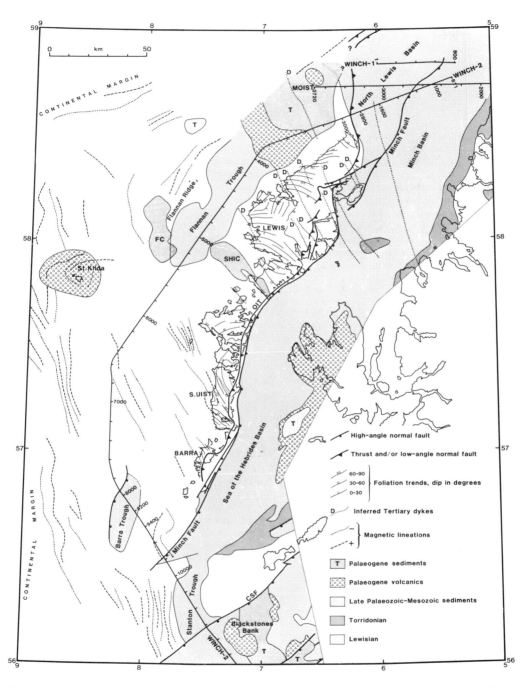

FIG. 2. Geology of the foreland relevant to the interpretation of deep reflection profiles. Foliation trends on the Outer Hebrides are taken from unpublished BGS tectonic maps. SHIC—South Harris igneous complex. FC—'Flannan complex' of high-amplitude magnetic anomalies. OIT—Outer Isles thrust. CSF—Camasunary-Skerryvore fault. Note how the throw of the Minch fault decreases to zero north and south of the Outer Hebrides (see text).

Hebrides (Fig. 1), crossing the boundary of the orogen again off the SW coast of Scotland near the island of Islay.

Figure 2 is a new compilation of the geology of the foreland region. It is based on interpretation of the BIRPS and commercial reflection data, and commercial, BGS and Hydrographic Office aeromagnetic and gravity surveys. Further details of these data are given in Brewer & Smythe (1986).

The Caledonian foreland is a complex of gneisses and granulites incorporating metasediments, metavolcanics and metamorphosed layered basic and anorthositic bodies, with various granites and pegmatites that constitute Lewisian basement rocks (see Watson 1975, for a review). The earliest recognizable structure (ductile shear zones, sometimes associated with gravity anomalies), generally characterized by a NNE grain, were established before the end of the Scourian episode (c. 2700 Ma). Tectonic and metamorphic activity continued intermittently until about 1600 Ma. The later phases, the Laxfordian deformation, created narrow NW–SE zones of strong deformation between blocks, within which pre-Laxfordian features are less severely modified. Granites and pegmatites were emplaced ubiquitously during the late stages of Laxfordian activity, accompanied by retrogression to amphibolite facies of granulites formed in earlier Laxfordian or Scourian episodes.

The Caledonian foreland is bounded to the west by the passive continental margin of the Rockall Trough (Fig. 1), a major rift formed during the early phases of opening of the North Atlantic.

Foreland Lewisian is overlain by two cover sequences: (1) the Torridonian, consisting of sandstones and conglomerates (1100–1040 Ma; Smith *et al.* 1983) thought to have been laid down in an extensional, block-faulted environment (Stewart 1982), and (2) Cambrian–Ordovician quartzites and carbonates thought to have been laid down in shallow, subtidal conditions on a continental shelf bounding the western margin of the 'proto-Atlantic' (Swett & Smit 1972).

To the east of the foreland lies the Caledonian orogen. On land, the orogenic front is defined by the Moine Thrust zone (Fig. 1). Proterozoic metasediments (originally mainly shallow marine or lacustrine sands or shales) of the Moine succession lie above this zone, and moved westward over the foreland an unknown distance during the late episodes (Silurian–Devonian) of the Caledonian orogeny (see the discussions in Watson & Dunning 1979, and Brewer & Smythe 1984).

The Moine Thrust is the structurally highest thrust of the Moine Thrust zone, and the zone itself consists of the intensely imbricated shelf sequence, including thrust slices of Lewisian and Torridonian, which were stripped off the autochthonous basement.

Lewisian-type inliers occur in the Moine schists either as basement onto which some of the Moines were laid down, or as thrust slices (Watson 1975). One of the key problems is the extent of foreland Lewisian basement under the orogen. Although estimates of the amount of shortening along individual thrusts range up to 60–70 km (Elliott & Johnson 1980), gravity and magnetic signatures suggest that autochthonous basement may only extend 20–30 km east of the Moine Thrust zone (Watson & Dunning 1979, p 73). Two groups of ideas have evolved, both based on surface mapping and on the interpretation of velocities obtained from the LISPB regional refraction survey (Bamford *et al.* 1978). Elliott and Johnson consider that the imbricated Cambrian–Ordovician succession under the Moine Thrust can be palinspastically restored. They suggest that up to 100 km of shortening has occurred in the region of the Assynt window. This implies that very gently-sloping foreland basement once extended this far east under the orogen. Thin-skinned models for the Moine Thrust zone have also been proposed by Coward (1980) and Butler & Coward (1984).

In contrast, a thick-skinned model has been postulated by Soper & Barber (1982), who consider that the thrust zone cuts through the crust at up to 45°, flattening out at the Moho. Blundell *et al.* (1985) have modified Soper & Barber's model to be compatible with the MOIST profile, which they have modelled with a synthetic seismogram. They show how the foreland is likely to have been cut by large, discrete thrusts propagating succesively deeper and farther west, as a consequence of the lower geothermal gradient there during the Caledonian orogeny, compared with the orogen.

Thrust faulting was apparently the only major effect of the Caledonian orogeny on the foreland. One major structure, which was compiled from earlier mapping and named the Outer Isles Thrust by Dearnley (1962), but is also known as the Outer Hebrides Fault (Sibson 1975, 1977) is subparallel to the Moine Thrust, and therefore assumed to be of Caledonian age, although it can only be said with certainty to be post-Laxfordian.

After the Caledonian orogeny the areas of the orogen and foreland which now lie offshore were subject to extension associated with the opening of the North Atlantic. Basins such as the Flannan Trough and Minch Basin were filled with Permo–Triassic and younger sediments. The general trend of these basins shows that their structure was controlled by the underlying Caledonian framework. The MOIST profile showed in detail that many of these basins formed by extensional reactivation of Caledonian thrusts (Smythe *et al.* 1982). In many areas, though, the sedimentary rocks in the deepest parts of the basins are undated, and it is possible that some of the basins are immediately post-orogenic (*ie* Devonian) in age. Some are probably as old as Torridonian (*c.* 1000 Ma); this is discussed below.

Other geophysical studies

Northern Scotland and the Scottish continental shelf have been the subject of many seismic studies on both regional and local scales, partly because of the extensive exposures of Precambrian basement, and the opportunity it allows to study rocks from deep within the crust. The regional refraction studies (LISPB, NASP and HMSE; see Fig. 1) have proved useful for locating the Moho (the crust–mantle boundary) whereas the local studies show velocity variations in the upper part of the crust possibly explicable in terms of varying basement geology. These refraction experiments are reviewed by Hall (this volume). However, the structure of the mid-crust, in particular along the boundary zone of the orogen, is not well understood.

Crustal structure of the foreland

The foreland is considered to extend as far to the SE as the Loch Skerrols Thrust (Fig. 1), which has long been thought to be the southwesterly extension of the Moine Thrust (Bailey 1917). The Loch Skerrols Thrust appears to mark a major sub-vertical offset of Lewisian basement (Westbrook & Borradaile 1978), and therefore may also mark the orogenic front to the Caledonian orogen.

The Outer Isles Thrust

The fault known on the Outer Hebrides as the Outer Isles Thrust (Dearnley 1962) was originally interpreted offshore, using commercial seismic reflection data, as a sequence of reflectors dipping at about 25° from the seabed north of Lewis into the lower crust (Smythe 1980). It was subsequently identified on MOIST (Smythe *et al.* 1982) and WINCH (Brewer *et al.* 1983), and traced into the lower crust. Figure 3 shows a newly-migrated version of WINCH–1, on which the thrust is clearly visible. It can be traced from WINCH and MOIST onto commercial seismic data, to within 4–5 km of the position of the fault onshore

(Fig. 4*a*). However, on the offshore data the only demonstrable offset on the fault is extensional, as shown by the formation of the major half-grabens. All the evidence of thrusting comes from onshore studies, suggesting that the normal faulting observed offshore must be simply a reactivation of the pre-existing thrust. Since Wernicke *et al.* (1985) and Wernicke (1986) have questioned this prior existence of the normal fault as a thrust, it is worth summarizing the evidence in support of thrust movements. It includes: (1) a thick (up to 1 km) sequence of mylonites, pseudotachylites and cataclastic rocks, more commonly seen around thrusts than around normal faults. (2) a schistosity developed in the ductile shear zones which intensifies and curves in from the margins to the centre in a thrust sense. (3) the presence in the hanging wall of granulite facies rocks, of higher metamorphic grade (and therefore presumably originating from greater depths) than the amphibolite facies rocks which make up the footwall. (4) a shallow (~25°) dip of the fault zone at the surface. See, however, White & Glasser (this vol.). Later dip-slip movement is indicated by a fairly ubiquitous series of late stage, asymmetric crenulations and chevron folds with consistent down-dip vergence (Sibson 1977).

Furthermore, if the Outer Isles fault feature mapped onshore were just the exposed plane of a low-angle normal fault, it would imply that the Minch-Sea of the Hebrides Basin (Fig. 2) once extended some way to the west over the Outer Hebrides, burying the present-day outcrop to a depth of several kilometres. There is no evidence for such a hypothetical burial and re-exhumation of the Outer Hebrides, which would have to have occurred in late Jurassic–Cretaceous time.

The age of the fault rocks is uncertain. They are definitely post-Laxfordian (they cut host rocks of this age), but the only radiometric investigations are whole-rock K–Ar experiments on micaceous mylonites which gave late Caledonian ages (see the discussion by R. H. Sibson in Steel & Wilson 1975).

The Outer Isles Thrust is conventionally regarded as of Caledonian age, but there is indirect evidence from offshore reflection interpretation that it may be of Grenville age. Williams (1969) interpreted the late Torridonian (Torridon Group) of NW Scotland as a piedmont fan deposit, with the source area of the retreating mountain front in the region of the present-day Minch Basin and Lewis. Extrapolation westwards of the mainland Torridonian outcrop below the Minches (Chesher *et al.* 1983), combined with the re-interpretation of earlier gravity modelling (Smythe *et al.* 1972), suggests that the basal part of the half-graben infill of the Minch and North

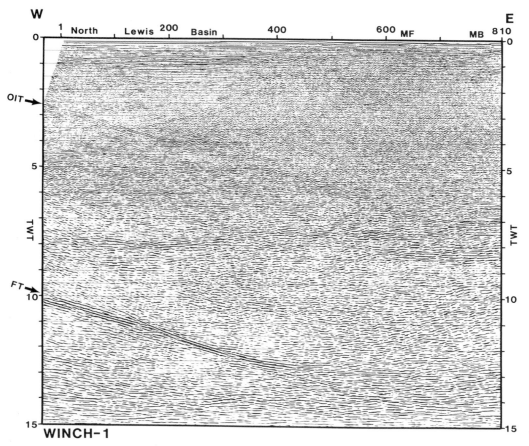

FIG. 3. WINCH–1 30-fold migrated section. Migration was done in the F–K domain using a 1–dimensional velocity function. 100 SP = 5 km. Processing through stack by GECO for BIRPS, 1982; post-stack migration and display by Western Geophysical for BGS, 1985. OIT—Outer Isles thrust. FT—Flannan thrust. MF—Minch fault. MB—Minch basin. To convert two-way time in seconds to approximate depth in kilometres, multiply by 3. Note that the Minch basin has almost died out this far north, and that upper crustal extension is taken up in the North Lewis basin, which directly overlies the Outer Isles thrust.

Lewis Basins is of Torridonian age, lying in the hanging wall of the Outer Isles Thrust. Given the palaeogeographic setting of these rocks, it is reasonable, firstly, that the fault now bounding the prism of sediment was the main normal fault active at *c.* 1000 Ma, controlling the deposition of the fan deposits. Secondly, and more specula-tively, if the Outer Isles Thrust was active then as a normal fault, it may have been a reactivated thrust fault, originating in, say, Grenville time, *c.* 1100–1200 Ma.

The first part of this interpretation is now strongly corroborated by new (1985) commercial seismic reflection data in the Sea of the Hebrides (Kilenyi & Standley 1985), where a thick prism of Torridonian (dated by offshore sampling and by tying along strike to the Isle of Rhum) can

now be clearly seen to be faulted on its western flank by the Minch Fault (the reactivated Outer Isles Thrust; see also Kilenyi & Standley 1985, Fig. 4). The Torridonian wedge is locally more than 6 km thick, making it rather unlikely that the fault which now truncates it on the west was simply a posthumous, as opposed to a syn-rift, fault.

Peddy (1984) has proposed, from reflection seismogram modelling of WINCH–1, that the Outer Isles Thrust does not flatten out near the base of the crust, as conventional stacked record sections or time migrations of them (such as Fig. 3) suggest. The crustal model used as the basis for the seismogram modelling has the thrust cutting the Moho near the eastern end of the line. Although the Moho is correctly offset at the place

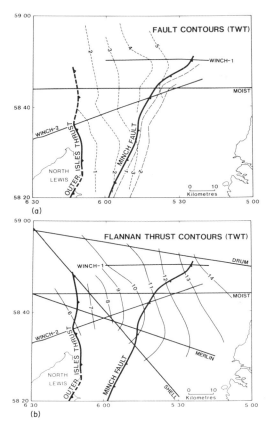

FIG. 4a. Unmigrated two-way time (TWT) contours on the Minch fault (long-dash lines) and the Outer Isles thrust (short dashed lines). MOIST, WINCH–1 and WINCH–2 are 15 s lines. The Outer Isles thrust offshore can be clearly identified with the same feature onshore on North Lewis by mapping it south using the other commercial data; see Brewer & Smythe (1986) for further details. The dashed portion of the Outer Isles Thrust, north of WINCH–2, is subcropping below sediments which overstep the fault to the west, hence the intersection of the fault trace with the 1 s contour.

FIG. 4b. Unmigrated two-way time (TWT) contours on the Flannan thrust, based on MOIST, WINCH–1 and WINCH–2 (Brewer and Smythe 1986), but also using the new 30 s DRUM line and a proprietary Shell line (McGeary & Warner 1985), together with a new Merlin Profilers 30 s line shot and processed in collaboration with BGS.

predicted by the synthetic seismogram, near the eastern end of the line (see Fig. 3), the new DRUM line (Fig. 1) does not show any sign of the thrust continuing in the mantle farther east (McGeary & Warner 1985), as might be expected from Peddy's hypothesis. Both alternatives—flattening out in the lower crust, or cutting

through the Moho—would appear to remain plausible at present.

Crustal reflection character

Most of the Lewisian basement crossed by WINCH is devoid of significant cover rocks, and the upper part of the crust (to 3–4 s, or 9–12 km depth) is remarkably featureless and transparent, at least on the scale of the wavelengths used in seismic surveys. However, full seismic coverage is achieved only below 3 s, and thus it is conceivable that the transparent upper crust simply is due to the incomplete coverage above this travel time.

Notwithstanding the acoustic imaging problems, it is probably a valid generalization (based on observations from all the various processing stages of the reflection data) that the upper crust in the Caledonian foreland is largely transparent to seismic energy in the frequency spectrum 10–50 Hz. The NW–SE trending shear zones associated with Laxfordian deformation (Watson 1975, 1977; see Fig. 2) have not been acoustically detected, at least in the upper crust.

In contrast to the upper crust, the lower crust is highly reflective between about 4 and 8–9 s (about 12–30 km depth). Figure 5 shows a sample of WINCH data from west of Lewis, at the intersection with HMSE (Fig. 1). Bands of discontinuous (up to 5–10 km long) antiformal reflections (some of which may be off-line), subhorizontal and apparently north-dipping reflections and diffractions make up the lower crustal reflection sequence. Reflector density is somewhat variable. The Moho appears as a discontinuous reflector or band of reflectors between 8 and 9 s (26–29 km depth) at the base of the lower crustal layer.

The reflection character of the Lewisian foreland is quite different from the character of the foreland to the Appalachian and Ouachita mountain belts, where they have been crossed by three COCORP profiles (Ando *et al.* 1983; Cook *et al.* 1979, 1981; Nelson *et al.* 1982). The Grenville age foreland basement in all these areas is essentially devoid of internal reflecting horizons, and in most areas there is no clear Moho reflection. If a seismically transparent crust is indeed characteristic of the Grenville province then the position of the Grenville front under Scotland might be detectable on this basis.

The Moho and upper mantle

On much of MOIST and DRUM there is a sharp, high-amplitude Moho, but no strongly reflective

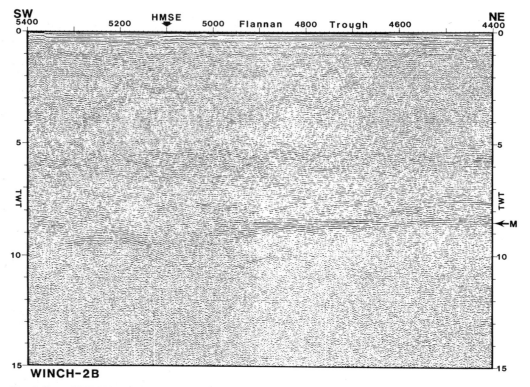

FIG. 5. Part of WINCH–2B (7.5–20 Hz bandpass display) over the foreland NW of Harris (Fig. 2). Gently N-dipping reflectors at 0–2 *s* are from within or just below the Flannan Trough, one of the few areas where upper crustal reflectors occur. The upper crust beneath (2–5 *s*) shows only incoherent reflections and diffractions, whereas the lower crust (5–8 *s*) is more reflective. The Moho band of reflections at around 8.4–9 *s* correlates well with the refraction-defined Moho on HMSE.

lower crust, whereas on WINCH a reflective lower crust occurs with a less well-defined Moho beneath. Jacob & Booth (1977) also inferred a sharp Moho boundary, based on a wide-angle seismic experiment which recorded good PS reflections east of the Outer Isles thrust. This result is consistent with the sharp Moho seen on MOIST and DRUM.

The Moho reflection differences between MOIST, DRUM and WINCH are not simply explicable by different processing parameters. Rather surprisingly, the travel time of the Moho reflection does not vary significantly with variations in upper crustal velocity structure. The most obvious example of this occurs under the North Lewis basin, where considerable velocity pulldown would be expected, but is not seen (Fig. 3).

The Flannan Thrust (Smythe *et al.* 1982) was interpreted as a thrust because it has a similar reflection character, and a similar geometry and Caledonian trend to the Outer Isles Thrust

(Fig. 3). However, no definite structural offsets have been identified across it, so this must remain a working hypothesis. The thrust dips easterly at 25–30° (from depth migration of line drawings), subparallel to the Outer Isles thrust, from at least 14 *s* (about 45 km depth) and passes updip through the Moho, which is not clearly offset. The 3-dimensional control on the geometry of the thrust is now constrained by no less than six seismic reflection lines shot to 15 or 30 *s* (Fig. 4*b*). It can also be traced down-dip right along the length of DRUM (Fig. 1), on which it can be seen at a depth of about 90 km at its eastern end (McGeary & Warner 1985). The possible continuation of the Flannan Thrust south of the Hebrides is seen on the WINCH line in that area (Brewer *et al.* 1983, Brewer & Smythe 1986), and also on a new Merlin Profilers proprietary 15 *s* line. It is apparently linked to an extensive upper mantle reflector (see Hall *et al.* 1984, for further discussion).

Lewisian basement beneath the orogen

The Moine Thrust has been interpreted as one of the series of pronounced easterly and south-easterly dipping (20°–25° migrated dip) reflections which characterize the eastern 60 km of the MOIST line (Fig. 1), and which give the upper and middle crust under the orogen a very different seismic character from that of the foreland. These reflections flatten or die out at around 17–20 km depth, and close to the surface are either directly overlain by westerly-dipping ?Devonian and Permo–Triassic sedimentary rocks occurring in half-grabens, or pass into acoustically transparent ('blank') zones beneath the half-grabens. Figure 6 shows a piece of a newly reprocessed and migrated segment of MOIST from the margin of the orogen offshore (Fig. 1), on which the easterly-dipping reflectors can be seen to be truncated against the overlying westerly-dipping reflectors. The easterly-dipping reflections can be mapped along strike on commercial seismic lines (Brewer & Smythe 1984). These authors have argued that the lozenge-shaped packages of easterly-dipping reflectors, within some of which the seismic layering is rather planar, could represent Moinian rocks above the thrust zone. Alternatively (their preferred interpretation), they may originate from an offshelf sequence of metasediments (of uncertain origin), imbricated with the underlying basement and stacked up against the undeformed Lewisian shelf edge. The Moine Thrust zone would then be a structurally higher thrust.

In neither of Brewer & Smythe's alternatives are the easterly-dipping reflectors part of the Lewisian foreland. However, Butler and Coward (1984) have proposed a reinterpretation of the MOIST data, in which the easterly-dipping reflectors are due to imbrication of Lewisian foreland in a crustal-scale duplex, below a large culmination in the Moine Thrust zone. Offshore, in the area of MOIST, the Caledonian cover and the thrust zone have been stripped off, so that the two sequences of westerly and easterly-dipping reflectors (Fig. 6) represent, respectively, the Devonian to Triassic sediments, and imbricated foreland beneath.

Resolution of the problem of how far the Lewisian foreland extends—'Caledonised' or not—below the orogen requires a reinterpretation of the offshore data, including that obtained recently. It will be especially desirable to link the west Orkney and northern Scottish mainland area to Shetland, where the equivalent of the Moine Thrust zone has been successfully taken offshore to the SW on to recent commercial reflection lines there (Andrews 1985).

Conclusions

Deep seismic reflection profiles across the Caledonian foreland demonstrate that: (1) the upper

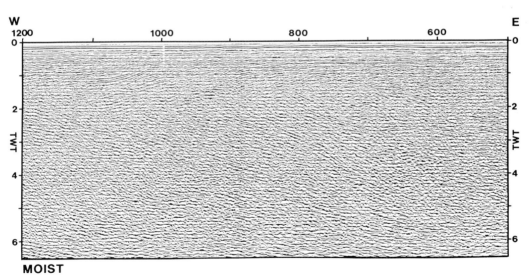

W   **E**

MOIST

FIG. 6. New, migrated version of part of MOIST, reprocessed for BGS by Western Geophysical, 1985. It shows the easterly-dipping reflectors of the mid-crust at the margin of the orogen (Fig. 1) truncated by the overlying west-dipping Devonian to Triassic age sediments. The easterly-dipping reflectors could be from imbricated Caledonian cover rocks (Brewer & Smythe 1984), or else represent imbricated Lewisian foreland, with no Caledonian cover present in this area offshore (Butler & Coward 1984).

crust is largely acoustically transparent, and little evidence of the trace of Precambrian structures is seen. (2) in contrast, the lower crust is acoustically highly reflective, and in some areas of the Hebridean shelf contains structures whose trends are possibly of Caledonian or Scourian age. (3) the crustal reflection character of the foreland to the Caledonides differs from the areas of the foreland to the Appalachians studied with COCORP data, where Grenville crust is largely non-reflective. (4) the Moho is a fairly continuous reflector or group of reflectors, and is remarkably uniform in travel time, at about 8.5 s ($\equiv 27$ km) below the foreland. It is apparently not significantly offset under the North Lewis and Minch basins, nor under the Outer Isles Thrust. (5) some of the basins on the Hebridean shelf are half-grabens formed by extensional reorientation of Caledonian thrusts. Conversely, where these thrusts do not exist, the shelf remained largely unaffected by extension. (6) the western margin

of the orogen contains reflection sequences whose geometry is remarkably similar to those observed on parts of COCORP profiles recorded in the northern and southern Appalachians. The Lewisian foreland of NW Scotland probably does not continue eastwards below the Caledonian overthrust belt for more than 20–30 km east of the Moine Thrust zone.

ACKNOWLEDGMENTS: I have benefited from discussions with many colleagues in Edinburgh and Cambridge, but especially from collaboration with Jon Brewer between 1981 and 1984. Western Geophysical were very cooperative and helpful in the reprocessing of the MOIST and WINCH data. Merlin Profilers kindly permitted early reference to their new proprietary surveys in the Minches.

The WINCH seismic reflection data were provided for BIRPS by the Deep Geology Committee of the Natural Environment Research Council. The paper is published by permission of the Director, British Geological Survey (NERC).

References

ANDO, C. J., COOK, F. A., OLIVER, J. E., BROWN, L. D. & KAUFMAN, S. 1983. Crustal geometry of the Appalachian orogen from seismic reflection studies. *Geol. Soc. Am. Mem.* **158**, 83–101.

ANDREWS, I. J. 1985. The deep structure of the Moine Thrust, southwest of Shetland. *Scott. J. Geol.* **21**, 213–17.

BAILEY, E. B. 1917. The Islay anticline (Inner Hebrides), *Quart. J. Geol. Soc. Lond.* **72**, 132–64.

BAMFORD, D., NUNN, K., PRODEHL, C. & JACOB, B. 1978. LISPB–IV. Crustal structure of northern Britain. *Geophys. J. R. astr. Soc.* **54**, 43–60.

BLUNDELL, D. J., HURICH, C. A. & SMITHSON, S. B. 1985. A model for the MOIST seismic reflection profile. *J. Geol. Soc. Lond.* **142**, 245–58.

BREWER, J. A. & SMYTHE, D. K. 1984. MOIST and the continuity of crustal reflector geometry along the Caledonian–Appalachian orogen, *J. Geol. Soc. Lond.* **141**, 105–20.

——— & SMYTHE, D. K. 1986. The BIRPS WINCH profile: deep structure of the foreland to the Caledonian orogen, NW Scotland. *Tectonics* **5**, 171–94.

———, MATTHEWS, D. H., WARNER, M. R., HALL, J., SMYTHE, D. K. & WHITTINGTON, R. J. 1983. BIRPS deep seismic reflection studies of the British Caledonides. *Nature, London* **305**, 206–10.

BUTLER, R. W. H. & COWARD, M. P. 1984. Geological constraints, structural evolution, and deep geology of the northwest Scottish Caledonides. *Tectonics* **3**, 347–65.

CHESHER, J. A., SMYTHE, D. K. & BISHOP, P. 1983. *The geology of the Minches, Inner Sound and Sound of Raasay.* Rep. Inst. Geol. Sci. No. 83/6.

COOK, F. A., ALBAUGH, D. S., BROWN, L. D., KAUFMAN, S., OLIVER, J. E. & HATCHER, R. D. 1979. Thin-skinned tectonics in the crystalline southern Appalachians: COCORP seismic reflection profiling of the Blue Ridge and Piedmont. *Geology* **7**, 563–7.

———, BROWN, L. D., KAUFMAN, S., OLIVER, J. E. & PETERSEN, T. A. 1981. COCORP seismic profiling of the Appalachian orogen beneath the coastal plain of Georgia. *Bull. geol. Soc. Am.* **93**, 738–48.

COWARD, M. 1980. The Caledonian thrust and shear zones of NW Scotland. *J. struct. Geol.* **2**, 11–17.

DEARNLEY, R. 1962. An outline of the Lewisian complex of the Outer Hebrides in relation to that of the Scottish mainland. *Q. J. Geol. Soc. Lon.* **118**, 143–76.

ELLIOTT, D. & JOHNSON, M. R. W. 1980. Structural evolution in the northern part of the Moine thrust belt, NW Scotland. *Trans. R. Soc. Edinb. Earth Sci.* **71**, 69–96.

HALL, J., BREWER, J. A., MATTHEWS, D. H., & WARNER, M. R. 1984. Crustal structure across the Caledonides from the 'WINCH' seismic reflection profile: Influences on Midland Valley evolution. *Trans. R. Soc. Edinb. Earth Sci.* **75**, 97–109.

JACOB, A. W. B. & BOOTH, D. C. 1977. Observations of PS reflections from the Moho. *J. Geophys.* **43**, 687–92.

KILENYI, T. & STANDLEY, B. 1985. Petroleum prospects in the northwest seaboard of Scotland. *Oil Gas J.* **83**, 100–108.

McGEARY, S. & WARNER, M. 1985. DRUM: seismic profiling of the lower continental lithosphere. *Nature, London* **317**, 795–7.

NELSON, K. D., LILLIE, R. J., DEVOOGD, B., BREWER, J. A., OLIVER, J. E., KAUFMAN, S. & BROWN, L. D. 1982. COCORP seismic reflection profiling in the Ouachita Mountains of western Arkansas: geometry and geologic interpretation, *Tectonics* **1**, 413–430.

PEDDY, C. P. 1984. Displacement of the Moho by Outer Isles Thrust shown by seismic modelling, *Nature, London* **312**, 628–30.

SIBSON, R. H. 1975. Generation of pseudotachylite by ancient seismic faulting, *Geophys. J. R. astr. Soc.* **43**, 775–94.

—— 1977. Fault rocks and fault mechanisms. *J. geol. Soc. Lond.* **133**, 191–213.

SMITH, R. L., STEARN, J. E. F. & PIPER, J. D. A. 1983. Palaeomagnetic studies of the Torridonian sediments, NW Scotland. *Scott. J. Geol.* **19**, 29–45.

SMYTHE, D. K. 1980. The deep structure of the Moine and Outer Isles Thrusts north of Cape Wrath and Lewis. *Geophys. J. R. astr. Soc.* **61**, 199.

——, DOBINSON, A., MCQUILLIN, R., BREWER, J. A., MATTHEWS, D. H., BLUNDELL, D. J. & KELK, B. 1982. Deep structure of the Scottish Caledonides revealed by the MOIST reflection profile. *Nature London* **299**, 338–40.

——, SOWERBUTTS, W. T. C., BACON, M. & MCQUILLIN, R. 1972. Deep sedimentary basin below northern Skye and the Little Minch, *Nature Phys. Sci.* **236**, 87–89.

SOPER, N. J. & BARBER, A. J. 1982. A model for the deep structure of the Moine Thrust Zone. *J. geol. Soc. Lond.* **139**, 127–38.

STEEL, R. J. & WILSON, A. C. 1975. Sedimentation and tectonism (?Permo-Triassic) on the margin of the North Minch Basin, Lewis. *J. Geol. Soc. Lond.* **131**, 183–202.

STEWART, A. D. 1982. Late Proterozoic rifting in NW Scotland: the genesis of the 'Torridonian'. *J. Geol. Soc. Lond.* **139**, 413–20.

SWETT, K. & SMIT, D. E. 1972. Paleogeography and depositional environments of the Cambro–Ordovician shallow marine facies of the North Atlantic. *Bull. geol. Soc. Am.* **83**, 3223–48.

WATSON, J. 1975. The Lewisian complex. *In:* HARRIS, A. L. *et al.* (eds) *A correlation of Precambrian rocks in the British Isles.* Spec. Rep. geol. Soc. Lond. **6**, 15–29.

——, 1977. The Outer Hebrides—a geological perspective, *Proc. Geol. Assoc.* **88**, 1–14.

—— & DUNNING, F. W. 1979. Basement-cover relations in the British Caledonides. *In:* HARRIS, A. L., HOLLAND, C. H. & LEAKE, B. E. (eds) *Caledonides of the British Isles—reviewed.* Spec. Publ. geol. Soc. Lond. **8**, 67–92.

WERNICKE, B. 1986. Whole-lithosphere normal simple shear: an interpretation of deep-reflection profiles in Great Britain. *In:* BARAZANGI, M. & BROWN, L. D. (eds). *Reflection Seismology: the continental crust.* Am Geophys. Union Geodynamics Series. **14**, 331–9.

——, WALKER, J. D. & BEAUFAIT, M. S. 1985. Structural discordance between Neogene detachments and frontal Sevier thrusts, central Mormon Mountains, southern Nevada. *Tectonics* **4**, 213–46.

WESTBROOK, G. K. & BORRODAILE, G. J. 1978. The geological significance of magnetic anomalies in the region of Islay. *Scott. J. Geol.* **14**, 213–24.

WILLIAMS, G. E. 1969. Petrography and origin of pebbles from Torridonian strata (Late Precambrian), northwest Scotland. *In:* KAY, M. (ed.) *North Atlantic—geology and continental drift. Mem. Am. Assoc. Petrol. Geol.* **12**, 609–29.

D. K. SMYTHE, British Geological Survey, Murchison House, West Mains Road, Edinburgh EH9 3LA, UK.

The palaeomagnetic record in the Lewisian terrain

J. D. A. Piper

SUMMARY: Palaeomagnetic investigations of the Lewisian rocks identify a diverse remanence record which varies from zone to zone. The characteristic (A) remanence in the central mainland zone is a strong and stable NW downward-directed and magnetite-held component. This occurs sporadically elsewhere but is largely displaced in the northern mainland zone and in Lewis and Harris by lower blocking temperature/coercivity components with more variable directions; in addition hematite overprints occur sporadically in the central zone and in the Loch Torridon area of the southern mainland zone. Geological relationships and palaeomagnetic field tests suggest that all of these components were acquired during post-Laxfordian uplift and cooling of this terrain but a steep E downward-directed component is a feature of pre-Laxfordian belts in the south and may be considerably older. The collective data define migration of the geomagnetic field axis during uplift and cooling of the terrain and are linked in general terms to mineral ages in the range c. 1720–1500 Ma; further rock magnetic and $^{39}Ar/^{40}Ar$ investigations are in progress to characterize the areal significance of the components of remanence and to date them more precisely.

Introduction

The palaeomagnetic study of metamorphic terrains is still in its infancy and the significance of their magnetizations is poorly understood. Often components with divergent directions but similar properties are observed in adjacent samples from the same site and it is evident that the remanence record was acquired at different times over a long interval. In place of one or more single coherent axes of magnetization, which are the outcome of palaeomagnetic studies in igneous and sedimentary rocks, distributions of directions are generally found which are interpreted to represent a composite record of the geomagnetic field during protracted periods of post-metamorphic uplift and cooling (see for example Buchan & Dunlop 1976, Piper 1985). These data are potentially very useful because not only do they record the magnitude of apparent polar wander (APW) over long periods of geological time, but they also define stages in the post-metamorphic history which may not be obvious from petrologic or structural studies. However, the interpretation is often very uncertain and, as will be evident from existing knowledge of the Lewisian terrain, it must be undertaken on a regional basis. Since metamorphic rocks acquire their remanence by a thermal process, the relaxation time of the remanence, and hence both the temperature interval over which it is acquired and its intensity, are dependent on cooling rate (Dodson & McClelland Brown 1980). It is predicted that progressive recovery of higher blocking temperature and/or blocking temperature fractions of the remanence by progressive cleaning will recover younger to older APW motion provided that the remanence resides in magnetite; this has been demonstrated, for example, in the Nagssugtoqidian terrain of West Greenland (Morgan 1976a). Furthermore, higher and earlier-cooled crustal levels may be expected to record older remanence than deeper, and therefore later-cooled, levels; this has also been demonstrated in West Greenland (Piper 1981). The trends suggested by these two predictions can be further tested by comparison of the remanences residing in high and low blocking temperature components at the same crustal levels. These predictions have not been widely demonstrated in the Lewisian terrain although the palaeomagnetic record has proved to be progressively more complex as the sampling here has been extended. The presence of a later chemical remanence residing in hematite is an indication of later pervasive alteration and in this instance blocking temperature sequence is not necessarily the same as the age sequence.

Published palaeomagnetic results from the Lewisian have been confined almost exclusively to the basic intrusions and their amphibolitized equivalents. It has not yet been suggested that any of these units records a remanence dating from the time of intrusion primarily because the metamorphic assemblages indicate that the dykes were intruded into hot crust at great depth. Tarney (1963) suggests that emplacement took place at depths of 15–25 km and into country rock at temperatures of about 500°C; O'Hara (1977) deduces a comparable temperature at somewhat greater depths (c. 20–25 km). However, this temperature estimate is sufficiently below the critical blocking temperature range of the high blocking temperature components (typically ex-

From: PARK, R. G. & TARNEY, J. (eds), 1987, *Evolution of the Lewisian and Comparable Precambrian High Grade Terrains*, Geological Society Special Publication No. 27, pp. 205–215.

205

tending several tens of degrees below 580°C (Piper 1979, Smith & Piper 1982) even when accommodating the revised effect of slow cooling (Dodson & McClelland Brown 1980) to suggest that some of these bodies could have been magnetized during initial emplacement; this possibility must await $^{39}Ar/^{40}Ar$ studies for proper evaluation. The disequilibrium metamorphic reactions suggest rapid regional uplift following the Laxfordian episode (Dickinson & Watson 1976) and it is in this interval of time that the remanence record is generally believed to have been acquired. It is convenient to consider this record in terms of the major regional subdivision of the mainland Lewisian and extend this consideration to the Outer Hebrides.

Central and northern mainland zones

Beckmann (1976) studied the remanence in samples from 38 sites in the central and northern zones between Lochinver and Laxford Bridge. Stable magnetizations with a northwesterly positive (downward) direction were recovered from ten sites in dykes and one in granulite from the interior part of the central zone; the remaining sites were classed as unstable. Observing that a fine-grained late dyke with a Laxfordian age (Evans & Tarney 1964) yielded an identical remanence direction to early dykes and the granulite, Beckmann inferred that the characteristic remanence recorded by this study was late Laxfordian in age (see also Morgan 1976b).

The stable sites were characterized by higher coercivities than the unstable sites which accorded with the only observable petrological difference between the two groups, namely a subdivision of the ilmenite grains by fine blades in the former case. It is possible that some regional effect has promoted sub-microscopic subdivision of the magnetite grains in the central zone to produce pseudo-single domain (PSD) remanence carriers here (in the approximate size range 1–15 μm). However, in view of the absence of visible subdivision in the discrete magnetite grains it is more likely that the carriers of stable remanence are exsolution blades or rods of magnetite along cleavage planes within the silicates; these have been observed in some samples exhibiting this stable remanence (Piper 1979) and such grains have been linked to PSD or SD remanence in slowly-cooled rocks (Morgan & Smith 1981). It is not yet clear why this promotion of the conditions for stable remanence should have occurred less readily where the Laxfordian metamorphism was more profound and it is possible that the magnetic structure is a relict one inherited from pre-Laxfordian times in response to an earlier subdivision of this terrain.

The NW positive direction of remanence was subsequently confirmed (Piper 1979) to be the predominant ('A') remanence in a further 40 dykes from the central zone (Fig. 1). This later study also identified a minority group of ten dykes within the swarm in the central zone containing high coercivity/blocking temperature components, residing in part in hematite with shallow dual-polarity directions in a W–NW direction. In view of its sporadic occurrence, this remanence group is probably younger than the 'A' group. It is also less well grouped and possibly of composite origin: a B1 group (mean direction $D = 252°$, $I = 9°$) is now known to correlate with remanence directions acquired late in the uplift history of the Lewisian terrain, and a second B2 group (mean direction $D = 297°$, $I = -33°$) correlates with the early part of the Grenville Track (c. 1000 Ma) defined from other Laurentian Shield data (e.g. McWilliams & Dunlop 1978) on the pre-drift reconstruction and is similar to the predominant remanence axis in the Torridonian sediments (Smith et al. 1983). The B1 direction is fairly close to a single stable component found by Beckmann (1976) in the northern zone from a dyke at Badcall. This dyke has been the subject of detailed geochronological investigations which yield the best estimate of the age of the B1 axis: Evans & Tarney (1964) report K-Ar ages of 1860 and 1440 Ma and Chapman (1978) dated this same dyke at 1630 Ma by Rb–Sr whole-rock study. Chapman interpreted the age to be due to metamorphic resetting possibly linked to intrusion of post-Laxfordian pegmatites which cut this dyke giving Rb–Sr ages of 1615, 1517 and 1467 Ma (Gilletti et al. 1961, recalculated); 1615 Ma is currently the best minimum estimate for this axis of magnetism.

A subsidiary ('C') group of sites in the central zone yields weak components generally of lower stability than the 'A' and 'B' groups and with NE positive directions. The origin of this component is not clear, sometimes it is present at sites showing the predominant 'A' remanence or is present as a lower blocking temperature component in these sites. Pyrrhotite and maghemite are possible contenders and maghemite alteration rims to magnetite grains have been recognized at some sites where both 'A' and 'C' components are present (Piper 1979) although most of these sites have very little opaque content. Since the mean remanence direction ($D = 43°$, $I = 40°$) diverges from both Torridonian and Phanerozoic field directions for this area, it is probable that these components are of Precambrian age and acquired late in the cooling history of the Lewisian

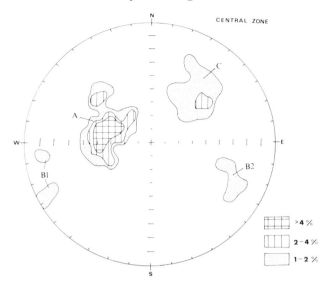

FIG. 1. Contoured equal area projection of the directions of magnetization (80) derived from 52 sites in the central zone of the Lewisian terrain after a.f. and/or thermal cleaning; antiparallel directions of magnetizations plotting in the upper hemisphere are taken to contour the distribution on the lower hemisphere. Data from Piper (1979).

terrain. Currently only one component, a sparse and low coercivity ('D') component with a mean direction $D = 161°$, $I = 48°$ is a possible contender for a Lower Palaeozoic overprint linked to the evolving Caledonian orogenic belt to the east.

The southern mainland zone

Smith & Piper (1982) reported results from 111 sites in this zone which come mainly from dykes and basic pods. The main feature of the collective data is that the characteristic directions of magnetization change from predominantly NW positive directions at the Gruinard Bay area in the north to NW shallow or negative directions in the Torridon area in the south (Fig. 2). The thermomagnetic studies suggest that the former components correlate with magnetite–sulphide assemblages while the latter correlate with magnetite–hematite assemblages. Conglomerate tests show that the remanence in the south predates deposition of the Torridonian sediments. It appears that a late event in the uplift and cooling history was responsible for oxidizing the magnetic assemblages in the Torridon area and overprinting the remanence here with a shallow NW-directed single-polarity field axis comparable to the B1 component recognized sporadically in the central zone. There is a further interesting complexity to the Lewisian remanence record in this zone; within the narrow belts and 'pips'

showing relict fabrics unreworked during the Laxfordian episode (Sutton & Watson 1951, Cresswell & Park 1973) a steep easterly positive component of remanence is present either as the only component, or recoverable by progressive demagnetization as the higher blocking temperature component (Fig. 3). Because it is confined largely to the zones with pre-Laxfordian fabric, this is inferred to be the oldest remanence recovered from the Lewisian terrain. K-Ar ages of 2230 (whole rock) and 2098 Ma (hornblende) from one of the large dykes in the Ruadh Mheallan zone (Moorbath & Park 1971) yielding this remanence suggest that it might possibly be pre-Laxfordian in age, although in the context of the uplift and cooling history of the terrain (Dickinson & Watson 1976) we believe this to be rather unlikely and K-Ar hornblende ages in the range 1712–1662 Ma from the less foliated dykes (Moorbath & Park 1971) probably yields a closer estimate of the age of this remanence.

Cresswell & Park (1973) recognize three structural episodes (LD1–LD3) in the Laxfordian of the southern zone associated with amphibolite (LM1 and LM2) and greenschist-facies (LM3) metamorphism respectively. LD3 is linked to the development of concentric folds which incorporate major rotations of the dykes in upright folds (Park 1973) in the zones affected by LD3. Adjustment of the palaeomagnetic directions for this folding disperses them and in particular

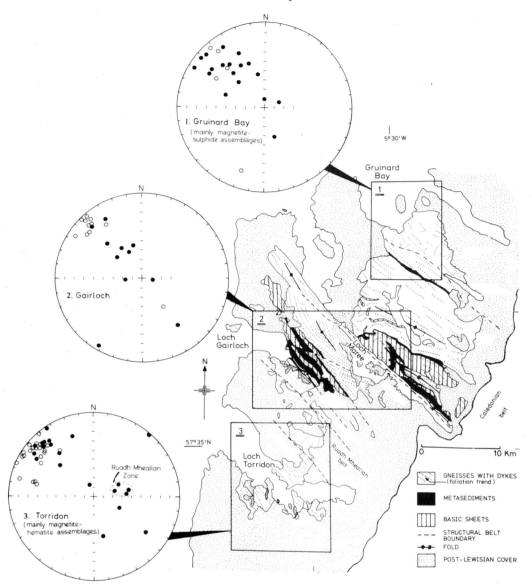

FIG. 2. The palaeomagnetic signature of the southern zone of the Lewisian terrain. The equal area projections show the distributions of magnetic vectors identified by a.f. and thermal cleaning subdivided according to the areas enclosed by the rectangles. The palaeomagnetic data are given by Smith & Piper (1982) and the geology is simplified after Park (1973).

shows no sign of movement towards the steep E positive direction preserved in the relict zones. Thus it appears that the magnetic remanence preserved in the belts affected by LD3 (at least) is syn- or post-folding in origin. The maximum age of this episode is 1700–1670 Ma by reference to pegmatite ages and is therefore the maximum age of the NW intermediate positive to shallow

negative directions in Fig. 3. The K-Ar mineral ages of Moorbath & Park (1971) give some control on the age of the remanence groups in Fig. 2, with hornblende ages ranging from 1723–1668 Ma on unfoliated basic dykes and regional gneisses in the Gruinard Bay area linked to the predominantly NW components of remanence. (Of the metamorphic mineral phases hornblende

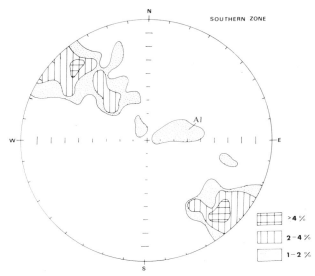

FIG. 3. Contoured equal area projection of the directions of magnetization (90) identified at 88 sites in the southern zone of the Lewisian terrain. Data from Smith & Piper (1982); plotted in the same way as Fig. 1.

is likely to become closed to argon at a temperature closest to the blocking temperature of the remanence although it cannot be precisely correlated because outgassing temperatures decrease from about 600–550°C for Mg^{2+}-rich amphiboles down to low temperatures comparable to medium-grained biotites (325–275°C) with increasing substitution of the larger Fe^{2+} ion (O'Nions *et al.* 1969)). Younger (hornblende) ages in the range 1504–1468 Ma on amphibolitized dykes from the Torridon area suggest that the shallow to NW negative components which predominate here may be appreciably younger although there is clearly a discrepancy with the 1615 Ma estimate on the comparable B1 remanence in the central zone.

The collective record to emerge from the southern zone is a distribution of predominantly steep to shallow NW directed components of remanence which are interpreted to record an equivalent migration of this region with respect to the palaeopole and provisionally dated by the K-Ar hornblende ages in the range 1690–1470 Ma (Moorbath & Park 1971, Smith & Piper 1982); current studies are aiming to date the components of remanence incorporated in the swathe more precisely by $^{39}Ar/^{40}Ar$ studies (T. J. Poppleton and author, in progress).

The Outer Hebrides

Studies in progress on the Lewisian of the Hebridean islands include a.f. demagnetized results from 68 sites on Lewis and Harris (Fig. 4) which come mainly from amphibolitized basic bodies on Lewis and in the South Harris igneous complex. The vectors recognized by line and plane search techniques (Kent *et al.* 1983) applied routinely to the vector plots yielded by the a.f. data are shown in Fig. 5. This figure shows only the better defined vectors shown by five or more demagnetization steps and with $\alpha_{95} \leqslant 25°$; it emphasizes the complexity of the remanence record in a slowly-cooled metamorphic terrain and the need to characterize each component by thermal demagnetization and rock magnetic studies. However, a number of important features emerge from these data. Only at one site (11) is the NW positive component predominant in the central zone present in all cores from the same sampling site (Fig. 6). Elsewhere it is present at many sites but only in a fraction of the cores as the strongest and highest coercivity component; elsewhere it is displaced by a more diverse range of components with lower coercivities. Of special interest are a number of sites on Lewis (30, 33, 35, 37) where SW negative components antiparallel to this NW positive group are present. This is the first indication from the Lewisian terrain that the geomagnetic field at the time of magnetization had dual polarity; it is a further indication that the time taken for the magnetization of these rocks in individual samples was not very protracted (i.e. nearer 10^6 than 10^7 Ma, see Morgan (1976a) and Smith & Piper (1982)). Some sites (*e.g.* 21 and 35 (Fig. 6)), show antiparallel

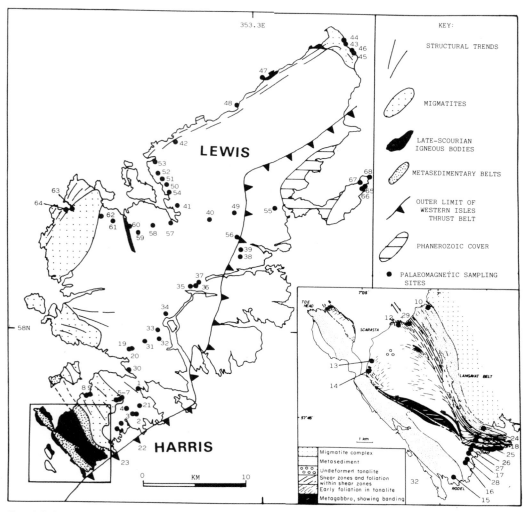

FIG. 4. Palaeomagnetic sampling sites in the Lewisian terrain of Lewis and Harris. The inset diagram shows the sampling sites in the vicinity of the South Harris igneous complex based on Graham & Coward (1973).

directions in different cores from the same site. The samples from the South Harris igneous complex show a more prominent group of NW shallow to negative components (15, Fig. 6) with antiparallel directions present through most of this range. As a preliminary step to interpretation it may be assumed that these remanences are dual polarity and the upper hemisphere directions can be reversed to produce a distribution on the lower hemisphere. This isolates a distribution of NW directions and also suggests a continuation of the distribution into very steep components with an easterly trend similar to the component in the pre-Laxfordian domains of the southern zone (Fig. 7). The distribution from Lewis is

broadly comparable although an appreciable number of ESE positive vectors are also present here. A number of components with NE positive directions occur in both Lewis and Harris comparable to the 'C' directions in the central zone. Since they again form no very coherent grouping their significance is unclear, but all of the samples illustrating this component have low coercivities and in several this component is removed by cleaning to recover the characteristic NW directions (4, Fig. 6); the arguments used in the case of the central zone to assign an age late in the uplift cooling history of the terrain are therefore applicable here.

Although large parts of the Lewisian complex

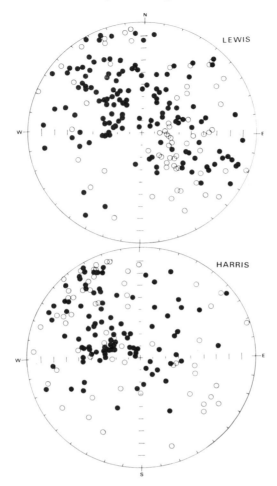

FIG. 5. Equal area projections showing the distributions of all vectors recognized in the Lewisian terrain of Lewis and Harris from a.f. cleaning and defined by five or more demagnetization steps and a within-sample grouping defined by $\alpha_{95} \leqslant 25°$. Closed symbols are lower hemisphere plots and open symbols are upper hemisphere plots.

in the Outer Hebrides were formed during the Scourian cycle (*e.g.* Lambert *et al.* 1970*b*, Watson 1977), the South Harris igneous complex was intruded at about 2000 Ma and metamorphosed to granulite facies at about 1870 Ma (Watson & Lisle 1973); some of the basic dykes here predate tonalites dated at 1870–1860 Ma (Cliff *et al.* 1983); this must define the maximum age of the magnetic remanences observed here. Stages in the Laxfordian uplift are recorded by K-Ar whole rock ages of 1782–1571 Ma (Lambert *et al.* 1970*a*). It is with this general spectrum of ages that the remanence record is likely to correlate.

Conclusions

It is already apparent that the remanence record in the Lewisian terrain varies considerably from area to area. Although the NW positive component is the most characteristic and widespread feature, it is variably displaced by other components; these are most commonly of lower coercivity and/or blocking temperature but in some cases hematite is the carrier. The extent of this overprinting is much greater in the zones affected by tectonic reworking during the Laxfordian episode. Further rock magnetic investigations will be necessary to characterize these reman-

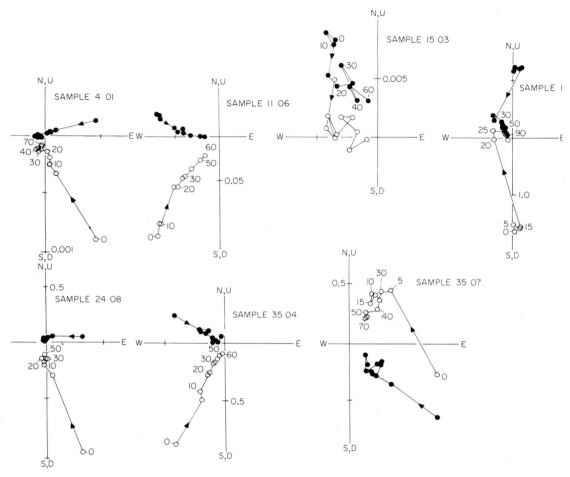

FIG. 6. Representative demagnetization behaviour of samples from Lewis and Harris showing some of the most typical directions recognized in this study and plotted as orthogonal vector plots. The projection of the vector on to the horizontal plane is shown by the closed symbol and the projection on to the vertical plane is shown by the open symbol; the demagnetization steps are in milli Teslas (mT) and the axes are calibrated in $Am^2 kg^{-1}$. This figure illustrates an example of the most typical NW positive component of remanence (11 06); more steep (24 08) and less steep (15 03) vectors are also common. Sometimes anti-parallel directions (35 04 and 35 07) are present in different samples from the same site and were presumably acquired before and after a reversal of the geomagnetic field. The NE positive ('C') remanence is typically removed in low fields (4 01) to recover the NW positive remanence; in other cases (15 08) this low coercivity component cannot be distinguished from a viscous component in the direction of the earth's present field.

ences and define their areal significance in the context of the later uplift and cooling history of the terrain. The case for assigning all of the remanence record to the Laxfordian episode or post-Laxfordian uplift rests on three observations, namely (i) the negative fold test on sites affected by the LD3 episode in the southern zone, (ii) the comparable directions of the magnetization observed in the basic bodies of different generations and (iii) the distinction of the bulk of the remanence record from the Torridonian and Phanerozoic palaeofield directions for NW Scotland. The possibility that some of the components of magnetizations may 'see through' the Laxfordian episode must await further $^{39}Ar/^{40}Ar$ studies.

A noteworthy feature of the contoured distributions of directions in Figs 1, 3 and 7 is the general tendency for the remanence record from each area to lie in a plane with a strike close to

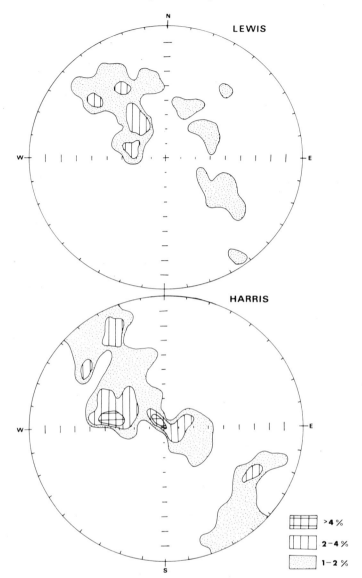

FIG. 7. Contoured equal area projection of the directions of magnetization identified in the Lewisian terrain of Lewis and Harris.

the trend of the Scourie dykes, and the regional fabric imposed by the Laxfordian mobile episode. This observation begs the question as to how much these remanence directions are influenced by the fabric of the rocks. Shape anisotropy is an important effect in magnetite and maghemite which have high susceptibilities, while crystalline anisotropy may be important in hematite because it is more readily magnetized in the basal plane than in any other crystallographic direction.

McElhinny (1973) shows that anisotropies of 10, 20 and 50% are equivalent to a maximum deflection of the remanence directions by 2.7, 5.2 and 11.6° respectively although these estimates would appear to be raised if the directional changes in the self-demagnetizing factor are taken into account (Nagata 1961). It is difficult to determine the deflection of the remanence by this effect in any specific case because the susceptibility ellipsoid, which is used as a laboratory estimate of the magnetic fabric, gives the total anistropy resulting from all magnetic phases rather than the anisotropy of the small fraction (usually a few per cent or less) of the magnetite phases contributing to the stable remanence. Laboratory studies of the TRM acquired in a known field may help to clarify this problem (Beckmann *et al.* 1977), but require that the magnetic phases should not be affected by the heating procedure; it is possible that use of an IRM in place of a TRM will enable this problem to be overcome (Stephenson *et al.* 1985). Although the remanence record in the Lewisian terrain is no doubt influenced in detail by the fabric of the rocks, there are two indications that the effect is not a gross one. Firstly, with this problem in mind, the palaeomagnetic studies have generally concentrated on late- to post-tectonic rocks with the least tectonic fabric, and secondly, there are many examples where stable remanences in rocks of different origins including granulites, amphibolitized and deformed basic bodies, early dykes and late dykes yield comparable directions of magnetization (Beckmann 1976, Smith & Piper 1982).

ACKNOWLEDGEMENT: Precambrian palaeomagnetic studies are supported by NERC grant, 3/4495.

References

BECKMANN, G. E. J. 1976. A Palaeomagnetic study of part of the Lewisian complex, North-west Scotland. *J. geol. Soc. London*, **132**, 45–59.

——, OLSEN, N. O. & SØRENSEN, K. 1977. A palaeomagnetic experiment on crustal uplift in West Greenland. *Earth planet. Sci. Lett.* **36**, 269–79.

BUCHAN, K. L. & DUNLOP, D. J. 1976. Palaeomagnetism of the Haliburton intrusions: superimposed magnetisations, metamorphism and tectonics in the late Precambrian. *J. Geophys. Res.* **81**, 2951–2967.

CHAPMAN, H. J. 1978. *Geochronology and isotope geochemistry of Precambrian rocks from North-west Scotland.* Unpubl. D. Phil. thesis, University of Oxford.

—— 1979. 2,390 Myr Rb-Sr whole-rock age for the Scourie dykes of North-west Scotland. *Nature, London* **277**, 642–3.

CLIFF, R. A., GRAY, C. M. & HUHMA, H. 1983. A Sm-Nd isotopic study of the South Harris Igneous Complex, The Outer Hebrides. *Contrib. Mineral Petrol.* **82**, 91–8.

CRESSWELL, D. & PARK, R. G. 1973. The metamorphic history of the Lewisian rocks of the Torridon area in relation to that of the remainder of the southern Laxfordian belt. *In*: R. G. PARK & J. TARNEY (eds) *The Early Precambrian of Scotland and related rocks of Greenland*, Univ. Keele. 77–83.

DICKINSON, B. B. & WATSON, J. 1976. Variations in crustal level and geothermal gradient during the evolution of the Lewisian Complex of North-west Scotland. *Precambrian Res.* **3**, 363–74.

DODSON, M. H. & MCCLELLAND BROWN, E. 1980. Magnetic blocking temperatures of single domain grains during slow cooling. *J. Geophys. Res.* **85**, 2625–37.

EVANS, C. R. & TARNEY, J. 1964. Isotopic ages of Assynt dykes. *Nature, London* **204**, 638–41.

GILLETTI, B., MOORBATH, S. & LAMBERT, R. ST. J. 1961. A geochronological study of the metamorphic complexes of the Scottish Highlands. *Q. J. geol. Soc. London*. **117**, 233–64.

GRAHAM, R. H. & COWARD, M. P. 1973. The Laxfordian of the Outer Hebrides. *In*: R. G. PARK & J. TARNEY (eds) *The Early Precambrian of Scotland and related rocks of Greenland,* Univ. Keele. 85–93.

KENT, J. T., BRIDEN, J. C. & MARDIA, K. V. 1983. Linear and planar structure in ordered multivariate data as applied to progressive demagnetisation of palaeomagnetic remanence. *Geophys. J. R. astr. Soc.* **75**, 593–622.

LAMBERT, R. ST. J., EVANS, C. R. & DEARNLEY, R. 1970a. Isotopic ages of dykes and pegmatite gneiss from the southern islands of the Outer Hebrides. *Scott. J. Geol.* **6**, 208–13.

——, MYERS, J. S. & WATSON, J. 1970b. An apparent age for a member of the Scourie dyke suite in Lewis, Outer Hebrides. *Scott. J. Geol.* **6**, 214–26.

McELHINNY, M. W. 1973. *Palaeomagnetism and Plate Tectonics.* Cambridge University Press, 358 pp.

McWILLIAMS, M. O. & DUNLOP, D. J. 1978. Grenville palaeomagnetism and tectonics. *Can. J. Earth Sci.* **15**, 687–95.

MOORBATH, S. & PARK, R. G. 1971. The Lewisian chronology of the southern region of the Scottish mainland. *Scott. J. Geol.* **8**, 51–74.

MORGAN, G. E. 1976a. Palaeomagnetism of a slowly-cooled plutonic terrain in Western Greenland. *Nature, London.* **259**, 382–85.

—— 1976b. Discussion of paper 'A palaeomagnetic study of part of the Lewisian Complex, NW Scotland', by G. E. J. BECKMANN. *Proc. Geol. Soc. Lond., 132,* 351–2.

—— & SMITH, P. P. K. 1981. Transmission electron microscope and rock magnetic investigations of remanence carriers in a Precambrian metadolerite. *Earth planet. Sci. Lett.* **53**, 226–40.

NAGATA, T. 1961. *Rock Magnetism.* Maruzen, Tokyo, 350 pp.

O'HARA, M. J. 1977. Thermal history of excavation of Archaean gneisses from the base of the continental crust. *J. geol. Soc. London.* **134**, 185–200.

O'NIONS, R. K., SMITH, D. G. W., BAADSGAARD, H. & MORTON, R. D. 1969. Influence of chemical compositions on argon retentivity in metamorphic calcic amphiboles from South Norway. *Earth planet. Sci. Lett.* **5**, 339–45.

PARK, R. G. 1973. The Laxfordian belts of the Scottish mainland. *In*: R. G. PARK & J. TARNEY, (eds) *The Early Precambrian of Scotland and related rocks of Greenland,* University of Keele. 65–76.

PIPER, J. D. A. 1979. The palaeomagnetism of the Central Zone of the Lewisian foreland, Northwest Scotland. *Geophys. J. R. astr. Soc.* **59**, 101–22.

—— 1981. The altitude-dependence of magnetic remanence in the slowly-cooled Precambrian plutonic terrain of West Greenland. *Earth planet. Sci. Lett.* **54**, 449–66.

—— 1985. Palaeomagnetic study of the Nagssugtoqidian mobile belt in central west Greenland. *Precambrian Res.* **28**, 75–110.

SMITH, R. L. & PIPER, J. D. A. 1982. Palaeomagnetism of the Southern Zone of the Lewisian (Precambrian) foreland, NW Scotland. *Geophys. J. R. astr. Soc.* **68**, 325–47.

——, Stearn, J. E. F. & PIPER, J. D. A. 1983.

Palaeomagnetic studies of the Torridonian sediments, NW Scotland. *Scott. J. Geol.* **19**, 29–45.

STEPHENSON, A., SADIKUN, S. & POTTER, D. K. 1985. A comparison of the anisotropy of magnetic susceptibility and remanence in rocks and minerals (abstract), *Geophys. J. R. astr. Soc.* **81**, 325.

SUTTON, J. & WATSON, J. V. 1951. The pre-Torridonian metamorphic history of the Loch Torridon and Scourie areas in the North-west Highlands and its bearing on the chronological classification of the Lewisian. *Quart. J. Geol. Soc. London.* **106**, 241–307.

TARNEY, J. 1963. Assynt dykes and their metamorphism. *Nature, London.* **199**, 672–4.

WATSON, J. 1977. The Outer Hebrides: a geological perspective. *Proc. Geol. Assoc.* **88**, 1–14.

—— & Lisle, R. J. 1973. The pre-Laxfordian complex of the Outer Hebrides. *In*: PARK R. G. & TARNEY J. (eds) *The early Precambrian of Scotland and related rocks of Greenland*, Univ. Keele. 45–50.

J. D. A. PIPER, Department of Geological Sciences, University of Liverpool, PO Box 147, Liverpool L69 3BX, UK.

Mineralogy, petrology and geochemistry of the Scourie dykes: petrogenesis and crystallization processes in dykes intruded at depth

J. Tarney & B. L. Weaver

SUMMARY: The mineral chemistry, petrology and geochemistry of representative members of the Scourie dyke swarm are described, and discussed in relation to crystallization processes in deep-seated dykes and to their petrogenesis. Four types of dykes can be defined on petrological and geochemical grounds: bronzite–picrites, norites, olivine-gabbros and quartz dolerites. The latter constitute by far the most abundant dyke-type. In the central Scourian granulite zone in particular the dykes were emplaced at depth into hot country rocks; this enables the through-flow behaviour of different magma types in dyke conduits to be compared. Whereas the dolerites and norites have chilled margins, the bronzite–picrites and olivine-gabbros have coarse grained orthopyroxene-rich and augite-rich margins respectively. This probably reflects turbulent-flow conditions in the less viscous, more ultramafic magmas which permitted rapid crystallization of pyroxenes on the dyke walls during intrusion. The picrite dykes, and to a lesser extent the olivine-gabbro dykes, display additional across-dyke modal and textural variations. These are not accompanied by significant variations in mineral composition, and can largely be attributed to crystal settling in variably inclined dyke sheets.

All dykes typically show a 'continental' trace element signature (enrichment in light rare-earth elements and large-ion-lithophile elements), but this must have been inherited from the sub-continental lithosphere because contamination by Lewisian gneisses would not generate the observed trace element characteristics. Both trace element and mineral chemical data indicate that the dykes were derived from at least two distinct mantle sources, that supplying the picrite and norite dykes being more refractory with respect to major elements, but showing a greater relative enrichment in light REE and LIL elements.

The emplacement of the Scourie dyke swarm represents considerable crustal extension, but also poses a thermal problem in the generation of high temperature picritic magmas. It is suggested that the dykes and their compositional characteristics reflect the processes of growth and evolution of the sub-continental lithosphere, and that the extensive retrogression of the granulites, which occurred penecontemporaneously with dyke intrusion, may also be linked with these processes.

Introduction

Early Proterozoic dyke swarms are a common feature of many Archaean gneiss terrains. They could, on the one hand, be regarded as marking the final stages of stabilization of Archaean cratonic nuclei, extensional tectonics having replaced the strong horizontal thrusting and deformation associated with the crust-generating processes. On the other hand, in the Lewisian complex their appearance is also linked in time with the initiation of major shear zones, and massive ingress of hydrous fluids up these shear zones, which essentially mark the development of Proterozoic intracratonic mobile belts. There is of course a 500 m.y. time gap between the generation of Lewisian gneisses at 2.92 Ga (Hamilton *et al.* 1979) and the start of emplacement of the Scourie dykes at 2.39 Ga (Chapman 1979); indeed there may have been minor dyke

emplacement at least 200 m.y. later than this (Evans & Tarney 1964). It is of interest to note that Ameralik mafic dykes in West Greenland (Chadwick 1981) were emplaced into the 3.8 Ga Amitsoq gneisses, but before the development of the Nûk gneisses at *c.* 3.0 Ga. There are other extensive Middle Proterozoic (1.2 Ga) dyke swarms in Canada which precede the Grenville events. Dyke swarms may therefore be a normal feature of the process of crustal evolution, but we do not yet fully understand their thermal, tectonic and petrogenetic significance. Geochemically they have much in common with the voluminous continental flood basalt extrusives of the Phanerozoic (Weaver & Tarney 1983).

The purpose of this contribution is to review some pertinent features of the Scourie dykes, using both previously published and new data, which are relevant to their petrogenesis. The Scourie dykes display a wider range of composi-

From: PARK, R. G. & TARNEY, J. (eds), 1987, *Evolution of the Lewisian and Comparable Precambrian High Grade Terrains*, Geological Society Special Publication No. 27, pp. 217–233.

tion than most Proterozoic dyke swarms, and can potentially provide more information on the nature of their sources. Additionally they occur in a variety of crustal rocks ranging from granulites in the central Scourian zone to lower grade terrains in the flanking zones to the north and south. Those in the central zone in particular were intruded at considerable depth into hot country rock (O'Hara 1961; Tarney 1963, 1973). This offers the opportunity to compare the behaviour of different magma types, ranging from high-Mg picrites to Fe-rich quartz dolerites, flowing through dyke channels at depth.

The Scourie dykes comprise four main petrological groups (Tarney 1973):

(1) Bronzite picrites
(2) Olivine gabbros
(3) Norites
(4) Quartz tholeiites

Perhaps 90% of all dykes fall into the last group. However the greatest concentration of dykes occurs in the central Scourie–Assynt granulite zone. The dykes are wider here and it is also where most of the more ultramafic dyke-types occur and where country rock temperatures were highest. Most of the Scourie dykes are silica-saturated to oversaturated; some olivine gabbro dykes are mildly nepheline-normative, but even these bear modal hypersthene.

Most of the present discussion is based on dykes from the central zone, partly because of the diversity of dyke types here, but also because the effects of Inverian and Laxfordian metamorphism are less pervasive. The bronzite picrites are concentrated just to the north of the Lochinver antiform, the olivine gabbro dykes just to the south of it (Tarney 1973); other examples are known at Geisgeil and Scourie Bay, Gruinard Bay, and at Braesclete and Maaruig on the Outer Hebrides. Norites also occur at Badcall (O'Hara 1962) and in the Torridon area.

Bronzite picrite dykes

Fresh picrite dykes have the primary mineralogy: olivine – orthopyroxene – clinopyroxene – plagioclase–phlogopite–chromite. Each dyke has a distinctive texture and modal composition, and also olivine size. The olivine size is constant within each dyke but varies from less than 1 mm to 5 mm between different dykes (Tarney 1973). This suggests that olivine had crystallized almost completely under conditions peculiar to each dyke before intrusion to the present level. Alternatively it could be that at the high degrees of mantle melting implied by a picritic composition, the source was completely disaggregated

and the whole crystal–liquid mush emplaced, the olivine grain size reflecting that of the source. Most of the orthopyroxene crystallized before clinopyroxene, and overgrowths of clinopyroxene on orthopyroxene are common (Tarney 1969). There are no Fe–Ti oxides and chromite is mostly present as inclusions within the olivines. In contrast to the dolerite and olivine gabbro dykes, the picrites have no hornblende (except rare crystals in late-stage veins) and phlogopite is the only hydrous mineral.

Mineralogy

A summary of representative modal and mineral composition data for the bronzite picrite dykes is given in Table 1. Representative microprobe analyses of olivines are given in Table 2, and of other ferromagnesian mineral phases in comparison with those from the other dyke-types in Tables 7–10.

Olivine: tends to be rounded, usually lacking well developed crystal faces. Compositions (Table 2) are surprisingly uniform (Fo_{85-82}) and unzoned except in late-stage veins (Fo_{79-69}).

Orthopyroxene has good crystal form and has fine exsolution lamellae parallel to (100). Compositions (Table 7) are more Mg-rich (En_{90-87}) than the olivines, except in zoned rims (En_{83-73}) and late stage veins (En_{67}). Calcium contents are high.

Clinopyroxenes are pale green Cr-endiopsides and display fine exsolution lamellae parallel to (100). Contrary to the normal relationship (Kretz 1961) *mg* values are *c.* 4% lower than in the coexisting orthopyroxene, thus compatible with the evidence from overgrowths that it crystallized later. Calcium contents are low (Table 8) and, together with the high CaO contents of the orthopyroxene, suggest considerable miscibility, indicative of high crystallization temperatures of the picritic magma.

Plagioclase is always interstitial to the pyroxenes and occasionally forms large poikilitic crystals 2–3 cm in diameter. Despite the highly magnesian nature of the picrites, plagioclase compositions are surprisingly sodic (An_{55-50}) and are strongly zoned to An_{25} or even An_{15}.

Phlogopite is a strongly pleochroic titanian variety (Table 10) with significantly lower *mg* values than the olivines and pyroxenes.

There is surprisingly little overlap in the crystallization sequence from petrographic evidence, confirmed by the progressive lowering of *mg* values in the mafic phases and the Ca-poor composition of the plagioclase. The picrite magmas are therefore far removed from low

TABLE 1. *Modal and mineral composition data for Scourie picrite dykes*

	Northern Leothaid dyke (16.5 m)									Suileag dyke	Beannach dyke		
	L582	L584	L584A	L585	L586	L587	L588	L589	L579	L448	L265	L252	L280
Distance from N. Margin (m)	0.3	0.9	3.7	4.3	5.0	6.9	7.3	7.5		Centre	Centre	Vein	Vein
Mode:													
Olivine	4.7	14.6	38.4	34.5	29.5	35.0	32.4	48.2	55.8	43.6	37.5	7.2	7.9
Orthopyroxene	78.5	61.8	18.6	13.6	11.0	10.9	26.3	4.4	1.0	31.1	30.3	4.4	24.3
Clinopyroxene	7.7	15.2	23.8	17.9	26.2	28.8	11.4	17.2	15.4	14.5	9.4	30.3	35.7
Plagioclase	8.1	7.4	16.9	30.4	20.4	22.5	26.8	29.2	25.1	8.8	19.3	54.7	29.8
Phlogopite	1.0	1.0	2.3	3.6	2.9	2.8	3.7	1.0	2.7	2.1	3.6	3.4	2.3
Mineral compositions (Mg/Mg + Fe)													
Olivine	82	—	83	—	83	—	82	—	83	85	84	79	69
Orthopyroxene	87–73	—	89–82	—	89–85	—	89–83	—	83	89–86	90–88	80–69	85–67
Clinopyroxene	84–77	—	85	—	86	—	85	—	85	87	88	85–73	84–72

pressure cotectic compositions and certainly represent high degrees of mantle melting.

Pyroxene-rich margins and transverse modal variations

Superimposed on inter-dyke variability there is locally considerable within-dyke modal and textural variation, although this is not always evident because of poor exposure. The dyke margins are not chilled, but coarse grained and orthopyroxene-rich. Some dykes have fairly uniform centres,

both modally and texturally, but some display moderate to quite marked transverse variations, which often tend to be asymmetric. Two examples will be briefly described.

Beannach dyke

Transverse variations are best displayed along parts of the Loch Beannach dyke; at Loch Beannach itself for instance, where the dyke is *c.* 100 m wide, coarse poikilitic orthopyroxenes, 2–3 cm diameter, are developed toward the northern

TABLE 2. *Representative analyses of olivines from bronzite picrite dykes*

	North Leothaid						Beannach			Suileag
	L582	L584A	L586	L588	L579	L118	L265	L252	L280	L448
SiO_2	39.22	39.34	39.93	39.05	39.28	40.25	39.71	39.10	37.11	40.07
FeO	16.54	16.04	15.93	16.93	15.80	14.22	15.52	19.13	27.57	14.69
MnO	—	—	—	—	—	—	—	0.26	0.36	—
MgO	43.25	43.80	44.10	42.98	44.08	44.92	45.08	41.30	34.09	45.06
NiO	0.53	0.37	0.44	0.43	0.36	0.40	0.34	—	—	0.42
Total	99.54	99.55	100.40	99.39	99.52	99.79	100.65	99.79	99.13	100.24
Cations on the basin of 4 oxygens										
Si	0.998	0.998	1.003	0.997	0.996	1.008	0.994	1.003	1.000	1.002
Fe^{2+}	0.352	0.340	0.335	0.362	0.335	0.298	0.325	0.410	0.622	0.307
Mn	—	—	—	—	—	—	—	0.006	0.008	—
Mg	1.641	1.656	1.651	1.636	1.666	1.677	1.681	1.579	1.370	1.680
Ni	0.011	0.008	0.009	0.009	0.007	0.008	0.007	—	—	0.008
Fo	82.3	83.0	83.1	81.9	83.3	84.9	83.8	79.4	68.8	84.5

L582–L118   N. Leothaid picrite (L118 centre)
L265–L280   Beannach picrite (L252, L280 differentiated veins)
L448   Suileag picrite (dyke centre)

margin of the dyke. The following gradational zones occur from the north margin to the south margin, though are not everywhere developed:

(1) Orthopyroxene-rich margins, 1–2 m wide, with a framework texture of orthopyroxene.
(2) Poikilitic harzburgite, low in clinopyroxene, plagioclase and phlogopite, with large orthopyroxenes 1–3 cm in diameter enclosing numerous small (<0.5 mm) olivines. May locally have narrow bands of orthopyroxenite parallel to dyke margin.
(3) Central zone with idiomorphic rather than poikilitic orthopyroxenes, typical of the dyke where asymmetry is poorly developed.
(4) Orthopyroxene-poor zone, locally developed near southern side of dyke; rock is correspondingly richer in olivine, clinopyroxene, plagioclase and phlogopite.
(5) Orthopyroxene-rich margin.

The scale of the maximum modal variations in the Beannach dyke is illustrated in Fig. 1.

Leothaid dyke

The dykes running west from Loch an Leothaid have a more even grained texture because the olivines are much larger (*c.* 3 mm). There are no poikilitic orthopyroxenes and there is little textural variation across the dykes. Considerable modal variations still occur however, orthopyroxene comprising 80% of the marginal facies, and 19% in the central zone (typical of most of the dyke), but is locally as low as 1% near the south side of the dyke. The orthopyroxene-rich margins are less wide than in the Beannach dyke, but are coarser grained and show a decrease in size of the orthopyroxenes away from the margin. Orthopyroxene crystals nearest the margin are elongated along their *c*-axes and oriented roughly perpendicular to the margin. The interstices of the pyroxene framework are filled with later crystallizing components: plagioclase, biotite and minor clinopyroxene. Compositions of orthopyroxenes making up the framework are close to En_{87} but are zoned sharply to En_{73} adjacent to these plagioclase-rich interstices. Corresponding clinopyroxene compositions are *mg* = 84 and *mg* = 77 respectively. Clearly a more fractionated Fe-rich liquid was trapped in the pore spaces within the pyroxene framework.

Modal and mineral composition variation across the dyke is shown in Table 1. Olivine shows negligible variation (Fo_{83-82}), consistent with having crystallized before intrusion. The lack of zoning and rounded form suggests in fact that they may have suffered slight resorption. Orthopyroxene cores are similarly invariant across the dyke (En_{89-87}), as are clinopyroxenes (*mg* = 86–84); however orthopyroxene from the orthopyroxene-poor zone is slightly less magnesian (En_{83}). The highly magnesian compositions of the mafic phases as well as the high Ni and Cr contents of the olivines and pyroxenes, respectively, confirms that the parental magma was ultrabasic and that the dykes are not a mobilized crystal cumulate mush from a mafic magma chamber.

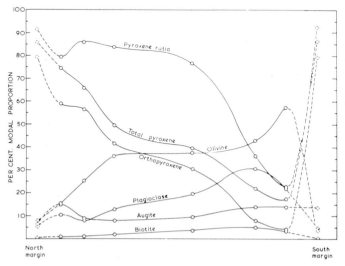

FIG. 1. Modal variations across the 12 m wide Beannach bronzite picrite dyke, *c.* 1 km W of Loch Assynt. This represents the extreme variation. Along other parts of the dyke the asymmetry may be reversed or absent.

Not only is there relatively little variation in mineral chemistry within dykes, but there is also surprisingly little variation between dykes (Table 1). Thus, although there are appreciable differences in grain size and texture between dykes, the invariant mineral compositions suggest that the magma compositions cannot have been very different. Essentially the modal and textural variations represent a mechanical sorting of crystals during and after intrusion.

Across-dyke chemical variations

Whole rock geochemical studies are to some extent hampered by variable serpentinization. Results for the Leothaid dyke (Table 3) show that SiO_2 is highest in the orthopyroxene-rich marginal facies and lowest in the orthopyroxene-poor olivine-rich southern zone. MgO and Ni distributions largely reflect olivine and CaO reflects clinopyroxene and plagioclase concentrations. However, despite the Cr-rich nature of the pyroxenes, Cr distributions follow olivine, which

TABLE 3. *Analytical data for samples from the North Leothaid dyke*

Sample	L582	L584A	L586	L588	L579
SiO_2	52.2	46.4	45.6	46.4	42.8
TiO_2	0.37	0.40	0.43	0.44	0.47
Al_2O_3	4.8	4.8	4.5	7.3	4.5
Fe_2O_3	9.43	9.97	10.31	10.04	11.97
MnO	0.22	0.20	0.22	0.18	0.22
MgO	26.16	29.63	29.39	26.71	31.65
CaO	4.95	5.86	5.53	4.86	4.29
Na_2O	1.15	1.02	0.98	1.62	0.96
K_2O	0.33	0.36	0.46	0.57	0.52
P_2O_5	0.04	0.04	0.06	0.05	0.05
Total	99.65	98.68	97.48	98.17	97.43
Cr	4600	4530	3836	3491	4230
Ni	980	1709	1891	1593	2278
Zn	59	61	59	60	72
Rb	8	7	12	11	11
Sr	79	102	110	183	131
Ba	115	144	156	218	197
Zr	34	42	48	43	53
Nb	1	1	2	<1	<1
La	8	6	8	7	10
Y	6	7	7	7	8
Pb	<3	3	<3	<3	6
Th	<3	<3	<3	<3	<3
Ga	10	8	9	11	11
Fe*/Mg	0.42	0.39	0.41	0.44	0.44
Ti/Zr	65	57	54	61	53
Zr/Y	5.7	6.0	6.9	6.1	6.6
Rb/Sr	0.101	0.069	0.109	0.060	0.084

Major elements are in weight percent and trace elements in parts per million. Fe* = total Fe as Fe^{2+}

contains most of the chromite inclusions. Incompatible elements Zr, Ti, Y, Rb, Sr, Ba, K and P correlate with the interstitial liquid, the proportion of which is generally greatest toward the southern side of the dyke.

Late stage products

The evidence presented above suggests that, despite the wide modal variations within and between dykes, they have not undergone much real magmatic evolution. The direction of *in situ* magmatic evolution can, however, be judged from late-stage veins and lenticular bodies within the Beannach dyke which are enriched in the late-crystallizing phases (clinopyroxene, plagioclase and phlogopite) but contain variable amounts of xenocrysts of early-crystallizing phases. These are interpreted as filter-press products, perhaps a consequence of deformation before the dykes were fully consolidated. The margins of the veins are enriched in pyroxene.

Modal analyses of two samples, vein margin and vein centre, are given in Table 1 along with mineral compositions. There are two distinct generations of pyroxenes. The first generation are similar to, but slightly less Mg-rich than, those in the main dyke, and there are numerous examples of augite overgrowths on orthopyroxene. The second generation are much more iron-rich, particularly orthopyroxene which now forms overgrowths on the augite (Tarney 1969), but augite is modally the dominant pyroxene. The margins of the veins are enriched in this second generation augite, the spherulitic aggregates forming a framework similar to that in the olivine-gabbro dykes (see below). The olivines are also more Fe-rich than in the main dyke, and are probably second generation too. However, although the *mg* values of these second generation mafic phases are similar to those in the olivine-gabbro dykes, the proportion of olivine is too low, and the veins lack the distinctive kaersutite and Fe–Ti oxides of the olivine-gabbro dykes. This, coupled with the trace element evidence (Weaver & Tarney 1981), casts doubt on a direct genetic link between the two dyke types.

Olivine gabbro dykes

In Assynt, olivine-gabbro dykes occur exclusively to the south of the Canisp Shear Zone. The dykes were originally mapped as ultrabasic on account of their dark colour (strongly clouded feldspar), but the one at Badnaban was termed a biotite diorite (presumably because of the sodic feldspar), and later renamed 'hornblende olivine

TABLE 4. *Modal and mineral composition data for Scourie olivine-gabbro dykes*

	Northern Loch Scionascaig dyke (14.6 m)					Southern L. Scionascaig dyke	Badnaban dyke
	L540	L541	L542	L543	L544	L537	L322
Distance from N. margin (m)	0.5	2.3	7.3	11.0	14.2	Centre	Centre
Mode:							
Olivine	20.7	23.7	17.3	18.3	13.4	19.0	14.3
Orthopyroxene	3.6	6.0	5.3	4.6	3.5	1.0	12.8
Clinopyroxene	37.9	34.3	30.4	23.9	26.1	27.8	23.2
Plagioclase	20.9	21.5	25.2	29.4	34.0	37.0	35.2
Biotite	3.6	3.5	6.6	4.7	7.7	4.9	1.5
Kaersutite	11.1	8.8	12.4	15.8	11.5	6.0	7.2
Ore	2.2	2.1	2.8	3.3	3.8	4.3	5.8
Mineral compositions (Mg/Mg + Fe)							
Olivine	68–72	67–69	59–67	63–70	63–64	71	68
Orthopyroxene	72	72	73	73	70	70	78–73
Clinopyroxene	80–75	79–72	81–70	80–72	81–71	81–72	83–73

norite' by MacGregor & Phemister (1958). In fact hypersthene is always subordinate to augite, they are always olivine-rich and normally coarse grained, so 'olivine-gabbro' is the best descriptive term. Thin chilled veins of this dyke type, carrying microphenocrysts of olivine and spherulitic augite aggregates, occur at Badcall Bay (O'Hara 1962), and are probably related to the larger dyke at Geisgeil. Although easily mapped as peat-filled trenches, exposures are rare. The following descriptions are largely based on remote exposures of two dykes on the eastern shore of Loch Scionascaig. Representative modal and mineral composition data are given in Table 4; microprobe analyses of olivines are given in Table 5 and data for the other main mineral phases are compared with those from other dykes in Tables 7–10.

Mineralogy

All of the olivine-gabbro dykes have the same mineralogy: olivine, clinopyroxene, orthopyroxene, plagioclase, kaersutite, biotite, Fe-Ti oxides. The mineral proportions vary from dyke to dyke (Table 4) and, as with the picrites, across dykes.

Olivine averages almost 20% of the mode; unlike the picrites there is little inter-dyke variation in grain size, but considerable within-dyke variation in grain size and composition (Table 5) of the olivines; they are 10–15% richer in Fa than the picrite olivines and, unlike the latter, are zoned. *Clinopyroxene* (augite) typically comprises 25–30% of the rock. Crystal faces are not well developed.

Orthopyroxene forms small pink pleochroic crystals, with better crystal form than, and frequently forming epitaxic overgrowths on, the augites (Tarney 1969). They are much more Fe-rich (Table 7) than those in the picrites.
Plagioclase is interstitial and often poikilitic, has a strong reddish-brown clouding, and is of andesine composition and strongly zoned (An_{45-27}).
Phlogopite is interstitial, forming between 1 and 7% of the mode and is a titanian variety (Table 10).
Kaersutite occurs as short stubby prisms forming

TABLE 5. *Representative analyses of olivines from olivine-gabbro dykes*

	North Loch Scionascaig					South Loch Scion	Bad-naban
	L540	L541	L542	L543	L544	L537	L322
SiO_2	37.39	37.27	36.96	36.74	36.31	37.66	37.10
FeO	26.26	28.41	31.75	31.05	31.32	26.55	28.91
MnO	0.37	0.51	0.50	0.48	0.44	0.37	0.36
MgO	35.77	33.64	31.30	31.23	30.94	36.07	34.00
Total	99.79	99.83	100.51	99.50	99.01	100.65	100.37
Cations on the basis of 4 oxygens							
Si	0.995	1.001	1.002	1.004	1.000	0.994	0.994
Fe^{2+}	0.584	0.638	0.720	0.710	0.721	0.586	0.648
Mn	0.008	0.012	0.011	0.011	0.010	0.008	0.008
Mg	1.418	1.347	1.265	1.272	1.269	1.418	1.357
Fo	70.8	67.9	63.7	64.2	63.8	70.8	67.7

L540–L544   N Loch Scionascaig olivine gabbro dyke
L537   S Loch Scionascaig olivine gabbro
L322   Badnaban olivine gabbro (centre)

up to 15% of the mode. It is Ti-rich (Table 9), deep reddish-brown and strongly pleochroic.

Titanomagnetite has partially unmixed to ilmenite lamellae with a little spinel (Stumpfl 1961). It forms between 2 and 6% of the mode. There are also accessory amounts of pyrrhotite intergrown with pentlandite and chalcopyrite.

Transverse modal variations

As with the picrite dykes, the olivine-gabbro dykes display quite marked mineralogical asymmetry which is well illustrated by the northernmost of the two Loch Scionascaig dykes (Table 4, Fig. 2). However, because the crystallization sequence is different, it is augite rather than orthopyroxene which is concentrated at the dyke margins. Moreover, contrasting with the coarse orthopyroxenes in the picrite dyke margins, the augites are finer grained than in the dyke centres, but the margins are not chilled.

The augites at the dyke margin have a peculiar almost spherulitic form. In crystallographic terms this is manifest as a rotation of the lattice about an axis parallel to *b*, and shows variable development from two adjacent crystals arranged in this manner to a complete spectrum of crystal domains with this orientation. This spherulitic form is restricted to the dyke margins and may be the result of rapid crystal growth. The spherulitic aggregates have grown out from the dyke margin to form a pyroxene framework, but this is not monomineralic as there are small olivine inclusions and also channels or pores filled with the later crystallizing minerals—orthopyrox-

ene, plagioclase, ore, phlogopite and kaersutite (the latter often forming overgrowths on the augite terminations).

The framework-textured augite-rich zone disappears within 1 m of the northern margin and there is a gradual increase in grain size, towards the centre and southern zone of the dyke, of all minerals including olivine. Plagioclase changes from small laths near the margin to large poikilitic crystals. The nature of the accompanying modal variations are shown in Table 4, and are broadly similar to those seen in the picrites except that augite takes the place of orthopyroxene.

Mineral composition data (Tables 4 & 5) show that there is not a great change in mineral compositions across the dyke. Augite core compositions are the same ($mg = 80$) and are zoned to the same degree ($mg = 72$). Orthopyroxenes are also uniform (En_{72}) though, compared with the picrites, are now more Fe-rich than the augites. However, olivine compositions are most magnesian in the pyroxene-rich margins and become more Fe-rich towards the centre of the dyke. This suggests that olivine was still crystallizing as the olivine-gabbro dykes were being intruded. This is confirmed by the thin chilled veins of this magma type at Badcall (O'Hara 1962) which have *c.* 15% of tiny olivines (0.2 mm diameter) and about 5% augite aggregates, suggesting that olivine had partly crystallized, and augite was beginning to crystallize, as the dykes were emplaced. It is curious then that in the case of both the picrites and the olivine-gabbros it is the second liquidus phase which is enriched at the margin.

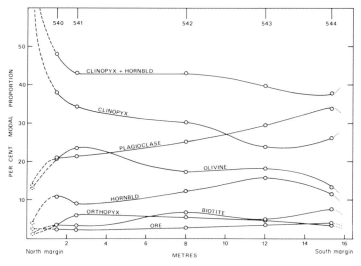

Fig. 2. Modal variations across the northern dyke at Loch Scionascaig.

Across dyke chemical variations

The analyses in Table 6 illustrate the chemical variations across the Scionascaig dyke. The variations are of lesser magnitude than in the picrite dykes. The decrease in MgO, Ni and Cr away from the pyroxene-rich margin reflects the comparable decrease in early-formed olivine and augite. The increase in Fe/Mg, Zr, Ti, K and P matches the increase in modal plagioclase and reflects the increasing proportion of interstitial liquid. Elemental ratios such as Ti/Zr, Zr/Y and Rb/Sr, which are fairly sensitive petrogenetic indicators, show little change across the dyke.

TABLE 6. *Analytical data for samples from the north Loch Scionascaig dyke*

	L540	L541	L542	L543	L544
SiO_2	46.4	46.0	46.3	47.0	47.1
TiO_2	1.57	1.46	1.78	1.89	1.98
Al_2O_3	8.6	7.9	9.4	10.0	10.0
Fe_2O_3	14.73	15.52	15.28	15.13	15.23
MnO	0.28	0.30	0.29	0.28	0.26
MgO	15.01	15.31	12.87	12.47	12.25
CaO	8.19	8.82	7.98	7.97	7.91
Na_2O	2.53	2.27	2.86	3.09	3.14
K_2O	0.58	0.49	0.72	0.75	0.77
P_2O_5	0.15	0.13	0.17	0.18	0.19
Total	98.04	98.20	97.65	98.76	98.83
Cr	1319	1234	1010	936	903
Ni	1106	1098	880	833	783
Zn	89	89	99	101	101
Rb	9	8	12	14	14
Sr	216	188	260	287	286
Ba	189	163	233	247	268
Zr	101	85	110	124	133
Nb	7	6	6	6	6
La	13	11	16	14	16
Y	14	13	16	16	18
Pb	4	<3	4	5	<3
Th	<3	<3	<3	<3	<3
Ga	16	16	20	21	20
Fe*/Mg	1.14	1.18	1.38	1.41	1.44
Ti/Zr	93	103	97	91	89
Zr/Y	7.2	6.5	6.9	7.7	7.4
Rb/Sr	0.042	0.043	0.046	0.049	0.049

Major elements are in weight percent and trace elements in parts per million. Fe* = total Fe as Fe^{2+}

Noritic dykes

The noritic dykes form a relatively minor proportion of the Scourie dyke swarm. The best examples of fresh dykes are found near Badcall (O'Hara 1962) and south of Loch Assynt (Tarney 1973), although altered varieties are more widespread.

Their primary mineral assemblage comprises plagioclase, hypersthene, clinopyroxene, with minor olivine or quartz and (always) biotite, and accessory Fe–Ti oxides, apatite and microperthite. The dykes have chilled margins, those of the Badcall norite bearing orthopyroxene and rare plagioclase microphenocrysts, whereas the dyke in Assynt has only rare clinopyroxene phenocrysts.

The compositions of the orthopyroxenes (Table 7) from the centre of the Assynt norite dyke (sample L639) and from the Badcall norite (N1) are quite magnesian (En_{81}) and similar to those of orthopyroxene rims in the bronzite picrites. However there are also discrete grains of a late stage, deeper brown pleochroic orthopyroxene which is much more Fe-rich (Table 7). Clinopyroxene compositions (Table 8) also resemble those of the bronzite picrite dykes, though they are more Fe-rich.

None of the fresh norite dykes shows any obvious transverse modal variations. Their chilled margins suggest a higher viscosity magma, perhaps too high to permit significant within-dyke differentiation.

Scourie dolerite dykes

Although the most abundant dyke type, the tholeiitic Scourie dykes are texturally and mineralogically rather uniform and have chilled dyke margins which bear only tiny plagioclase microlites. The mineralogy of the 'type' Scourie dolerite from Poll Eorna at Scourie has been described by O'Hara (1961), and Tarney (1973) has briefly described the petrology of dolerite dykes from Assynt. Only limited additional information is given here. The dolerites have a primary mineralogy composed of plagioclase, clinopyroxene and titanomagnetite with variable amounts of orthopyroxene, green hornblende, biotite, quartz and minor apatite.

Mafic phases have been analysed in four dolerite dykes covering the range of fractionation observed. Within this range the clinopyroxene composition varies from augite in the most primitive dolerite (L613), to subcalcic ferroaugite in the most evolved dyke (831) (Table 8). The latter is similar to the clinopyroxene from the Poll Eorna dyke (O'Hara 1961). The small amount of orthopyroxene in L613 is a ferrohypersthene (Table 7). The primary green hornblendes (Table 9) have much lower titanium contents than those in the olivine-gabbro dykes and range from ferro-edenitic hornblende to ferro-pargasite (Leake 1978) in composition.

TABLE 7. *Representative analyses of orthopyroxenes from Scourie dykes*

	picrites						olivine-gabbros		norite		dolerite
	L582		L588		L280		L540	L543	L639		L613
	c	r	c	r	c	r					
SiO₂	55.45	53.06	56.58	53.60	54.60	51.77	51.38	52.11	55.39	51.02	49.01
TiO₂	—	0.38	—	0.26	—	0.57	0.71	0.55	—	0.48	—
Al₂O₃	1.46	2.03	1.19	3.82	2.92	2.94	3.66	3.06	1.21	1.64	1.77
FeO	8.32	16.43	7.24	10.57	9.48	19.97	17.20	16.57	11.59	25.58	35.44
MnO	—	0.42	—	—	—	0.44	0.24	0.37	0.29	0.49	0.65
MgO	30.98	25.43	32.97	29.40	29.61	22.58	24.54	24.95	28.63	18.75	11.37
CaO	2.30	1.45	1.74	1.89	2.36	1.62	1.83	1.73	2.47	1.91	1.91
Cr₂O₃	0.94	—	0.91	0.54	0.56	—	—	—	—	—	—
Total	99.45	99.20	100.63	100.08	99.53	99.89	99.56	99.34	99.58	99.87	100.15

Formula on the basis of 6 oxygens

Si	1.955	1.943	1.958	1.895	1.931	1.917	1.886	1.910	1.976	1.944	1.956
Ti	—	0.010	—	0.007	—	0.016	0.020	0.015	—	0.014	—
Al	0.061	0.088	0.049	0.159	0.122	0.128	0.158	0.132	0.051	0.074	0.083
Fe	0.245	0.503	0.210	0.313	0.280	0.618	0.528	0.508	0.346	0.815	1.183
Mn	—	0.013	—	—	—	0.014	0.007	0.011	0.009	0.016	0.022
Mg	1.628	1.388	1.700	1.549	1.561	1.246	1.343	1.363	1.522	1.065	0.676
Ca	0.087	0.057	0.065	0.072	0.089	0.064	0.072	0.068	0.094	0.078	0.082
Cr	0.026	—	0.025	0.015	0.016	—	—	—	—	—	—

c = centre of crystal, r = rim.

TABLE 8. *Representative clinopyroxene analyses from Scourie dykes*

	picrites				olivine-gabbros				norite	dolerites		
	L582	L588	L280		L540		L543		L639	L613	919	831
			c	r	c	r	c	r				
SiO₂	52.94	52.03	51.46	49.09	51.85	50.74	51.13	49.33	53.10	52.66	51.03	49.83
TiO₂	0.19	0.35	0.23	0.73	0.38	0.71	0.68	1.14	—	0.36	0.50	0.69
Al₂O₃	2.86	4.95	4.33	6.14	3.10	4.31	3.60	6.04	2.72	2.23	2.83	2.81
FeO	6.69	5.85	6.35	10.76	8.14	9.37	6.90	10.08	8.24	8.95	13.62	21.61
MnO	—	—	—	—	—	—	—	—	—	—	0.35	0.40
Mgo	20.05	18.30	18.18	15.48	17.92	15.93	15.51	14.55	19.60	16.37	15.41	12.52
CaO	14.91	16.77	16.61	15.59	16.43	17.34	20.41	17.12	14.80	19.02	15.52	11.68
Na₂O	0.73	0.77	0.78	0.83	1.01	1.10	0.75	1.10	0.58	0.60	0.53	0.71
Cr₂O₃	0.92	1.06	0.90	0.24	1.10	0.28	1.00	0.29	0.69	—	—	—
Total	99.29	100.08	98.84	98.86	99.93	99.78	99.98	99.65	99.73	100.19	99.79	100.25

Formula on the basis of 6 oxygens

Si	1.931	1.887	1.895	1.841	1.907	1.882	1.890	1.839	1.939	1.943	1.918	1.917
Ti	0.005	0.010	0.006	0.021	0.011	0.020	0.019	0.032	—	0.010	0.014	0.020
Al	0.123	0.212	0.188	0.271	0.134	0.189	0.157	0.265	0.117	0.097	0.125	0.127
Fe	0.204	0.177	0.196	0.337	0.250	0.291	0.213	0.314	0.252	0.276	0.428	0.695
Mn	—	—	—	—	—	—	—	—	—	—	0.011	0.013
Mg	1.090	0.989	0.998	0.865	0.982	0.881	0.855	0.808	1.066	0.900	0.863	0.718
Ca	0.583	0.652	0.655	0.626	0.647	0.689	0.808	0.684	0.579	0.753	0.625	0.482
Na	0.052	0.054	0.056	0.060	0.072	0.079	0.054	0.080	0.041	0.043	0.039	0.053
Cr	0.027	0.030	0.026	0.007	0.032	0.008	0.029	0.009	0.020	—	—	—

c = centre of crystal, r = rim.

TABLE 9. *Representative analyses of amphiboles from Scourie dykes*

	olivine-gabbros		dolerites	
	L540	L543	L613	831
SiO_2	41.35	41.79	42.37	39.57
TiO_2	4.81	5.06	0.96	1.52
Al_2O_3	11.50	11.41	11.70	12.14
FeO	13.10	12.34	21.53	25.42
MgO	12.60	12.64	7.44	4.78
CaO	9.91	9.74	10.66	10.67
Na_2O	3.03	3.37	1.20	1.71
K_2O	0.82	0.85	1.36	1.87
Total	97.12	97.20	97.22	97.68

Formula on the basis of 23 oxygens
Si	6.163	6.210	6.522	6.234
Ti	0.539	0.566	0.111	0.180
Al	2.021	1.999	2.123	2.258
Fe	1.633	1.543	2.772	3.354
Mg	2.799	2.799	1.707	1.124
Ca	1.583	1.551	1.758	1.804
Na	0.876	0.971	0.358	0.523
K	0.156	0.161	0.267	0.376

Trace element geochemistry of Scourie dykes

The geochemistry of the different types of Scourie dykes has been described in detail by Weaver & Tarney (1981, 1983), and only the main points are outlined and illustrated here. All the dykes, with a single exception, have rare earth patterns showing light rare earth enrichment (Fig. 3). The light REE enrichment is greater in the picrite and norite dykes than in the olivine-gabbros and the dolerites, and the patterns in the two groups are different in shape. Modelling of the REE in combination with other trace elements suggested that (a) the norites could not be derived from the picrites by fractional crystallization, but could be derived from a similar mantle source as the picrites at lower degrees of melting, (b) the quartz dolerites and olivine gabbros are not related by fractional crystallization, but could be derived from a similar mantle source provided the olivine-gabbro magmas were generated at greater depth in the stability field of garnet, (c) the mantle sources of the two groups were different, that which gave rise to the picrites and norites being

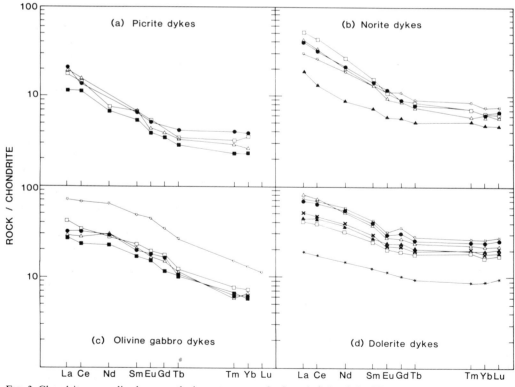

FIG. 3. Chondrite-normalized rare earth element patterns for Scourie dykes (after Weaver & Tarney 1981).

Mg-rich and Ti-poor, and (d) both these mantle sources had undergone enrichment in light REE prior to magma generation.

Comparison of other trace element abundances using multi-element primordial mantle normalized diagrams (Fig. 4) also demonstrates that all dykes are enriched in large ion lithophile (LIL) elements relative to high field strength (HFS) elements, but that this relative enrichment is greater in the picrites and norites than in the dolerites and olivine-gabbro dykes. The norite and picrite dykes have essentially parallel normalized patterns, implying consanguinity, and likewise the olivine-gabbro and dolerite patterns are closely similar. Both types of pattern display marked negative Nb anomalies, the magnitude of this anomaly being greater in the picrite and norite dykes.

Such trace element patterns are typical of continental flood basalts (Weaver & Tarney 1983) and there is debate as to whether this 'continental'

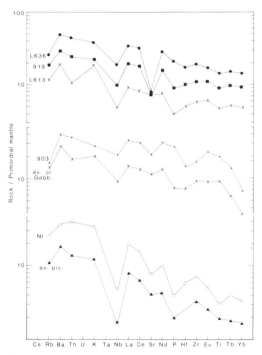

FIG. 4. Trace element abundances in Scourie dykes normalized to primordial mantle values (after Weaver & Tarney 1981). Above: 3 samples representing the compositional range of Scourie quartz dolerites. Below: pattern for the norite N1 is very similar to that of the average picrite. Centre: patterns for the average olivine-gabbro, and a related more fractionated sample, 903, show closer similarities with the dolerites than with the picrites and norite.

trace element signature has resulted from crustal contamination of ascending magmas or is a characteristic of the mantle source. Weaver & Tarney (1983) were able to demonstrate however that assimilation of Lewisian gneisses could not possibly generate the observed trace element patterns in the Scourie dykes, a prime difficulty in a contamination model being that the concentrations of LIL elements such as Rb and Th are too low, by an order of magnitude, in the Lewisian gneiss country rocks.

Discussion

The occurrence of widely different magma compositions among the Scourie dyke swarm allows interesting comparisons to be made of the behaviour of magmas flowing through dyke channels at depth. Questions to be asked might be: (1) Can significant mineral fractionation take place *en route* to higher levels? (2) With higher magma temperatures at depth, will the combined effects of lower viscosity and rapid flow rate permit sufficiently high Reynolds numbers to be attained that the flow becomes turbulent rather than laminar? (3) If turbulent flow takes place might this bring about thermal erosion and assimilation of wall rock?

Most of the dykes in the central zone appear to have been intruded through granulite- or amphibolite-facies gneisses with country rock temperatures of the order of 500°C (O'Hara 1961; Tarney 1963; Sills & Rollinson, this vol.). There is no evidence that dykes with chilled margins were emplaced into cooler host rocks; indeed field relationships suggest the reverse is true. Rather, differences in crystallization behaviour seem directly to reflect differences in the physical properties of the respective magmas. Quartz dolerite dykes have chilled margins with few if any phenocrysts, norite dykes have chilled margins with pyroxene phenocrysts, olivine-gabbro dykes have finer grained augite-rich margins whilst the picrites have wide, coarse-grained orthopyroxene-rich margins. This correlates with increasing basicity of the magma: the more ultrabasic magmas have lower ratios of glass-former elements (Si, Al) to oxygen, which implies lower viscosities and more favourable diffusion rates.

Pyroxene-rich margins

The fact that there are both orthopyroxene-rich or augite-rich margins and clear igneous textures rules out reaction with the country rock as possible explanations for this feature. Nor, since enrichment occurs on both sides of the dykes, can they be cumulate in origin. A point worth noting is that it is the second liquidus phase, orthopyroxene or augite, rather than the first liquidus phase, olivine, which is enriched at the margin of the dyke. One implication of this is that some mechanism must be invoked to remove olivines from the marginal zone of the dykes and prevent olivines being incorporated in the margins. Flowage differentiation (Bhattacharji & Smith 1964), which would concentrate suspended crystals toward the centre during emplacement, is a probable explanation. Indeed in the thin ultramafic veins at Badcall Bay (O'Hara 1962) olivine microphenocrysts are concentrated at the centre of the veins. However there is rather a sharp change in behaviour from the chilled, almost glassy margins of the dolerites and norites to the coarse almost monomineralic pyroxene-rich margins of the olivine-gabbros and picrites, which suggests a first order change in magma behaviour. The most obvious explanation is that this marks a change from laminar flow in the case of the basic dykes to turbulent flow during intrusion of the higher temperature, lower viscosity ultramafic magmas.

During laminar flow temperatures at the contact are intermediate between that of the magma and that of the country rock. This position is maintained as heat transferred to the wall rocks is matched by crystallization at the margin and the solid–liquid interface moves into the dyke, but the thermal profile becomes flatter. Even with hot country rocks this situation will still produce chilled margins.

Under turbulent flow conditions the temperatures at the contact can be much higher and, particularly with superheated magmas, could produce thermal erosion and assimilation of wall rock. In the more normal condition of magmas without superheat, any heat transferred to the wall rocks must be accompanied by crystallization of liquidus phases. If these are transported upwards by the moving magma, then thermal erosion could still occur. However if these liquidus phases crystallize on the dyke wall, thermal erosion will be inhibited and the dyke margin will be enriched in those phases crystallizing at the time of intrusion. These were orthopyroxene in the case of the picrite dykes and augite in the olivine-gabbro dykes. The observed framework textures in both are perfectly compatible with this. Turbulent motion of the uprising magma would prevent significant numbers of suspended olivines being incorporated in the marginal pyroxene framework, and the higher temperatures at the margin would also prevent significant precipitation of later crystallizing phases, except later at lower temperatures in pores within the framework.

An important factor in the formation of such margins may have been the ease of nucleation of the liquidus phases. This is particularly relevant in the case of the olivine-gabbro dykes where olivine was apparently also crystallizing at the time of intrusion but was not enriched significantly at the dyke margin. Olivine nucleates easily however and rarely forms aggregates. The abundance of overgrowth relationships amongst the dyke pyroxenes (Tarney 1969) suggests that

TABLE 10. *Representative analyses of micas from Scourie dykes*

	picrites			olivine-gabbros		norite	dolerite
	L582	L588	L280	L540	L543	L639	L613
SiO_2	36.23	37.54	36.12	36.62	37.43	36.87	34.79
TiO_2	4.40	5.22	5.42	5.32	4.47	3.46	4.84
Al_2O_3	15.43	14.82	15.33	13.91	14.59	16.00	15.40
FeO	12.88	7.74	16.03	16.92	11.95	16.91	22.75
MgO	15.68	19.80	12.87	13.47	17.77	13.27	8.29
Na_2O	0.51	0.59	0.41	0.47	0.89	—	0.36
K_2O	9.53	9.78	9.64	9.59	8.98	9.89	9.32
Total	94.66	95.49	95.82	96.30	96.08	96.40	95.75

Formula on the basis of 22 oxygens

Si	5.419	5.436	5.419	5.494	5.473	5.501	5.399
Ti	0.495	0.568	0.612	0.600	0.492	0.388	0.565
Al	2.721	2.530	2.712	2.460	2.515	2.814	2.817
Fe	1.611	0.937	2.011	2.123	1.461	2.110	2.953
Mg	3.495	4.272	2.878	3.012	3.873	2.950	1.917
Na	0.148	0.166	0.119	0.137	0.252	—	0.108
K	1.819	1.807	1.845	1.836	1.675	1.882	1.845

they nucleate with difficulty and would tend to nucleate, where possible, on earlier crystals, in this case at the dyke margin.

An important implication of these observations is that thermal erosion of country rock and contamination of ascending magmas may be very much less than assumed, even with high temperature picritic magmas. Indeed, far from magmas becoming more silicic through assimilation, the curious fact is that extraction of orthopyroxene from the magma by wall crystallization actually leaves the uprising magma relatively richer in olivine, and more ultramafic.

Asymmetric variations

Explanations for the asymmetric mineral distributions follow that of the pyroxene-rich margins, but refer to the position after flow had ceased. At this point, in the picrites, the centre of the dyke would largely have been composed of suspended olivines and also orthopyroxenes which had nucleated independently from the marginal zone. Thick dykes emplaced into hot country rock can be considered as magma chambers with infinite height and no floor. Crystal settling becomes a steady state process: and would not manifest itself unless the sheet was inclined. In this case settling crystals would preferentially concentrate near the footwall. Orthopyroxenes, being larger, if not denser, would (according to Stokes' Law) congregate nearer the footwall, and would continue to grow, and in the case of the Beannach dyke, poikilitically enclose numerous olivines. The liquid carrying components of the later crystallizing constituents, clinopyroxene, plagioclase and biotite, would be displaced towards the hanging wall side of the dyke. Such a model permits varying degrees of asymmetry (even, as

is observed in the Beannach dyke, local reversed asymmetry) depending on the inclination of the dyke, or no asymmetry at all if the dyke is vertical. It is a situation where no great change in mineral composition across the dyke need occur. The asymmetry in the olivine-gabbro dykes may be explained similarly, except that augite was the early crystallizing pyroxene and not all the olivine had crystallized before intrusion.

One final item needs comment. Such mineralogical and modal variations that occur within the Scourie dykes are restricted to those of ultramafic composition and low viscosity. Their magnitude is not significant in a petrogenetic sense. No variations are apparent in the quartz dolerite dykes, and simple extrapolation would suggest that this is unlikely even at greater depth. They have no phenocrysts. Yet the Fe-rich quartz dolerites have compositions that correspond to basaltic liquids which have suffered extensive low pressure crystal fractionation.

Significance of variations in mineral chemistry

Before discussing the petrogenetic relationships between the four types of dykes it is worth considering the constraints provided by the mineralogy and mineral chemistry. The picrites and norites have a mineralogy dominated by orthopyroxene but have no amphibole; the mineralogy of the olivine gabbros and quartz dolerites is dominated by clinopyroxene and appreciable hornblende. On the other hand it is tempting to relate the picrite and olivine-gabbro dykes petrogenetically, particularly as the late stage products of the picrites have some similarities with the olivine-gabbro dykes, including similar pyroxene compositions (Fig. 5). However,

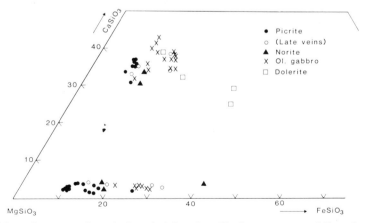

FIG. 5. Compositions of pyroxenes from the Scourie dykes plotted in the pyroxene quadrilateral.

in detail, these clinopyroxene compositions are not quite so closely comparable. Figure 6 shows Al–Ti distributions in clinopyroxenes from all the dykes. The picrites and norites have coherent Ti/Al ratios which are appreciably lower than the ratio in the clinopyroxenes from the dolerites and olivine-gabbros. This must reflect a real difference in the chemistry of the magmas from which the pyroxenes crystallized, and possibly of the source too.

Although for the picrite, norite and olivine-gabbro dykes the whole rock chemistry is generally controlled by the presence of 'cumulus' olivine and pyroxene, some indication as to the primary composition of the dyke magmas can be gained from the mineral chemistry of the ferromagnesian phases. Using the olivine–liquid Mg–Fe partitioning data of Roeder & Emslie (1970), olivine of composition Fo_{83} (typical of most picrite dykes, Table 2) would have been in equilibrium with a liquid having an *mg* number $(100.Mg/(Mg+Fe^{2+}))$ of 62. The olivines in the evolved veins of the Beannach dyke (Table 2) equilibrated with liquids of *mg* numbers of 42–55. In the olivine-gabbro dykes, the liquids in equilibrium with olivine that ranged in composition from Fo_{71} to Fo_{64} would have had *mg* numbers of 37–45. These liquid compositions are far removed from those of primary magmas (*mg* = *c*. 79) derived from the mantle with olivine of composition Fo_{92}. Either the magmas had undergone significant fractionation of ferromagnesian phases prior to emplacement at the presently exposed crustal level, or the primary

magmas were derived from a more iron-rich mantle source (as proposed by, for instance, Wilkinson & Binns 1977). Similarly, the picrite olivines are too iron-rich to represent disaggregated olivines from an upper mantle source, unless this source was less magnesian than normal upper mantle. However, Ni and Cr contents of the ferromagnesian phases in the picrite, olivine-gabbro and norite dykes indicate the primitive nature of the dyke magmas. The picrite olivines typically have NiO contents of about 0.40% (Table 2). Using the olivine–liquid Ni partition coefficient data of Hart & Davis (1978), and assuming liquids with MgO contents of 10–15% (although this is not well constrained except from some simple olivine subtraction mass balance calculations), the equilibrium liquids would have contained *c*. 270–340 ppm Ni. Adopting a clinopyroxene–liquid partition coefficient for Cr of about 10 (Sun *et al*. 1979), clinopyroxene cores in both the picrite and olivine-gabbro dykes having *c*. 1% Cr_2O_3 equilibrated with liquids containing *c*. 680 ppm Cr, while norite dykes having clinopyroxenes with *c*. 0.69% Cr_2O_3 equilibrated with liquids containing 470 ppm Cr. Similarly, using an orthopyroxene–liquid partition coefficient for Cr of about 7 (average of megacryst/host data of Irving & Frey 1984), picrite orthopyroxene cores having 0.91% Cr_2O_3 (Table 7) equilibrated with liquids containing 890 ppm Cr. The calculated abundances of Ni and Cr in the liquids giving rise to the picrite, norite and olivine-gabbro dykes are close to those expected in primary mantle melts (*c*. 250 ppm Ni, 600 ppm Cr, although Cr abundances are controlled by the amount of spinel in the residue; Bougault *et al*. 1979; Sun *et al*. 1979). This suggests that the magmas can have undergone only limited fractionation of ferromagnesian phases prior to emplacement, and is in apparent contradiction to the indications from Fe–Mg relations in olivines, unless the magmas were derived from a relatively iron-rich mantle source.

Petrogenesis

The mineral data and the trace element data for the Scourie dykes indicate that the four types of dykes cannot be part of a single co-genetic suite. There must be at least two different sources supplying the dyke magmas, one more Mg-rich and refractory which provided the bronzite picrite and the norite magmas, the other more Fe-rich and fertile which supplied the olivine-gabbro and quartz dolerite magmas. In each case differing degrees of melting and/or depths of melting are involved. Moreover the trace element data indicate that these mantle sources must have

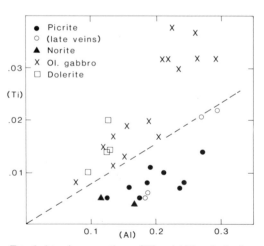

FIG. 6. Atomic proportions of Ti and Al (on the basis of 6 oxygens) in Scourie dyke clinopyroxenes. Line separates bronzite picrite (including late stage veins) and norite dyke pyroxenes, with lower Ti/Al ratios, from olivine-gabbro and dolerite pyroxenes.

been enriched in LIL elements and light REE. The timing of this mantle enrichment event is uncertain, but Weaver & Tarney (1981) argued that enrichment some 500 m.y. earlier, at the time of generation of the Lewisian gneisses at 2.9 Ga, was compatible with available Sr isotope data on the dykes and the modelled Rb/Sr ratios of the dolerite dyke source. The simplest explanation for the enrichment is that crustal components generated from subduction zones contaminated, and were incompletely extracted from, the overlying mantle wedge: this material ultimately became part of the subcontinental mantle, being stabilized in hydrous mineral phases such as phlogopite or hornblende. As average crustal material is enriched in LIL elements and is characterized by a prominent negative Nb anomaly (Weaver & Tarney 1983), there is no difficulty in accounting for the geochemistry of the dykes if subsequent thermal events mobilized the sub-continental mantle.

A point worth making is that Scourie dykes are by no means unique in having these geochemical characteristics. In the Napier Complex of Antarctica, Sheraton & Black (1981) have described dykes of essentially the same age, and intruded into country rocks of similar age and composition as the Lewisian, which are almost identical in their geochemistry to the quartz dolerite and norite dykes of Assynt. Continental flood basalt provinces such as the Karoo, Deccan, Columbia River and many others have basalts with similar trace element signatures (Weaver & Tarney 1983; Thompson *et al.* 1983; Cox 1983), although sometimes it is possible to invoke crustal assimilation as well as contamination of the mantle source (Cox & Hawkesworth 1985). Picritic lavas also occur in these provinces and it is interesting that, like the Scourie bronzite picrites, they frequently show greater relative enrichment in LIL elements and the light REE than the associated dolerites. That these characteristics are present in ancient subcontinental lithosphere is apparent from isotopic studies of mantle nodules (Menzies 1983; Hawkesworth *et al.* 1983; Richardson *et al.* 1985).

Dyke swarms emplaced over a wide region, and including magmas such as the picrites and olivine-gabbros which represent high degrees of mantle melting, pose a thermal problem in accounting for the large volume of magma produced and also in how the thermal energy is focused to generate high degree mantle melts. The fact that dykes are wider, more abundant and include denser ultramafic types in the central granulite zone, whereas dykes in the flanking high level amphibolite facies zones are thinner and more sparse, suggests there may not have been equivalent extrusives. Because the height to which a magma column can rise is dependent on its density in relation to that of the combined weight of crust + mantle supporting the column, the probability is that the source of the dyke magmas was relatively shallow. Radiogenic heat alone is unlikely to generate high degrees of mantle melts.

Adiabatic uprise of mantle diapirs is the most potent way of generating the required thermal energy to provide high degrees of mantle melting (Weaver & Tarney 1979; McKenzie 1984). Diapirism may be thermally induced. Alternatively high-Mg refractory harzburgitic mantle, a result of basalt extraction at mid-ocean ridges, is less dense than fertile mantle (Boyd & McCallister 1976), and inherently buoyant. It has been suggested by Oxburgh & Parmentier (1978) that such subducted residues from basalt extraction may eventually rise diapirically to underplate the continental lithosphere. The thermal effects are likely to be substantial. In particular, extensive melting of the phlogopite and/or hornblende-rich subcontinental lithosphere might occur, producing voluminous tholeiitic magmas or, at deeper level, magmas with the characteristics of the olivine-gabbro dykes. The refractory harzburgitic material of the diapir might also melt and, interacting with the overlying phlogopite-rich mantle, be a suitable source for the orthopyroxene-rich picrite and norite magmas. Although necessarily speculative, such a model does account for the different magma types observed and the thermal energy required to generate them. Interestingly, mantle xenoliths include those which are fertile with respect to major elements and those which are refractory; it is the latter which generally show greater relative enrichment in the more incompatible trace elements (Harte 1983), broadly corresponding with the features seen in the Scourie dykes.

Thermal breakdown of hydrous phases in the subcontinental lithosphere might also have provided extensive volumes of hydrous fluids, which preceded and were associated with dyke intrusion, and which migrated up shear zones to cause extensive retrogression of the gneisses and metamorphism of the early dykes. The volumes of these retrogressive fluids were substantial (Beach & Tarney 1978), but no reasoned explanation has hitherto been advanced to account for them.

Conclusions

The Scourie dyke swarm represents considerable extension of the Lewisian crust in the early

Proterozoic. Various original depths of dyke emplacement are seen in the segmented Lewisian outcrop as a result of the juxtaposition of different crustal levels. Throughflow behaviour of basic and picritic magmas in hot country rocks can be compared. The pyroxene-rich margins of the latter dykes may be attributable to turbulent, as opposed to laminar, flow, but if so, turbulent flow conditions are not associated with significant thermal erosion of the country rocks. Indeed, although most dykes have a 'continental' trace element signature, this is not a result of assimilation of country rock, but must be an inherited feature from the sub-continental mantle. Trace element data and mineral chemistry indicate that the four main types of dyke magma must be derived from at least two different mantle sources, one fertile with respect to major elements and one more refractory, but showing a greater relative enrichment in incompatible trace elements. Different depths and degrees of melting are necessary to account for the trace element differences between the dykes. The picritic and olivine-gabbro dykes represent high degrees of mantle melting, which presents a significant thermal problem. The answer may lie in the processes of development of the sub-continental lithosphere. Conversely, studies of Proterozoic dyke swarms may provide significant information on the nature and development of the sub-continental mantle and supplement information provided by studies of mantle xenoliths.

References

BEACH, A. & TARNEY, J. 1978. Major and trace element patterns established during retrogressive metamorphism of granulite facies gneisses, NW Scotland. *Precambrian Res*, 7, 325–348.

BHATTACHARJI, S. & SMITH, C. H. 1964. Flowage differentiation. *Science*, 145, 150–153.

BOUGAULT, H., CAMBON, P., JORON, J-L. & TREUIL, M. 1979. Evidence for variability of magmatic processes and upper mantle heterogeneity in the axial region of the Mid-Atlantic Ridge near 22°N and 36°N. *Tectonophysics*, 55, 11–44.

BOYD, F. R. & McCALLISTER, R. H. 1976. Densities of fertile and sterile garnet peridotites. *Geophys Res Let*, 9, 509–512.

CHADWICK, B. 1981. Field relations, petrography and geochemistry of Archaean amphibolite dykes and Malene supracrustal amphibolites, northwest Buksefjorden, southern west Greenland. *Precambrian Res*, 14, 221–259.

CHAPMAN, H. J. 1979. 2390 Myr Rb-Sr whole rock age for the Scourie dykes of north-west Scotland. *Nature, London*. 277, 642–643.

COX, K. G. 1983. The Karoo Province of southern Africa: origin of trace element enrichment patterns. *In*: HAWKESWORTH, C. J. & NORRY, M. J. (eds) *Continental Basalts and Mantle Xenoliths*. Shiva Publications, Nantwich, pp. 139–157.

—— & HAWKESWORTH, C. J. 1985. Geochemical stratigraphy of the Deccan Traps at Mahabaleshwar, Western Ghats, India, with implications for open system magmatic processes. *J. Petrol*. 26, 355–377.

EVANS, C. R. & TARNEY, J. 1964. Isotopic ages of Assynt dykes. *Nature, London* 204, 638–641.

HAMILTON, P. J., EVENSEN, N. M., O'NIONS, R. K. & TARNEY, J. 1979. Sm-Nd systematics of Lewisian gneisses: implications for the origin of granulites. *Nature, London* 277, 25–28.

HART, S. R. & DAVIES, K. E. 1978. Nickel partitioning between olivine and silicate melt. *Earth planet Sci. Lett*. 40, 203–219.

HARTE, B. 1983. Mantle peridotites and processes—the kimberlite sample. *In*: HAWKESWORTH, C. J. & NORRY, M. J. (eds) *Continental Basalts and Mantle Xenoliths*, Shiva Publications, Nantwich, pp. 46–91.

HAWKESWORTH, C. J., ERLANK, A. J., MARSH, J. S., MENZIES, M. A. & VAN CALSTERN, P. 1983. Evolution of the continental lithosphere: evidence from volcanics and xenoliths in southern Africa. *In*: HAWKESWORTH, C. J. & NORRY, M. J. (eds) *Continental Basalts and Mantle Xenoliths*. Shiva Publications, Nantwich, pp. 111–138.

IRVING, A. J. & FREY, F. A. 1984. Trace element abundances in megacrysts and their host basalts: Constraints on partition coefficients and megacryst genesis. *Geochim. Cosmochim. Acta*, 48, 1201–1221.

KRETZ, R. 1961. Some applications of thermodynamics to coexisting minerals of variable composition. Examples: orthopyroxene-clinopyroxene and orthopyroxene-garnet. *J. Geol*. 69, 361–387.

LEAKE, B. E. 1978. Nomenclature of amphiboles. *Min. Mag*. 42, 533–563.

MacGREGOR, M. & PHEMISTER, J. 1958. *Geological excursion guide to the Assynt District*, Oliver & Boyd, London, 50 pp.

McKENZIE, D. 1984. The generation and compaction of partially molten rock. *J. Petrol*. 25, 713–765.

MENZIES, M. A. 1983. Mantle ultramafic xenoliths in alkaline magmas: evidence for mantle heterogeneity modified by magmatic activity. *In*: HAWKESWORTH, C. J. & NORRY, M. J. (eds) *Continental Basalts and Mantle Xenoliths*. Shiva Publications, Nantwich, pp. 92–110.

O'HARA, M. J. 1961. Petrology of the Scourie dyke, Sutherland. *Min. Mag*. 32, 848–865.

—— 1962. Some intrusions in the Lewisian complex near Badcall, Sutherland. *Trans. Edinburgh Geol. Soc*. 19, 201–207.

OXBURGH, E. R. & PARMENTIER, E. M. 1978. Thermal processes in the formation of the continental lithosphere. *Phil. Trans. R. Soc. London, A* 288, 415–429.

RICHARDSON, S. H., ERLANK, A. J. & HART, S. R. 1985. Kimberlite-borne garnet peridotite xenoliths from old enriched subcontinental lithosphere. *Earth planet. Sci. Lett.* **75**, 116–128.

ROEDER, P. L. & EMSLIE, R. F. 1970. Olivine-liquid equilibrium. *Contrib. Mineral. Petrol.* **29**, 275–289.

SHERATON, J. W. & BLACK, L. P. 1981. Geochemistry and geochronology of Proterozoic tholeiitic dykes of East Antarctica: evidence for mantle metasomatism. *Contrib. Mineral. Petrol.* **78**, 305–317.

STUMPFL, E. F. 1961. Contribution to the study of ore minerals in some igneous rocks from Assynt. *Min. Mag.* **32**, 767–777.

SUN, S-S., NESBITT, R. W. & SHARASKIN, A. YA. 1979. Geochemical characteristics of mid-ocean ridge basalts. *Earth planet. Sci. Lett.* **44**, 119–138.

TARNEY, J. 1963. Assynt dykes and their metamorphism. *Nature, London* **199**, 672–674.

—— 1969. Epitaxic relations between coexisting pyroxenes. *Min. Mag.* **37**, 115–122.

—— 1973. The Scourie dyke suite and the nature of the Inverian event in Assynt. *In*: PARK, R. G. & TARNEY, J. (eds) *The Early Precambrian of Scotland and related rocks of Greenland.* Univ. Keele, pp. 105–118.

THOMPSON, R. N., MORRISON, M. A., DICKIN, A. P. & HENDRY, G. L. 1983. Continental flood basalts . . . arachnids rule OK? *In*: HAWKESWORTH, C. J. & NORRY, M. J. (eds) *Continental Basalts and Mantle Xenoliths.* Shiva Publications, Nantwich, pp. 158–185.

WEAVER, B. L. & TARNEY, J. 1979. Thermal aspects of komatiite generation and greenstone belt models. *Nature, London* **279**, 689–692.

—— & —— 1981. The Scourie dyke suite: petrogenesis and geochemical nature of the Proterozoic subcontinental mantle. *Contrib Mineral. Petrol.* **78**, 175–188.

—— & —— 1983. Chemistry of the sub-continental mantle: inferences from Archaean and Proterozoic dykes and continental flood basalts. *In*: HAWKESWORTH, C. J. & NORRY, M. J. (eds) *Continental Basalts and Mantle Xenoliths.* Shiva Publications, Nantwich, pp. 209–229.

WILKINSON, J. F. G. & BINNS, R. A. 1977. Relatively iron-rich lherzolite xenoliths of the Cr-diopside suite: a guide to the primary nature of anorogenic tholeiitic andesitic magmas. *Contrib. Mineral. Petrol.* **65**, 199–212.

J. TARNEY, Department of Geology, University of Leicester, Leicester LE1 7RH, UK.

B. L. WEAVER, School of Geology and Geophysics, University of Oklahoma, Norman, Oklahoma 73019, USA.

The East Greenland Nagssugtoqidian mobile belt compared with the Lewisian complex

J. S. Myers

SUMMARY: The rocks, structures and geological history of the Lewisian complex are similar to those of the Nagssugtoqidian mobile belt in East Greenland. Both regions comprise a heterogeneous, mainly tonalitic, gneiss complex which formed 2900–2700 Ma. Both gneiss complexes were intruded by basic dykes and intensely deformed and metamorphosed during two major episodes. The first episode, called Inverian in Scotland, is broadly equivalent to the Nag. 1 episode in Greenland dominated by major dextral strike-slip shear zones about 2600–2300 Ma. The second episode, the Laxfordian of Scotland, is broadly equivalent to the Nag. 2 episode of Greenland associated with the southward translation of sheets of rock along northward-dipping thrusts and shear zones about 1900–1700 Ma. Both gneiss complexes were raised to a high crustal level by 1600–1400 Ma and extensively eroded.

Introduction

Anyone who crosses the North Atlantic from the Lewisian complex of Scotland to the Precambrian gneisses of southern Greenland will be struck by the similarity of the rocks. Both regions comprise a variety of quartzo-feldspathic gneisses and a lesser quantity of amphibolite and metasedimentary rocks. The rocks of both regions are heterogeneously deformed, and show evidence of repeated deformation and metamorphism in amphibolite or granulite facies. In these respects they resemble many other Precambrian gneiss terrains, but in detail, both in the kinds of rocks and in the sequence of geological events, they have much in common which distinguishes them from other early Precambrian cratons such as Australia (Myers, this vol.).

The early Precambrian gneisses of both the Lewisian complex and southern Greenland are intruded by swarms of basic dykes. These dykes are strongly deformed in the Nagssugtoqidian mobile belt in Greenland and in much of the Lewisian complex. Where the dykes are deformed, the host gneisses are tectonically reworked, their banding is distorted and in many cases transposed into a new gneissosity.

In East Greenland this tectonic reworking is most intense in the Nagssugtoqidian mobile belt, 240 km wide, which cuts sharply across the older gneiss complex. Basic dykes are especially abundant within and adjacent to this mobile belt. The rocks, structures and sequence of geological processes seen in this mobile belt more closely resemble those of the Lewisian complex than do those of the rest of SE Greenland. Before the Cainozoic formation of the North Atlantic Ocean, the Lewisian complex lay directly along

strike of the Nagssugtoqidian mobile belt, about 500 km from the present coast of East Greenland, and a correlation of geology between these regions seems likely (Fig. 1).

Most readers will be familiar with the geology of the Lewisian complex, and it is dealt with by other contributors to this volume. Therefore this paper concentrates on the geology of the Nagssugtoqidian mobile belt of East Greenland and the Archaean gneiss complex which it cuts, and then makes broad comparisons with similar aspects of Lewisian geology.

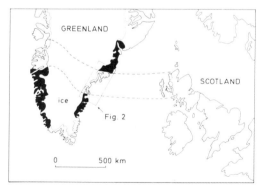

FIG. 1. Map showing the relative position of Greenland and Scotland before the formation of the Atlantic Ocean (after Le Pichon *et al.* 1977). Thin closely spaced lines show the strike of Nagssugtoqidian structures in Greenland and Inverian–Laxfordian structures in Scotland which formed 2600–1700 Ma. Black—Archaean gneisses stable since 2600 Ma; stipple—Archaean and Proterozoic gneisses deformed and metamorphosed 1900–1700 Ma.

From: PARK, R. G. & TARNEY, J. (eds), 1987, *Evolution of the Lewisian and Comparable Precambrian High Grade Terrains*, Geological Society Special Publication No. 27, pp. 235–246.

Archaean gneiss complex in East Greenland

The Nagssugtoqidian mobile belt cuts across, and appears to be superimposed on, the Archaean gneiss complex (Fig. 2). The gneiss complex was heterogeneous in composition and structure (Fig. 3), and was metamorphosed in granulite or upper amphibolite facies. About 80–90% of the gneiss complex was derived from granodioritic or tonalitic plutonic rocks, and a small amount from dioritic or granitic rocks. About 10–20% of the complex consists of metamorphosed volcanic and sedimentary rocks and layered basic intrusions, that were all fragmented by the granitoid intrusions which form the bulk of the complex. Various intensities of Archaean deformation can be seen, from undeformed to intensely deformed. With increasing deformation a variety of planar elements were brought into parallelism (Fig. 4) and, together with heterogeneities such as agmatite fragments, were streaked out; grain sizes and the thickness of individual layers were progressively reduced (as in West Greenland; Myers 1978).

In some regions of West Greenland it can be seen that typical quartzo-feldspathic gneisses were derived from sheets of tonalite, granodiorite or granite emplaced into now metamorphosed volcanic and sedimentary rocks and layered anorthosite intrusions (Myers 1981). All these rocks were interleaved in a sub-horizontal tectonic regime and then folded by two sets of upright folds into large scale dome-and-basin interference structures (Myers 1981). Similar structures are seen in the Archaean gneiss complex in East Greenland but have not been mapped out on a regional scale.

The components and tectonic history of the gneiss complex on both sides of the mobile belt in East Greenland are similar to those of the gneiss complex in SW Greenland which mainly formed 2900–2700 Ma (Bridgwater *et al.* 1976), although no early Archaean rocks such as the 3800–3650 Ma Amîtsoq gneisses and Isua supracrustal rocks have been identified in East Greenland. The Nagssugtoqidian mobile belt appears to have formed within a single craton rather than to have joined different Archaean cratons.

Nag. 1 deformation and metamorphism

The heterogeneous Archaean gneiss complex of

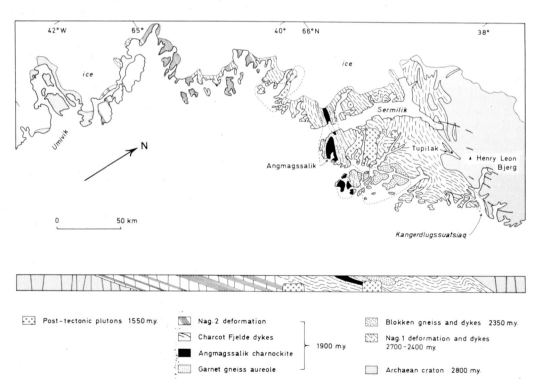

FIG. 2. Geological map and section of the Nagssugtoqidian mobile belt in East Greenland (after Bridgwater & Myers 1979).

FIG. 3. Heterogeneous Archaean gneiss with deformed networks of pegmatite veins. The veins are little deformed in amphibolite fragments (foreground) but are strongly deformed and rotated into sub-parallelism in granitoid pegmatite-banded gneiss beyond. The gneiss is cut by metamorphosed basic dykes (on distant hills) but is not deformed by Nagssugtoqidian tectonism. Umivik, 25 km south of the Nagssugtoqidian mobile belt.

East Greenland was cut by swarms of dolerite dykes (Fig. 5), and the dykes are especially abundant within and adjacent to the Nagssugtoqidian mobile belt. The boundaries of the mobile belt are marked by major shear zones in which dykes and Archaean structures and fabrics are strongly deformed, attenuated and brought into parallelism (Fig. 6). The tectonic and metamorphic history of the mobile belt in East Greenland is divided into two major episodes called Nag. 1 and Nag. 2 (Bridgwater & Myers 1979), and the shear zones which define the mobile belt are Nag. 1 structures.

Within the mobile belt the Nag. 1 deformation was accompanied by metamorphism which, in the north, caused retrogression of Archaean granulite-facies gneisses to amphibolite facies, and in the south led to the recrystallization of Archaean amphibolite-facies gneisses with new tectonic fabrics in amphibolite facies. Retrogression from granulite to amphibolite facies also occurred in shear zones in the Archaean craton to the north of the mobile belt, and many of these shear zones were intruded by dolerite dykes (Myers 1984, fig. 11). A Rb–Sr age of about 2635 was obtained from one of these shear zones by Pedersen & Bridgwater (1979). In the Archaean craton immediately adjacent to the north of the mobile belt the shear zones were preceded by broader zones in which retrogression occurred in vein-like networks isolating an irregular breccia-like complex of granulite-facies blocks and patches (Figs 7 and 8).

Nag. 1 deformation within the mobile belt formed steep belts with pronounced planar fabrics (Fig. 9) associated with regional dextral transcurrent movements (Myers 1984, fig. 13). This deformation continued intermittently during the major episode of dyke intrusion; early dykes were deformed, cut by younger dykes, and then all deformed together. Many dykes were intruded into active Nag. 1 shear zones and show primary pinch-and-swell structures (Bridgwater & Myers 1979, fig. 2a and b; Myers 1984, fig. 14). Most little-deformed dykes have relict sub-ophitic textures and contain garnets. Strongly deformed dykes were converted to schistose amphibolite. The development of Nag. 1 fabrics and structures was heterogeneous; lenses of unmodified Archaean gneisses occur sporadically throughout the mobile belt (Fig. 10), and complex fold and fold interference structures were generated by deformation of Archaean banding and Nag. 1 schistosity and dykes.

FIG. 4. Strongly deformed Archaean dykes and gneiss at Kangerdlugssuaq, 250 km north of the Nagssugtoqidian mobile belt, which resemble the younger Nag. 1 dykes and deformation within the mobile belt. (Cliff section is about 2 m high.)

Supracrustal rocks

Supracrustal rocks, mainly metasedimentary pelitic and semi-pelitic schists with minor marbles and graphite schists (Wright *et al.* 1973), are much more abundant within the Nagssugtoqidian mobile belt than in the Archaean gneiss complex of the craton. Amphibolites of probably metavolcanic origin occur within the mobile belt but are relatively less abundant than in the craton. Kyanite is abundant in pelitic rocks within the mobile belt but has not been seen in pelitic rocks in the adjacent craton.

Similar features are seen in West Greenland where Kalsbeek *et al.* (1984) point out the similarity of the supracrustal rocks in the Nagssugtoqidian mobile belt with those in the Rinkian mobile belt to the north (Escher & Pulvertaft

FIG. 5. Undeformed but metamorphosed basic dykes (garnet amphibolite) sub-parallel to the boundary of the Nagssugtoqidian mobile belt, cutting heterogeneous Archaean gneiss at Umivik, 25 km south of the mobile belt.

FIG. 6. Profile section (450 m) of the northward-dipping southern boundary of the Nagssugtoqidian mobile belt. Below the boundary (located between two arrows) undeformed basic dykes cut Archaean gneisses, whereas at and above the boundary basic dykes and Archaean structures are strongly deformed, attenuated and brought into parallelism to form a new, pronounced, Nag. 1 schistosity and banding. 60 km north of Umivik.

FIG. 7. Archaean gneiss in granulite facies (grey) with banding dipping to the NW (towards top left), showing vein-like networks of Nag. 1 retrogression to amphibolite facies (white) cut by metadolerite dykes (mid-left and bottom right). The mountain face is 1000 m high and located 10 km west of Tupilak, 2 km north of the Nagssugtoqidian boundary.

FIG. 8. Archaean gneiss in amphibolite facies in a region of patchy and vein-like Nag. 1 retrogression from granulite facies, cut by undeformed Nag. 1 amphibolite dykes. North of Sermilik, 2 km north of the boundary of the Nagssugtoqidian mobile belt.

FIG. 9. Typical, pronounced, steep Nag. 1 schistosity and banding derived by rotation and attenuation of dykes (black) and Archaean gneiss (grey), veined by post-tectonic granite. In the centre of the mobile belt, 60 km WNW of Angmagssalik.

FIG. 10. Undeformed Nag. 1 amphibolite dyke in a large lens of recrystallized, but otherwise unmodified, Archaean gneiss in the southern part of the mobile belt, 100 km north of Umivik.

FIG. 11. Steeply dipping, tectonically interleaved layers of strongly deformed pelitic, semi-pelitic and amphibolite schists (black) and Archaean gneiss (grey), with pronounced Nag. 1 schistosity and banding. Section about 1 km wide on the NW shore of Sermilik.

1976). Kalsbeek *et al.* (1984) found that supracrustal rocks in both these belts gave similar Pb-Pb ages of between 1930–1840 Ma. They also found isotopic evidence that some quartzo-feldspathic gneisses in the Nagssugtoqidian belt of West Greenland were derived from Proterozoic intrusions, although most gneisses are thought to be of Archaean origin (Escher *et al.* 1976).

The supracrustal rocks of the Nagssugtoqidian mobile belt in East Greenland are intensely deformed, they are concordant with, and show pronounced Nag. 1 schistosity parallel to, the banding of adjacent quartzo-feldspathic gneiss (Fig. 11). By analogy with West Greenland, most of these supracrustal rocks may be of early Proterozoic age.

Blokken gneiss

The Blokken gneiss (Fig. 2) is derived from plutons of tonalite which were emplaced into the northern part of the mobile belt. These intrusions cut across Nag. 1 folds, banding, fabrics and deformed dykes, but are themselves intruded by basic dykes which are deformed by Nag. 2 deformation (Fig. 12). Samples of Blokken gneiss have given a poorly-defined Rb-Sr age of about 2350 Ma (Bridgwater & Myers 1979).

FIG. 12. Blokken gneiss and amphibolite dyke folded by Nag. 2 deformation. Plagioclase clusters after garnets act as strain markers in the folded dyke.

Nag. 2 deformation, metamorphism and plutonic intrusions

A major swarm of basic dykes called Charcot Fjelde dykes (Myers *et al.* 1979) was intruded into the mobile belt and the adjacent craton to the

north (Fig. 2). In the craton most of these dykes are undeformed except for narrow schistose margins, and have relict sub-ophitic textures containing garnets. In the mobile belt the dykes cut Nag. 1 structures and the Blokken gneiss, and many are intensely deformed and are schistose amphibolite (Fig. 13).

The nature of the Nag. 2 structures and metamorphism varies northward across the mobile belt (Fig. 2) from northward-dipping shear and thrust zones in greenschist facies, to shear and thrust zones in amphibolite facies (Myers 1984, fig. 16) and open folds with northward-dipping axial surfaces (Myers 1984, fig. 17). These structures are associated with the southward translation of rocks along thrust and shear zones (Fig. 14), both within the mobile belt and the Archaean craton to the north. The spatial variations in the nature of Nag. 2 structures and metamorphism suggest that progressively deeper crustal levels are exposed northward across the mobile belt, probably reflecting greater uplift of the northern part of the belt after deeper burial during overthrusting from the north (Myers 1984, fig. 13).

Northward-dipping sheets of leuconorite (Fig. 15) and charnockite were emplaced into the northern portion of the mobile belt and cut across Nag. 1 structures. They were not seen to be cut by the Charcot Fjelde dykes but are deformed and folded by Nag. 2 deformation. An outline of their petrology is given by Wright *et al.* (1973). The adjacent gneisses contain abundant garnet, are in granulite facies, and show blotchy quartzo-feldspathic segregations associated with partial melting. This recrystallization and the segregations overprint Nag. 1 fabrics and gneissose banding, and progressively increase in intensity as the charnockite complex is approached. This is most clearly seen along the western shore of Sermilik (Fig. 2). Gneisses from this zone of intense recrystallization around the Angmagssalik charnockite complex have given a poorly-defined Rb-Sr isochron of about 1900 Ma (Bridgwater *et al.* 1978).

Post-tectonic intrusions

Plutons of mainly diorite and granite (Wright *et al.* 1973) cut across the Nag. 2 structures (Figs 2 and 9). They were emplaced by stoping with brittle deformation of their host rocks and narrow metamorphic aureoles about 1550 Ma ago (Bridgwater & Myers 1979). Their high-level nature suggests that major uplift of the northern part of the mobile belt occurred between 1900 and 1550 Ma.

FIG. 13. Archaean gneiss and deformed network of amphibolite dykes, all showing flat-lying Nag. 2 recumbent folds, foliation and amphibolite facies metamorphism. Cliff face 200 m high on the right, 110 km WSW of Angmagssalik.

FIG. 14. Belt of gently northward-dipping Nag. 2 schistosity (top right) and thrust contact (centre) over steep Nag. 1 schistosity and banding (bottom left). In the centre of the mobile belt, 80 km west of Angmagssalik.

Fig. 15. Leuconorite with network of felsic veins (foreground and low ground in distance). The distant mountain ridge comprises the garnet-gneiss aureole of the leuconorite–charnockite complex. View to NNE from Angmagssalik.

Comparison with Lewisian complex

The Lewisian complex, like the Nagssugtoqidian mobile belt of East Greenland, mainly consists of heterogeneous quartzo-feldspathic gneisses, generated 2900–2700 Ma (Hamilton *et al.* 1979), subsequently intruded by dykes and repeatedly deformed and metamorphosed between 2600 and 1700 Ma.

The Lewisian metasedimentary rocks of South Harris, Coll, Tiree and Iona bear closer resemblance to early Proterozoic rocks in the Rinkian belt of NW Greenland and to metasedimentary rocks within the Nagssugtoqidian mobile belt than to supracrustal rocks of the Archaean gneiss complex of Greenland. Likewise, the anorthosite complexes of South Harris, Ness and Iona do not resemble the widespread, distinctive Archaean anorthosite complexes of Greenland (Bridgwater *et al.* 1976); and Sm-Nd model ages obtained from the South Harris anorthosite complex by Cliff *et al.* (1983) suggest that this complex was generated during the early Proterozoic.

The Inverian and most Scourie dykes may be equivalent to the Nag. 1 episode of East Greenland. Many Scourie dykes were emplaced into shear zones associated with tectonic reworking of Archaean (Scourian) gneiss and amphibolite-facies metamorphism (Fig. 16) (Park 1973). Some Scourie dykes show deformed primary pinch-and-swell structures (Myers 1971a, fig. 2) which resemble the primary structures of many Nag. 1

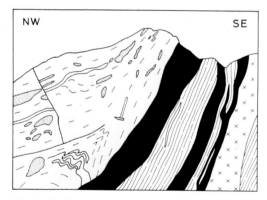

Fig. 16. Profile section of Scourie dykes (black) emplaced into a shear zone (with closely spaced lines indicating intense new schistosity), analogous to Nag. 1 dykes and shear zones in East Greenland. The shear zone cuts relatively little deformed Scourian (Archaean) gneiss (grey) with fragments of amphibolite (stippled) and pegmatite veins (white). The shear zone is cut by an undeformed Laxfordian pegmatite (crosses). Aird Fenish, western Lewis.

dykes in Greenland (Bridgwater & Myers 1979; Nash 1979). Many Scourie dykes and Nagssugtoqidian dykes crystallized with igneous textures containing garnets. The nature of Inverian deformation closely resembles Nag. 1 deformation in Greenland and shows compatible strike-slip movements on major shear zones (Watterson 1978).

The Laxfordian, with an early episode of flatlying shear zones folded by upright structures (Coward 1974), may be broadly equivalent to the Nag. 2 episode of Greenland which was dominated by southward translation of rock slabs along northward-dipping thrusts and shear zones. By analogy with Nag. 2 tectonics in East Greenland, the Scourian complex of the Scottish mainland may be a slab of the northern hinterland of the mobile belt, translated southward during the Laxfordian.

There do not appear to be any traces of Laxfordian-style granites and migmatites (Myers 1971*b*) in the Nagssugtoqidian mobile belt of East Greenland, nor equivalents of the 1550 Ma post-tectonic high-level intrusions of East Greenland in the Lewisian.

Both the Lewisian Complex and Nagssugtoqidian mobile belt of East Greenland were affected by similar kinds of tectonic processes at depth in the crust, and then elevated to a high crustal level by 1600–1400 Ma and extensively eroded.

ACKNOWLEDGEMENTS: Thanks are expressed to the Director of the Geological Survey of Greenland for permission to publish this work which was carried out for that Survey in 1977–80.

References

BRIDGWATER, D. & MYERS, J. S. 1979. Outline of the Nagssugtoqidian mobile belt of East Greenland. *Rapp. Grønlands geol. Unders.* **89**, 9–18.

——, KETO, L., McGREGOR, V. R. & MYERS, J. S. 1976. Archaean gneiss complex of Greenland. *In:* ESCHER, A. & WATT, W. S. (eds) *Geology of Greenland.* Grønlands geol. Unders., Copenhagen, 18–75.

——, DAVIES, F. B., GILL, R. C. O., GORMAN, B. E., MYERS, J. S., PEDERSEN, S. & TAYLOR, P. 1978. Precambrian and Tertiary geology between Kangerdlugssuaq and Angmagssalik, East Greenland. *Rapp. Grønlands geol. Unders.* **83**, 17 pp.

CLIFF, R. A., GRAY, C. M. & HUHMA, M. 1983. A Sm-Nd isotopic study of the South Harris igneous complex. *Contr. Mineral. Petrol.* **82**, 91–98.

COWARD, M. P. 1974. Flat-lying structures within the Lewisian basement gneiss complex of NW. Scotland. *Proc. Geol. Ass.* **85**, 459–472.

ESCHER, A. & PULVERTAFT, T. C. R. 1976. Rinkian mobile belt of West Greenland. *In:* ESCHER, A. & WATT, W. S. (eds) *Geology of Greenland.* Grønlands geol. Unders., Copenhagen, 104–119.

——, SØRENSEN, K. & ZECK, H. P. 1976. Nagssugtoqidian mobile belt in West Greenland. *In:* ESCHER, A. & WATT, W. S. (eds) *Geology of Greenland.* Grønlands geol. Unders., Copenhagen, 76–95.

HAMILTON, P. J., EVENSEN, N. M., O'NIONS, R. K. & TARNEY, J. 1979. Sm-Nd systematics of Lewisian gneisses: implications for the origin of granulites. *Nature, London.* **277**, 25–28.

KALSBEEK, F., TAYLOR, P. N. & HENRIKSEN, N. 1984. Age of rocks, structures, and metamorphism in the Nagssugtoqidian mobile belt, West Greenland—field and Pb-isotope evidence. *Can. J. Earth. Sci.* **21**, 1126–1131.

LE PICHON, X., SIBUET, J. C. & FRANCHETEAU, J. 1977. The fit of the continents around the North Atlantic Ocean. *Tectonophysics,* **38**, 169–209.

MYERS, J. S. 1971*a*. Zones of abundant Scourie dyke fragments and their significance in the Lewisian complex of western Harris, Outer Hebrides. *Proc. Geol. Ass.* **82**, 365–375.

—— 1971*b*. The Late Laxfordian granite–migmatite complex of western Harris, Outer Hebrides. *Scott. J. Geol.* **7**, 254–284.

—— 1978. Formation of banded gneisses by deformation of igneous rocks. *Precambrian Res.* **6**, 43–64.

—— 1981. The Fiskenaesset anorthosite complex—a stratigraphic key to the tectonic evolution of the West Greenland gneiss complex 3000–2800 m.y. ago. *Spec. Publ. geol. Soc. Australia,* **7**, 351–360.

—— 1984. The Nagssugtoqidian mobile belt of Greenland. *In:* KRÖNER, A. & GREILING, R. (eds) *Precambrian tectonics illustrated.* Schweizerbart'sche Verlagsbuchhandlung, Stuttgart, 237–250.

——, AUSTRHEIM, H., GILL, R. C. O., GORMAN, B. E. & REX, D. 1979. Field work on the Nagssugtoqidian boundary north of Angmagssalik and Tertiary igneous rocks of Kialineq and Kap Gustav Holm, East Greenland. *Rapp. Grønlands geol. Unders.* **95**, 82–85.

NASH, D. 1979. An interpretation of irregular dyke forms in the Itivdleq shear zone, West Greenland. *Rapp. Grønlands geol. Unders.* **89**, 77–83.

PARK, R. G. 1973. The Laxfordian belts of the Scottish mainland. *In:* PARK, R. G. & TARNEY, J. (eds) *The Early Precambrian of Scotland and related rocks of Greenland.* Univ. Keele, 65–76.

PEDERSEN, S. & BRIDGWATER, D. 1979. Isotopic re-equilibration of Rb-Sr whole rock systems during reworking of Archaean gneisses in the Nagssug-

toqidian mobile belt, East Greenland. *Rapp. Grønlands geol. Unders.* **89**, 133–146.
WATTERSON, J. 1978. Proterozoic intraplate deformation in the light of south-east Asian neotectonics. *Nature, London.* **273**, 636–640.
WRIGHT, A. E., TARNEY, J., PALMER, K. F., MOORLOCK, B. S. P. & SKINNER, A. C. 1973. The geology of the Angmagssalik area, East Greenland and possible relationships with the Lewisian of Scotland. *In*: PARK, R. G. & TARNEY, J. (eds) *The early Precambrian of Scotland and related rocks of Greenland.* Univ. Keele, 157–177.

J. S. MYERS, Geological Survey of Western Australia, 66 Adelaide Terrace, Perth, Western Australia 6000.

The boundary between Proterozoic and Archaean crustal blocks in central West Greenland and northern Labrador

J. Korstgård, B. Ryan & R. Wardle

SUMMARY: The contact between the Early Proterozoic Nagssugtoqidian Mobile Belt and the Archaean craton in West Greenland, and that between the Churchill Province and the Archaean (Nain) craton in Northern Labrador represent two cross-sections of an Early Proterozoic orogenic boundary. The Archaean cratons in both regions display the peripheral effects of Proterozoic orogenic events. The best indicators of Proterozoic effects on the Archaean cratons are the Late Archaean–Early Proterozoic dykes and the Early Proterozoic supracrustal rocks which unconformably overlie the gneisses and dykes. In Greenland the boundary zone evolution is characterized by Late Archaean (Nag. 1) transcurrent shearing, Early Proterozoic Kangâmiut dyke intrusion and subsequent (Nag. 2) ductile overthrusting. Ductile overthrusts are characteristic of the Nagssugtoqidian–Archaean boundary and attest to substantial shortening of the crust in this region. In Labrador the boundary region has been divided into several distinct zones. Although facets of its evolution are analogous to the boundary in Greenland there are several fundamental differences, the most important of which is that transcurrent movement appears to have been dominant over ductile overthrusting. These differences are provisionally related to contrasting tectonic settings of the two areas during Early Proterozoic continental collision, the Greenland segment being the frontal collision zone whilst the Labrador segment documents slightly oblique transcurrent motion.

Introduction

By analogy with Phanerozoic orogenic belts, the border zones of Proterozoic orogens are presumed to have developed by some combination of accretion, involving addition of new or exotic crustal elements, and the reworking of pre-existing sialic 'basement'. The deeply eroded level of the border zones of these orogens effectively precludes analysis by traditional stratigraphic methods and instead one must focus on the crystalline rocks for insight into the tectonic processes through which they have evolved. In this paper, we examine the spectacularly exposed northern and western margins of the North Atlantic Craton with the adjacent Early Proterozoic orogens of the Nagssugtoqidian Mobile Belt in Greenland and the Churchill Province of Labrador (Fig. 1). More studies have been undertaken on the Greenland segment of this junction (*cf* Korstgård 1979*a*) than on the Labrador segment, therefore we present firstly an overview and analysis of the northern boundary before providing an account of the western boundary. We then present a brief comparative discussion of the two areas and speculate on the tectonic processes involved in the evolution of the boundary zones.

Nagssugtoqidian–Archaean boundary, West Greenland

One of the most spectacular boundaries of a Precambrian orogenic belt can be viewed along Søndre Strømfjord (Fig. 2) where a swarm of basic dykes intruded into Archaean gneisses is progressively reworked during the Proterozoic. The boundary was first described by Ramberg (1948) who named the Proterozoic belt the Nagssugtoqides. Since then, the Geological Survey of Greenland (GGU) has carried out reconnaissance mapping of the boundary area in 1966 (Escher 1966) and 1977 (Allaart *et al.* 1978). A Liverpool–GGU project in 1972–75 concentrated on boundary problems in the Holsteinsborg–Itivdleq region (Watterson 1974). Results from the GGU reconnaissance work and the Liverpool project are summarized in a series of papers in Korstgård (1979*a*). More recently Myers (1984, this vol.) has provided a review of the boundary both in West and East Greenland.

The Archaean block

The central part of the Archaean block in West Greenland is a classic area for Archaean studies, mainly through the work of McGregor (1973) and GGU. The major Archaean events (McGregor 1973; Bridgwater *et al.* 1976) are best defined in the Godthåbsfjord region (Fig. 1) where *c.* 3.8 Ga supracrustal remnants are found enclosed in the slightly younger quartzo-feldspathic Amîtsoq gneisses, both of which were intruded at *c.* 3.2–3.0 Ga by a swarm of basic (Ameralik) dykes and overlain by the Malene supracrustals. Major thrusting followed, produc-

From: PARK, R. G. & TARNEY, J. (eds), 1987, *Evolution of the Lewisian and Comparable Precambrian High Grade Terrains*, Geological Society Special Publication No. 27, pp. 247–259.

FIG. 1. Early Proterozoic orogenic belts of the North Atlantic region. Pre-Mesozoic continental drift reconstruction after Bullard *et al.* (1965). G = Godthåbsfjord, SS = Søndre Strømfjord.

ing a pile of alternating sheets of Amîtsoq gneisses and Malene supracrustals. Emplacement of a major syntectonic suite of calc-alkaline rocks (Nûk gneisses) took place around 3.0 Ga, followed by widespread intense deformation and high-grade metamorphism at *c.* 2.8 Ga.

The northern sector of the Archaean block adjacent to the Nagssugtoqidian front has not been investigated in any detail. Most of the quartzo-feldspathic gneisses are in granulite facies and are thought to correspond to the 2.8–3.0 Ga Nûk gneisses (Allaart & Jensen 1979). Supracrustal rocks form either trains of inclusions in the gneisses or continuous, strongly folded,

belts and are believed to represent units corresponding to the *c.* 3.0 Ga Malene supracrustals of the Godthåbsfjord region.

Supracrustal rocks comprising subaqueous volcanics, basic and ultrabasic sills and clastic carbonate sediments rest unconformably on the Archaean gneisses at Sarfartup nuna just north of the main Nagssugtoqidian front (Fig. 2). These form a small klippe of imbricate thrust slices metamorphosed at low amphibolite facies, and may represent Nagssugtoqidian (Early Proterozoic) supracrustals transported southwards from a Nagssugtoqidian zone of strong ductile overthrusting (Talbot 1979).

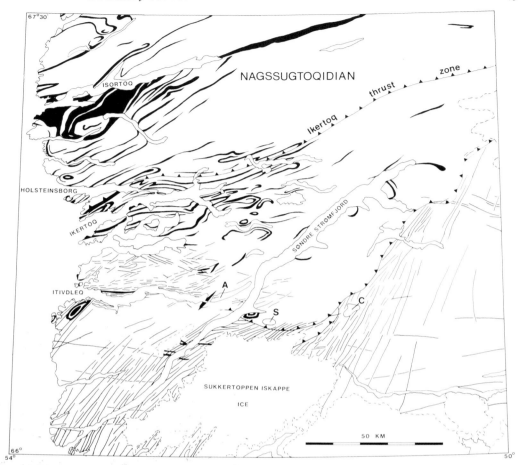

FIG. 2. Sketch map of the Archaean–Nagssugtoqidian boundary in West Greenland. Black areas are supracrustal rocks and black lines are undeformed Kangâmiut dykes. A) indicates an anorthosite body, C) a carbonatite body, and S) the Sarfartup nuna klippe of supracrustal rocks (after Geological Map of Greenland, 1:500,000, sheet 3, compiled by A. Escher, and sheet 2 compiled by J. H. Allaart; published by the Geological Survey of Greenland).

The Nagssugtoqidian front

The gneisses forming the northern part of the Archaean block are cut by dense swarms of dolerite (diabase) dykes (Fig. 2). Escher *et al.* (1975) recognized two main sets, a dominant ENE-striking swarm (the Kangâmiut dykes) post-dating an E–W-striking swarm. The Kangâmiut dykes give Rb–Sr ages around 1.9 Ga (Kalsbeek *et al.* 1978). Towards the north the dykes and their host rocks are progressively deformed and metamorphosed resulting in the transposition of both dykes and country rock structures into the Nagssugtoqidian trend.

The Nagssugtoqidian boundary in the inner parts of Søndre Strømfjord is a transition zone about 20 km wide in which retrogression of the Archaean granulite-facies gneisses and rotation of the dyke swarm takes place progressively. The boundary represents the limit of rocks that have undergone intense simple shear strain in response to ductile overthrusting of Nagssugtoqidian rocks over the Archaean craton (Bridgwater *et al.* 1973; Myers 1984). This relatively simple picture from the inner parts of Søndre Strømfjord is more complicated in the coastal areas around Itivdleq (Fig. 2; Watterson 1974) where intrusion of Kangâmiut dykes was predated by strong deformation and metamorphism in an event referred to as Nagssugtoqidian 1 or Nag. 1.

Nag. 1 deformation and metamorphism

Along the coast of Itivdleq the trend of the

compositional layering and schistosity of the gneisses is uniformly E–W and subvertical. This broad band, about 6 km in width, is made up of a number of Nag. 1 ductile shear zones which collectively constitute the Itivdleq shear zone. The sense of shear in the zone is dextral, the shear plane subvertical, and the movement direction, as estimated from stretching lineations on schistosity planes, plunges shallowly to the west. In the shear zone the quartzo-feldspathic gneisses are retrogressed from granulite or upper amphibolite facies to low amphibolite facies (epidote-amphibolite).

Dyke intrusion

The Nag. 1 deformation was followed by intrusion of the Kangâmiut dykes. Adjacent to the Itivdleq shear zone the dykes are subvertical and trend mainly NE and ESE (Fig. 2). Contradictory cross-cutting relationships suggest that the dykes of both trends are effectively contemporaneous. The northern limit of the Kangâmiut dyke swarm is on the islands just south of Holsteinborg in the western part of the region (Grocott 1979). In the eastern part, at the head of the fiords, the northern boundary is not yet established, but is north of the Ikertoq thrust (Fig. 2).

The pattern of orientation of the dykes shows a marked change along Itivdleq where there is a strong concentration of E–W trending dykes (Fig. 2). Field evidence (Nash 1979; Korstgård 1979*b*) indicates that this change in trend is due to a primary change in the orientation of the fracture system into which the dykes intruded, rather than to structural rotation. Whereas dykes in the gneisses outside the shear zone are tabular in shape, continuous along strike and clearly cross-cut the gneisses with sharp, angular contacts, the dykes in the Itivdleq shear zone are subparallel to the Nag. 1 shear fabric and may show irregular primary shapes and discontinuity along strike (Fig. 3).

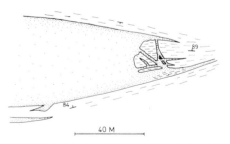

FIG. 3. Field sketch of undeformed Kangâmiut dyke in the Itivdleq shear zone showing primary pinch and swell structure.

Nag. 2 deformation and metamorphism

Along the coast of Itivdleq and Holsteinborg Grocott (1979) demonstrated that the strong planar E–W fabric in the southern part of these areas is mainly of Nag. 1 origin and that the Kangâmiut dykes have intruded along Nag. 1 schistosity planes. However, the effects of the Nag. 1 deformation are masked progressively northwards by the subsequent Nag. 2 deformation and metamorphism. In the fiords just north of Itivdleq, the effects of Nag. 2 deformation on the country rocks are relatively slight and are mainly expressed as a folding of the Nag. 1 fabric around E–W subhorizontal axes. The dykes, whilst clearly recognizable as intrusive bodies, are folded and completely converted into amphibolites. The Nag. 2 folds in this region are tight to isoclinal with an axial plane schistosity dipping steeply to the NNW. Metadykes are often broken up into lenses on what appear to be the limbs of major folds. Fold axes and lineations plunge shallowly to the WNW. In the north arm of inner Ikertoq there is an abrupt change in the plunge of the linear structures to steeply down-dip. This change is associated with development of a strong planar fabric in the gneisses, in what is interpreted as a ductile shear zone characterized by over-thrusting towards the SSE on a moderately steep shear plane (the Ikertoq thrust zone).

In concert with the progressive Nag. 2 deformation of the dykes northwards there is also a progressive increase in metamorphic grade which is clearly revealed by the metamorphosed basic dykes. The assemblage hornblende + plagioclase (oligoclase–andesine) with accessory sphene and quartz gives way northwards near Ikertoq to clinopyroxene + garnet + hornblende + plagioclase (An_{30-40}) with accessory ilmenite after sphene. North of the Ikertoq thrust zone (Fig. 2) the appearance of orthopyroxene in gneisses and metadykes marks the transition to granulite facies. A common assemblage is plagioclase + hornblende + orthopyroxene + clinopyroxene. Sphene is no longer present, hornblende is brown and the An-content in plagioclase is mostly above 40%.

Summary of structural and metamorphic evolution

In middle Archaean times (*c.* 3.0 Ga) rocks now exposed were stabilized in granulite and upper amphibolite facies (Fig. 4*a*). Uplift brought these rocks to crustal levels where granulite and upper amphibolite facies assemblages were metastable (Fig. 4*b*). Nag. 1 shearing (*c.* 2.5 Ga; Hickman 1979), mainly transcurrent, produced the Itivdleq

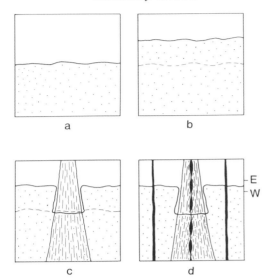

FIG. 4. Schematic, vertical, N–S sections through the crust across the Itivdleq shear zone. a) The crust in Archaean times. The lower part of the section was stabilized in granulite facies (dotted), the upper part in amphibolite facies. b) Uplift brought granulite-facies assemblages into regions where they were metastable (dotted area above the dashed line). c) Nag. 2 shearing (transcurrent along vertical shear planes) retrogressed the metastable granulite-facies assemblages. d) In the shear zone the Kangâmiut dykes intruded subparallel to the shear fabric and developed primary pinch and swell structures. E and W indicate present erosion levels in eastern and western parts of Itivdleq (from Korstgård 1979*b*).

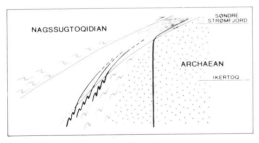

FIG. 5. Schematic cross-section of the Nagssugtoqidian front envisaged as one or several thrust zones. Erosion levels at Søndre Strømfjord and Ikertoq are indicated.

shear zone (Fig. 4*c*) and most likely similar shear zones farther north between Itivdleq and Ikertoq (Fig. 2). Within the shear zones, rocks recrystallized under amphibolite-facies conditions with new fabrics. Following the Nag. 1 shearing the crust was invaded by swarms of dolerite dykes, the Kangâmiut dykes (*c.* 1.9 Ga; Kalsbeek *et al.*

1978). In older Archaean rocks the dykes intruded along NE–SW and WNW–ESE ductile 'fractures' (Escher *et al.* 1976*a*) and in Nag. 1-affected rocks they intruded subparallel to Nag. 1 planar fabrics where they developed primary pinch and swell structures (Fig. 4*d*). Nag. 2 deformation occurred at *c.* 1.8 Ga, and involved development of the Ikertoq shear zone and a zone of overthrusting south of inner Søndre Strømfjord (Fig. 2). The latter shear zone is envisaged in Fig. 5 to represent a higher structural level than that seen in the Ikertoq shear zone.

The distribution and relative age of metamorphic facies in the Itivdleq–Ikertoq region as summarized above is outlined in Fig. 6.

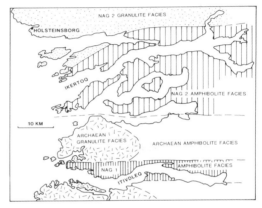

FIG. 6. Distribution of Middle Archaean, Late Archaean (Nag. 1), and Early Proterozoic (Nag. 2) metamorphic zones in the Itivdleq–Ikertoq region (from Korstgård 1979*b*).

Churchill Province–Archaean boundary, Labrador

The geology of northernmost Labrador, simplified after Taylor (1979), is shown in Fig. 7. The region is divided into the Archaean Nain Province (equivalent to the Archaean block of Greenland) in the east and the Early Proterozoic Churchill Province (equivalent to the Nassugtoqidian of Greenland) in the west. This original division (Fig. 7, inset), made by Stockwell (1963) largely on the basis of K–Ar ages, assigned the last major tectonism in the Nain Province to the Kenoran orogeny (*c.* 2.5 Ga) and that in the Churchill Province to the Hudsonian orogeny (*c.* 1.8 Ga). Stockwell (1964) and Taylor (1971) further refined the position of the boundary, in general moving it eastwards (Fig. 7, inset).

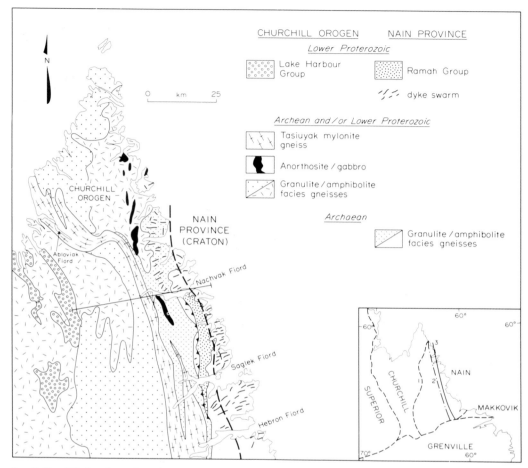

FIG. 7. Simplified geology of northernmost Labrador, modified after Taylor (1979) and Greene (1972). Inset shows interpretations of the Nain–Churchill boundary: 1) Stockwell 1963, 2) Taylor 1971, 3) this paper. E–W line through Nachvak Fiord represents cross-section of Fig. 10 and is the approximate line of traverse for the Nachvak Fiord transect referred to in the text.

Despite a challenge by Douglas (1972) the position of Taylor (1971) has generally been accepted by subsequent workers (eg Greene 1972) with modifications by Morgan (1975).

Our work in northern Labrador has been concentrated in the Saglek Fiord–Hebron Fiord area (Ryan et al. 1983, 1984) and to a lesser extent the Nachvak Fiord area (Wardle 1983, 1984) where we have recognized the junction to be a broad zone of progressive Hudsonian structural reworking of Archaean crust. We have followed Morgan (1975) in locating the Nain–Churchill boundary at the most easterly limit of this reworking. In Fig. 8, we propose a new subdivision of the boundary zone which we believe more clearly reflects the transitional nature common to most deeply eroded orogen boundaries.

Nain craton

The Nain craton (Nain Province) comprises crust essentially undisturbed since Archaean time, the history of which has only been established in detail in the Saglek Fiord–Hebron Fiord area. The main events from the Saglek–Hebron area are summarized as follows (cf Bridgwater et al. 1975; Collerson & Bridgwater 1979; Collerson, et al. 1982; Ryan et al. 1983, 1984).

Small rafts and belts of >3.7 Ga supracrustal rocks occur within a multiphase orthogneiss group (Uivak gneisses). A major deformational and metamorphic–metasomatic event occurred at c. 3.6 Ga followed by intrusion of a basic dyke swarm (Saglek dykes), and accumulation of sedimentary, volcanic and basic intrusive rocks

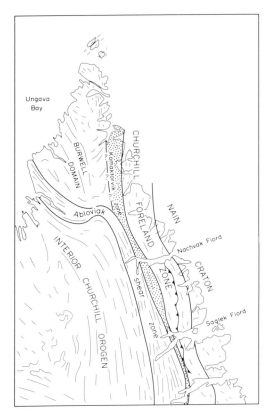

FIG. 8. Tectonic elements of the Nain–Churchill boundary, northernmost Labrador. Structural trends interpreted from geological maps of Taylor (1979) and aeromagnetic maps (GSC 1985).

known as the Upernavik supracrustals. Tectonic interleaving of the Uivak gneisses and the Upernavik supracrustals occurred *c.* 3.0 Ga giving rise to a regional layered complex of paragneiss and orthogneiss. The complex was remobilized to produce a heterogeneous suite of migmatities at *c.* 2.8 Ga coeval with granulite-facies metamorphism (Ryan 1977; Kerr 1980; Collerson *et al.* 1982). As such, this chronology is very similar to that of the Gothåbsfjord area, with the major exception that there is no local equivalent to the Nûk gneisses. Nain Province gneisses in the Nachvak Fiord area comprise similar migmatites at granulite grade which, on the basis of a single U-Pb zircon date (Morgan 1979), formed at 2.8 Ga. It is not clear, however, whether they are derived from old Uivak-type crust, or later intrusive material (Wardle 1983) such as that which comprises the Nûk gneisses of Greenland. The injection of regional predominantly E–NE-trending dolerite (diabase) dyke

swarms at *c.* 2.3 Ga is the last major event to affect the Archaean complex prior to Early Proterozoic erosion, uplift, and deposition of the Ramah Group.

Hudsonian effects on the Nain craton in both the Saglek and Nachvak areas are restricted to a patchy static retrogression of the high-grade gneisses and brittle faulting. The dolerite dykes show local development of actinolitic coronas on clinopyroxene.

Churchill foreland zone

This zone (Figs 7 and 8) is underlain by Nain-type Archaean crust, locally overlain by the Ramah Group supracrustals, which has been zonally reworked in Hudsonian shear zones that range from brittle and locally mylonitic in the east, to progressively more ductile in the west. Hudsonian effects in this zone are best exemplified by the Proterozoic diabase dykes which, whilst retaining their rectiplanar form, become progressively recrystallized to pseudomorphous and schistose secondary amphibolite-facies assemblages across the zone from east to west. A number of pre-dyke ductile shear zones have been recognized in eastern Nachvak Fiord (Wardle 1983), where they have been reactivated as Hudsonian shears, a situation analogous to the Nag. 1 and Nag. 2 deformations in western Greenland.

The Archaean gneisses in the foreland zone are variably affected by an amphibolite-facies Hudsonian overprint. Areas of relict Archaean (pre-dyke) granulite-facies assemblages are locally well-preserved in zones with strong Hudsonian imprint in the western part of Nachvak Fiord. Retrogression of these Nachvak granulites becomes more pronounced in areas adjacent to and underneath the supracrustal Ramah Group. We infer this differing response of the Archaean gneisses to Hudsonian metamorphism to have been controlled by the availability of hydrous fluids, produced mainly from the de-watering of the Ramah Group; the area under, and east of, the Ramah Group represents shallow hydrated crust whereas the granulites of western Nachvak comprise deeper-level crust which remained out of the range of these fluids.

The Ramah Group is a synformal succession of basinal to deep water sedimentary rocks and associated diabase sills that unconformably overlies peneplained Archaean gneisses and Proterozoic dykes (Morgan 1975; Knight & Morgan 1982; Fig. 7). The eastern margin of the Ramah Group along the northern and central parts of the belt is gently west-dipping and little disturbed. However, the western margin of the

Group is highly deformed, and is overthrust by gneisses of the Komaktorvik zone (see below; Morgan 1975; Mengel 1985). From Saglek Fiord southwards the group is very strongly tectonized, as exemplified by numerous intra-Ramah thrusts and thrusts which interleave basement and cover, polyphase folding, and Hudsonian metamorphism at amphibolite (staurolite, kyanite, sillimanite) facies (Ryan *et al.* 1983, 1984; Mengel 1984, 1985). The Ramah Group at its southernmost extension is preserved only as narrow subvertical slivers intercalated and infolded with reworked Archaean basement (Ryan *et al.* 1983, 1984).

Komaktorvik zone

The foreland zone passes gradationally west into the Komaktorvik zone which is characterized by pervasive Hudsonian amphibolite to granulite-facies reworking of the Archaean gneisses to produce finely banded, straightened and mylonitic gneisses. The dolerite (diabase) dyke swarm dies out within this zone (Figs 7 and 8) but, where present, the dykes are largely transposed into the Hudsonian foliation. Pseudotachylite veining is a common feature throughout the zone.

In the Saglek Fiord–Hebron Fiord area, rocks of the Komaktorvik zone are faulted against the western margin of the Ramah Group (Morgan 1975; Ryan *et al.* 1983). Here, Hudsonian reworking has occurred in both granulite and amphibolite facies, the contact between the two being a steep reverse fault. Between Saglek Fiord and Nachvak Fiord, Archaean structures and discordant Proterozoic dykes locally persist in the gneisses (Morgan 1981; Mengel 1985). Local discordances between the dykes and granulite-facies gneissic layering indicate that the orthopyroxene-bearing assemblage is an inherited Archaean feature which has remained stable during the Hudsonian reworking. The Komaktorvik zone from Nachvak northwards is also characterized by a series of elongate anorthosite bodies (Fig. 7). These are generally strongly recrystallized and foliated but locally retain primary igneous layering. This layering is cut by the dyke swarm indicating that the anorthosites are probably Archaean in age and likely to be comparable with those of the Fiskenaesset region in West Greenland (Myers 1975).

Abloviak shear zone

This is a major feature of the boundary zone that is strikingly apparent on aeromagnetic maps (GSC 1985) and Landsat imagery. The shear zone, named after Abloviak Fiord (Fig. 7),

follows a distinctive garnetiferous mylonite gneiss referred to as the Tasiuyak gneiss (Wardle 1983) but also affects adjacent granitoid gneiss units. The Tasiuyak gneiss is a finely banded quartz-feldspar - garnet - sillimanite - biotite - graphite gneiss interpreted by Ryan *et al.* (1984) and Wardle (1984) to represent a diatexite derived from an aluminous (Archaean?) metasedimentary protolith. The migmatitic banding of the diatexite has been isoclinally folded and transposed into a subvertical, planar, mylonitic fabric containing a strong subhorizontal quartz lineation. Wardle (1984) has compared the metasedimentary component of the gneiss to the Archaean Upernavik supracrustals, and Ryan *et al.* (1983, 1984) noted the compositional similarity between granitoid melts in the Upernavik supracrustals and the Tasiuyak gneiss. The eastern boundary of the Tasiuyak gneiss is a zone of tectonic intercalation with reworked Archaean gneisses of the Komaktorvik zone. On its western boundary the Tasiuyak gneiss is intercalated with thick bands of lineated granitoid granulite. These granulites lack the complex fabrics seen in granitoid gneisses east of the Tasiuyak gneiss and are of unknown age.

North of Nachvak Fiord the Abloviak shear zone swings west to Ungava Bay and in so doing it isolates a triangular shaped segment of crust between itself and the Komaktorvik zone, which we designate the Burwell domain (Fig. 8). We have no data to speculate on the continuity of the Abloviak shear zone west of Ungava Bay.

Burwell domain

This sector of the Churchill Province is underlain by a mixture of granulite and amphibolite-facies granitoid gneisses interspersed with bands of supracrustal gneiss, all shown by Taylor (1979) as Early Proterozoic in age. We have not seen this part of northern Labrador but on the basis of its irregular aeromagnetic signature (GSC 1985) would venture to suggest that it is probably a Nain-type Archaean terrain, which may have been only mildly affected by Proterozoic tectonism. The Burwell domain could possibly be an analogue of the Archaean lacunae preserved between straight belts within the Greenland Nagssugtoqidian (*cf* Escher *et al.* 1976*b*).

Interior Churchill orogen

Taylor (1979) showed this area to be underlain by a mixed assemblage of granulite to amphibolite-facies granitoid and supracrustal gneisses inferred to be of Early Proterozoic age. We have examined these rocks only in the Nachvak Fiord transect (Wardle 1984; Fig. 7) where the predominant lithology is a grey, banded, migmatitic granitoid gneiss interspersed with bands, ranging from a metre to several kilometres in width, of psammitic to pelitic metasedimentary gneiss, with minor marble and quartzite. These bands correlate well with narrow linear aeromagnetic lows (GSC 1985) and appear to have considerable N–S extent. Wardle (1984) has compared the metasedimentary gneisses to the Upernavik supracrustals and suggested that much of the gneiss terrain in the Nachvak transect area may represent reworked Archaean crust. This is supported by the mixed 2.6 Ga and 1.8 Ga isochrons determined by Taylor (1979) for granulites of this general area. We do not imply, however, that this Archaean crust is necessarily a direct extension of the Nain craton.

The western end of the Nachvak transect lies in the Lake Harbour Group (Fig. 7), a supracrustal sequence of psammitic–pelitic gneiss, marble, quartzite and amphibolite of Early Proterozoic age (Jackson & Taylor 1972). The contrast between the relatively simple structural style of these rocks compared to the adjacent migmatitic tonalitic and supracrustal gneisses of suspected Archaean age led Wardle (1984) to suggest that their contact may be a reworked unconformity. The group may be a broad temporal equivalent of the Ramah Group.

Structural evolution of the boundary area in Labrador

An east–west profile of the Nain–Churchill boundary in northern Labrador shows the following zonation. Nain-type Archaean lithologies can be traced through the foreland zone into the Komaktorvik zone. The enigmatic Tasiuyak gneiss in the Abloviak zone separates these from the interior Churchill Province rocks which we also believe are largely of Archaean age, reworked in the Proterozoic, but not necessarily of Nain Province parentage. We therefore envision juxtaposition of two Archaean blocks, one of which (Nain) has undergone only peripheral deformation, the other (Churchill) exhibiting widespread crustal reactivation.

The *foreland zone* structural pattern is one of eastward-directed overthrusting of Archaean basement across Ramah Group. Intra-Ramah thrusts are more prominent at Saglek Fiord, and from there southward the openly folded and thrusted aspect of the Ramah Group is replaced by a subvertical structural style in which belts of polydeformed and strongly metamorphosed Ramah Group occur as slices interleaved with refoliated basement.

The *Komaktorvik zone* is characterized by Hudsonian refoliated Archaean gneisses which have been thrust eastward over the Ramah Group. The gneisses are interleaved along their western margin with the Tasiuyak gneiss of the *Abloviak shear zone*, a belt of blastomylonitic, subhorizontally lineated, steeply-dipping rocks derived largely from a deep crustal diatexite. These mylonitic gneisses have been interpreted as the site of major transcurrent movement during the Hudsonian (Morgan 1975; Bridgwater *et al.* 1973; Wardle 1983, 1984; Mengel 1985). The relationship between this transcurrent motion and the folding and thrusting in the Ramah Group is not firmly established.

The *interior Churchill orogen* and the *Burwell domain* are poorly known but appear dominated by steep structures (Taylor 1979). However, planar structures in the Nachvak transect are locally gently east-dipping, and folds have a westerly sense of vergence (Wardle 1984), in contrast to the foreland and Komaktorvik zones which are dominated by east-verging folds and associated thrusts (Wardle 1983). Wardle (1984) suggested that the progressive fanning of structures across the Nachvak transect (Fig. 9) developed in response to E–W crustal shortening, characterized both by east-directed and west-directed translation.

Comparison of the Archaean–Proterozoic tectonic boundaries in Greenland and Labrador

The comparison and correlation of the geological history of the Archaean craton in southwest Greenland and northern Labrador have been firmly established (Bridgwater *et al.* 1975; Bridgwater *et al.* 1978), most especially in the resemblance of the 3.8–3.0 Ga gneisses of the Saglek–Hebron area to those of the Godthåbsfjord area. Most of the gneisses of the northern Nain craton however appear to be granulites related to a 2.8 Ga crustal reworking event. A similar situation exists in the Søndre Strømfjord area where the Archaean granulites are *c.* 2.8 Ga in age and appear to be derived from older gneisses. The Late Archaean shear zone development in the Nachvak Fiord sector of the Churchill foreland zone is strikingly similar to the Nag. 1 shear zone deformation in the Proterozoic of West Greenland. The Proterozoic dykes in Labrador occupy exactly the same relative stratigraphic position as the Kangâmiut dykes, although the presently available radiometric ages suggest they differ by a surprising 0.4–0.5 Ga (Table 1).

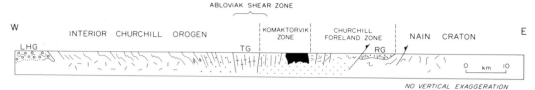

NO VERTICAL EXAGGERATION

FIG. 9. Cross-section of the Nachvak Fiord transect showing structural fan (after Wardle 1983, 1984). RG = Ramah Group, TG = Tasiuyak gneiss, LHG = Lake Harbour Group. Other lithological units keyed as on Fig. 7.

Early Proterozoic supracrustals are present on the (Archaean) foreland of both the Nagssugtoqidian and Churchill orogens. The Ramah Group in the Churchill foreland has a possible counterpart in the more areally restricted Sarfartup nuna supracrustals in West Greenland. Within the interior zone of both orogens there are extensive belts of quartzitic, pelitic and carbonate metasediments (*eg* Lake Harbour Group) which likewise seem to be of Early Proterozoic age and which in both areas are highly deformed and infolded with gneisses of probable Archaean age.

Both the Nagssugtoqidian Mobile Belt and the Churchill Province are characterized by granulite-facies gneisses. Granulites of Proterozoic age first appear in the Nagssugtoqidian some 40 km north of the Søndre Strømfjord thrust front, whereas in Labrador they constitute the easternmost units (the Abloviak and Komaktorvik zone) which occur within 30 km (Nachvak) and 12 km (Saglek) of the Nain Province. These granulites persist for some 30–60 km westward into the interior before giving way to lower-grade rocks (Taylor 1979).

In both Greenland and Labrador the main structural boundary between Archaean and Proterozoic terrains takes the form of thrust zones directed over a foreland of gneisses. The well defined, low angle, overthrust boundary found in the inner parts of Søndre Strømfjord is not found in Labrador, where instead the gneisses in the contact zone are steeply dipping and the overthrust zone is either a single major, or a series of anastomosing, steeper reverse faults. The amount of compressional translation along Nagssugtoqidian thrust zones has been estimated to be well in excess of 100 km (Bridgwater *et al.* 1973). The telescoping of Hudsonian metamorphic zones in Labrador, as exemplified by a greenschist to granulite-facies transition distance of only 8 km at Saglek Fiord, also indicates substantial shortening along reverse faults, thrusts and ductile shear zones between and within the foreland and Abloviak zones.

In summary we note that there are close comparisons between West Greenland and La-

brador in the relative age and lithological character of rocks affected by Early Proterozoic thermo-tectonism (Table 1). However, important differences also exist. For instance, the Abloviak shear zone, which apparently post-dates dyke intrusion, has no counterpart in Greenland where transcurrent movements appear to be largely of Nag. 1 age. Neither can we correlate specific tectonic zones between Labrador and Greenland. These differences, however, should not be surprising given the original separation of the areas and the probability that they formed in somewhat

TABLE 1. *Highlights of major events across the Archaean–Proterozoic boundary of West Greenland and Labrador*

West Greenland	Northern Labrador
1.8 Ga Nag. 2 ductile overthrusting Greenschist to granulite facies metamorphism	1.8 Ga Hudsonian thrusting in foreland zone and transcurrent shearing in Abloviak zone. Greenschist to granulite facies metamorphism.
1.9 Ga Kangâmiut dykes	
	2.0 Ga Uplift, erosion, and deposition of Ramah Group
2.3 Ga Nag. 1 Shearing	2.3–2.4 Ga Mafic dyke swarm
2.5–2.4 Ga Uplift of crust to levels where granulites are unstable	2.5 Ga Shearing
3.8–2.5 Ga Development of polycyclic gneiss complex from several supracrustal and plutonic associations Granulite-facies metamorphism at 2.8 Ga	3.8–2.5 Ga Development of polycyclic complex from several supracrustal and plutonic associations Granulite-facies metamorphism at 2.8 Ga.

different tectonic environments, a theme we elaborate on below.

Tectonics of the North Atlantic Archaean–Proterozoic boundary

The well-documented ductile overthrusts in the Nagssugtoqidian of West Greenland indicate substantial crustal shortening by an overriding mechanism between the Proterozoic and Archaean blocks, whereas the Labrador boundary is dominated by the Abloviak transcurrent shear zone. This difference in character of the junction in Greenland and Labrador was noted by Bridgwater *et al.* (1973), who suggested that the Greenland boundary represents a frontal collison of two crustal blocks, whereas the Labrador junction is a zone of lateral shear. Watterson (1978) elaborated on this model by invoking a rigid continental plate pushing north against the North Atlantic craton, thus inducing frontal thrusting around the apex of the craton, and conjugate transcurrent shear zones on its sides. This model offered a ready explanation of dyke swarm orientations within Greenland (Fig. 10) based on evidence that dykes were emplaced parallel to planes of high shear stress rather than into the plane of minimum stress as in normal crustal rifting.

Although appealing for its overall elegance, this model does not fit all features of the Labrador boundary, where perhaps the main uncertainty is that we cannot, as yet, confirm the predicted sinistral sense of displacement on the Abloviak shear zone (Fig. 10). Dykes trend at a high angle

to this zone and predate its development, thus demonstrating it to be younger than similar features in West Greenland. Also, the Abloviak shear zone diverges westwards from the craton in a fashion not readily accommodated in the model. This may simply be a 'wrap-around' effect around the Burwell domain; alternatively it may be a major divergence.

It is also apparent that development of the Labrador boundary has involved both transcurrent shear and compressional overthrusting (Fig. 10). Thrusts trend parallel, rather than oblique to, the Abloviak shear zone, and are thus unlikely to be genetically related to transcurrent shearing. Rather, we suspect that the Labrador boundary developed by some sequential combination of frontal collision and transcurrent shearing, whose relative timing has yet to be established. This probably occurred in an environment of overall oblique convergence. A broad analogy is drawn with the southwestern U.S. Cordillera where oblique plate motion first produced Laramide thrusting, then gave way to Late Tertiary transcurrent motion on the San Andreas fault zone (*cf* Atwater 1970). A net result of this type of deformation in Labrador has been to 'turn up' the eastern edge of the Churchill Province crust to expose very deep crustal levels in the form of the granulites and Tasiuyak diatexite on the Abloviak shear zone.

The above problems aside, it is clear that the Labrador boundary is dominated by the Abloviak transcurrent shear zone whereas the Greenland boundary is thrust dominated. We thus concur with the general principle of Watterson's (1978) model that Proterozoic deformation in the two areas can be interpreted in terms of collision and northwards indentation of the North Atlantic Craton into other continental terrains now obscured in the interior of the Proterozoic orogens. The presence of metamorphosed Early Proterozoic shelf sequences with modified unconformity against adjacent gneisses within the interior of both the Nagssugtoqidian and Churchill belts indicates that the interiors of the Proterozoic orogens in both cases comprise reconstituted Archaean continental crust with infolded younger cover. However, insufficient work has been conducted to determine if these areas of possible Archaean crust are simple reworked extensions of the adjacent Archaean cratons, or whether they represent accreted terrains.

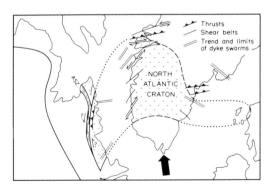

FIG. 10. Boundary tectonics of the North Atlantic craton (after Watterson 1978). ASZ—Abloviak shear zone. Dotted area represents probable limit of North Atlantic craton crust. Dyke swarms limited to areas bounded by double lines.

ACKNOWLEDGMENTS: J. K.'s field work in Greenland was sponsored by Grønlands Geologiske Undersøgelse, Copenhagen, and the University of Liverpool. Field work in Labrador (B. R., R. W., and J. K.) was conducted under a co-operative provincial-federal agreement between the Newfoundland Department of Mines and Energy, St. John's and Energy, Mines and Resources Canada, Ottawa. We thank F. C. Taylor of

the Geological Survey of Canada for his comments on an early draft of this paper, and two anonymous reviewers for suggestions which improved the final script.

References

ALLAART, J. H. & JENSEN, S. B. 1979. Completion of 1:500,000 reconnaissance mapping in the Precambrian of the Evighedsfjord–Søndre Strømfjord–Itivdleq region, southern West Greenland. *Rapp. Grønlands geol. Unders.* **95**, 72–76.

——, FRIEND, C. R. L., HALL, R. P., JENSEN, S. B. & ROBERTS, I. W. N. 1978. Continued 1:500,000 reconnaissance mapping in the Precambrian of the Sukkertoppen region, southern West Greenland. *Rapp Grønlands geol. Unders.* **90**, 50–54.

ATWATER, T. 1970. Implications of plate tectonics for the Cenozoic evolution of western North America. *Bull. Geol. Soc. Amer.* **81**, 3813–3536.

BRIDGWATER, D., ESCHER, A. & WATTERSON, J. 1973. Tectonic displacements and thermal activity in two contrasting Proterozoic mobile belts from Greenland. *Phil. Trans. R. Soc. Lond.* **A273**, 513–533.

——, COLLERSON, K. D., HURST, R. W. & JESSEAU, C. W. 1975. Field characters of the early Precambrian rocks from Saglek, coast of Labrador. *In: Report of Activities, Part A.* Geol. Surv. Canada, Paper 75–1A, 287–296.

——, KETO, K., McGREGOR, V. R. & MYERS, J. S. 1976. Archaean gneiss complex of Greenland. *In:* ESCHER, A. & WATT, W. S. (eds). *Geology of Greenland*, Grønlands geol. Unders. Copenhagen, 19–75.

——, COLLERSON, K. D. & MYERS, J. S. 1978. The development of the Archaean gneiss complex of the North Atlantic region. *In:* TARLING, D. H. (ed.). *Evolution of the Earth's Crust*, London Academic Press, 19–69.

BULLARD, E., EVERETT, J. E. & SMITH, A. G. 1965. The fit of the continents around the Atlantic. *In: A Symposium on Continental Drift. Phil. Trans. R. Soc. Lond.* **A258**, 41–51.

COLLERSON, K. D. & BRIDGWATER, D. 1979. Metamorphic development of early Archaean tonalitic and trondhjemitic gneisses, Saglek area, Labrador. *In:* BARKER, F. (ed.). *Trondhjemites, Dacites and Related Rocks*, Elsevier, 205–273.

——, KERR, A., VOCKE, R. D. & HANSON, G. 1982. Reworking of sialic crust as represented in late Archaean-age gneisses, northern Labrador. *Geology*, **10**, 202–208.

DOUGLAS, R. J. W. 1972. A revision of Precambrian Structural Provinces in northeastern Quebec and northern Labrador: a discussion. *Can. J. Earth Sci.* **8**, 925–930.

ESCHER, A. 1966. New geological reconnaissance mapping in the area between Nordre Strømfjord and Ikertoq fjord. *Rapp. Grønlands geol. Unders.* **11**, 24–25.

——, ESCHER, J. C. & WATTERSON, J. 1975. The

reorientation of the Kangâmiut dyke swarm, West Greenland. *Can. J. Earth Sci.* **12**, 158–173.

——, JACK, S. & WATTERSON, J. 1976a. Tectonics of the North Atlantic Proterozoic dyke swarm, West Greenland. *Phil. Trans. R. Soc. Lond.* **A280**, 529–539.

——, SØRENSEN, K. & ZECK, H. P. 1976b. Nagssugtoqidian mobile belt in West Greenland. *In:* ESCHER, A. & WATT, W. S. (eds). *Geology of Greenland*, Grønlands geol. Unders. Copenhagen, 77–95.

GREENE, B. 1972. *Geological map of Labrador, 1:1,000,000.* Mineral Resources Division, Department of Mines, Agriculture and Resources, Province of Newfoundland and Labrador, St. John's, Newfoundland.

GROCOTT, J. 1979. Controls of metamorphic grade in shear belts. *In:* KORSTGÅRD, J. A. (ed.): *Nagssugtoqidian Geology.* Rapp. Grønlands geol. Unders. **89**, 47–62.

GSC. 1985. *Torngat Mountains, magnetic anomaly map, 1:1,000,000.* Geol. Surv. Canada, Map NO–20–M.

HICKMAN, M. H. 1979. A Rb-Sr age and isotope study of the Ikertoq, Nordre Strømfjord and Evighedsfjord shear belts, West Greenland—outline and preliminary results. *In:* KORSTGÅRD, J. A. (ed.): *Nagssugtoqidian Geology.* Rapp. Grønlands geol. Unders. **89**, 125–128.

JACKSON, G. D. & TAYLOR, F. C. 1972. Correlation of major Aphebian rock units in the northeastern Canadian Shield. *Can. J. Earth Sci.* **9**, 1659–1669.

KALSBEEK, F., BRIDGWATER, D. & ZECK, H. P. 1978. A 1950 ± 60 Ma Rb-Sr whole-rock isochron age from two Kangâmiut dykes and the timing of the Nagssugtoqidian (Hudsonian) orogeny in West Greenland. *Can. J. Earth Sci.* **15**, 1122–1128.

KERR, A. 1980. *Late Archaean igneous, metamorphic and structural evolution of the Nain Province at Saglek, Labrador.* Unpubl. M.Sc. thesis, Memorial University, St. John's, Nfld., Canada.

KNIGHT, I. & MORGAN, W. C. 1982. The Aphebian Ramah Group, northern Labrador. *In:* CAMPBELL, F. H. A. (ed.). *Geol. Surv. Canada, Paper 81–10*, 313–330.

KORSTGÅRD, J. A. 1979a (ed.). *Nagssugtoqidian Geology.* Rapp. Grønlands geol. Unders. **89**, 146 pp.

——, 1979b. Metamorphism of the Kangâmiut dykes and the metamorphic and structural evolution of the southern Nagssugtoqidian boundary in the Itivdleq-Ikertoq region, West Greenland. *In:* KORSTGÅRD, J. A. (ed.): *Nagssugtoqidian Geology.* Rapp. Grønlands geol. Unders. **89**, 63–75.

McGREGOR, V. R. 1973. The early Precambrian gneisses of the Godthåb district, West Greenland. *Phil. Trans. R. Soc. Lond.* **A273**, 343–358.

MENGEL, F. 1984. Preliminary results of mapping in the Ramah Group and adjacent gneisses south of Saglek Fiord, northern Labrador. *In: Current Research*, Newfoundland Department of Mines and Energy, Report 84–1, 21–29.

——, 1985. Nain–Churchill Province boundary: a preliminary report on a cross-section through the Hudsonian front in the Saglek Fiord area, northern Labrador. *In: Current Research*, Newfoundland Department of Mines and Energy, Report 85–1, 33–42.

MORGAN, W. C. 1975. Geology of the Precambrian Ramah Group and basement rocks in the Nachvak Fiord-Saglek Fiord area, north Labrador. *Geol. Surv. Canada, Paper 74–54.*

——, 1979. *Geology, Nachvak Fiord–Ramah Bay.* Geol. Surv. Canada, Map 1469A.

——, 1981. *Geology, Bears Gut-Saglek Fiord.* Geol. Surv. Canada, Map 1478A.

MYERS, J. S. 1975. Igneous stratigraphy of Archaean anorthosite at Majorqap qâva, near Fiskenaesset, South-West Greenland. *Rapp. Grønlands geol. Unders.* **74**, 27 p.

——, 1984. The Nagssugtoqidian mobile belt of Greenland. *In:* KRÖNER, A. & GREILING, R. (eds). *Precambrian Tectonics Illustrated.* E. Schweizer bart'sche Verlagsbuchhandlung (Nagele u. Obermiller), Stuttgart, 237–250.

NASH, D. 1979. An interpretation of irregular dyke forms in the Itivdleq shear zone, West Greenland. *In:* KORSTGÅRD, J. A. (ed.): *Nagssugtoqidian Geology.* Rapp. Grønlands geol. Unders. **89**, 77–83.

RAMBERG, H. 1948. On the petrogenesis of the gneiss complexes between Sukkertoppen and Christianshaab, West Greenland. *Meddr dansk geol. Foren.* **11**, 312–327.

RYAN, A. B. 1977. *Progressive structural reworking of the Uivak gneisses, Jerusalem Harbour, northern Labrador.* Unpubl. M.Sc. thesis, Memorial University, St. John's, Nfld., Canada.

——, MARTINEAU, Y., BRIDGWATER, D., SCHIØTTE, L. & LEWRY, J. 1983. The Archaean–Proterozoic boundary in the Saglek Fiord area, Labrador: Report 1. *In: Current Research, Part A.*, Geol. Surv. Canada, Paper 83–1A, 297–304.

——, MARTINEAU, Y., KORSTGÅRD, J. & LEE, D. 1984. The Archaean–Proterozoic boundary in northern Labrador: Report 2. *In: Current Research, Part A.* Geol. Surv. Canada, Paper 84–1, 545–551.

STOCKWELL, C. H. 1963. Second report on structural provinces, orogenies and time classification of rocks of the Canadian Precambrian Shield. *Geol. Surv. Canada, Paper 62–17*, 123–133.

——, 1964. Fourth report on structural provinces, orogenies, and time-classification of rocks of the Canadian Precambrian Shield. *Geol. Surv. Canada, Paper 64–17*, 1–21.

TALBOT, C. J. 1979. A klippe of Nagssugtoqidian supracrustal rocks at Sarfartup nuna, central West Greenland. *In:* KORSTGÅRD, J. A. (ed.): *Nagssugtoqidian Geology.* Rapp. Grønlands geol. Unders. **89**, 23–42.

TAYLOR, F. C. 1971. A revision of Precambrian structural provinces in northeastern Quebec and northern Labrador. *Can. J. Earth Sci.* **8**, 579–584.

——, 1979. Reconnaissance geology of a part of the Precambrian Shield, northeastern Quebec, northern Labrador and Northwest Territories. *Geol. Surv. Canada, Mem. 393.*

WARDLE, R. J. 1983. Nain–Churchill Province cross-section, Nachvak Fiord, northern Labrador. *In: Current Research*, Newfoundland Department of Mines and Energy, Report 83–1, 68–90.

——, 1984. Nain–Churchill province cross-section; Riviere Baudancourt—Nachvak Lake. *In: Current Research*, Newfoundland Department of Mines and Energy, Report 84–1, 1–11.

WATTERSON, J. 1974. Investigation of the Nagssugtoqidian boundary in the Holsteinsborg district, central West Greenland. *Rapp. Grønlands geol. Unders.* **65**, 33–37.

——, 1978. Proterozoic intraplate deformation in the light of southeast Asian neotectonics. *Nature, London* **273**, 636–640.

J. KORSTGÅRD, Geologisk Institut, Aarhus Universitet, 8000 Aarhus C, Denmark.

B. RYAN, Department of Mines and Energy, Mineral Development Division, P.O. Box 4750, 95 Bonaventure Avenue, St. John's, Newfoundland, Canada A1C 5T7.

R. WARDLE, Department of Mines and Energy, Mineral Development Division, P.O. Box 4750, 95 Bonaventure Avenue, St. John's, Newfoundland, Canada A1C 5T7.

Mid-Archaean basic magmatism of southern West Greenland

R. P. Hall, D. J. Hughes & C. R. L. Friend

SUMMARY: Three groups of metamorphosed basic igneous rocks post-date the Amîtsoq gneisses (c. 3700 Ma) and pre-date the Nûk gneisses (c. 2900 Ma) in the Archaean craton of southern West Greenland. These are the Malene metavolcanic amphibolites, the Ameralik dykes within the Amîtsoq gneisses and a series of large metagabbro–anorthosite complexes. The Malene rocks range from komatiitic to tholeiitic in chemical affinities and occur as extensive intermixed horizons throughout the craton. Metavolcanic amphibolites which are intercalated with the older Amîtsoq gneisses are chemically similar to those which are isolated from them. They probably all represent lavas erupted in an oceanic environment, some of which were subsequently tectonically intercalated with the older sialic crust. Significant geochemical differences between the Malene metavolcanic rocks and the Ameralik basic dykes, which intrude the Amîtsoq gneisses, suggest that these dykes could not have acted as feeders to the Malene lavas. The petrogenesis of the Malene rocks is considered in terms of normative behaviour and of the system $CaO–MgO–Al_2O_3–SiO_2$ (CMAS). Both demonstrate the importance of olivine and clinopyroxene in the evolution of the Malene magmas and suggest that they were derived from relatively garnet-depleted and clinopyroxene-enriched mantle compared to average modern mantle. Evidence for a complementary aluminous portion of the Archaean mantle is provided by the abundance of metagabbro–anorthosite rocks and associated aluminous tholeiitic metavolcanic amphibolites.

The lithostratigraphy of the Archaean craton of southern West Greenland has been determined from field relationships which have been described by several authors (eg McGregor 1973; Bridgwater et al. 1976; Chadwick & Coe 1976; Coe 1980; Hall & Friend 1979, 1983) and which has been corroborated by a wealth of isotopic data (eg Moorbath et al. 1977; Kalsbeek & Pidgeon 1980; Taylor et al. 1980; Hamilton et al. 1983). The region is dominated by two generations (c. 3700 and 2900 Ma) of dioritic–granitic gneiss which have been termed the Amîtsoq and Nûk gneisses respectively (McGregor 1973) (Table 1). The older of these two gneisses contains abundant relics of a still older supracrustal suite termed the Akilia association (McGregor &

TABLE 1. *Simplified Archaean stratigraphy of southern West Greenland*

6. Nûk quartzo-feldspathic gneisses	c. 2900 Ma
5. Fiskenaesset-type metagabbro–anorthosites	
4. Malene-type metavolcanics	
3. Ameralik basic dykes	
2. Amîtsoq quartzo-feldspathic gneisses	c. 3700 Ma
1. Akilia–Isua supracrustals	

Relationships between arrowed lithostratigraphic units are discussed in the text.

Mason 1977). These composite ancient gneisses are restricted to the Godthåb–Isukasia region (Fig. 1) apart from a few enclaves which occur in the eastern Sukkertoppen region (Hall 1981, 1985). The c. 2900 Ma Nûk gneisses occur throughout the craton (Taylor et al. 1980; Kalsbeek & Pidgeon 1980; A. A. Garde, pers. comm. 1984). In between the formation of the two gneiss complexes, episodes of basic magmatism occurred throughout the region. These resulted in the emplacement of the Ameralik basic dyke swarm into the Amîtsoq sialic crust (Fig. 2a) (McGregor 1973; Gill & Bridgwater 1979; Chadwick 1981), the extrusion of ubiquitous and voluminous basic lavas which now comprise the Malene amphibolites (Fig. 2b) (McGregor 1973; Hall 1980; Chadwick 1981; Friend et al. 1981) and the emplacement of large gabbro–anorthosite complexes (Fig. 2c), typified by that in the Fiskenaesset region (Windley et al. 1973; Windley & Smith 1974; Myers 1975, 1981).

Despite overall agreement about the stratigraphic ordering of the predominant basic lithostratigraphic units (Table 1; cf McGregor 1973; Bridgwater et al. 1976; Coe 1980; Chadwick 1981; Hall & Friend 1983), some problems still remain concerning their mutual relationships. Firstly, it has been suggested that some contact relationships between the Malene supracrustal rocks and the Amîtsoq gneisses in the Godthåb area (Fig. 1) are primary, and that the Malene rocks formed a supracrustal cover to an Amîtsoq sialic basement (Chadwick & Nutman 1979;

From: PARK, R. G. & TARNEY, J. (eds), 1987, *Evolution of the Lewisian and Comparable Precambrian High Grade Terrains*, Geological Society Special Publication No. 27, pp. 261–275.

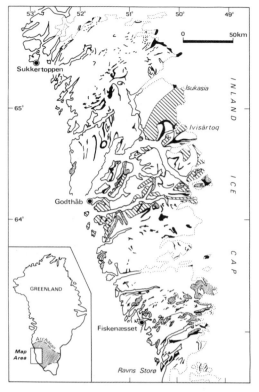

FIG. 1. Simplified sketch-map of the central part of the Archaean craton of southern West Greenland showing the distribution of the main horizons of Malene metavolcanic amphibolites (black), metagabbro–anorthosite complex rocks (stippled) and Amîtsoq gneisses (line-shading) (after Allaart 1982).

Nutman & Bridgwater 1983), having been fed by Ameralik dykes (Chadwick 1981). Secondly, Weaver *et al.* (1981, 1982) have suggested a genetic link between the metavolcanic amphibolites of the southern part of the craton and the metagabbro–anorthosites of the same region. Clearly, if both of these hypotheses are correct then the Malene amphibolites, the Ameralik dykes and the Fiskenaesset-type metagabbro–anorthosites simply represent volcanic, hypabyssal and plutonic equivalents of the same general magmatic suite. This assertion has been tested by examining the geochemistry of two of the largest and best preserved belts of supracrustal amphibolites, one from the heart of the Amîtsoq gneiss terrain (Ivisârtoq) and the other distant from these older gneisses in the southern Fiskenaesset region (Ravns Storø, Fig. 1) and by comparing their geochemistry with that of the Ameralik dykes and the Fiskenaesset metagabbro–anorthosite complex.

Malene metavolcanic amphibolites

Ivisârtoq

An extensive belt of Malene supracrustal rocks approximately two kilometres wide crops out on the Ivisârtoq semi-nûnatak 100 km NE of Godthåb (Fig. 1) and comprises a variety of metasediments, metavolcanics and intercalated ultrabasic rocks (Hall 1981). This belt was deformed during two major phases of large-scale folding, during which the granitic (*s.l.*) precursors of the Nûk gneisses were emplaced as sheets and diapirs (Hall & Friend 1979, 1983; Chadwick 1985). The metavolcanic rocks consist predominantly of variably deformed pillow-structured fine-grained

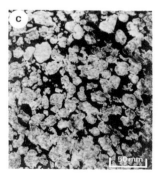

FIG. 2. The three types of metabasic igneous rocks which post-date the Amîtsoq gneisses (*c.* 3700 Ma) and pre-date the Nûk gneisses (*c.* 2900 Ma) on Ivisârtoq. a) Deformed Ameralik dyke which retains a discordant relationship with the banding in the host Amîtsoq gneisses; b) relict pillow-structured Malene metavolcanic amphibolites; c) coarse-grained plagioclase-cumulus leucogabbro.

amphibolites (Hall 1980) which strongly implies that they originated as subaqueous basic lavas. While relict cumulus textures are common in various gabbroic and ultrabasic rocks in the region (*eg* Fig. 2*c*), none are preserved in the pillow-structured metavolcanics. No original mineralogy is preserved in the amphibolites and their present mineralogy comprises predominantly normal epidote-amphibolite facies assemblages. Fifty samples of these rocks have been analysed using a Philips PW1410 semi-automatic X-ray fluorescence spectrometer in the Department of Geology at Portsmouth Polytechnic. The

data retrieval techniques and programs of Brown *et al.* (1973) were used for data reduction and six USGS reference samples (AGV1, BCR1, DTS1, G2, GSP1 and PCC1) were analysed concurrently as an accuracy check, and these show a good overall correspondence with the values quoted by Flanagan (1973) and Abbey (1980) (Hall 1981; details available on request). Representative analyses of the metavolcanic amphibolites are presented in Table 2, arranged in order of decreasing MgO. All iron is presented as Fe_2O_3. FeO was not analysed since the oxidation state of the iron in such amphibolites

TABLE 2. *Representative analyses of komatiitic and tholeiitic Malene metavolcanic amphibolites from Ivisârtoq*

	Komatiitic amphibolites					Tholeiitic amphibolites				
	200887	207624	207625	207637	207616	200422	207613	207622	200456	207615
wt%										
SiO_2	44.52	45.17	46.49	48.28	46.61	46.62	50.15	46.67	48.03	54.19
Al_2O_3	8.65	9.58	9.37	10.83	10.28	14.48	13.04	13.90	13.58	13.14
Fe_2O_3	12.87	13.09	12.35	12.45	14.35	12.41	12.21	13.82	14.83	8.34
MgO	21.78	17.83	17.05	14.00	11.93	11.57	9.99	9.05	8.12	6.71
CaO	10.49	11.88	11.96	10.93	13.74	11.80	10.79	13.25	11.65	14.98
Na_2O	0.77	1.32	2.03	2.12	2.00	2.24	2.68	1.99	2.16	1.73
K_2O	0.19	0.32	0.02	0.06	0.23	n.d.	0.24	0.03	0.01	0.11
TiO_2	0.38	0.47	0.55	0.89	0.57	0.67	0.64	0.98	1.24	0.53
MnO	0.24	0.24	0.23	0.13	0.29	0.23	0.23	0.24	0.27	0.20
P_2O_5	0.10	0.11	n.d.	0.32	0.01	n.d.	0.03	0.06	0.10	0.07
ppm										
Sc	36	39	41	48	42	43	41	47	46	45
V	191	199	206	199	223	261	235	299	353	242
Cr	2467	2296	1765	784	811	468	497	244	146	814
Ni	723	623	566	321	322	194	109	113	85	194
Rb	9	25	9	3	14	n.d.	15	1	n.d.	1
Sr	13	32	37	79	56	65	78	150	80	89
Y	7	8	9	22	8	15	13	22	25	13
Zr	24	26	28	40	33	33	41	59	75	36
Nb	n.d.	n.d.	1	3	n.d.	n.d.	1	1	1	1
Ba	8	128	n.d.	13	20	n.d.	27	24	12	33
Ce	2	1	7	24	6	4	4	9	11	9
CIPW norms										
Q	—	—	—	—	—	—	—	—	—	7.52
or	1.12	1.89	0.12	0.36	1.36	—	1.42	0.18	0.06	0.65
ab	6.52	8.13	12.18	17.94	11.30	18.24	22.68	16.84	18.28	14.64
an	19.59	19.27	16.40	19.86	18.39	29.46	22.84	28.91	27.33	27.76
ne	—	1.65	2.71	—	3.05	0.39	—	—	—	—
di	25.39	31.22	34.41	25.96	40.36	23.52	24.76	29.76	24.48	37.43
hy	3.22	—	—	11.45	—	—	12.14	1.81	16.00	7.83
ol	38.60	32.01	28.77	17.56	19.26	22.65	9.50	15.59	5.94	—
mt	3.58	3.64	4.34	3.47	4.00	3.60	3.39	3.84	4.13	2.32
il	0.72	0.89	1.05	1.69	1.08	1.27	1.22	1.86	2.36	1.01
ap	0.23	0.26	—	0.74	0.02	—	0.07	0.14	0.23	0.16

Major element XRF analyses recalculated to 100% on a water-free basis. Data presented in order of decreasing MgO. All Fe presented as Fe_2O_3. C.I.P.W. norms calculated on the basis of an Fe^{2+}/total Fe ratio of 0.8.
n.d. = not detected.
* All sample numbers should carry the prefix GGU (Grønlands Geologiske Undersøgelse = Geological Survey of Greenland).

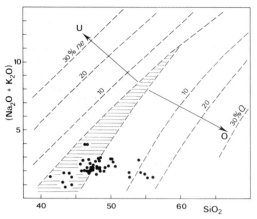

FIG. 3. Alkalis versus silica diagram showing the field
of Malene metavolcanic amphibolites from Ivisârtoq
and the potential normative character of igneous rock
compositions. The contours represent the normative
wt% of nepheline and quartz for basaltic rocks
plotting in the silica-undersaturated (U) and
oversaturated (O) fields respectively. The line-shaded
area represents the range of rock compositions which
would usually contain neither nepheline nor quartz in
the norm (after Cox et al. 1979).

bears no relation to, and is therefore not appropriate in considering the petrogenesis of, their
igneous precursors. An FeO value was adopted
for CIPW norm calculation based on an average
Fe^{2+}/total Fe ratio of 0.8 (equivalent to Fe_2O_3/
FeO $= 0.27$) in basaltic rocks (Engel et al. 1965;
Manson 1967; Sun et al. 1979). The samples were
mainly collected from horizons of little deformed
pillow-structured units (Fig. 2b) where structural
disruption and chemical alteration were considered to be minimal. Zeck et al. (1983) have
demonstrated that basic dykes may partially
adopt the K/Rb character of their host rocks
during penecontemporaneous or subsequent
metamorphism. However, chemical alteration
suggested by increased alkali and Rb contents is
only rarely apparent in the analysed metavolcanic
amphibolites. All except two of the fifty samples
have alkali ($Na_2O + K_2O$) contents $< 3\%$ (K_2O
$< 1\%$) (Fig. 3). Thirty-eight have K_2O contents
$< 0.25\%$. Similarly, Rb values in thirty-seven
samples are between 0 and 10 ppm; only four
samples (including the two high-K samples) have
markedly high Rb values (> 190 ppm) and nine
have between 10 and 70 ppm Rb (those with
between 0.25 and $1\% K_2O$).

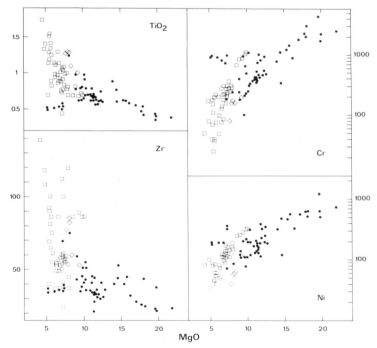

FIG. 4. Plot of TiO_2 (wt%), Zr, Cr and Ni (ppm) against MgO (wt%) for Malene metavolcanic amphibolites from
Ivisârtoq (filled circles) and Ameralik dykes from the Godthåb–Isua region (squares, data from Gill &
Bridgwater 1979) and Ivisârtoq (diamonds). Note that there is only a small degree of overlap between the two
lithostratigraphic groups.

The geochemical affinities of the metavolcanic amphibolites range from tholeiitic to komatiitic in character. They all have the SiO_2:alkali relationships typical of tholeiites (Fig. 3) as well as low Ti and Zr and high Mg, Ni and Cr contents (Fig. 4; *cf* Miyashiro & Shido 1975; Arndt *et al.* 1977; Pearce & Norry 1979; Sun *et al.* 1979). The range in ratios of alkalis with respect to Fe and Mg (Fig. 5) is very similar to that of primitive tholeiites as it is for the metavolcanic amphibolites from other areas in the craton (Rivalenti 1976; Friend *et al.* 1981; Weaver *et al.* 1982). However, many of the Ivisârtoq metavolcanics have unusually high MgO contents (up to 22%) compared with typical modern basaltic rocks. The Ni and Cr contents of these magnesian samples are correspondingly high (up to 1200 and 4400 ppm respectively) while TiO_2 and Zr abundances are low (*c.* 0.5% and 25 ppm respectively) (Fig. 4). Similarly, while the Fe/Mg ratios are akin to those of abyssal tholeiites (Miyashiro 1975; Hall 1980), the Mg-rich samples also have low Al_2O_3 (6–12%) (Fig. 6), K_2O (0–0.9%) and SiO_2 (41–51%). The CaO/Al_2O_3 ratios of these rocks are high (>0.9) (Fig. 7). The sum of these chemical characteristics is very similar to that of many komatiitic suites (see Arndt & Nisbet 1981*a*), and consequently on geochemical grounds the Malene metavolcanic amphibolites can be subdivided into komatiitic and tholeiitic basalt types (Hall 1980).

The definition of komatiite has been frequently reviewed and most recently Arndt & Nisbet (1981*b*) defined komatiite as a volcanic rock representing a liquid composition with MgO > 18%. However, the high-MgO (10–22%), high CaO/Al_2O_3 (>0.9) Malene metavolcanic amphibolites satisfy the earlier chemical definitions given by Brooks & Hart (1974) and Arndt *et al.* (1977) for pyroxenitic and basaltic komatiites, although there is a chemical continuum from these komatiitic rocks to the simple tholeiitic amphibolites (Figs 6 and 7).

Ravns Storø

The Malene supracrustal amphibolites on Ivisârtoq are structurally interleaved with *c.* 3700 Ma Amîtsoq gneisses (Hall & Friend 1979) which could originally have formed a sialic crustal basement to them, whereas the equivalent supracrustal amphibolites in the northern and southern parts of the Archaean craton are apparently the oldest crustal rocks. One of the largest and best preserved supracrustal belts in the southern part of the craton is the Ravns Storø belt in the

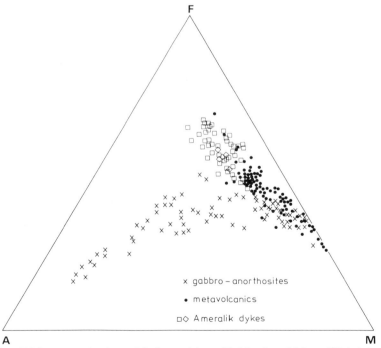

FIG. 5. AFM plot of Malene metavolcanic amphibolites and Ameralik dykes from Ivisârtoq (filled circles and open diamonds respectively), Ameralik dykes from the Godthåb–Isua region (squares, data from Gill & Bridgwater 1979) and the Fiskenaesset metagabbro–anorthosite complex (crosses, data from Myers 1975 and Windley *et al.* 1973).

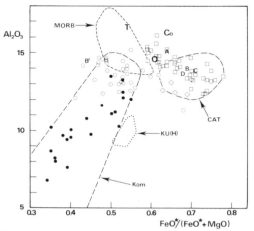

FIG. 6. Plot of Al_2O_3 versus $FeO^*/(FeO^* + MgO)$ for Malene komatiitic (filled circles) and tholeiitic (open circles) metavolcanic amphibolites and Ameralik dykes (diamonds) from Ivisârtoq. $FeO^* = $ total Fe as FeO. Dashed lines enclose fields of komatiites (Kom) from Canada, Australia, India, Zimbabwe and South Africa (Arndt *et al.* 1977), Canadian and Australian Archaean tholeiites (CAT) (Arndt *et al.* 1977) and typical mid-ocean ridge basalts (MORB) (Sun *et al.* 1979). T: average oceanic tholeiite of Engel *et al.* (1965); O and Co: average oceanic and continental tholeiites respectively of Manson (1967); A–D: Ameralik dyke types of Chadwick (1981).

Fiskenaesset region (Fig. 1), approximately 150 km south of the Amîtsoq gneiss terrain. Thus, it is considered that the predominantly metavolcanic rocks in this belt represent oceanic crust.

Just as the tectonic provincialism of modern basaltic suites is reflected in the distinctive geochemical characters of, for example, mid-ocean ridge, island arc and continental basalts, so the geochemistry of the Ravns Storø and the Ivisârtoq metavolcanic rocks might be expected to reflect any major difference in the crustal environment in which they were erupted. This possibility was investigated by Friend *et al.* (1981) who showed that there is no significant geochemical or petrogenetic difference between the composite metavolcanic suites of the two belts. The two have similar ranges of major and trace elements and vary from high magnesian, low-Al komatiitic types to normal tholeiitic members.

Rare-earth element (REE) abundances confirm this interpretation. REE concentrations were determined by neutron activation analysis at the Universities of Liverpool and Manchester Research Reactor, Risley. The REE contents of five typical samples from Ivisârtoq and six samples from Ravns Storø are shown in Figs 8*a* and 8*b* respectively, normalized to the average chondrite values quoted by Nakamura (1974) and chondrite

values for Pr, Tb and Ho of 0.129, 0.05 and 0.067 respectively (interpolated from Schilling & Winchester 1969 and Evensen *et al.* 1978). The REE patterns are almost flat for all the samples, ranging from approximately three to twenty times chondritic values. The REE values show an overall increase with decreasing MgO content. Only one of the tholeiitic samples (GGU 129988; $MgO = 12.48\%$) from Ravns Storø shows a positive Eu anomaly. The relatively flat distribution illustrates the primitive character of the metavolcanic amphibolites, while their low concentration with respect to mid-ocean ridge basalts may indicate higher degrees of partial melting of the source material (*cf* Jahn *et al.* 1974; Arth & Hanson 1975; Condie & Harrison 1976; Sun & Nesbitt 1978*a*).

Petrogenesis of the amphibolites

The normative compositions of the metavolcanic amphibolites of Ivisârtoq are shown in Fig. 9. Perhaps surprisingly, they vary from slightly nepheline-normative to quartz-normative types. The Mg-rich komatiitic rocks tend to contain normative nepheline while the low-MgO (c. 6%) rocks are quartz-normative. In general, this change in normative character parallels the increase in SiO_2 with decreasing MgO content. The migration of alkalis during metamorphism alters the normative character of basic rocks. For example, Gill & Bridgwater (1979) showed that the addition of 1.2% Na_2O and 0.5% K_2O transfers a quartz-normative tholeiitic Ameralik dyke sample through the olivine-tholeiite field to a nepheline-normative composition. However, such a large secondary addition of alkalis is clearly unlikely in the metavolcanic amphibolite samples in question which, apart from two, contain between 0.2 and 3% total alkalis. The alkalis/silica ratios of these metavolcanic amphibolites suggest that none should contain normative nepheline (Fig. 3). Equally, the influence of iron oxidation state on the apparent silica saturation (Cox *et al.* 1979) is not relevant since a constant basaltic Fe^{3+}/Fe^{2+} ratio was of necessity applied to these metamorphosed rocks.

One chemical characteristic which distinguishes most komatiitic rocks from other high-Mg basaltic rocks is their high CaO/Al_2O_3 ratio (> 0.9) (Fig. 6). The $CaO:Al_2O_3$ balance can influence the apparent silica saturation defined in terms of the absence or presence of normative nepheline. Subsequent to its allocation to normative apatite, anorthite and sphene, residual CaO is allotted to normative diopside with equal amounts of $(Mg + Fe^{2+})$. Obviously, in these low-

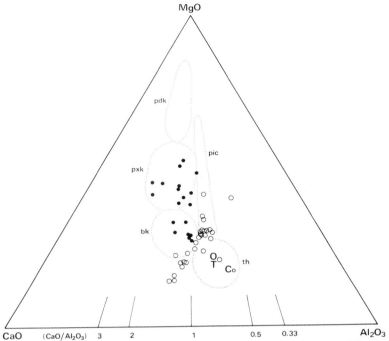

FIG. 7. Plot of CaO:MgO:Al₂O₃ for the Malene metavolcanic amphibolites from Ivisârtoq. The fields of peridotitic komatiites (pdk), pyroxenitic komatiites (pxk) and basaltic komatiites (bk) (after Viljoen & Viljoen 1969; Arndt *et al.* 1977; Green & Schulz 1977) and picritic (pic) and tholeiitic (th) basalts are drawn schematically for comparison. Symbols as in Fig. 6.

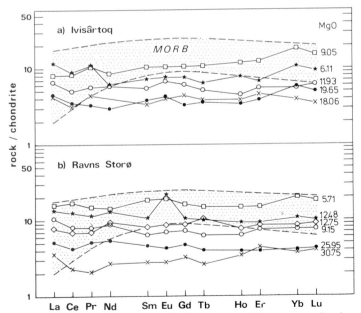

FIG. 8. Chondrite-normalized rare-earth element distributions of typical Malene metavolcanic amphibolites from a) Ivisârtoq and b) Ravns Storø. Symbols: (a) crosses: 200870; filled circles: 207623; open circles: 207616; asterisks: 200890; open squares: 207622; (b) crosses: 119858; filled circles: 129990; open circles: 129974; diamonds: 119816; asterisks: 129988; squares: 119822. Field of mid-ocean ridge basalts (*MORB*) after Frey *et al.* (1974) and Schilling (1975).

TABLE 3. *Representative analyses of metavolcanic amphibolites from Ravns Storø and Ameralik dykes from Ivisârtoq*

	Metavolcanic amphibolites					Ameralik dykes				
	129978	129964	129980	129974	119822	200851	207655	200820	200837	200836
wt%										
SiO_2	47.26	46.88	46.64	50.86	48.11	46.98	47.54	47.98	47.11	47.25
Al_2O_3	6.63	9.15	9.61	11.55	12.41	13.13	12.34	12.60	13.34	12.53
Fe_2O_3	11.91	13.78	12.93	12.30	18.50	14.44	15.55	15.26	15.17	16.62
MgO	23.95	19.81	17.72	9.15	5.71	9.34	8.43	8.06	7.97	7.66
CaO	9.19	8.28	10.71	12.59	10.30	11.28	11.55	11.02	10.99	10.62
Na_2O	0.47	1.09	1.50	2.27	2.05	2.49	2.55	2.59	2.90	2.64
K_2O	4.01	0.07	0.07	0.14	0.26	1.01	0.59	0.83	0.83	1.01
TiO_2	0.32	0.65	0.60	0.75	2.15	1.00	1.09	1.28	1.29	1.27
MnO	0.23	0.22	0.17	0.22	0.26	0.27	0.28	0.27	0.28	0.29
P_2O_5	0.03	0.07	0.06	0.17	0.24	0.07	0.08	0.11	0.12	0.11
ppm										
Sc	20	32	30	38	38	43	50	46	46	47
V	138	206	202	294	348	291	326	353	336	342
Cr	2633	1994	1557	177	n.d.	204	159	173	163	82
Ni	1312	705	625	77	10	123	62	59	57	38
Rb	n.d.	n.d.	n.d.	n.d.	2	11	6	5	6	5
Sr	11	29	119	101	147	119	97	111	135	240
Y	8	13	11	18	30	7	24	27	27	29
Zr	19	36	31	53	95	53	60	82	85	77
Nb	1	1	1	1	n.d.	1	1	3	4	1
Ba	n.d.	4	3	15	58	74	22	102	57	76
Ce	4	5	9	14	9	10	4	12	17	16
CIPW norms										
Q	—	—	—	0.01	—	—	—	—	—	—
or	0.06	0.41	0.06	0.83	0.71	6.04	3.53	4.97	4.97	6.05
ab	3.98	9.31	3.05	19.29	21.58	16.33	21.17	22.19	19.89	21.09
an	16.03	19.96	20.10	21.03	21.98	21.92	20.74	20.56	21.19	19.62
ne	—	—	—	—	—	2.70	0.37	—	2.68	0.84
di	23.52	16.70	13.20	33.01	21.43	27.97	30.21	28.00	27.30	44.24
hy	35.59	24.61	29.42	19.48	14.41	—	—	1.30	—	—
ol	25.76	22.53	27.71	—	13.04	18.89	17.32	15.97	16.94	17.72
mt	4.38	5.07	5.39	4.52	4.99	4.06	4.39	4.30	4.27	4.69
il	0.61	1.23	0.91	1.42	1.69	1.92	2.10	2.46	2.48	2.45
ap	0.07	0.15	0.15	0.41	0.17	0.16	0.19	0.26	0.28	0.26

n.d. = not detected.

Al_2O_3 (originally feldspar-poor or absent) komatiitic rocks, significant amounts of CaO will be residual. Hence large amounts of relatively silica-rich normative diopside will be formed in the calculation prior to relatively silica-poor normative olivine. In the final re-allocation of silica a deficiency can thus arise which has to be compensated for by the desilication to normative nepheline of earlier formed normative albite. Thus, the normative nepheline of the basaltic komatiites is probably an artefact of the calculation, possibly added to by the influence of slight alkali migration during metamorphism. This suggests that the earlier subdivision of Malene amphibolites from the Fiskenaesset region into

tholeiitic and alkali olivine basalt types (Rivalenti & Rossi 1975; Rivalenti 1976) is erroneous.

Assuming that in reality all of these amphibolites were originally tholeiitic (hypersthene-normative) in character, a projection from quartz onto the plane Ol–Cpx–Pl in the simple normative basalt system (Fig. 10) shows clear clustering of the basaltic rocks of the suite on the clinopyroxene and olivine-poor side of the rocks with komatiitic affinities. If the komatiitic and basaltic components of the amphibolite suite are regarded as being co-genetic then this implies either that olivine and clinopyroxene were significant fractionating phases in its evolution or that the komatiitic members of the suite originated by a

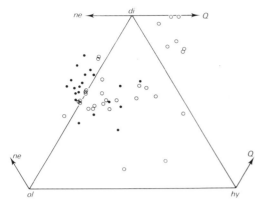

FIG. 9. Malene metavolcanic amphibolite data from Ivisârtoq projected into the normative system *ne–ol–di–hy–Q*. Symbols as in Fig. 6.

larger degree of partial melting of lherzolitic mantle than the tholeiitic rocks.

The more rigorous CaO–MgO–Al$_2$O$_3$–SiO$_2$ (CMAS) system (O'Hara 1968) can be used to clarify the nature of phases controlling the evolution of basic magmatic systems. As in the normative system, projections from controlling phase compositions result in a close grouping of genetically related data points while projections onto planes containing controlling phase compositions will result in linear arrays of points away from that phase.

As in the normative system, projections in CMAS clearly demonstrate the importance of both olivine and clinopyroxene as controlling phases in the evolution of the Malene metavolcanics. The projection from enstatite (MS) onto the plane C$_2$S$_3$–M$_2$S–A$_2$S$_3$ containing diopside (CMS$_2$), pyrope (M$_3$AS$_3$) and forsterite (M$_2$S) shows that the lower magnesian tholeiitic Malene rocks plot on the diopside and forsterite-poor side of the komatiites (Fig. 11) while in contrast, a typical picritic suite (Baffin Bay picrites) forms a linear array towards the forsterite apex in this plane (Clarke 1970). Projections from diopside (CMS$_2$) onto the plane C$_3$A–M–S and from forsterite (M$_2$S) onto CS–MS–A show an evolutionary trend away from forsterite and diopside respectively (Hall 1981).

The fact that the Malene komatiites fall on the diopside-rich side of the tholeiitic rocks, as do typical komatiites from elsewhere (Fig. 11), suggests that increasing degrees of melting of the source mantle produced melts progressively enriched in olivine and clinopyroxene. However,

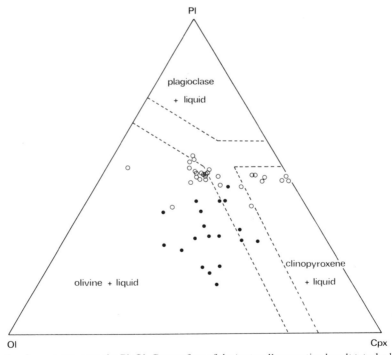

FIG. 10. Projection from quartz onto the Pl–Ol–Cpx surface of the 'natural' normative basalt tetrahedron of the Malene metavolcanic amphibolites from Ivisârtoq (after Cox *et al.* 1979). Symbols as in Fig 6. Pl $= an + ab$; Ol $= fo + fa + (hy_{en} \times 0.713) + (hy_{fs} \times 0.766)$; Cpx $= di$.

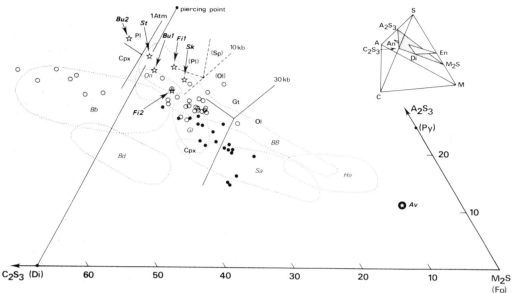

FIG. 11. CMAS (wt%) plot of the Malene metavolcanic amphibolites from Ivisârtoq projected from enstatite (MS) onto the plane C_2S_3–M_2S–A_2S_3. Filled circles: komatiitic amphibolites; open circles: tholeiitic amphibolites; Av: average garnet lherzolite from kimberlite pipe nodules (Ito & Kennedy 1967). The fields of South African komatiites are taken from Cawthorn & Strong (1974). Bb: Barberton type; Bd: Badplaas type; Gl: Geluk type; Sa: Sandspruit type; On: Onverwacht metatholeiites; Ho: Hoogenoeg metatholeiites. The linear array of the Baffin Bay picrite suite (BB) illustrates a clearly defined simple olivine control (Clarke 1970). Estimated parent liquid compositions of the Skaergaard (Sk), Bushveld ($Bu1$, $Bu2$) and Stillwater (St) intrusions were calculated from data presented by Wager & Brown (1968). Estimated parent liquid compositions of the Fiskenaesset metagabbro–anorthosite complex ($Fi1$, $Fi2$) are taken from Windley et al. (1973) and Weaver et al. (1981) respectively. Experimentally determined phase boundaries are shown for pressures of 1 atmosphere, 10 kilobars and 30 kilobars (after O'Hara 1968).

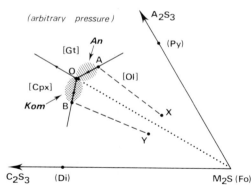

FIG. 12. Schematic clinopyroxene (Cpx)–garnet (Gt)–olivine (Ol) phase boundaries showing the lines of evolution of melt composition derived from a normal garnet lherzolite (X) and a garnet-depleted (clinopyroxene-enriched) lherzolite (Y) in the projection from enstatite (MS) onto the plane C_2S_3–M_2S–A_2S_3 (after O'Hara 1970; Cawthorn & Strong 1974). (Fo), (Di) and (Py) indicate the relative positions of the forsterite, diopside and pyrope composition points. An and Kom indicate the fields of liquids produced by large degrees of partial melting of mantle sources X and Y respectively.

progressive melting of an 'average' garnet lherzolite source ('Av' in Fig. 11) would produce relatively more aluminous liquids (O'Hara 1970; Cawthorn & Strong 1974). This implies that the Malene komatiitic amphibolites and genetically associated tholeiitic amphibolites were derived from a less aluminous, presumably relatively garnet-poor, mantle peridotite. This distinction is illustrated schematically in Fig. 12. In this diagram the lines of liquid descent of an average garnet lherzolite (X) and a relatively garnet-depleted, clinopyroxene-enriched lherzolite (Y) are represented by paths X–A–O and Y–B–O respectively. The first liquids of both lherzolite compositions plot at the invariant point (O). During progressive melting of garnet lherzolite source X, clinopyroxene is the first phase to be exhausted, leaving a garnet harzburgite residuum and the liquid composition subsequently moves along the path O–A until garnet is exhausted, leaving harzburgite. Further melting moves the liquid along the line A–X until orthopyroxene is exhausted and only olivine (dunite) is left. For a garnet lherzolite source with composition Y, the locus of liquid compositions during progressive melting follows the path O–B–Y and lherzolite, harzburgite and dunite residua are left successively as garnet, clinopyroxene and orthopyroxene are removed. It is considered that a mantle composition equivalent to Y must account for the generation of the Malene komatiite–tholeiite metavolcanic suite. Complementary aluminous basaltic amphibolites derived from relatively garnet-enriched mantle might be expected to coexist with the komatiitic–tholeiitic amphibolite suite. This possibility is discussed in the final section. This further suggests that the source of these Archaean komatiitic and tholeiitic lavas and complementary aluminous basaltic rocks involves a wider range of compositions than that inferred for modern mantle from, for example, the variety of garnet lherzolite nodules in kimberlites (Ito & Kennedy 1967; Ringwood 1975).

The Ameralik dykes

Among the most fundamental unresolved problems in the tectonic modelling of the Archaean craton of West Greenland is the environment in which the Malene supracrustal rocks were formed and the relationship of these rocks to the pre-existing Amîtsoq sialic crust in the region east of Godthåb at the centre of the craton (Fig. 1). The present intercalation of Malene supracrustal and Amîtsoq gneiss units is predominantly the result of an early phase of thrusting and subsequent large scale folding (Bridgwater *et al.* 1974; Hall & Friend 1979). However, whether the juxtaposition of the two suites also represents an original cover–basement relationship or was brought about purely tectonically has been the subject of considerable discussion.

If the Amîtsoq gneisses formed an early Archaean continental crust through which the Malene basic lavas were originally injected to form a cover to that crust then basic feeder dykes of equivalent composition to the lavas should be preserved within the Amîtsoq gneisses. Since abundant metamorphosed basic dykes are a characteristic feature of the Amîtsoq gneisses (McGregor 1973) these rocks, known as the Ameralik dykes, could obviously be postulated as feeders to Malene basic lavas erupted on to an Amîtsoq gneiss basement. Hence, the geochemistry of the Ameralik dykes and Malene metavolcanics is fundamental in determining whether the two are genetically related.

An extensive suite of Ameralik dykes from the Godthåb–Isukasia region has been analysed and described by Gill & Bridgwater (1979) and Ameralik dykes from the region to the south of Godthåb (the Buksefjorden region) have been

examined by Chadwick (1981). Apart from a group of recognizably cumulus-textured dykes described by Chadwick (1981), the dykes from the two areas are very similar. Chadwick (1981) has also shown that in the Buksefjorden region there is a considerable geochemical overlap between the Ameralik dykes, Malene metavolcanics and Malene dykes, and that the Ameralik dykes may well have been feeders for the Malene lavas in that region.

However, there are important geochemical differences between the Malene komatiitic–tholeiitic metavolcanic suite of Ivisârtoq and the Ameralik dykes from the Godthåb–Isukasia region (Fig. 13). The wide separation of the two groups in terms of the major element discriminant 'F' functions defined by Pearce (1976) reflects the more primitive character of the metavolcanic rocks. This is also shown by the higher Mg:Fe ratios of these rocks and also by their higher absolute values of Mg, Ni and Cr and lower Zr and Ti compared to the Ameralik dykes (Figs 4–6).

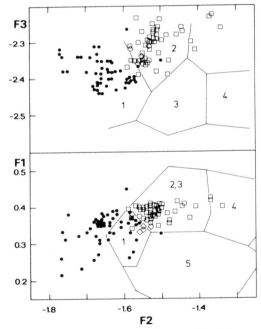

FIG. 13. Plot of major element chemistry discriminant functions F3 versus F2 and F1 versus F2 (after Pearce 1976) showing the clear distinction between the Malene metavolcanic amphibolites from Ivisârtoq (closed circles) and the Ameralik dykes from the Godthåb–Isukasia region (squares) and from Ivisârtoq (diamonds). The statistically-defined fields are 1) ocean-floor basalts, 2) low-K tholeiites, 3) calc-alkali basalts, 4) shoshonites and 5) within-plate basalts.

Severe olivine and clinopyroxene fractionation is the only tenable fractionation model which could link the relatively evolved Ameralik dykes to the more magnesian, komatiitic Malene metavolcanic rocks. However, plagioclase is the only common relict phenocryst phase in the Ameralik dykes and no fractionation relationship is suggested by the REE distribution patterns of the Malene komatiites (Fig. 8) and the Ameralik dykes (Gill & Bridgwater 1979; Chadwick 1981). Extensive plagioclase fractionation to produce a residuum equivalent to the Malene komatiitic metavolcanics from a magma of Ameralik dyke composition can be simply dismissed on physical grounds. Thus, there is strong geochemical evidence that the Ameralik dykes did not feed the Malene komatiitic–tholeiitic metavolcanic suite on Ivisârtoq and, hence, that these Malene lavas were not originally erupted through the Amîtsoq 'continent'.

The only so-called Ameralik dykes which are geochemically similar to the Malene komatiitic metavolcanics are those of the Kangerdluk–Ugpik (KU) suite (Gill & Bridgwater 1976, 1979) with which Chadwick (1981) correlates his 'H' Ameralik dykes (Fig. 6). However, these dykes are also remarkable in that unlike all the other rocks in this amphibolite-facies terrain they retain both igneous textures and mineralogy, comprising clino- and orthopyroxene poikilitically enclosed by plagioclase. Chadwick (1981) considers them to be '. . . of probable Nûk age . . .' (c. 2900 Ma), but it is also possible that these dykes are altered early Proterozoic noritic dykes which are abundant in this part of the Archaean craton and which have a very similar geochemistry and are also characterized texturally by orthopyroxene enclosed by plagioclase oikocrysts (Hall et al. 1985). In either case, they cannot be stratigraphically equated with the Malene metavolcanic amphibolites which are distinctly older than the dioritic–granitic precursors of the Nûk gneisses (McGregor 1973; Bridgwater et al. 1976; Coe 1980; Hall & Friend 1983; Chadwick 1985). Similarly, Mg-rich, so-called 'E'-type Ameralik dykes which cut these KU ('H') dykes (Chadwick 1981) clearly cannot be correlated with the Malene metavolcanic rocks, and they have a distinctive and unusual geochemistry (relatively rich in Mg, Cr, Ni, Rb, Sr and light REE) very similar to that of the early Proterozoic norites.

Discussion

Several significant points emerge from this examination of the geochemistry of the various Archaean basic lithostratigraphic units in southern West Greenland.

1) The metavolcanic amphibolites from Ivîsartoq comprise a suite which ranges from komatiitic to tholeiitic in chemical affinities.

2) The petrogenetic evolution of the suite was dominated by both olivine and clinopyroxene either as controlling phases during fractional crystallization or during progressive melting. The important rôle of clinopyroxene suggests that the source mantle was relatively rich in clinopyroxene (and correspondingly garnet-poor) compared to average garnet lherzolite mantle.

3) There is no significant geochemical difference between the komatiitic–tholeiitic metavolcanics from the large and well preserved Ivisârtoq belt in the heart of the Amîtsoq gneiss terrain and the Ravns Storø belt which is remote from (approximately 150 km to the south of) the Amîtsoq gneisses. There are no geochemical grounds for invoking origins in different crustal environments for these two supracrustal belts. Both probably originated as oceanic crust.

4) Although the Malene metavolcanic amphibolites on Ivisârtoq are presently intercalated with the older Amîtsoq gneisses, their geochemistry does not correspond to that of the Ameralik dykes which intrude the Amîtsoq gneisses of the region (Gill & Bridgwater 1979). The geochemical differences between these Malene metavolcanics and the Ameralik dykes thus suggest that the Ameralik dykes do not represent feeders to the Malene lavas and hence, given that no dykes with Malene-type komatiitic compositions occur, that the Malene lavas were not erupted through the pre-existing Amîtsoq sialic crust. The fact that the Ameralik dykes and the Malene metavolanics of the southern Godthåb region (Fig. 1) are approximately geochemically equivalent (Chadwick 1981) and that unconformable relationships between the Malene supracrustals and Amîtsoq gneisses are preserved in this region (Chadwick & Nutman 1979; Nutman & Bridgwater 1983) suggests that these Malene rocks were possibly fed by Ameralik dykes through the Amîtsoq sialic crust (Chadwick 1981; Nutman & Bridgwater 1983). Hence, the Malene amphibolites probably represent more than one basic metavolcanic suite.

5) A third major type of Archaean basic magmatism comprises large intrusive complexes of aluminous metagabbro–anorthosite, typified by the Fiskenaesset complex (Fig. 1) (Myers 1975, 1981; Windley et al. 1973). These are associated with petrogenetically related metavolcanic amphibolites (Weaver et al. 1981, 1982). The Fiskenaesset complex has been interpreted by Weaver et al. (1981) as a 'tholeiitic layered

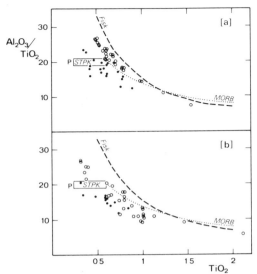

FIG. 14. Plot of Al_2O_3/TiO_2 versus TiO_2 for the Malene metavolcanic amphibolites from a) Ivisârtoq and b) Ravns Storø (open circles: tholeiitic amphibolites; filled circles: komatiitic amphibolites). The trend of the aluminous tholeiitic amphibolites of the Fiskenaesset region (*Fisk*) which are related to the Fiskenaesset metagabbro–anorthosite complex is taken from Weaver *et al.* (1982). Model pyrolite (P), the field of spinifex-textured peridotitic komatiites (*STPK*) and trend of mid-ocean ridge basalts (*MORB*) are taken from Sun & Nesbitt (1978*b*).

complex which has undergone extensive plagioclase fractionation' having been derived from a magma which 'approximates a moderately aluminous tholeiitic basalt'. These anorthositic rocks and their metavolcanic equivalents clearly represent a petrogenetic counterpart to the aluminium-poor komatiite–tholeiite metavolcanic assemblages. Different petrogenetic affinities are immediately suggested by the ratios of alkalis to Fe and Mg (Fig. 5) and are confirmed by the different evolutionary paths with respect to Al and Ti (Fig. 14). These latter elements clearly distinguish the petrogenetic development of the aluminous and Al-poor types of metavolcanics. It is difficult to envisage a mechanism by which

the komatiitic metavolcanic rocks could be related to such aluminous parent liquids (Fig. 14) without, for example, producing a strongly fractionated REE distribution pattern (*cf* Fig. 8). It is still more difficult to relate the komatiitic metavolcanic amphibolites to the Fiskenaesset metagabbro–anorthosite complex parent magma which was estimated by Windley *et al.* (1973) to have an Al_2O_3/TiO_2 ratio of 62.6 with an Al_2O_3 content of 23.15%.

The high-magnesium members of the komatiitic suites were presumably derived by large degrees of melting of a relatively clinopyroxene-rich mantle peridotite (Fig. 12). Conversely, an equal degree of partial melting of a complementary relatively clinopyroxene-poor, garnet-rich mantle would give rise to correspondingly more aluminous melts. Compositional estimates of the parent magma of the Fiskenaesset metagabbro–anorthosite complex by Windley *et al.* (1973) and Weaver *et al.* (1981) are plotted in the projection from enstatite (MS) onto the plane C_2S_3–M_2S–A_2S_3 in Fig. 11 (*Fi1* and *Fi2* respectively). Estimates of the Bushveld (*Bu1* and *Bu2*), Skaergaard (*Sk*) and Stillwater (*St*) parent magma compositions are shown for comparison (data from Wager & Brown 1968, table 7). These all plot on the aluminous and diopside-poor side of typical komatiitic suites (Cawthorn & Strong 1974). Thus, there is abundant geological evidence for essentially bimodal aluminous and komatiitic basic magmatism during the Archaean in West Greenland, derived from a heterogeneous Archaean mantle. It remains unclear whether the mantle was simply layered (*cf* Cawthorn & Strong 1974) or more irregularly heterogeneous (*cf* Erlank *et al.* 1980; Davies 1981; White & Hofmann 1982) and whether or not there are basic metavolcanics which were derived from a mantle source compositionally intermediate to the komatiite–tholeiite and aluminous tholeiite sources.

ACKNOWLEDGEMENTS: We are grateful to the Director of the Geological Survey of Greenland for inviting us to work in Greenland and for permission to publish this paper. We thank R. C. O. Gill and an anonymous reviewer for their helpful comments.

References

ABBEY, S. 1980. Studies in "standard samples" for use in the general analysis of silicate rocks and minerals. *Geostandards Newsletter*, **4**, 163–90.

ALLAART, J. H. 1982. (compiler) *1:500,000 scale geological map Frederikshåb Isblink–Søndre Strømfjord.* Geol. Surv. Greenland.

ARNDT, N. T., NALDRETT, A. J. & PYKE, D. R. 1977. Komatiitic and iron-rich tholeiitic lavas of Munro township, north-east Ontario. *J. Petrol.* **18**, 319–69.

—— & NISBET, E. G. (eds.) 1981*a*. *Komatiites*. George Allen & Unwin, London, 526 pp.

—— & —— 1981*b*. What is a komatiite? *In*: ARNDT, N. T. & NISBET, E. G. (eds.) *Komatiites*. George Allen & Unwin, London, 19–27.

ARTH, J. G. & HANSON, G. N. 1975. Geochemistry and

origin of the early Precambrian crust of N.E. Minnesota. *Geochim. cosmochim. Acta*, **39**, 325–62.

BRIDGWATER, D., McGREGOR, V. R. & MYERS, J. S. 1974. A horizontal tectonic regime in the Archaean of Greenland and its implications for early crustal thickening. *Precambrian Res.* **1**, 179–97.

——, KETO, L., McGREGOR, V. R. & MYERS, J. S. 1976. Archaean gneiss complex of Greenland; *In*: ESCHER, A. & WATT, W. S. (eds) *Geology of Greenland*, Geol. Surv. Greenland, Copenhagen, 18–75.

BROOKS, C. & HART, S. R. 1974. On the significance of komatiite. *Geology*, **2**, 107–10.

BROWN, G. C., HUGHES, D. J. & ESSON, J. 1973. New X.R.F. data retrieval techniques and their application to U.S.G.S. standard rocks. *Chem. Geol.* **11**, 223–9.

CAWTHORN, R. G. & STRONG, D. F. 1974. The petrogenesis of komatiites and related rocks as evidence for a layered upper mantle. *Earth planet. Sci. Lett.* **23**, 369–75.

CHADWICK, B. 1981. Field relations, petrography and geochemistry of Archaean amphibolite dykes and Malene supracrustal amphibolites, northwest Buksefjorden, southern West Greenland. *Precambrian Res.* **14**, 221–59.

—— 1985. Contrasting styles of tectonism and magmatism in the late Archaean crustal evolution of the northwestern part of the Ivisârtoq region, inner Godthåbsfjord region, southern West Greenland. *Precambrian Res.* **27**, 215–38.

—— & COE, K. 1976. New evidence relating to Archaean events in southern West Greenland. *In*: WINDLEY, B. F. (ed.) *The Early History of the Earth*. Wiley, London, 203–11.

—— & NUTMAN, A. P. 1979. Archaean structural evolution in the northwest of the Buksefjorden region, southern West Greenland. *Precambrian Res.* **9**, 199–226.

CLARKE, D. B. 1970. Tertiary basalts of Baffin Bay: possible primary magma from the mantle. *Contrib. Mineral. Petrol.* **25**, 203–24.

COE, K. 1980. Nûk gneisses of the Buksefjorden region, southern West Greenland, and their enclaves. *Precambrian Res.* **11**, 357–71.

CONDIE, K. C. & HARRISON, N. M. 1976. Geochemistry of the Archaean Bulawayan Group, Midlands greenstone belt, Rhodesia. *Precambrian Res.* **3**, 253–71.

COX, K. G., BELL, J. D. & PANKHURST, R. J. 1979. *The Interpretation of Igneous Rocks*. George Allen & Unwin, London, 450 pp.

DAVIES, G. F. 1981. Earth's neodymium budget and structure and evolution of the mantle. *Nature, London*. **290**, 208–13.

ENGEL, A. E. J., ENGEL, C. G. & HAVENS, R. G. 1965. Chemical characteristics of oceanic basalts and the upper mantle. *Bull. geol. Soc. Am.* **76**, 719–34.

ERLANK, A. J., ALLSOPP, H. L., DUNCAN, A. R. & BRISTOW, J. W. 1980. Mantle heterogeneity beneath southern Africa: evidence from the volcanic record. *Phil. Trans. R. Soc. Lond. A* **297**, 295–307.

EVENSEN, N. M., HAMILTON, P. J. & O'NIONS, R. K.

1978. Rare-earth abundances in chondritic meteorites. *Geochim. cosmochim. Acta*, **42**, 1199–212.

FLANAGAN, F. J. 1973. 1972 values for international geochemical reference samples. *Geochim. cosmochim. Acta*, **37**, 1189–200.

FREY, F. A., BRYAN, W. & THOMPSON, G. 1974. Atlantic Ocean floor: geochemistry and petrology of basalts from Legs 2 and 3 of the Deep-Sea Drilling Project. *J. geophys. Res.* **79**, 5507–27.

FRIEND, C. R. L., HALL, R. P. & HUGHES, D. J. 1981. The geochemistry of the Malene (mid-Archaean) ultramafic–mafic amphibolite suite, southern West Greenland. *In*: GLOVER, J. E. & GROVES, D. I. (eds.) *Archaean Geology*. Spec. Publ. geol. Soc. Aust. **7**, 301–12.

GILL, R. C. O. & BRIDGWATER, D. 1976. The Ameralik dykes of West Greenland, the earliest known basaltic rocks intruding continental crust. *Earth planet. Sci Lett.* **29**, 276–82.

—— & —— 1979. Early Archaean basic magmatism in West Greenland: the geochemistry of the Ameralik dykes. *J. Petrol.* **20**, 695–726.

GREEN, J. C. & SCHULZ, K. J. 1977. Iron-rich basaltic komatiites in the early Precambrian Vermilion District, Minnesota. *Can. J. Earth Sci.* **14**, 2181–92.

HALL, R. P. 1980. The tholeiitic and komatiitic affinities of the Malene metavolcanic amphibolites from Ivisârtoq, southern West Greenland. *Rapp. Grønlands geol. Unders.* **97**, 20 pp.

—— 1981. *The Archaean geology of Ivisârtoq, inner Godthåbsfjord, southern West Greenland*. Unpubl. PhD thesis, CNAA, Portsmouth Polytechnic.

—— 1985. Mg-Fe-Mn distribution in amphiboles, pyroxenes and garnets and implications for conditions of metamorphism of high-grade early Archaean iron-formation, southern West Greenland. *Mineralog. Mag.* **49**, 117–28.

—— & FRIEND, C. R. L. 1979. Structural evolution of the Archaean rocks in Ivisârtoq and the neighbouring inner Godthåbsfjord region, southern West Greenland. *Geology*, **7**, 311–5.

—— & —— 1983. Intrusive relationships between young and old Archaean gneisses: evidence from Ivisârtoq, southern West Greenland. *Geol. J.* **18**, 77–91.

——, HUGHES, D. J. & FRIEND, C. R. L. 1985. Geochemical evolution and unusual pyroxene chemistry of the MD tholeiite dyke swarm from the Archaean craton of southern West Greenland. *J. Petrol.* **26**, 253–82.

HAMILTON, P. J., O'NIONS, R. K., BRIDGWATER, D. & NUTMAN, A. 1983. Sm-Nd studies of Archaean metasediments and metavolcanics from West Greenland and their implications for the Earth's early history. *Earth planet. Sci. Lett.* **62**, 263–72.

ITO, K. & KENNEDY, G. C. 1967. Melting and phase relations in a natural peridotite to 40 kilobars. *Am. J. Sci.* **265**, 519–38.

JAHN, B.-M., SHIH, C.-Y. & MURTHY, V. R. 1974. Trace element geochemistry of Archaean volcanic rocks. *Geochim. cosmochim. Acta*, **38**, 611–27.

KALSBEEK, F. & PIDGEON, R. T. 1980. The geological significance of Rb-Sr whole-rock isochrons of polymetamorphic Archaean gneisses, Fiskenaesset area, southern West Greenland. *Earth planet. Sci. Lett.* **50**, 225–37.

MANSON, V. 1967. Geochemistry of basaltic rocks: major elements; *In*: HESS, H. H. & POLDERVAART, A. (eds) *Basalts, I*, Wiley, London, 215–69.

MCGREGOR, V. R. 1973. The early Precambrian gneisses of the Godthåb district, West Greenland. *Phil. Trans. R. Soc. Lond. A* **273**, 343–78.

—— & MASON, B. 1977. Petrogenesis and geochemistry of metabasaltic and metasedimentary enclaves in the Amîtsoq gneisses, West Greenland. *Am. Mineral.* **62**, 887–904.

MIYASHIRO, A. 1975. Classification, characteristics and origin of ophiolites. *J. Geol.* **83**, 249–81.

—— & SHIDO, F. 1975. Tholeiitic and calc-alkalic series in relation to the behaviours of titanium, chromium and nickel. *Am. J. Sci.* **275**, 265–77.

MOORBATH, S., ALLAART, J. H., BRIDGWATER, D. & MCGREGOR, V. R. 1977. Rb-Sr ages of early Archaean supracrustal rocks and Amîtsoq gneisses at Isua. *Nature, London,* **270**, 43–5.

MYERS, J. S. 1975. Pseudo-fractionation trend of the Fiskenaesset anorthosite complex, southern West Greenland. *Rapp. Grønlands geol. Unders.* **75**, 77–80.

—— 1981. The Fiskenaesset anorthosite complex—a stratigraphic key to the tectonic evolution of the West Greenland gneiss complex 3000–2800 m.y. ago. *In*: GLOVER, J. E. & GROVES, D. I. (eds.) *Archaean Geology.* Spec. Publ. geol. Soc. Aust. **7**, 351–60.

NAKAMURA, N. 1974. Determination of REE, Ba, Fe, Mg, Na and K in carbonaceous and ordinary chondrites. *Geochim. cosmochim. Acta,* **38**, 757–75.

NUTMAN, A. P. & BRIDGWATER, D. 1983. Deposition of Malene supracrustal rocks on an Amîtsoq basement in outer Ameralik, southern West Greenland. *Rapp. Grønlands geol. Unders.* **112**, 43–51.

O'HARA, M. J. 1968. The bearing of phase equilibria studies in synthetic and natural systems on the origin and evolution of basic and ultrabasic rocks. *Earth Sci. Rev.* **4**, 69–133.

—— 1970. Upper mantle composition inferred from laboratory experiments and observations of volcanic products. *Phys. Earth Planet. Interiors,* **3**, 236–45.

PEARCE, J. A. 1976. Statistical analysis of major element patterns in basalts. *J. Petrol.* **17**, 15–43.

—— & NORRY, M. J. 1979. Petrogenetic implications of Ti, Zr, Y and Nb variations in volcanic rocks. *Contrib. Mineral. Petrol.* **69**, 33–47.

RINGWOOD, A. E. 1975. *Composition and Petrology of the Earth's Mantle.* McGraw-Hill, New York, 618 pp.

RIVALENTI, G. 1976. Geochemistry of metavolcanic amphibolites from South-west Greenland. *In*: WINDLEY, B. F. (ed.) *The Early History of the Earth.* Wiley, London, 213–23.

—— & ROSSI, A. 1975. Geochemistry of Precambrian amphibolites in an area near Fiskenaesset, South West Greenland. *Boll. Soc. geol. Ital.* **94**, 27–49.

SCHILLING, J. G. 1975. Rare-earth variations across 'normal segments' of the Reykjanes Ridge, 60–53 N, mid-Atlantic ridge, 29 S, and east Pacific rise, 2–19 S, and evidence of the composition of the underlying low-velocity layer. *J. geophys. Res.* **80**, 1459–73.

—— & WINCHESTER, J. A. 1969. Rare-earth contribution to the origin of Hawaiian lavas. *Contrib. Mineral. Petrol.* **23**, 27–37.

SUN, S. S. & NESBITT, R. W. 1978*a*. Petrogenesis of Archaean ultrabasic and basic volcanics: evidence from rare-earth elements. *Contrib. Mineral. Petrol.* **65**, 301–25.

—— & —— 1978*b*. Geochemical regularities and genetic significance of ophiolitic basalts. *Geology,* **6**, 689–93.

——, —— & SHARASKIN, A. Y. 1979. Geochemical characteristics of mid-ocean ridge basalts. *Earth planet. Sci. Lett.* **44**, 119–38.

TAYLOR, P. N., MOORBATH, S., GOODWIN, R. & PETRYKOWSKI, A. C. 1980. Crustal contamination as an indicator of the extent of early Archaean continental crust; Pb isotopic evidence from the late Archaean gneisses of West Greenland. *Geochim. cosmochim. Acta,* **44**, 1437–53.

VILJOEN, M. J. & VILJOEN, R. P. 1969. The geology and geochemistry of the lower ultramafic unit of the Onverwacht Group and a proposed new class of igneous rock. *Spec. Publs. geol. Soc. S. Afr.* **2**, 55–85.

WAGER, L. R. & BROWN, G. M. 1968. *Layered Igneous Rocks.* Oliver & Boyd, Edinburgh, 588 pp.

WEAVER, B. L., TARNEY, J. & WINDLEY, B. F. 1981. Geochemistry and petrogenesis of the Fiskenaesset anorthosite complex, southern West Greenland: nature of the parent magma. *Geochim. cosmochim. Acta,* **45**, 711–25.

——, ——, —— & LEAKE, B. E. 1982. Geochemistry and petrogenesis of Archaean metavolcanic amphibolites from Fiskenaesset, S.W. Greenland. *Geochim. cosmochim. Acta,* **46**, 2203–15.

WHITE, W. M. & HOFMANN, A. W. 1982. Sr and Nd isotope geochemistry of oceanic basalts and mantle evolution. *Nature, London,* **296**, 821–5.

WINDLEY, B. F., HERD, R. K. & BOWDEN, A. A. 1973. The Fiskenaesset complex, West Greenland, Part I. A preliminary study of stratigraphy, petrology and whole rock chemistry from Qeqertarssuatsiaq. *Bull. Grønlands geol. Unders.* **106**, 80 pp.

—— & SMITH, J. V. 1974. The Fiskenaesset complex, West Greenland, Part II. General mineral chemistry from Qeqertarssuatsiaq. *Bull. Grønlands geol. Unders.* **108**, 54 pp.

ZECK, H. P., MORTHORST, J. R. & KALSBEEK, F. 1983. Metasomatic control of K/Rb ratios in amphibolites. *Chem. Geol.* **40**, 313–21.

R. P. HALL & D. J. HUGHES, Department of Geology, Portsmouth Polytechnic, Portsmouth PO1 3QL, UK.

C. R. L. FRIEND, Department of Geology and Physical Sciences, Oxford Polytechnic, Oxford OX3 0BP, UK.

High-grade terrains in and around the Yilgarn Block of Western Australia

J. S. Myers

SUMMARY: Two kinds of high-grade terrain occur in the western part of the Archaean Yilgarn Block. One consists of repeatedly deformed and metamorphosed granites (3650 and 3500 Ma), layered basic rocks (3750 Ma), and siliceous metasedimentary rocks, which were metamorphosed to granulite facies at 3300 Ma. The other consists of much less deformed granites and some basic rocks which form deeper, granulite-facies equivalents of the adjacent high-level 3000–2600 Ma granite-greenstone terrain.

The Yilgarn Block is bounded by Proterozoic belts of intense deformation and high-grade metamorphism. These belts were active between 2000 and 1600 Ma and comprise both reworked Archaean and early Proterozoic rocks. Two belts were mobile again and metamorphosed to granulite or amphibolite facies between 1300 and 1000 Ma, and one of these belts was also intruded by plutonic rocks, deformed and metamorphosed to granulite facies at about 650 Ma.

The main outcrop of early Precambrian rocks in Australia is in the Western Shield of Western Australia (Fig. 1). This consists of two Archaean cratons: the Pilbara craton which formed between 3500 and 2800 Ma and the Yilgarn craton (generally known as the Yilgarn Block, Gee 1979) which formed between 3800 and 2500 Ma. These cratons are separated and surrounded by Proterozoic mobile belts in which old crust was reworked and new sialic crust was generated. The mobile belts were established by 2000 Ma (Fletcher et al. 1983a,b) and thereafter were the sites of all major tectonic activity, the cratons remaining as intact blocks.

The exposed surfaces of most of the Yilgarn, and all of the Pilbara, craton (except for the Hamersley Basin) consist of granite–greenstone terrain (Fig. 1)—volcanic and sedimentary rocks intruded by granitoid plutons and metamorphosed to low to moderate grade. Although some of these volcanic and sedimentary rocks were locally metamorphosed to granulite facies, regional high-grade metamorphism is only seen in a belt called the Western Gneiss Terrain (Gee et al. 1981) along the western margin of the Yilgarn craton (Fig. 1). An outline of the geology of the Western Gneiss Terrain is given in the first part of this paper. The geology of the whole Western Shield (Fig. 1) is summarized by Gee (1979).

The Gascoyne mobile belt (Fig. 1) developed between the Pilbara and Yilgarn cratons about 2000 Ma. Field and isotopic evidence suggest the presence of abundant reworked Archaean rocks in the south, but similar kinds of evidence suggest that the central and northern parts of the belt consist entirely of early Proterozoic rocks— deformed high-grade metasedimentary rocks and granitoid intrusions (field evidence, Williams

1986; isotopic evidence, Fletcher et al. 1983a). To the north of the Gascoyne belt, contemporaneous metasedimentary rocks form a broad synclinorium in the Ashburton Trough, metamorphosed to low amphibolite or greenschist facies. To the SE, contemporaneous rocks occur in a relatively little-deformed and metamorphosed state in the Nabberu Basin (Fig. 1). All these rocks are partly overlain by a thin veneer of 1100 Ma clastic sedimentary rocks in the Bangemall Basin (Fig. 1) (Gee 1979).

The Albany–Fraser mobile belt to the south of the Yilgarn craton (Fig. 1) also developed at about 2000 Ma but was reactivated between 1300 and 1050 Ma (Fletcher et al. 1983b; Rosman et al. 1980). An outline of part of this belt is given in this paper as an example of the Proterozoic mobile belts.

The western boundary of the Yilgarn craton (Fig. 1) is the Darling Fault. This fault was active about 430–130 Ma during the separation of the Indian sub-continent from Western Australia, with a downthrow of the belt through Perth of over 10 km (Playford et al. 1976). Mylonite zones in Archaean granites along the western margin of the craton are thought to have formed about 2575 Ma (Rb–Sr isochron) during early movements along the line of the present Darling Fault (Blight et al. 1981). Sm–Nd model ages of about 2.0–1.8 Ma of crystalline rocks obtained from boreholes from beneath the Phanerozoic rocks to the west of the Darling Fault, and from outcrops to the NNW of Perth, indicate the presence of an early Proterozoic mobile belt along the western margin of the Yilgarn craton beneath the Phanerozoic Perth Basin (Fletcher et al. 1985). Some of these crystalline rocks, at granulite facies, give Rb–Sr ages of about 1000 Ma (Compston &

From: PARK, R. G. & TARNEY, J. (eds), 1987, *Evolution of the Lewisian and Comparable Precambrian High Grade Terrains*, Geological Society Special Publication No. 27, pp. 277–284.

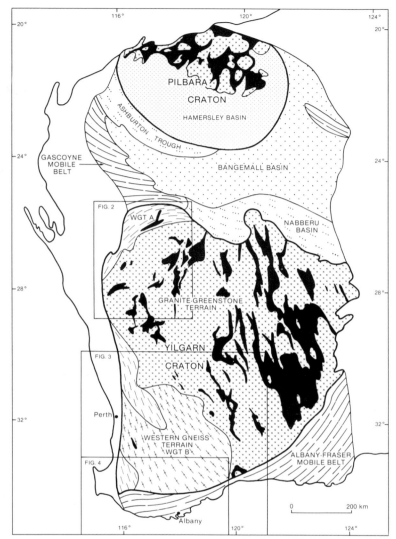

FIG. 1. Tectonic outline of the Western Shield of Western Australia (with ornament; regions of Phanerozoic rocks are blank). The granite–greenstone terrains are subdivided into greenstones (black) and granites (cross ornament). The Western Gneiss Terrain is subdivided into an early gneiss complex (WGT A) and a region containing younger deformed granites in granulite facies (WGT B).

Arriens 1968) suggesting a further episode of tectonic and metamorphic activity in this mobile belt. Deformed crystalline rocks at granulite facies north of Cape Leeuwin (located on Fig. 4), to the west of the Phanerozoic basin, give Sm-Nd model ages of about 750–600 Ma (Fletcher *et al.* 1985; I.R.Fletcher pers. comm. 1985), indicating another major episode of crustal mobility in this belt.

Western Gneiss Terrain—northern sector

The northern sector of the Western Gneiss Terrain (Fig. 1) consists of two groups of gneiss: Meeberrie gneiss derived from a complex of mainly monzogranite, and Dugel gneiss mainly derived from syenogranite (Fig. 2) (Myers &

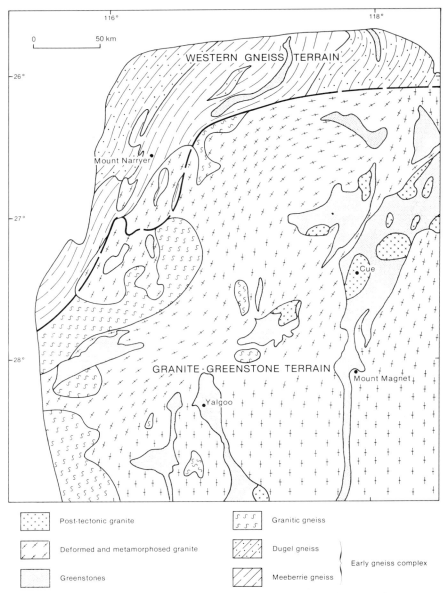

FIG. 2. Map of the northern sector of the Western Gneiss Terrain and adjacent granite–greenstone terrain, located on Fig. 1. The thick broken line marks the SE boundary of the Western Gneiss Terrain. Most rocks dip steeply and linear ornament indicates tectonic trends.

Williams 1985), which give Sm-Nd model ages of 3630 ± 40 and 3510 ± 50 Ma respectively (De Laeter *et al.* 1981*a*). The Dugel gneiss contains inclusions of a layered gabbro-anorthosite complex called the Manfred Complex which gives Sm-Nd model ages of about 3800–3700 Ma (I. R. Fletcher pers. comm. 1984).

Narrow strips of quartzite and banded quartz-

magnetite rocks, and lesser amounts of pelitic and semi-pelitic schists are prominent in both groups of gneiss. They are strongly deformed together with the gneisses, and primary contact relations are obliterated. The thickest sequence of these rocks occurs at Mount Narryer (Fig. 2) where the metasedimentary rocks are also least deformed. Cross-bedding and graded-bedding

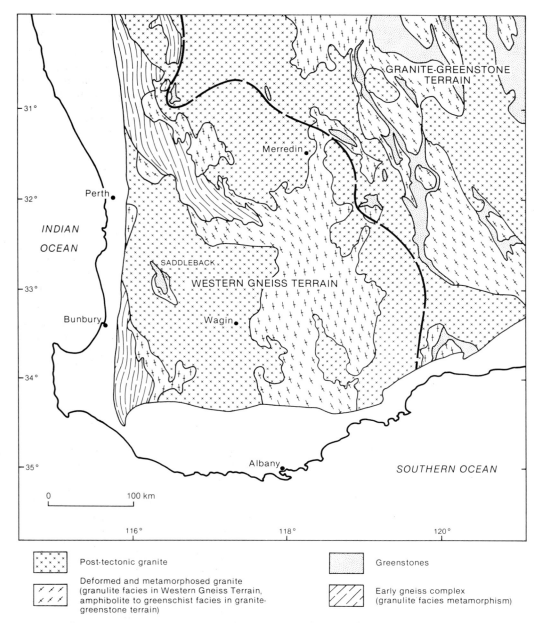

FIG. 3. Map of the southern sector of the Western Gneiss Terrain and adjacent granite–greenstone terrain, located on Fig. 1. The thick broken line marks the NE boundary of the Western Gneiss Terrain.

structures are preserved in a sequence of mainly quartzite and metaconglomerate (Myers & Williams 1985). Detrital zircons from these quartzites studied by ion microprobe (Froude *et al.* 1983) were mostly found to have U-Pb ages of 3750–3500 Ma, but a few zircons were identified with

ages of 4200–4100 Ma, far older than any known terrestrial rocks.

This group of ortho- and para-gneisses is collectively called the early gneiss complex (Myers & Williams 1985). It does not appear to contain any rocks of metavolcanic origin, in contrast to the dominance of metavolcanic rocks in the greenstones of the granite-greenstone terrain. The early gneiss complex was deformed and recrystallized to granulite facies, and Rb-Sr whole rock isochron ages of about 3350 Ma from the Meeberrie gneiss (De Laeter *et al.* 1981*b*; De Laeter *et al.* 1985) may be associated with this episode of high-grade regional metamorphism.

The boundary of the early gneiss complex is a major zone of tectonic displacement (Fig. 2). The granite–greenstone terrain to the SE of this boundary contains a distinctly different complex of granitic gneiss (Fig. 2) which does not appear to have been metamorphosed to granulite facies. This complex of granitic gneiss, together with the greenstones and all the components of the early gneiss complex were intruded by sheets and plutons of granites (deformed and metamorphosed granite on Fig. 2). All these rocks were subsequently deformed together and the main tectonic fabrics and structures of both the early gneiss complex and the granite–greenstone terrain formed at the same time. Associated metamorphism ranges from retrograde high amphibolite facies in the early gneiss complex, to prograde high amphibolite facies in the NW part of the granite–greenstone terrain, to prograde low amphibolite or greenschist facies to the SE. The present erosion surface appears to be tilted towards the SE relative to the crustal level during this last major episode of deformation and metamorphism. Some deformed and metamorphosed granites which intrude the early gneiss complex at Mount Narryer (Fig. 2) give a Sm-Nd model age of 3120 ± 30 Ma and a Rb-Sr isochron of 2579 ± 122 Ma (De Laeter *et al.* 1985).

Western Gneiss Terrain—southern sector

The southern sector of the Western Gneiss Terrain consists of two distinct groups of rocks. An older group (WGT A, Fig. 1) appears to be broadly similar in composition, age and geological history to the early gneiss complex which forms the northern sector of the Western Gneiss Terrain (Fig. 2). A younger group (WGT B, Fig. 1) consists of deformed and metamorphosed granite which intruded the older gneiss complex and has syn- or post-tectonic metamorphic textures in granulite facies. These deformed and metamorphosed granites (Fig. 3) appear to be similar in relative age and deformation state to the widespread syn-tectonic granitoid intrusions of the Yilgarn granite–greenstone terrain (Gee *et al.* 1981), but differ in their higher metamorphic grade. The region (Fig. 3) has not been mapped

in detail but an outline of the geology, including descriptions of the early gneiss complex, is given by Gee *et al.* (1981).

In this region (Fig. 3) the boundary of the Western Gneiss Terrain is a metamorphic boundary between regional granulite facies to the SW and regional amphibolite facies to the NE. The present surface of the Yilgarn craton here appears to be tilted NE relative to the level during high-grade regional metamorphism. This tilting may have occurred before the intrusion of post-tectonic, post-regional metamorphism, granite plutons which are relatively uniform throughout the region (Fig. 3).

Basic pyroxene granulites occur as small bodies in the deformed and metamorphosed granite in the southern sector of the Western Gneiss Terrain (Fig. 3), and have syn- or post-tectonic fabrics in granulite facies similar to those of the enclosing granite. Some of these bodies have relict igneous layering from melanogabbro to gabbro to anorthosite, whereas others are banded with mafic and felsic schlieren which resemble deformed pillow lave structures (*cf* Myers 1978, figs 7,8,9). The latter may be xenoliths or tectonic fragments of greenstones whereas the former are derived from layered basic intrusions which could be remnants of either a pre-greenstone gneiss complex, intrusions into the enclosing granites, or xenoliths of intrusions into greenstone belts.

Albany–Fraser mobile belt

The Albany–Fraser mobile belt extends along the southern margin of the Yilgarn craton and major tectonic trends within the belt are sub-parallel to the edge of the craton (Fig. 1). Only isolated parts of the belt have been studied and the region has not been mapped in detail. Previous work is summarized by Gee (1979). The map of the western part of the belt (Fig. 4) is based on 1:250 000 scale geological maps and a 1:1 million scale aeromagnetic map. It outlines the main tectonic units of the mobile belt.

Two dense swarms of basic dykes cut the Yilgarn craton adjacent to the mobile belt (Fig. 4). One dyke swarm parallels the mobile belt whereas the other is at a high angle to it. The relative age of the two dyke swarms is unknown, but neither swarm cuts the mobile belt. Strongly deformed and recrystallized basic dykes are abundant within the mobile belt and they may be equivalents of the two dyke swarms seen in the adjacent craton.

Proterozoic psammite and quartzite occur on the southern edge of the Yilgarn craton (Fig. 4); most are deformed and recrystallized to greensch-

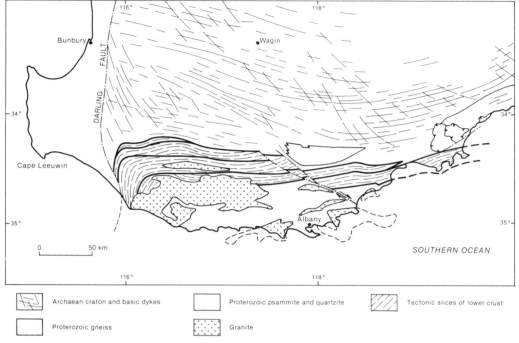

FIG. 4. Tectonic outline of the western part of the Albany–Fraser mobile belt, located on
Fig. 1. Map based on 1:250 000 scale geological maps, published or in preparation by the
Geological Survey of Western Australia, and the Albany 1:1 million scale total magnetic
intensity, pixel map, D. Tucker, Bureau of Mineral Resources, Canberra, 1985.

ist facies. In the northern part of the outcrop
shown in the eastern part of Fig. 4, these rocks
rest unconformably, with a basal conglomerate,
on the Archaean craton and are undeformed
(Thom *et al.* 1984). To the S they are more
deformed and recrystallized to greenschist facies.
Farther S they are overlain by thrust slices (Fig.
4) of similar rocks at greenschist facies, then by
pelites and psammites with cordierite-staurolite-
garnet assemblages, and then by kyanite-silli-
manite quartzites which appear to have been
transported northwards from progressively
deeper levels within the mobile belt. The thrust
zones are marked by retrogression of higher-
grade rocks to greenschist facies, the intense
development of schistosity, and in some cases the
formation of zones of phyllonite.

The regional magnetic pattern of the high-
grade mobile belt shows two major tectonic
divisions (interpreted on Fig. 4 as 'tectonic slices
of lower crust' and 'Proterozoic gneiss'). The
former occurs in the N of the mobile belt as a
zone of gneisses which show generally high
magnetism and pronounced magnetic layering
which dips steeply southward. This layering is
truncated by major zones of dislocation, and the

whole zone appears to consist of a number of
tectonic slices. The gneisses include both reworked Archaean and early Proterozoic rocks
(Sm-Nd model ages, Fletcher *et al.* 1983*b*), and
have syn- or post-tectonic mineral assemblages
in either granulite facies or in amphibolite facies
with textures indicating retrogression from granulite facies. A similar magnetic pattern is seen
600 km to the NE of Albany where thick slices
(5–10 km thick and over 160 km long) of metagabbro (Fraser Complex) are tectonically interleaved with quartzite, banded iron formation and
gneiss (Myers 1985).

The southern part of the mobile belt in the
vicinity of Albany consists of Proterozoic gneiss
Fig. 4) derived from both igneous and metasedimentary rocks, mainly granites and semi-pelitic
schists. Some of these gneisses have given Sm-
Nd model ages of about 2100 Ma (Fletcher *et al.*
1983*b*). These rocks are much less magnetic than
the gneisses in the northern part of the mobile
belt and lack the pronounced magnetic layering.
They are deformed and metamorphosed in
prograde amphibolite to granulite facies and are
intruded by thick sheets of granite (Fig. 4). These
granites were subsequently deformed and recrys-

tallized; some give Sm-Nd model ages of 2000–1800 Ma (Fletcher *et al.* 1983*b*) and Rb-Sr isochron ages between 1300 and 1050 Ma (Rosman *et al.* 1980; Turek & Stephenson 1966).

Conclusions

The Yilgarn Block and surrounding mobile belts show a variety of high-grade terrains. The Proterozoic mobile belts are zones of intense deformation and plutonic intrusions, and comprise mixtures of reworked Archaean crust and Proterozoic metasedimentary rocks and granites. Possible remnants of oceanic crust have not been recognised within them and the belts may therefore be ensialic.

Proterozoic metasedimentary rocks in granulite and high amphibolite facies indicate tens of kilometres of vertical movement within the mobile belts relative to the adjacent craton. In the north-eastern part of the Albany–Fraser belt, major thrust slices of granulite facies rocks were emplaced upwards into amphibolite facies and then greenschist facies environments. The stacking of these thrust slices indicates considerable tectonic shortening. A similar mechanism could have thickened the sequence of rocks in all the mobile belts and subsequent isostatic adjustment and erosion could have brought deeply buried Proterozoic sedimentary rocks back to the surface.

The Western Gneiss Terrain of the Yilgarn Block comprises two different kinds of high-grade terrain. In the SW Yilgarn, an extensive region of granites and minor basic rocks in granulite facies appears to be a deeper level of the adjacent granite–greenstone terrain, exposed by north-eastward tilting and deeper erosion of this corner of the Yilgarn Block. The rocks at granulite facies are no more deformed than the relatively high level rocks of the granite–greenstone terrain. These high-grade rocks are of great regional extent and show neither the linearity nor the intense deformation of the high-grade rocks in the mobile belts.

The main tectonic fabrics and fold structures of the early gneiss complex of the Western Gneiss Terrain formed at the same time, and in the same tectonic regime, as deformation of the adjacent granite–greenstone terrain about 2800 Ma. They are associated with retrogression of granulite facies assemblages to amphibolite facies. Pronounced tectonic fabrics did not generally develop during regional granulite facies metamorphism of the early gneiss complex at about 3300 Ma, and the tectonic environment of this early high-grade metamorphism is unknown.

ACKNOWLEDGMENTS: Thanks are expressed to the Director of the Geological Survey of Western Australia for permission to publish this work which was carried out for that Survey in 1984–85.

References

BLIGHT, D. F., COMPSTON, W. & WILDE, S. A. 1981. The Logue Brook Granite: age and significance of deformation zones along the Darling Scarp. *West. Australia Geol. Survey Ann. Rept. 1980*, 72–80.

COMPSTON, W. & ARRIENS, P. A. 1968. The Precambrian geochronology of Australia. *Canadian J. Earth. Sci.* **5**, 561–583.

DE LAETER, J. R., FLETCHER, I. R., ROSMAN, K. J. R., WILLIAMS, I. R., GEE, R. D. & LIBBY, W. G. 1981*a*. Early Archaean gneisses from the Yilgarn Block, Western Australia. *Nature*, **292**, 322–324.

——, WILLIAMS, I. R., ROSMAN, K. J. R. & LIBBY, W. G. 1981*b*. A definitive 3350 m.y. age from banded gneiss, Mount Narryer area, Western Gneiss Terrain. *West. Australia Geol. Survey Ann. Rept. 1980*, 94–98.

——, FLETCHER, I. R., BICKLE, M. J., MYERS, J. S., LIBBY, W. G. & WILLIAMS, I. R. 1985. Rb-Sr, Sm-Nd and Pb-Pb geochronology of ancient gneisses from Mt. Narryer, Western Australia. *Australian J. Earth Sci.* **32**, 349–358.

FLETCHER, I. R., WILLIAMS, S. J., GEE, R. D. & ROSMAN, K. J. R. 1983*a*. Sm-Nd model ages across the margins of the Archaean Yilgarn Block, Western

Australia; northwest transect into the Gascoyne Province. *J. geol. Soc. Australia*, **30**, 167–174.

——, WILDE, S. A., LIBBY, W. G. & ROSMAN, K. J. R. 1983*b*. Sm-Nd model ages across the margins of the Archaean Yilgarn Block, Western Australia—II; southwest transect into the Proterozoic Albany-Fraser Province. *J. geol. Soc. Australia*, **30**, 333–340.

——, & ROSMAN, K. J. R. 1985. Sm-Nd model ages across the margins of the Archaean Yilgarn Block, Western Australia—III. The western margin. *Australian J. Earth Sci.*, **32**, 73–82.

FROUDE, D. O., IRELAND, T. R., KINNY, P. D., WILLIAMS, I. S., COMPSTON, W., WILLIAMS, I. R. & MYERS, J. S. 1983. Ion microprobe identification of 4100 to 4200 Ma-old terrestrial zircons. *Nature, London*, **304**, 616–618.

GEE, R. D. 1979. Structure and tectonic style of the Western Australian Shield. *Tectonophysics*, **58**, 327–369.

——, BAXTER, J. L., WILDE, S. A. & WILLIAMS, I. R. 1981. Crustal development in the Archaean Yilgarn Block, Western Australia. *Geol. Soc. Australia, Spec. Publ.* **7**, 43–56.

MYERS, J. S. 1978. Formation of banded gneisses by deformation of igneous rocks. *Precambrian Res.* **6**, 43–64.

—— 1985. The Fraser Complex—a major layered intrusion in Western Australia. *West. Australia Geol. Survey, Professional Papers for 1983, Rept.* **14**, 57–66.

—— & WILLIAMS, I. R. 1985. Early Precambrian crustal evolution at Mount Narryer, Western Australia. *Precambrian Res.* **27**, 153–163.

PLAYFORD, P. E., COCKBAIN, A. E. & LOW, G. H. 1976. Geology of the Perth Basin, Western Australia. *West. Australia Geol. Survey Bull.* **124**, 311 pp.

ROSMAN, K. J. R., WILDE, S. A., LIBBY, W. G. & DE LAETER, J. R. 1980. Rb-Sr dating of granitic rocks in the Pemberton area. *West. Australia Geol. Survey Ann. Rept. 1979*, 97–100.

THOM, R., CHIN, R. J. & HICKMAN, A. H. 1984. *Explanatory notes on the Newdegate 1:250 000 geological sheet, Western Australia.* West. Australia Geol. Survey, Perth, 24 pp.

TUREK, A. & STEPHENSON, N. C. N. 1966. The radiometric age of the Albany granite and the Stirling Range Beds, southwest Australia. *J. geol. Soc. Australia,* **13**, 449–458.

WILLIAMS, S. J. 1986. *Geology of the Gascoyne Province, Western Australia.* West. Australia Geol. Survey Rept. 15.

J. S. MYERS, Geological Survey of Western Australia, 66 Adelaide Terrace, Perth, Western Australia 6000.

The Archaean geological evolution of Enderby Land, Antarctica

S. L. Harley & L. P. Black

SUMMARY: The Napier Complex of Enderby Land, Antarctica, is a major terrain exhibiting Archaean granulite-facies metamorphism at extreme PT conditions. Combined Rb-Sr, Sm-Nd and U-Pb zircon isotope systematics define an age of 3070 Ma for initial granulite-facies metamorphism and intense D_1 deformation. Orthogneissic sheets intruded into the tectonically thickened crust at times up to 3070 Ma resulted in the attainment of peak regional metamorphic conditions of 950°C and 7–10 kb subsequent to D_1. These high-grade conditions prevailed through a second, less intense, deformation (D_2) after which the Napier Complex became a stable craton for some 500 Ma. The presently exposed granulites record a near-isobaric cooling path over this time interval prior to reactivation at 700–650°C and 5–8 kb in a deformation event (D_3) at $c.$ 2450 Ma. The D_3 event resulted in open dome-and-basin folding of the pre-existing recumbent- and isoclinally-folded pile. Protolith ages for some granulite-facies gneisses, obtained from conventional and ion-microprobe investigation of zircons and deduced from Sm-Nd modelling, are in the range 3750–3950 Ma, some 700–900 Ma prior to the first recognized metamorphism.

The granulite-facies gneiss terrain (Napier Complex) of Enderby Land, east Antarctica (Fig. 1), has, in recent years, become the focus of detailed geochronological, geochemical and petrological studies, inspired by the results of initial investigation by Australian and Soviet scientists in the 1960s and early 1970s. These early studies demonstrated the presence in Enderby land of very high-grade mineral parageneses such as sapphirine + quartz (Dallwitz 1968), and suggested the existence of crust with an apparent isotopic age of 4000 Ma (Sobotovich *et al.* 1976). More recent investigations of the general geology and structural relationships (Ravich & Kamenev 1975; Sheraton *et al.* 1980; James & Black 1981), coupled with detailed geochronological (Black & James 1983; James & Black 1981; Black *et al.* 1983*a, b*, 1984), geochemical (Sheraton 1980;

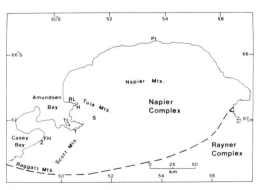

FIG. 1. Locality map of Enderby Land, Antarctica featuring localities mentioned in the text.
PI: Proclamation Island; RL: Mt Riiser Larsen; H: Mt Hardy; S: Mt Sones; T: Mt Todd; TI: Tonagh Island; FH: Fyfe Hills; Z: Zircon Point.

Sheraton & Black 1981, 1983) and petrological studies (Ellis *et al.* 1980; Ellis 1980, 1983; Grew 1980, 1982; Harley 1983, 1985*b*) established the geological framework of Enderby Land. In this paper, the framework is summarized and a model for the Archaean development of Enderby Land is presented which utilizes the available data. The post-Archaean evolution and eventual exhumation of the Napier complex, are beyond the scope of present review. (See Black *et al.* 1983*b*; Harley 1985*a*).

Geological setting and summary of features

Granulite-facies gneisses that crop out as isolated nunataks and coastal exposures in Enderby Land are separated into two distinct but overlapping complexes, the Napier Complex and the Rayner Complex (Fig. 1). Sheraton *et al.* (1980) distinguished the two complexes primarily on the basis of the exclusive presence of unmetamorphosed dykes in the former. Geochronological studies (Grew 1978; Black *et al.* 1983*b*, 1984) provide a Late Proterozoic age for a major orogeny, which, except for a small region at the SW margin of the Napier Complex, was confined to the Rayner Complex. In this review we focus on the Archaean block, the Napier Complex. This consists almost entirely of granulite-facies ortho- and para-gneisses, metamorphosed and deformed in a series of tectonothermal events between 3100 and 245 Ma.

Within the Napier Complex, Ravich & Kamenev (1975) have recognized two broad types of granulite-facies gneisses. 1) A locally promi-

From: PARK, R. G. & TARNEY, J. (eds), 1987, *Evolution of the Lewisian and Comparable Precambrian High Grade Terrains*, Geological Society Special Publication No. 27, pp. 285–296.

TABLE 1. *Mineral assemblages in Napier complex granulites*

Rock types	Initial Metamorphic Assemblages (D_1–D_2)	Subsequent mineral development (post-D_2 and D_3)
Felsic gneisses	opx qz msp ilm	ga developed on opx-plag contacts, biotite
Mafic	opx cpx plag (qz) ilm	ga on opx-plag
		ga qz on opx-cpx-plag
	cpx plag sph	ga on cpx-plag
		ga on ilm-opx-cpx
	subcalcic cpx-pigeonite	opx-cpx ($\pm$ga)
	ga cpx opx	
Ironstones	mt opx qz $\pm$ ga	
	mt ga cpx qz (pig)	opx cpx ga
Pelites	ga sill qz ksp/msp ilm (mt)	
	ga sill plag qz ilm	
	ga opx qz ksp $\pm$ plag	ga on opx and ga
	ga sill opx $\pm$ qz ksp $\pm$ plag	ga on opx, sill
	ga cd opx qz ksp (Napier)	
	sa qz opx rut msp	cd between sa qz
	sa ga phl rut msp	cd between sa opx
	sa ga phl ($\pm$opx)	
	sa opx sill rut	
	numerous osu bearing types	ksp cd opx
	sp qz	sa on sp qz, cd on sa

Abbreviations:

cpx	clinopyroxene	osu	osumilite	sill	sillimanite
cd	cordierite	plag	plagioclase	sa	sapphirine
ga	garnet	phl	phlogopite	sp	spinel
ilm	ilmenite	qz	quartz		
ksp	K-feldspar	rut	rutile		
msp	mesoperthite	mt	magnetite		
opx	orthopyroxene				

nent, but regionally less important, well-layered granulite sequence, the Tula Series. This includes a proportion of aluminous, siliceous, ferruginous and pelitic rock types (paragneisses) of probable sedimentary derivation, in addition to basic, intermediate and felsic gneisses (orthogneisses) of igneous and possibly volcanic provenance. All are metamorphosed in the granulite facies, the aluminous rock types containing some of the exotic and extremely high-grade mineral assemblages previously documented in the Complex (Ellis *et al.* 1980; Grew 1980). 2) A dominant poorly-layered to massive gneiss group, the Raggatt Series. This consists mainly of pyroxene-quartz-feldspar orthogneiss with subordinate two-pyroxene mafic granulites and ultramafic granulites (Sheraton *et al.* 1980). Mineral assemblages in the various rock types occurring within these series are summarized in Table 1 and further considered in subsequent sections.

James & Black (1981) report instances of discordant relations between massive orthogneisses and layered gneiss sequences, with the former being intrusive. Such observations are important in the context of models for the evolution of the Complex. In general, however, the relationships between orthogneisses and layered gneisses are obscure because of the intense deformation events which took place subsequent to orthogneiss emplacement. This history will be described below, followed by a consideration of the pre-deformational–metamorphic protolith histories as revealed by recent detailed isotopic investigations.

The first deformation (D_1)

The first recognized deformation event in the Napier Complex produced tight to isoclinal folds with flat-lying axial planes and symmetric style. F_1 folds are seldom preserved on a large scale, but are reported by James & Black (1981). Parasitic folds are uncommon, although outcrop-scale F_1 folds may occasionally be recognized, refolded by later open folds. It is widely considered (Black & James 1983; Sheraton *et al* 1980;

TABLE 2. *P-T estimates for the Napier Complex*

Method (References)		D1–D2 (peak)	Post D2 (cooling)	D3
Temperature (°C)				
garnet-clinopyroxene Fe-Mg	(1)	890–850	—	720–620
garnet-orthopyroxene Fe–Mg	(2)	950 max	780–700	720–650
pigeonite stability	(3)	960–925	—	—
sapphirine-quartz	(4)	950	—	—
garnet-biotite Fe–Mg	(5)	—	—	650–600
two pyroxene solvus	(6, 7)	950–900	850–750	>750
Pressures (Kb)				
garnet-orthopyroxene	(8)			
Tula Mts		6–8	5–7	5–7
Scott Mts–Casey Bay		8–11	5–9	5–9
Napier Mts		3–5	<5	<5
garnet-sill-plag-qz	(9)	6–8	—	—
garnet-opx-plag-qz	(10, 11)	7–9	—	8

Key for methods:

1. Ellis & Green (1979)
2. Harley (1984*b*)
3. Ross & Huebner (1975)
4. Ellis *et al.* (1980)
5. Ferry & Spear (1978)
6. Wood & Banno (1973)
7. Wells (1977)

8. Harley (1984*a*)
9. Newton & Haselton (1981)
10. Perkins & Newton (1981)
11. Bohlen, Wall & Boettcher (1983)

data summarized from Harley (1983 and 1985*b*)

Sandiford & Wilson 1983) that the first deformation resulted in nappe formation and the interleaving of diverse rock types on at least the larger (100 m–km) scales.

On a smaller scale, D_1 produced high ductile strains in many rock types, evidenced in the development of an intense flat-lying layer-parallel fabric defined by elongation of quartz ribbons, pyroxene aggregates, and dimensional orientation of prismatic grains, particularly in paragneisses. Such S_1 axial planar fabrics are often randomized by syntectonic and post-tectonic recrystallization (Black & James 1983) to produce largely granoblastic textures.

Metamorphic conditions during D_1 are summarized in Table 2. Important mineral assemblages indicative of very high grade granulite facies conditions, developed during and following D_1, are now recorded from a wide geographic area in the Napier Complex (Fig. 2). Of particular interest is the regional occurrence in aluminous metapelites of the high temperature parageneses sapphirine + quartz, orthopyroxene + sillimanite, and osumilite + garnet (Ellis *et al.* 1980; Sheraton *et al.* 1980; Motoyoshi & Matsueda 1984; Grew 1980, 1982). These parageneses generally suggest maximum metamorphic temperatures of 950°C, a figure supported by several independent Fe–Mg exchange thermometers (Harley 1983, 1985*b*; Ellis 1980) (Table 2) and by

the recognition of the occurrence of pigeonite in the more Fe-rich metabasites and ironstones (Grew 1980; Sandiford & Wilson 1983; Harley 1983). The occurrence of Mn-free pigeonite with $(Mg/Mg + Fe^{2+})$ of 0.42 at Tonagh Island in SW Enderby Land (Harley, unpubl.) implies metamorphic temperatures of at least 980°C. The spatial distribution of mineral assemblages (Fig. 2), and regional thermometry calculations (Harley 1983) suggest that the highest temperatures were experienced in granulites exposed in the Amundsen Bay region. These high temperatures prevailed under relatively 'dry' ($P_{H_2O} \ll P_{total}$) conditions. Evidence for relatively low P_{H_2O} in the D_1 event includes the occurrence of Ca-rich mesoperthite (Sheraton *et al.* 1980), the stability of osumilite, the absence of migmatites in mafic rocktypes (Ellis *et al.* 1980; Ellis 1980; Grew 1982), and the presence of orthogneisses derived from water-undersaturated melts (Sheraton & Black 1983).

Pressures of metamorphism during and subsequent to D_1 are summarized in Table 2. Pressures in the range 7–10 kbars are inferred both from mineral parageneses (opx-sill-qz and sa-opx) and from geobarometry based on several independently calibrated barometers (Ellis 1980; Grew 1980; Harley 1983; Sandiford & Wilson 1983; Black *et al.* 1983*a*). A regional increase in pressure towards the region south of Amundsen Bay,

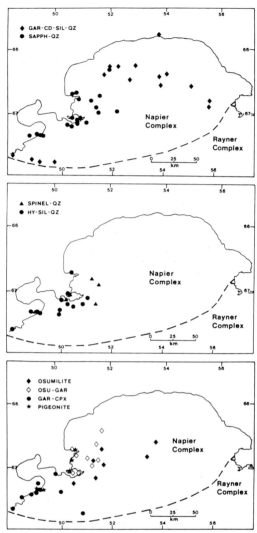

FIG. 2. Spatial distribution of key assemblages in granulites from the Napier Complex. sapph = sapphirine; hy = hypersthene; sil = sillimanite; cd = cordierite.

indicated by the restriction of garnet-cordierite assemblages to the Napier Mountains and of orthopyroxene-sillimanite and garnet-clinopyroxene assemblages to SW Enderby Land (Fig. 2 and Sheraton et al. 1980), has been verified by regional geobarometry based mainly on garnet-orthopyroxene assemblages (Harley 1983, 1985b) (Table 2).

Thus high-grade, dry, granulite-facies conditions of up to 950°C and at 7–10 kb pressure were established during and subsequent to D_1 over a large area ($> 15,000$ km^2) of this Archaean crustal

block. The evidence for the continuation of these high-grade conditions after D_1 include 1) randomization of axial planar fabrics resulting in no mineralogical change, 2) occasional garnet porphyroblast overgrowths on early sillimanite fabric, and 3) textural evidence related to D_2 (see below).

The age of D_1 is now well constrained by a range of isotopic data (Table 3). The best constraint is provided by a Rb-Sr whole rock isochron age of 3072^{+35}_{-33} Ma for syn-D1 orthogneiss from Proclamation Island (Sheraton & Black 1983). This orthogneiss is concordant with D_1 deformation structures within adjacent layered gneisses. Data from other orthogneisses (eg Fyfe Hills, Black et al. 1983a) and paragneisses (eg Mt Sones, Black & James 1983) yield less precise estimates of the age of this event. Sm-Nd whole rock isotopic data (McCulloch & Black 1984) on orthogneisses from Fyfe Hills indicates redistribution and partial re-equilibration of Sm and Nd at 3060 ± 160 Ma, on a scale of up to 1 m. McCulloch & Black (1984) furthermore argue, on the basis of scattered negative ε_{Nd} values for the samples, that this isochron indeed reflects isotopic homogenization during the D_1 granulite-facies metamorphic event.

U-Pb zircon systematics for Napier Complex granulites are often complicated by the presence of inherited, pre-metamorphic, zircon; new zircon growth, overgrowth, and probable Pb loss in D_1; and new zircon growth, overgrowth, and profound Pb-loss associated with a later event, D_3. Hence, several zircon populations may exist in both ortho- and paragneisses, and older populations are often highly discordant. Brown zircon fractions from orthogneisses at Fyfe Hills (Black et al. 1983a) and paragneiss at Mt Sones (James & Black 1981), which occur as inclusions within early high-grade minerals and are therefore believed to have formed at least as early as D_1, lie on discordia with upper intercepts in excess of 3000 Ma (3500–3800 Ma).

The second deformation (D_2)

Second-generation folds (F_2) are developed on meso- to macroscopic scales in the Napier Complex. These are typically asymmetric tight and isoclinal folds with shallower axial planes (recumbent to reclined) and common parasitic vergent folds (eg Black & James 1983; James & Black 1981). That D_2 was contemporaneous with continued high-grade granulite-facies metamorphism is implied by the general lack of development of D_2-associated axial-planar fabrics and microstructural readjustments. Over

TABLE 3. *Archaean geological history of the Napier complex*

Event	Age (Ma)	Features	Metamorphism	Sources
pre-D_1 evolution	3955 ± 10	Premagmatic zircons, initial crust.	—	2, 3, 6, 14
	3700–3800	Deposition of precursors of layered series, intrusion of some orthogneisses (Mt. Sones, Fyfe Hills) possible tectonothermal episodes; partial melting	?	
	> 3100	Intrusion of many orthogneisses, both depleted and undepleted in Y	— ?	7
D_1	$3072 \begin{smallmatrix} +35 \\ -33 \end{smallmatrix}$	Further orthogneiss emplacement. Resetting of most isotopic systems. Flat-lying isoclinal folds layer-parallel foliation, elongation lineations, symmetric folds, axial planar fabrics in hinge regions	Granulite facies. Coarse elongate polygonal granoblastic textures 950–900°C 6–10 kb	1, 2, 6, 9 5, 10, 11, 12, 14
D_2	> 2900	Assymetric-tight folds, parasitic folds common. Inclined axial planes, no penetrative foliation, rodding and sillimanite lineations, boudinage	Granulite facies. Coarse granoblastic textures, elongate pretectonic porphyroblasts 850–900°C 6–10 kb	1, 3, 5, 10, 13
B1		Emplacement of rare mafic/ultramafic dykes	—	1, 4
			Cooling, granulite facies. Garnet coronas, exsolution. 800–700°C 5–7 kb	5, 10, 1, 13
D_3	2463 ± 35	Resetting of Rb-Sr; disturbance of zircon isotopics. Upright close to open folds, large scale domes and basins, weak vertical foliation. Localized intense deformation, contemporaneous shearing	Granulite–upper amphibolite facies. Variable recrystallization to fine grain-sizes, local development of garnet biotite and amphibole. 700–650°C 5–8 kb	1, 7, 8, 5, 3, 12, 13, 14
B2	2400 ± 250	Mafic dykes intruded	Granulite-facies metamorphism, fine two-pyroxene granulites.	1, 4, 3
B^3	2350 ± 48	Mg-tholeiite dykes emplaced	—	1, 4

Key for sources:
1. Sheraton *et al.* (1980)
2. Black *et al.* (1983*a*)
3. Black & James (1983)
4. Sheraton & Black (1981)
5. Harley (1983)
6. McCulloch & Black (1984)
7. Sheraton & Black (1983)
8. Black *et al.* (1984)
9. James & Black (1981)
10. Ellis (1980)
11. Grew (1980)
12. Sandiford & Wilson (1983)
13. Harley (1985*a*, 1985*b*)
14. Williams *et al.* (1984)

most of the Napier Complex, and in most rock types, the results of the superposition of D_2 and D_1 are a relative randomization of early (D_1) elongate fabrics (see above) to granoblastic textures, and a static recrystallization of mineral phases with little change in parageneses or indeed apparent mineral compositions (Harley 1983). Most workers conclude that D_2 was tectonically related to D_1, and that peak granulite-facies conditions prevailed throughout the D_1-D_2 time interval (Sheraton *et al.* 1980; James & Black 1981; Black *et al.* 1983*a*).

Metamorphic conditions probably corresponding to the D_1-D_2 interval are summarized in Table 2, based on the data of Harley (1983, 1985*b*), Black *et al.* (1983*a*) and Sandiford & Wilson (1983). The high-temperature mineral parageneses developed in D_1 were apparently stable throughout D_2, although some mineralogical compositional zoning related to relative changes in *PT* conditions could have occurred in the D_1-D_2 interval. It is also possible (*eg* Harley 1983, 1985*b*) that measured core compositions for many of the high-grade minerals (*eg* sapphirine, orthopyroxene, garnet) particularly in granoblastic-textured samples, reflect equilibration during recrystallization during or just after D_2. 'Memory' of earlier (D_1?) peak metamorphic conditions may actually be obscured or even erased because of the relatively rapid diffusion rates at the temperatures in excess of 900°C which were experienced by these granulites.

In general, *P-T* conditions prevailing in the Napier Complex prior to the onset of post-D_2 cooling (see below) are calculated, based on rim compositions and using similar thermometers and phase equilibrium constraints to those applied to D_1 assemblages, to be in the range 800–850°C and 5–8 kbar. Data presented by Harley (1985*b*) for coexisting garnet and orthopyroxene rims from felsic and pelitic granulites probably indicate both *minimum* pressure and temperature conditions for D_2 as local Fe-Mg and Al reequilibration subsequent to D_2 is likely to have occurred.

Isotopic rehomogenization in D_2 was hampered by the lack of pervasive fabric development. For example, zircons enclosed within coarse D_1 pyroxene or garnet grains are unlikely to have been affected by the recrystallization which proceeded without significant mineral destruction or regrowth. Black & James (1983) have derived an imprecise Rb-Sr whole rock isochron age of 2934^{+146}_{-127} Ma for orthogneiss from Mt. Tod, which correlates well with a 2900 Ma age for concordant zircons from a paragneiss at Mt Riiser-Larsen (Black & James 1983). These results are possibly consistent with Rb-Sr whole-

rock data for metagabbros and meta-anorthosites from Fyfe Hills (Black *et al.* 1983*a*), which yield an imprecise age of 2790 ± 270 Ma. The high reported MSWD (320) of this latter example cautions us against accepting these data at face value, however. An U-Pb zircon age of 2780^{+173}_{-108} Ma (Black *et al.* 1983*b*) for a paragneiss at Zircon Point, derived from the upper intercept of a discordia, is believed to be a result of the mixing of two unrelated zircon components and not a reflection of any real geological event.

Thus the timing of D_2 remains equivocal, although some authors (Black & James 1983) prefer an age of approximately 2900 Ma based on some of the above information. This age needs confirmation, and one of us (SLH) believes that it is unrealistic in the light of the observed metamorphic history (continued granulite facies) and calculated timescales for the thermal relaxation of abnormally 'hot' continental crust in regions of either magmatic accretion (*eg* Wells 1980) or tectonic thickening (*eg* England & Thompson 1984).

Post-D_2 cooling

Following the D_2 deformation and associated recrystallization, the granulites of the Napier Complex underwent a period of near-isobaric cooling from 900°C and 6–9 kbars to *c.* 700–750°C and 5–9 kbars (Harley 1983, 1985*b*). This metamorphic evolution has been documented from studies of post-D_2 reaction and corona textures involving the growth of new mineral phases, the regrowth of new generations of pre-existing minerals, and rimward compositional zoning in early-formed coexisting mineral pairs (Harley 1983; Ellis 1980: Sheraton *et al.* 1980). A summary of the secondary textural features is given in Table 1, and geothermobarometry for post-D_2 corona assemblages are presented in Table 2.

Petrographic and mineralogical evidence for the proposed near-isobaric cooling path includes:
1) reaction coronas of sapphirine $\pm$ sillimanite on spinel in quartz-bearing aluminous rock types (Ellis *et al.* 1980);
2) coronas of cordierite-sillimanite-garnet or cordierite-sillimanite-hypersthene between D_1–D_2 sapphirine-quartz (Ellis *et al.* 1980);
3) the development of fine-grained sillimanite-orthopyroxene ($\pm$ garnet) aggregates as coronas or rims on D_1–D_2 orthopyroxene-sillimanite assemblages (Harley 1983);
4) symplectites of cordierite-orthopyroxene-Kfeldspar $+$ quartz after osumilite (Ellis *et al.* 1980);

5) well-developed pyroxene exsolution lamellae within D_1–D_2 clinopyroxene in mafic granulites. In the more Fe-rich mafic rock types, euhedral, sugary, and lamellar garnet may be developed between adjacent pyroxene and plagioclase grains and within pyroxene grains (Harley 1983). This garnet often post-dates exsolution lamellae. The production of garnet in the quartz-bearing meta-basic rock types is indicative of cooling into the 'high-pressure granulite' field of Green & Ringwood (1967);

6) growth of fine euhedral secondary garnets as rims on earlier orthpyroxene and garnet, or of lamellar garnet within or marginal to original orthopyroxenes (Harley 1983, 1985*b*). Fe–Mg–Al compositional zoning in the orthopyroxene, and differences between Fe-Mg values for early and later garnets, are consistent with this regrowth occurring during cooling at elevated pressure (Harley 1983).

In some cases it can be demonstrated that the post-D_2 textures listed above are disrupted or cut by seams of recrystallization associated with D_3 (see below). Generally, however, conclusive textural evidence of the timing of such features with respect to D_3 is lacking.

The time-span for this cooling from the perturbed geotherm of D_1–D_2 to the conditions indicated in Table 2 is not well constrained by isotopic data, which only provides a maximum possible interval of 400–600 Ma—the interval between D_1 and D_3 (see below). Thermal models for the cooling of lithosphere thickened by magmatic accretion (Wells 1980) or by collision (England & Thompson 1984) however, limit the timescales for equilibration to 'normal' geothermal gradients to between 50 and 200 Ma. As magmatic accretion appears to have played a major role in the early tectonothermal events (see below for discussion), the shorter end of the re-equilibration timescale is considered appropriate for the Napier Complex as a whole. If this is the case, then post-D_2 cooling occurred within 50–100 Ma of the D_2 event, after which the Napier Complex remained buried and stable (*ie* isostatically and thermally equilibrated) until reactivated in the D_3 tectono-thermal episode considered below.

The third deformation (D_3)

The last Archaean event to affect the Napier Complex was a refolding of the recumbent gneiss pile to produce a large scale (1–10 km) dome and basin pattern consisting of NE and SW plunging folds. F_3 folds are commonly open, with steeply dipping axial planes (James & Black 1981). Over most of the Napier Complex the D_3 deformation

was not intense enough to produce a penetrative fabric, however locally in hinge zones of F_3 folds and more extensively in the SW part of the Napier Complex a more or less pervasive axial planar (S_3) fabric was produced (Black & James 1983; Black *et al.* 1983*b*).

Features of the microfabric development in areas of more intense D_3 overprinting (James & Black 1981; Black *et al.* 1983*a, b*) include:

1) minor to variable or extensive grain boundary recrystallization of felsic minerals to produce sutured textures, and a bimodal grain size distribution, with coarser (0.5–3 mm) D_1-D_2 grains and fine (0.01–0.1 mm) polygonal aggregates of recrystallized grains (D_3). The latter may form trails or seams defining S_3, with opaque and ferromagnesian phases (ilmenite, magnetite, biotite, garnet, pyroxenes) as additional constituents. These trails sometimes overprint corona textures ascribed above to post-D_2 cooling;

2) intracrystalline deformation features such as undulose extinction, deformation bands, kink bands or deformation twinning. These occur mainly in felsic minerals but some are apparent in pyroxenes and sillimanite;

3) fracturing, rotation or reorientation, and disruption of D_1-D_2 porphyroblasts (pyroxene, garnet, sillimanite, sapphirine);

4) pronounced bleb-like and irregular exsolution features in feldspars. Such exsolution overprints previous lamellar exsolution in mesoperthites.

Metamorphic conditions related to partial recrystallization of the granulites during and subsequent to D_3 are summarized in Table 2. These estimates are based on a variety of corona and recrystallized assemblages (Table 1) which can be correlated with D_3 based upon recognition of the features given above (1 to 4) (Harley 1983). Many of the *PT* estimates for D_3 are based on the development of garnet as a new phase in metabasites, particularly in the Casey Bay region. In many cases the recrystallized grains form trails consistent with S_3, and in some cases fine garnets (D_3) have formed in cracks and disrupted margins of earlier pyroxene grains.

The *P-T* conditions of 650–720°C and 5–8 kb inferred for D_3 recrystallization (Harley 1983; Black *et al.* 1983*a, b*) lie on the lower-temperature continuation of the near-isobaric *PT* path defined by D_1-D_2 and post-D_2 assemblages. A slight increase in pressure may be inferred from the data (Fig. 3), and a distinct thermal pulse associated with D_3 cannot be excluded (McCulloch & Black 1984). However, the lower granulite to upper amphibolite-facies conditions related to D_3, and the generally localized recrystallization which occurred, suggest that this event represents only a slight readjustment or pertur-

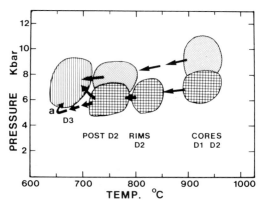

FIG. 3. Archaean *P-T*-time path for granulites of the Napier complex, based on data from Harley (1983 and 1985*b*), Ellis (1980) and Black *et al.* (1983*a,b*). Arrowed line a) depicts an alternative P-T-time path which includes a phase of heating and burial associated with D₃.

Key: stippled fields: granulites from Casey Bay and Scott Mountains. cross-hatched fields: granulites from the Tula Mountains and Amundsen Bay. vertical ruled field: all estimates for D₃.

bation to a deeply buried, relatively stable, terrain.

The age of D₃ is controlled by the presence of essentially undeformed mafic dykes to be older than 2350 Ma (Sheraton & Black 1982). Most isotopic systems have been reset to some extent by the D₃ event. Resetting was particularly severe in the Fyfe Hills and Casey Bay regions (Black *et al.* 1983*a,b*; Black *et al.* 1984).

At Fyfe Hills, while whole-rock samples preserve a D₁ Rb-Sr age, Rb-Sr isotopic re-equilibration occurred in D₃ up to a distance of about 10 cm. Thus, thin rock slabs define a Rb-Sr isochron yielding an age of 2463 ± 35 Ma for D₃ (Black *et al.* 1983*a*). This age is further substantiated by somewhat less precise Rb-Sr whole rock data for localities in the Field Islands (Black *et al.* 1983*b*). Sm-Nd isotope data presented by McCulloch & Black (1984) indicate resetting of the Sm-Nd system on a mineral scale at 2300 ± 300 Ma, an age consistent with D₃.

The best estimates for the age of D₃ are given by U-Pb isotope studies of zircons and monazites, for two reasons. 1) Extensive Pb loss in D₃ from old (pre-D₃) zircons, whether of D₁-D₂ or older age, has resulted in most lying on the younger end of discordia and hence being near-concordant at a D₃ age. Subsequent Pb loss has often only been of minor significance, 2) New zircon growth occurred in D₃. These zircons are nearly concordant, and have distinct morphology, colour, and often chemistry (*eg* Black *et al.* 1983*b*; James &

Black 1981). Such new zircon also forms overgrowths on earlier distinct zircon. In Casey Bay (Black *et al.* 1983*b*), D₃ zircons grown in gneiss and a syn-D₃ pegmatite are affected by post-Archaean Pb-loss.

The U-Pb zircon data yield ages of, for example, 2467 $^{+24}_{-16}$ Ma for D₂ (Black *et al.* 1983*b*), consistent with the other isotopic systems. In contrast to DePaolo *et al.* (1982), who contend that the highest-grade mineral assemblages in the Napier Complex developed at 2500 Ma, it is considered here that this age relates only to the last Archaean event (D₃) affecting rocks, most of which were metamorphosed previously at 3070 Ma.

Pre-D₁ history

Despite the substantial isotopic resetting induced by the D₁ and D₃ deformation episodes, a combination of isotopic approaches has enabled the elucidation of a prolonged pre-D₁ crustal history for at least some of the ortho- and paragneisses of the Napier Complex. While the 4000 Ma age reported by Sobotovich *et al.* (1976) based on $^{207}Pb/^{206}Pb$ whole rock data is not considered meaningful in the light of subsequent work (Black *et al.* 1983*a*; see also De Paolo *et al.* 1982), recent studies provide evidence for the presence of rocks approaching this age within the Napier Complex.

Although the complex, high-grade, Archaean tectonic history documented above renders Sr model ages meaningless, the high initial Sr^{87}/Sr^{86} values for some granulites nevertheless demonstrate a prolonged pre-D₁ history, *eg* 0.724 (average $^{87}Sr/^{86}Sr$ is 2.1) for a syn-D₁ charnockitic orthogneisses from Fyfe Hills (Black *et al.* 1983*a*). It is thus considered that at least some of the D₁ orthogneisses in the Napier Complex were either derived from considerably older crustal material or emplaced at times much earlier than D₁. In contrast, some orthogneisses (*eg* Proclamation Island, Sheraton & Black 1983) were emplaced, with little crustal prehistory, synchronous with or just prior to D₁ (Sheraton & Black 1983). Furthermore, Sheraton & Black (1983) have distinguished two groups of orthogneiss on the basis of trace-element geochemistry. 1) a Y-depleted group, believed to have been formed from melts derived by partial melting under hydrous conditions of hornblende ± garnet-bearing mafic crustal or sub-crustal rocks, 2) a Y-undepleted group, thought to have been generated from partial melting of predominantly felsic crustal material, under water-undersaturated conditions.

An interesting possibility (see Sheraton & Black 1983) is that the formation and migration of the Y-depleted orthogneiss precursors may have partially dewatered the lower crust, which could then have become the locus for the generation of water-undersaturated melts (type (2) precursors) and formation of dry granulite metamorphic assemblages as temperatures rose in the D_1 event.

Separate Sm-Nd studies of granulites from Fyfe Hills (DePaolo *et al.* 1982; McCulloch & Black 1984) give conflicting results for the age of the main metamorphism and the timing and extent of disturbance to the Sm-Nd system. Given the wealth of isotopic data which documents a major event at 3070 Ma, and for other reasons discussed in Black *et al.* (1983*a*) we prefer the data and interpretations presented by McCulloch & Black (1984). Rehomogenization of Nd isotopes at *c.* 3060 Ma leads to uncertainties in model age calculations for the orthogneiss suite from Fyfe Hills. However, the ε_{Nd} value of -2.0 ± 1.8 at that time is indicative of a significant crustal prehistory. Assumption of a depleted mantle source with ε_{Nd} of $+2.0$ leads to an average model age (T_{DM}) of 3500 Ma (McCulloch & Black 1984). Still older crustal-formation ages are possible if there was a large decrease in Sm-Nd during metamorphism.

Conventional U-Pb analysis of zircons in tonalitic orthogneiss from Mount Sones has identified a pre-D_1 zircon population. This defines a discordia from extending 2500 Ma to about 3700 Ma, presumably close to the crystallization age of the tonalite (Black & James 1983). Recent high-resolution ion-microprobe study of these zircons (Williams *et al.* 1984) has provided a better definition of the pre-D_1 history of the orthogneiss. An age of 3750 Ma has been established for magmatic zircon zones, and zircon cores preserve an apparent age of 3955 ± 10 Ma. The last age is thought to represent that of pre-magmatic zircon, *ie* magmatism at 3750 Ma at least partly involved the melting of pre-existing crust as old as 3955 Ma. Zircon cores from orthogneiss at Fyfe Hills yield an ion-microprobe age of 3800 Ma (Compston & Williams 1982).

The isotopic data summarized above indicate a substantial crustal pre-history for some of the Napier Complex protoliths affected by high-grade metamorphism and deformation at 3070 Ma. A gap of up to 800–900 Ma is implied between the earliest appearance of felsic crust in this area and the comparative stabilization represented by the earliest preserved (3070 Ma) metamorphic-deformation event. However, the ion-probe zircon data show that there was at least one phase of magmatic activity during this period

(at 3750–3800 Ma). Some components of the Napier Complex therefore probably experienced crustal metamorphism and partial melting in tectonothermal episodes preceding the pervasive D_1 episode at 3070 Ma (Sheraton & Black 1983).

Discussion and synthesis

The pressure-temperature-time paths experienced by the Napier Complex granulites in the 3070–2456 Ma interval provide important constraints on any tectonic models for the Archaean evolution of this area. These paths are summarized in Fig. 3, based on data discussed above (Harley 1983, 1985*b*; Ellis 1980). The *P-T* data are interpreted as reflecting both cooling following early tectonothermal events and the superposition of a much later, discrete, event of somewhat different style (D_3). The geological *P-T*-time trajectory is one of near-isobaric cooling over a prolonged period of time. Post-D_2 cooling through some 200–250°C, probably complete long before the advent of D_3, involved a maximum uplift of only some 6–9 kilometres from crustal depths of at least 21–30 km attained at 3070 Ma. It is considered likely that large areas of the Napier Complex remained deep and stable upon this cooling to steady-state geothermal conditions, to be only slightly thermally perturbed again at the time of D_3. *P-T* estimates for D_3 are broadly similar over a large area, and no prograde sequences of D_3 assemblages are found, features which are consistent with the above interpretation and indicated here by the small deflection in the overall *P-T* path depicted in Fig. 3.

The post-tectonic path for a metamorphic complex is a product of the interaction between erosion rates of thickened crust and rates of thermal relaxation to a steady-state geothermal condition. The near-isobaric cooling path followed by the Napier Complex subsequent to D_1–D_2 is inconsistent with models of tectonic thickening of the crust by continental collisional or overthrusting processes. In these models near-isothermal decompression paths are generated as a result of the predominance of rapid erosion rates (England & Richardson 1977; England & Thompson 1984). Such a steep dP–dT post-tectonic path would be expected for the Napier Complex if tectonic thickening, as recorded by the intense D_1 deformation, was alone responsible for the metamorphism. On the other hand, shallow dP–dT cooling paths may be possible in crust which is thickened by the accretion of large volumes of magma (30–60% of the crust) over sufficiently long periods of time (Wells 1980; Thompson 1981). Such accretion models, and somewhat similar 'hot diapir' models discussed with reference to the Napier Complex (*eg* Ellis 1980; Grew 1980; Ellis 1983; Harley 1983, 1985*b*), are given some support by the recent isotopic evidence which suggests that considerable magmatic material (orthogneiss precursors) was emplaced just prior to and within D_1. The Y-depleted orthogneiss at Proclamation Island, for example, was derived from a very short-lived crustal precursor at 3072 Ma (Sheraton & Black 1983).

The D_1 event in the Napier Complex was therefore a time of both tectonic and magmatic thickening of the crust (Harley 1985*b*). The gross tectonic setting was not collisional, but may have been extensional with thinned subcrustal lithosphere allowing an elevated mantle heat source. Intra-crustal melting occurred, resulting in Y-undepleted granitic intrusives (orthogneisses), and new felsic material was added to the crust (Y-depleted orthogneisses) to provide a substantial heat input. The D_1–D_2 tectonothermal events were the last and most profound of Archaean episodes to affect the Napier Complex prior to its stabilization as a cratonic area, affected only by weak compression in D_3 and marginal remobilization in the late Proterozoic. The Napier Complex probably remained deeply buried until at least 1000 Ma, when partial exhumation may have occurred as a result of marginal underplating by Proterozoic rocks of the adjacent Rayner Complex (Ellis 1983; Harley 1985*a*,1985*b*).

The Napier Complex is thus found to contrast with many other Precambrian high-grade terrains (*eg* the Scourian) which preserve petrographic and mineral chemical evidence for a pressure

decrease at elevated temperatures. The near-isobaric cooling path, at very low P_{H_2O}, deduced for the Napier Complex has allowed the preservation of the highest-grade assemblages by inhibiting anatexis, often considered to be associated with uplift subsequent to the attainment of maximum metamorphic temperatures (Ellis 1980). Composite migmatitic mafic–felsic gneisses, often described from other high-grade belts, are therefore rarely observed in the Napier Complex. On the other hand, metapelites and aluminous rock types which record the highest grades of metamorphism are of widespread occurrence in the Napier Complex whereas they are either rare, localized, or present only as relics in many other well-documented granulite belts such as the Lewisian. While other Archaean high-grade terrains may have attained similar pressures and temperatures to these documented for the Napier Complex, the very low P_{H_2O} and near-isobaric cooling history of the latter are distinctive features which have allowed the preservation of this remarkable granulite-facies terrain.

ACKNOWLEDGEMENTS: We thank D. H. Green, J. W. Sheraton, R. J. Tingey and J. Tarney for constructive criticism of the manuscript, and Mrs. J. Houlsby for typing the manuscript. The officers and expeditioners of the Australian National Antarctic Research Expedition (ANARE) are thanked for their help and support in Antarctica. L. P. Black publishes with the permission of the Director, Bureau of Mineral Resources, Geology and Geophysics, Canberra, Australia.

References

BLACK, L. P. & JAMES, P. R. 1983. Geological history of the Archaean Napier complex of Enderby Land. *In*: OLIVER, R. L., JAMES, P. R. & JAGO, J. B. (eds) *Antarctic Geoscience*. Aust. Acad. Sci., Canberra, 697 pp.

——, —— & HARLEY, S. L. 1983*a*. The geochronology, structure, and metamorphism of early Archaean rocks at Fyfe Hills, Enderby Land, Antarctica. *Precambrian Res.* **21**, 197–222.

——, —— & —— 1983*b*. Geochronology and geological evolution of metamorphic rocks in the Field Islands area, East Antarctica. *J. Metamorphic Geol.* **1**, 277–303.

——, FITZGERALD, J. D. & HARLEY, S. L. 1984. Pb isotopic composition, colour, and microstructure of monazites from a polymetamorphic rock in Antarctica. *Contrib. Mineral. Petrol.* **85**, 141–48.

BOHLEN, S. R., WALL, V. J. & BOETTCHER, A. L. 1983. Geobarometry in granulites. *In*: SAXENA, S. K.

(ed.) *Kinetics and Equilibrium in Mineral Reactions*. Advances in physical geochemistry, Vol. 3. Springer-Verlag, New York, 273 pp.

COMPSTON, W. & WILLIAMS, I. S. 1982. Protolith ages from inherited zircon cores measured by a high mass resolution ion microprobe. *Fifth Intern. Conf. on Geochronology, Cosmochronology and Isotope Geology*, Nikko, Japan, 63–64 (abs).

DALLWITZ, W. B. 1968. Coexisting sapphirine and quartz in granulite from Enderby Land, Antarctica. *Nature, London*, **219**, 476–477.

DE PAULO, D. J., MANTON, W. I., GREW, E. S. & HALPERN, M. 1982. Sm-Nd, Rb-Sr and U-Th-Pb systematics of granulite facies rocks from Fyfe Hills, Enderby Land, Antarctica. *Nature, London*, **298**, 614–618.

ELLIS, D. J. 1980. Osumilite-sapphirine-quartz granulites from Enderby Land, Antarctica: P-T conditions of metamorphism, implications for garnet-cordierite equilibria and the evolution of the deep crust. *Contrib. Mineral. Petrol.* **74**, 201–210.

—— 1983. The Napier and Rayner Complexes of Enderby Land, Antarctica: Contrasting styles of metamorphism and tectonism. *In:* OLIVER, R. L., JAMES, P. R. & JAGO, J. B. (eds) *Antarctic Geoscience.* Aust. Acad. Sci., Canberra, 697 pp.

——, SHERATON, J. W., ENGLAND, R. N. & DALLWITZ, W. B. 1980. Osumilite-sapphirine-quartz granulites from Enderby Land, Antarctica-mineral assemblages and reactions. *Contrib. Mineral. Petrol.* **72**, 123–143.

ENGLAND, P. C. & RICHARDSON, S. W. 1977. The influence of erosion upon the mineral facies of rocks from different metamorphic environments. *J. geol. Soc. Lond.* **134**, 201–213.

—— & THOMPSON, A. B. 1984. Pressure-temperature-time paths of regional metamorphism I. Heat transfer during the evolution of regions of thickened continental crust. *J. Petrol.* **25**, 894–928.

FERRY, J. M. & SPEAR, F. S. 1978. Experimental calibration of the partitioning of Fe and Mg between biotite and garnet. *Contrib. Mineral. Petrol.* **66**, 113–17.

GREEN, D. H. & RINGWOOD, A. E. 1967. An experimental investigation of the gabbro to eclogite transformation and its petrological applications. *Geochim. Cosmochim. Acta.* **31**, 767–833.

GREW, E. S. 1978. Precambrian basement at Molodezhaya station, East Antarctica. *Bull. Geol. Soc. Am.* **89**, 801–813.

—— 1980. Sapphirine + quartz association from Archaean rocks in Enderby Land, Antarctica. *Am. Mineralogist,* **65**, 821–36.

—— 1982. Osumilite in the sapphirine-quartz terrane of Enderby Land, Antarctica: implications for osumilite petrogenesis in the granulite facies. *Am. Mineralogist,* **67**, 762–787.

HARLEY, S. L. 1983. Regional geobarometry—geothermometry and metamorphic evolution of Enderby Land, Antarctica. *In:* OLIVER, R. L., JAMES, P. R. & JAGO, J. B. (eds) *Antarctic Geoscience.* Aust. Acad. Sci., Canberra, 697 pp.

—— 1984*a*. The solubility of alumina in orthopyroxene coexisting with garnet in FeO-MgO-Al$_2$O$_3$-SiO$_2$ and CaO-FeO-MgO-Al$_2$O$_3$-SiO$_2$. *J. Petrol.* **25**, 3, 665–96.

—— 1984*b*. An experimental study of the partitioning of Fe and Mg between garnet and orthopyroxene. *Contrib. Mineral. Petrol.* **86**, 395–373.

—— 1985*a*, Paragenetic and mineral-chemical relationships in orthoamphibole-bearing gneisses from Enderby Land, east Antarctica: a record of Proterozoic uplift. *J. Metamorphic Geol.* **3**, 179–200.

—— 1985*b*, Garnet-orthopyroxene bearing granulites from Enderby Land, Antarctica: metamophric pressure-temperature-time evolution of the Archaean Napier Complex. *J. Petrology,* **26**, 819–856.

HENSEN, B. J. & GREEN, D. H. 1973. Experimental study of the stability of cordierite and garnet in pelitic compositions at high pressures and temper-atures. III synthesis of experimental data and geological applications. *Contrib. Mineral. Petrol.* **38**, 151–166.

JAMES, P. R. & BLACK, L. P. 1981. A review of the structural evolution and geochronology of the Archaean Napier Complex of Enderby Land, Australian Antarctic Territory. *Geol. Soc. Aust. Spec. Publ.* **7**, 71–83.

McCULLOCH, M. T. & BLACK, L. P. 1984. Sm-Nd isotopic systematics of Enderby Land granulites and evidence for the redistribution of Sm and Nd during metamorphism. *Earth planet. Sci. Lett.* **71**, (1), 46–58.

MOTOYOSHI, Y. & MATSUEDA, H. 1984. Archaean granulites from Mt Riiser-Larsen in Enderby Land, East Antarctica. *Memoirs of Nat. Institute of Polar Research, Japan.* Special issue No. 33, 103–125.

NEWTON, R. C. & HASELTON, H. T. 1981. Thermodynamics of the garnet-plagioclase-Al$_2$SiO$_5$-quartz geobarometer. *In:* NEWTON, R. C., NAVROTSKY, A. & WOOD, B. J. (eds) *Thermodynamics of Minerals and Melts.* Springer-Verlag, New York.

PERKINS, D. III & NEWTON, R. C. 1981. Charnockite geobarometers based on coexisting garnet-pyroxene-plagioclase-quartz. *Nature, London,* **292**, 144–146.

RAVICH, M. G. & KAMENEV, E. N. 1975. *Crystalline basement of the Antarctic Platform.* John Wiley and Sons, New York, 582 pp.

ROSS, M. & HUEBNER, J. S. 1975. A pyroxene geothermometer based on composition-temperature relationships of naturally occurring augite, pigeonite and orthopyroxene. Extended abstracts. *Int. Conf. on Geothermometry and Geobarometry.* Penn. State University.

SANDIFORD, M. A. & WILSON, C. J. L. 1983. The geology of the Fyfe Hills-Khmara Bay region, Enderby Land. *In:* OLIVER, R. L., JAMES, P. R. & JAGO, J. B. (eds). *Antarctic Geoscience.* Aust. Acad. Sci., Canberra, 697 pp.

SHERATON, J. W. 1980. Geochemistry of Precambrian metapelites from east Antarctica: secular and metamorphic variations. *BMR J. Aust. Geol. geophys.* **5**, 279–288.

—— & BLACK, L. P. 1981. Geochemistry and geochronology of Proterozoic tholeiite dykes of East Antarctica: evidence for mantle metasomatism. *Contrib. Mineral. Petrol.* **78**, 305–17.

—— & —— 1983. Geochemistry of Precambrian gneisses: relevance for the evolution of the East Antarctic shield. *Lithos,* **16**, 273–296.

——, OFFE, L. A., TINGEY, R. J. & ELLIS, D. J. 1980. Enderby Land, Antarctica—an unusual Precambrian high grade metamorphic terrain. *J. Geol. Soc. Aust.* **27**, 305–17.

SOBOTOVICH, E. V., KAMENEV, YE. N., KOMARISTYY, A. A. & RUDNIK, V. A. 1976. The oldest rocks of Antarctica (Enderby Land). *Int. Geol. Rev.* **18**, 371–88.

THOMSPON, A. B. 1981. The pressure-temperature (P-T) plane viewed by geophysicists and petrologists. *Terra Cognita,* **1**, 11–20.

WELLS, P. R. A. 1977. Pyroxene thermometry in simple and complex systems. *Contrib. Mineral. Petrol.* **62**, 129–39.

—— 1980. Thermal models for the magmatic accretion and subsequent metamorphism of continental crust. *Earth planet. Sci. Lett.* **46**, 253–265.

WILLIAMS, I. S., COMPSTON, W., BLACK, L. P., IRELAND, T. R. & FOSTER, J. J. 1984. Unsupported radiogenic Pb in zircon: a cause of anomalously high Pb-Pb, U-Pb and Th-Pb ages. *Contrib. Mineral. Petrol.* **88**, 322–27.

WOOD, B. J. 1974. The solubility of alumina in orthopyroxene co-existing with garnet. *Contrib. Mineral. Petrol.* **46**, 1–15.

—— & BANNO, S. 1973. Garnet-orthopyroxene and orthopyroxene-clinopyroxene relationships in simple and complex systems. *Contrib. Mineral. Petrol.* **42**, 109–23.

S. L. HARLEY, Department of Earth Sciences, University of Oxford, Oxford OX! 3PR, UK.

L. P. BLACK, Division of Petrology and Geochemistry, Bureau of Mineral Resources, Geology and Geophysics, G.P.O. Box 378, Canberra, ACT 2601, Australia.

The Archaean high grade gneiss terrain in E Hebei Province, NE China: geological framework and conditions of metamorphism

J. D. Sills, K. Wang, Y. Yan & B. F. Windley

SUMMARY: The Archaean high-grade gneiss terrain of eastern Hebei Province, N.E. China, is unusual in that it contains abundant banded iron-formations at amphibolite or granulite facies. The Archaean terrain is divisible into three: an area between Taipingzhai and Malanyu comprising granulite-facies tonalitic gneisses formed about 2.5 Ga (the Qianxi Gneisses); farther south is an amphibolite-granulite-facies terrain consisting of enclaves of iron-formations and metasediments (Shuichang supracrustal association) within ortho-gneisses (Qianan Gneisses) which are in general more potassic; in the extreme south of the Archaean outcrop the oldest rocks, the Caozhuang group (c. 3.5 Ga in age) consist of a series of amphibolites, iron-formations and metasediments enclosed within granodioritic and granitic gneisses. The Qianan Gneisses comprise 'charnockites' of c. 2.7 Ga age, tonalitic to granodioritic gneisses and a variety of highly deformed granodioritic and granitic gneisses of uncertain age. P–T conditions range from 7–8 kb and c. 700°C in the north near Taipingzhai to 5–6.5 kb and 650–750°C near Shuichang and 4.5–6.0 kb and 600–650°C in the southernmost area. Thus deeper crustal levels are exposed in the north, but it is not known whether the transition is gradual or whether different crustal levels have been brought together by thrusting or by vertical movements along shear zones.

Introduction

The Archaean high-grade gneiss terrain of E. Hebei, containing the oldest rocks in China, has recently received considerable attention from geochronologists and geochemists (Compston *et al.* 1983; Jahn & Zhang 1984; Wang *et al.* 1985). The aim of this paper is to describe the rock types, structural relationships and mineral assemblages in more detail, in order to provide a framework for the geochemical and isotopic studies. We also present new data concerning the pressure–temperature conditions of metamorphism.

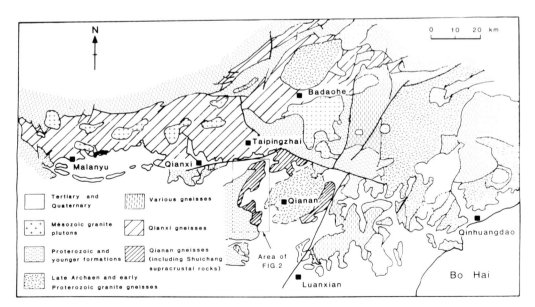

FIG. 1. General map of the Archaean geology of E. Hebei. Modified from Jahn & Zhang (1984) following Zhao Zhangpu (pers. comm.).

From: PARK, R. G. & TARNEY, J. (eds), 1987, *Evolution of the Lewisian and Comparable Precambrian High Grade Terrains*, Geological Society Special Publication No. 27, pp. 297–305.

Geological setting

Archaean gneisses are widespread in NE China where they form part of the Sino-Korean para-platform (Huang 1978). In E. Hebei Province, about 200 km east of Beijing, the gneisses have been dated as late Archaean (Compston *et al.* 1983; Jahn & Zhang 1984). Because of the presence of undoubted metasediment, Sun & Wu (1981) proposed that the Archaean was a sequence of highly metamorphosed sediments with a complicated stratigraphy (summary in Jahn & Zhang 1984). The calc-alkaline nature of the intermediate–acid gneisses led Ma & Wu (1981) and Cheng *et al.* (1982) to conclude that the Archaean was a sedimentary suite intercalated with calc-alkaline volcanics. The Archaean was divided into a series of formations, each of which was considered to be a separate volcano-sedimentary cycle (Cheng *et al.* 1982); however, the isotopic data cannot distinguish between such separate formations. More recently, from a consideration of the geochemistry and from a comparison with other high-grade terrains, a plutonic origin for most of the intermediate–acid gneisses is preferred (Jahn & Zhang 1984; Wang *et al.* 1985), although rocks of undoubted sedimentary origin (banded iron-formations (BIF), marbles, quartzites, metapelites *etc.*) and associated amphibolites do occur as enclaves within the gneisses.

In this paper, we discuss a revised nomenclature for the rocks from E. Hebei (Table 1) because the present nomenclature (as summarized by Jahn & Zhang 1984) is confusing and not supported by our data. The northern area between Taipingzhai and Malanyu (Fig. 1) comprises two-

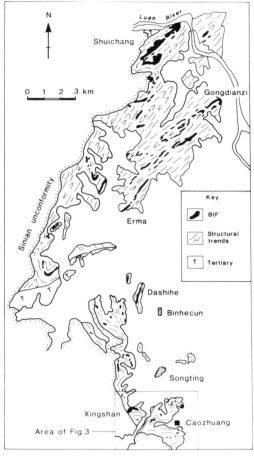

FIG. 2. General map of the area south of the Luan River, modified from Bai *et al.* (1980).

TABLE 1. *Outline of the chronology of the Archaean gneisses of E. Hebei*

Northern Area Taipingzhai to Malanyu	Southern Area Shuichang to Huangbeyu
Qianxi Gneisses ∼2.5 Ga (granulite facies tonalitic gneisses)	
	Qianan Gneisses ∼2.6–2.7 Ga (charnockites, tonalite-granodiorites, granitic-gneisses)
	Shuichang Supracrustal Association ??
	'grey gneisses' >3.0 Ga
	Caozhuang Supracrustal Association ∼3.5 Ga

pyroxene granulites with amphibole and minor garnet which range from basic to acid in composition with intermediate compositions predominating (the Qianxi Gneisses). Radiometric data suggest that the gneisses south of the Luan River (Fig. 2) are slightly older and, as will be shown later, experienced different metamorphic conditions. These are the Qianan Gneisses which include the charnockites and tonalitic–granodioritic gneisses of Wang *et al.* (1985) as well as various other granitic gneisses. The Qianan Gneisses enclose metasediments with abundant BIF (the Shuichang supracrustal association). Structural mapping (Bai *et al.* 1980) showed that the oldest rocks, the Caozhuang supracrustal association (Table 1), occur in the south of the area, near the village of Caozhuang (Figs 2, 3).

The Archaean rocks are unconformably overlain by conglomerates of the Proterozoic Sinian suberathem (Figs 1, 2).

Review of radiometric data

Most isotopic data consistently give late Archaean ages close to 2.5 Ga *eg*: 2.48 ± 0.02 Ga—zircon U–Pb (Pidgeon 1980); 2.63 ± 0.03 Ga—Rb–Sr whole rock (Compston *et al.* 1983); 2.48 ± 0.13 Ga—Rb–Sr whole rock (Jahn & Zhang 1984) and 2.48 ± 0.13 Ga—Sm–Nd whole rock (Jahn & Zhang 1984). These isochrons are almost exclusively from the area between Malanyu and Taipingzhai (Fig. 1). Jahn & Zhang (1984) argued that the time between generation of the precursor magmas and granulite-facies metamorphism was short.

Bai *et al.* (1980) showed on structural grounds that the oldest rocks in the region are a group of amphibolites, metasediments and BIF in the extreme south, near the village of Caozhuang—a time relation confirmed by a whole-rock Sm–Nd isochron 3.52 ± 0.12 Ga from amphibolites (Jahn & Zhang 1984). A Sm–Nd model age of > 3.0 Ga has been reported from a 'grey gneiss' just south of the village of Huangbeyu (Qiao, unpublished data; Fig. 3). Charnockitic gneisses enclosing the Caozhuang supracrustal rocks, give a Rb–Sr whole-rock isochron of 2.65 ± 0.05 Ga (Wang *et al.* 1985), but the age of most of the orthogneisses in this area is unknown. Tonalitic and granodioritic gneisses farther east (near Qianan, Fig. 1) give a slightly younger Rb–Sr whole-rock age of 2.13 ± 0.06 Ga (Wang *et al.* 1985) but it is not clear whether these gneisses are significantly younger, or if this age reflects a remobilization event. The gneisses west and south of Qianan are different from those of the Taipingzhai area in composition and metamorphic grade, and the isotopic data suggest that they may be up to 200 Ma older. The available age data from the entire region (Compston *et al.* 1983; Jahn & Zhang 1984) point to a major gneiss-forming event in the late Archaean, with relics of much older supracrustal assemblages preserved as enclaves within the orthogneisses.

In the Caozhuang area there are numerous late granite-pegmatites, the ages of which are unknown. Myrmekite replacing feldspars in many gneisses points to a late K-metasomatic event, possibly related to late shear zones or to the intrusion of pegmatites. This metasomatism may also be responsible for the difficulty in obtaining precise Rb–Sr isochrons (*eg* Compston *et al.* 1983). Pegmatites in the Taipingzhai area may have formed at about 2.1–2.0 Ga (Compston *et al.* 1983). Mineral isochrons indicate an important thermal event at about 1.7 Ga (Compston *et al.* 1983, Jahn & Zhang 1984).

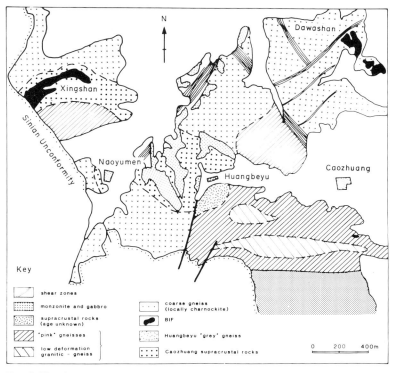

FIG. 3. Sketch geological map of the Caozhuang–Huangbeyu area.

Structural and field relationships

The field relationships of the various gneiss types are difficult to evaluate due to the lack of exposed contacts and diagnostic markers such as mafic dykes which may be useful in constructing a chronology of events. In all areas, early metasediments, amphibolites and iron-formations occur as enclaves within younger quartzofeldspathic gneisses, which have suffered several phases of deformation.

In the Taipingzhai area (Fig. 1) Xu & Zhang (1984) recognized four periods of folding, with metasediments isoclinally folded with the tonalitic gneisses. However, in places it is clear that the tonalitic gneisses invade and break up amphibolites.

In the southern area (Fig. 2) the BIF and associated metasediments occur in isoclinal synforms, commonly refolded, within quartzofeldspathic gneisses (Qian 1981). The Shuichang supracrustal association BIF form layers up to 40 m thick and several hundred metres long, although some blocks are only a few cm across. Around Shuichang a coarse charnockite predominates, while farther south, near Huangbeyu, granites and granodiorites are more abundant.

In the Caozhuang–Xingshan area (Fig. 3) the structure is known to be more complex as there is better exposure (Bai *et al.* 1980). The oldest unit, the Caozhuang supracrustal association, is highly folded with the BIF occurring in a refolded synform (Fig. 3). Unpublished geomagnetic maps produced by the Capital Steel Co. of Beijing show that highly folded BIF continues under the Quaternary cover. The Caozhuang supracrustal association is enclosed within highly deformed granodioritic to granitic grey and pink gneisses of uncertain age. The gneisses contain generally concordant blocks and lenses, up to 5 m thick, of amphibolite which are particularly abundant in the 'grey gneisses'; it is not clear whether these amphibolites are disrupted basic dykes or inclusions of the Caozhuang supracrustal association. The chemistry of the amphibolites within the 'grey gneiss' and the Caozhuang amphibolites is comparable (Sills *et al.* unpubl. data). In the same area there are very coarse (up to 1.5 cm) tonalitic to granodioritic gneisses locally with orthopyroxene, which are very similar to the charnockite near Shuichang, and which are believed to belong to the same unit, which has been dated at about 2.65 Ga (Wang *et al.* 1985). The relationship between the 'charnockite' and the pink and grey gneisses is unclear. The charnockite also contains inclusions of amphibolite, BIF and metasediment, but the amphibolite inclusions are generally smaller than in the grey gneiss. The pink and

TABLE 2. *Mineral assemblages for orthogneisses, metasediments and iron formations from the Taipingzhai, Shuichang and Caozhuang areas*

	Orthogneisses	Metasediments	BIF
Taipingzhai Area	Qz-plag-opx-cpx-hb-bi ± gt Plag-hb-qz ± bi Qz-plag-kspar Plag-cpx-opx-hb ± gt	Qz-plag-bi-gt Qz-plag-kspar-bi-sill-gt Qz-plag-bi-opx	opx-cpx-hb-magt-gt
Shuichang–Qianan Area	Qz-plag-kspar-bi ± opx Qz-plag-bi-hb-cpx-perthite Qz-perthite-plag-bi Qz-plag-bi-antiperthite	Qz-plag-bi-gt ± opx Qz-plag-bi-opx-perthite Qz-plag-gt-cord-bi-sill Qz-plag-kspar-bi-gt ± sill Opx-gt-qz-magt	Qz-magt-opx-cpx Qz-magt-cumm-cpx ± talc Qz-magt-opx ± talc ± cc Qz-magt-cumm ± trem ± opx ± cpx
Caozhuang–Xingshan Area	Qz-plag-kspar-bi ± opx ± hb Qz-plag ± kspar-bi Hb-plag ± cpx ± scap ± epidote ± qz Hb	Qz ± plag-bi-gt-opx Qz-plag-bi Qz-plag-bi-gt-sill ± kspar Qz-plag-bi-cord-sill ± gt Qz-plag-bi-gt-cumm(anth) Qz Qz-sill-fuchsite-chrome spinel-rut Plag-andradite-epidote Cc-olivine	Qz-magt ± trem ± cumm Qz-magt-dol Qz-magt-cc Magt-trem-cpx Magt-cc-olivine

Mineral abbreviations for table and text: qz—quartz, plag—plagioclase, kspar—alkali feldspar, bi—biotite, hb—hornblende, gt—garnet, opx—orthopyroxene, cpx—clinopyroxene, cord—cordierite, sill—sillimanite, magt—magnetite, trem—tremolite, cumm—cummingtonite, anth—anthophyllite, dol—dolomite, cc—calcite, rut—rutile.

grey gneisses are highly deformed and thus could include highly deformed charnockite, supracrustal rocks and other granitic gneisses.

The whole area is traversed by a series of shear zones which have an extremely heterogeneous pattern of strain; early shear zones have given rise to a strong E–W fabric and later shears range from NNW to NNE. Small later bodies of monzonite and gabbro (Fig. 3) cut the shear zones.

The BIF from Xingshan in the Caozhuang area (Figs 2, 3) is interfolded with amphibolites and metasediments and exhibits the same structural history as the amphibolites (Bai *et al.* 1980), thus this BIF could be as old as the amphibolites (*ie* 3.5 Ga). The vast majority of the BIF forms part of the Shuichang supracrustal suite, *eg* near Shuichang, and is associated with quartzofeldspathic metasediments and only minor amphibolites. It clearly predates the main phase of gneiss generation, but it is probably younger than 3.5 Ga. It is cut by largely undeformed granitegneiss and rare gabbro of unknown age.

Rock types and petrography

In order to discuss the rock types and parageneses more fully we divide the region into three areas: 1) around Taipingzhai (Fig. 1); 2) near Shuichang (Fig. 2) and 3) around Caozhuang (Fig 3). The main mineral assemblages and abbreviations used in the text are given in Table 2.

Taipingzhai area

In the Taipingzhai area, the dominant rock type is a granoblastic two-pyroxene granulite with subsidiary hornblende, only some of which is retrogressive. Garnet occurs in the more mafic gneisses. Garnet–biotite quartzites are the most common metasediment, but qz-plag-opx-bi ± gt gneisses also occur with opx containing rare biotite inclusions. Iron-formations are only a very minor constituent and consist of hb-opx-gt-cpx-plag-kspar-magt.

Shuichang area

There is a greater variety of rocks here than at Taipingzhai (Table 2). BIF may be pyroxene- or amphibole-bearing. Metasediments include gt ± opx-bi ± sill gneisses, uncommon gt-cord-sill-bi gneisses and rare gneisses (associated with BIF) contain > 80% opx and reaction rims with garnet between opx and magnetite. Most orthogneisses in the area covered by Fig. 2 are coarse grained charnockitic gneisses with or without opx and

with large rectangular (up to 1.5 cm) grains of feldspar, usually plagioclase with blebs of quartz, and more rarely microcline. Large feldspar grains are locally rimmed by biotite and/or opaque oxide. Plagioclase is commonly replaced along grain boundaries by blebs of myrmekite. More mafic lenses comprise medium-grained granoblastic qz-plag-opx-hb-bi rocks with a much higher proportion of opx, which either occurs as relics within hornblende grains or is partly replaced by a fine-grained intergrowth of hb + bi + qz. Farther east (Wang *et al.* 1985) there are homogeneous tonalitic to granodioritic gneisses containing small mafic lenses a few cm across. Both gneisses and mafic lenses comprise qz + plag + kspar + bi + cpx ± hb with cpx partly replaced by hornblende. Coarse pegmatite veins, a few cm across, are composed of kspar + qz + plag, but it is not clear whether these were injected or are locally derived segregations. Strongly deformed gneisses have a mortar texture and contain the most myrmekite.

In some metasedimentary gneisses opx contains inclusions of biotite, suggesting that the granulite-facies metamorphism was prograde. In other samples opx is partly replaced by biotite and garnet by qz + sill + bi. In the orthogneisses there is no evidence to suggest whether the granulite-facies metamorphism was prograde or retrograde. Most rocks contain retrogressive bi + hb.

Near Louzishan, N of Qianan, there is a very unusual metamorphosed iron-formation containing eulysite, garnet, ferrifayalite, fayalite, cpx, hb, bi, plag and kspar (Zhang *et al.* 1981; Jahn & Zhang 1984).

Caozhuang area

This area has the greatest variety of rock types (Table 2). The oldest gneisses (the Caozhuang supracrustal association) contain amphibole- and carbonate-bearing BIF, amphibolites, thin ultramafic layers and a wide variety of metasediments including quartzite, sillimanite quartzite, fuchsite quartzite, marble, calc-silicate gneiss, cord-bi-sill gneiss and gt-opx ± plag-qz gneiss. The enclosing quartzofeldspathic gneisses are generally at amphibolite facies (qz-plag-kspar-bi) but opx occurs locally in the 'charnockites' near Dawashan (Fig. 3). The pink and grey gneisses are generally medium grained with a granoblastic texture.

Conditions of metamorphism

The *P–T* conditions of metamorphism will be discussed with reference to the above three areas.

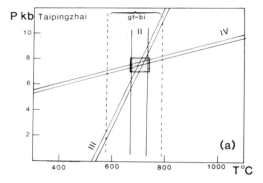

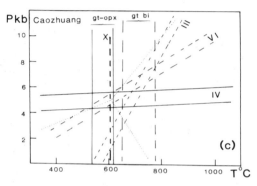

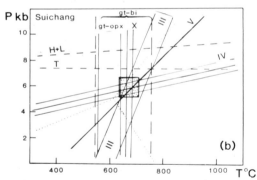

FIG. 4. Estimated conditions of equilibration for the Taipingzhai, Shuichang and Caozhuang areas. The range given for each technique covers the range of mineral compositions. *a*) II is the range of gt-cpx temperatures (Ellis & Green 1979), and gt-opx temperatures (Harley 1984*a*). III is the pressure range estimated from gt-opx (Harley & Green 1982). IV is the pressure for gt-opx-plag-qz (Newton & Perkins 1982). *b*) III and IV as above. V–pressure estimated from gt-sill-plag-qz (Newton & Haselton 1981). X–gt-cord temperatures (Thompson 1976), H + L–pressure estimated from gt-cord-sill-qz (Holdaway & Lee 1977), T—the same reaction (Thompson 1976). *c*) as above but VI is the pressure estimated from gt-opx-plag-qz (Bohlen *et al.* 1983). In *b*) and *c*) the Al$_2$SiO$_5$ phase diagram is shown dotted.

Taipingzhai area

The *P–T* data (Fig. 4*a*), were calculated by a variety of methods. The two-pyroxene temperatures according to Wood & Banno (1973) and Wells (1977) are about 800°C, but these thermometers may overestimate the temperature (Lindsley 1983). Temperatures obtained from the Lindsley (1983) model are about 700°C. Garnet–clinopyroxene compositions give temperatures (Ellis & Green 1979) in the range 680–720°C; this thermometer is thought to be reliable for granulite-facies temperatures (Johnson *et al.* 1983). Garnet–hornblende temperatures (Graham & Powell 1984) are in the same range, 690–730°C, but garnet–orthopyroxene temperatures (Harley 1984*a*) are lower, 650–700°C. Garnet–biotite temperatures (Hodges & Spear 1982) are variable; from biotite inclusions within garnet they are commonly quite high (~ 800°C), whereas from garnet edges and adjacent biotites they are much lower (< 600°C). Pressures estimated from the assemblage gt-opx-plag-qz (Newton & Perkins 1982; Bohlen *et al.* 1983; Perkins & Chipera 1985) are in the range 7.5 to 7.7 kb at 700°C (Newton & Perkins 1982), but are slightly higher for other calibrations. In common with granulite terrains elsewhere (*eg* Sills & Rollinson, this vol.), the garnet–orthopyroxene barometer (Harley & Green 1982; Harley 1984*b*) gives erratic results, with the Harley & Green (1982) model being more consistent. Our data (Fig. 4*a*) suggest the Taipingzhai area was metamorphosed at about 700–750°C and 7–8 kb, and they do not support the 11 kb (minimum) of Zhang & Cong (1982).

Shuichang area

Granulite-facies assemblages are not fully developed south of the Luan River (Fig. 2). In the area around Taipingzhai (Fig. 1) tonalitic gneisses show the characteristic depletion in Rb, U and Th, with K/Rb ratios > 1000 reported for many granulites (Jahn & Zhang 1984), whereas the Qianan gneisses generally have much lower K/Rb ratios of < 500 (Jahn & Zhang 1984; Wang *et al.* 1985). Orthopyroxene occurs in some orthogneisses and there are no biotite-free assemblages except in some BIF and related rocks. Orthogneisses contain no assemblages suitable for known geothermometers or geobarometers, therefore we made *P–T* estimates (Fig. 4*b*) from gt-bi $\pm$ sill gneisses, one gt-cord-sill gneiss and gt-plag-opx-qz rocks associated with BIF.

Two-pyroxene temperatures from BIF are < 680°C (Lindsley 1983). Garnet–cordierite gives temperatures of ~ 650°C (Thompson 1976; Holdaway & Lee 1977). Garnet–orthopyroxene temperatures for Fe-rich samples are 550–640°C.

Garnet–biotite temperatures vary widely between 550 and 750°C (Hodges & Spear 1982). Pressure calculated from the assemblage gt-sill-plag-qz (Newton & Haselton 1981), is 5–6 kb for 650–700°C. There may be a substantial error in this result because the garnet has an extremely low grossular content. Gt-cord-sill-qz gives a much higher pressure (> 8 kb; Holdaway & Lee 1977). The gt-opx-plag-qz geobarometer gives 5.0–5.5 kb (Newton & Perkins 1982), but slightly higher pressures of 5.0–6.0 kb are obtained from the Fe-end member calibration (Bohlen *et al.* 1983). This latter result is considered the more reliable as the rocks are fairly Fe-rich. From the Mg- and Fe- end member calibrations of Perkins & Chipera (1985) pressures are *c.* 8 kb and 6–6.5 kb respectively.

We estimate the *P–T* conditions for the Shuichang area to be 650–700°C and 5–6.5 kb. The pressure is significantly lower than at Taipingzhai and is consistent with the presence of sillimanite.

Caozhuang area

The assemblages farther south are similar except for the higher proportions of amphibole-bearing BIF and biotite-granite gneiss. Granulite facies assemblages occur in some charnockites, but they are extensively retrogressed. TiO_2 in biotite from charnockite is high but is very low (< 1.5 wt%) in biotite from granite-gneiss. *P–T* estimates were made from metasediments (Fig. 4c). The assemblage cord-gt-bi-sill is not found, but one gt-cord-bearing sample produces a temperature of 610°C (Thompson 1976). Gt-opx pairs give 540–620°C; most samples range from 600 to 620°C (Harley 1984a). Gt-bi temperatures vary widely in the range 660–720°C (Hodges & Spear 1982) but they are about 60°C lower using the original calibration of Ferry & Spear (1978). The assemblage gt-opx-plag-qz gives pressures of 4.5–5.5 kb (Newton & Perkins 1982), 5.0–6.8 kb (Bohlen *et al.* 1983) and 5.7–6.8 kb (Perkins & Chipera 1985) for the temperature range 600–700°C. If the temperature given by the gt-opx and gt-cord is correct, pressures would be in the range 4.0–5.5 kb for 600–700°C, but if the higher temperatures estimated from gt-bi pairs are correct, pressures would be somewhat higher (Fig. 4c).

These data suggest that the Caozhuang area may have experienced slightly lower pressures and temperatures than the Shuichang area, but there is an overlap between the two estimates. However there is more retrogression in the Caozhuang area associated with shear zones and intrusion of pegmatites and this may have removed evidence of higher *P–T* conditions.

Because these estimates were made from metasediments which predate the orthogneisses, it is possible that the orthogneisses did not experience the same *P–T* conditions, but this idea is not supported by the presence of opx + bi and cpx + bi assemblages in the charnockites and tonalitic gneisses.

There is an appreciable decrease in pressure from the Taipingzhai area to Caozhuang and this is accompanied by a decrease in temperature and an increase in the abundance of rocks rich in K_2O.

Discussion

The Archaean gneisses of eastern Hebei are heterogeneous and have had a complex history. New radiometric data suggest that the southern area between Shuichang and Caozhuang is older than the Taipingzhai–Malanyu area (Fig. 1).

The mineral assemblages indicate that the Taipingzhai–Malanyu area (Fig. 1) comprises medium-pressure granulites metamorphosed at about 7–8 kb and 700°C. Farther south where the rocks are more potassic, the pressure was significantly lower, 5–6 kb, with temperatures of about 650–700°C. In the extreme south near Caozhuang pressures and temperatures were even lower (mostly 4.0–5.5 kb, 540–700°C). Thus there is a significant decrease in pressure from north to south, but because there is no exposure between Taipingzhai and the Luan River, it is not known whether the contact is transitional or abrupt. It is possible that these two areas were juxtaposed at some later date by thrusting or by vertical movements along shear zones.

The presence of such large amounts of banded iron-formation within a high-grade gneiss terrain is unique (Prasad *et al.* 1982). In NE China, near Anshan, BIF of this type is so extensive that it makes a significant contribution to China's steel industry. Although some workers (Li *et al.* 1982) have concluded that some of the BIF is associated with greenstone belts, there is no evidence for the existence of classical greenstone belts in E. Hebei. The BIF is not comparable to the iron-formation associated with metavolcanics in greenstone belts nor to that within large sedimentary basins (Gross 1973). The BIF in E. Hebei is highly disrupted due to deformation, highly metamorphosed and locally retrogressed, so that the original mineralogy, texture and rock association has been obscured. Smaller amounts of BIF are reported from the high-grade gneisses of southern India (Prasad *et al.* 1982) and it is interesting to note that the southern Indian terrain also contains K_2O-rich gneisses (Weaver & Tarney 1983). The lithologies of the Caozhuang supracrustal association can be compared with the Isua and Akilia supracrustal associations of West Greenland (Nutman *et al.* 1983), both containing metavolcanic amphibolites, BIF, felsic metasediments and metapelites. The younger Shuichang supracrustal formation contains more BIF and felsic metasediments and less amphibolite.

The BIF in NE China and other high-grade gneiss terrains which are consistently associated with quartzites, marbles, metapelites and metavolcanic amphibolites probably formed in shallow water shelf environments on unstable continental margins which did not survive the dynamic conditions of the Archaean (Windley

1984). They may represent precursors to the major early Proterozoic BIF which typically developed along stable continental margins and in sedimentary basins in continental interiors.

ACKNOWLEDGEMENTS: JDS and BFW acknowledge the receipt of an NERC research grant GR3/5222 and both thank the Academia Sinica for hospitality during visits to China. Wang KY and Yan YH gratefully acknowledge the support of the Royal Society of London during their stay at Leicester. We would all like to thank the Capital Steel Co. of Beijing who allowed us to visit their mines and for excellent hospitality during the field work. We thank Li Wanbing and Wang Jingguo who have allowed us to use some of their data in Fig. 3.

References

BAI, Y. L., LI, Z. Z. & KU, T. L. 1980. Palaeofolds as seen from the metamorphic rocks of the Qianan region, E. Hebei. *Geol. Res.* **3**, 68–90 (in Chinese).

BOHLEN, S. R., WALL, V. J. & BOETTCHER, A. L. 1983. Experimental investigation and application of garnet granulite equilibria. *Contrib. Mineral. Petrol.* **83**, 52–61.

CHENG, Y. Q., BAI, J. & SUN, D. Z. 1982. The lower Precambrian of China. *Rev. Brasiliera de Giociências*, **12**, 65–73.

COMPSTON, W., ZHONG, F. D., FOSTER, J. J., COLLERSON, K. D., BAI, J. & SUN, D. C. 1983. Rubidium-strontium geochronology of Precambrian rocks from the Yenshan region, North China. *Precambrian Res.* **22**, 175–202.

ELLIS, D. J. & GREEN, D. H. 1979. An experimental study of the effect of Ca on garnet–clinopyroxene Fe–Mg exchange equilibria. *Contrib. Mineral. Petrol.* **71**, 13–22.

FERRY, J. M. & SPEAR, F. S. 1978. Experimental calibration of the partitioning of Fe and Mg between biotite and garnet. *Contrib. Mineral. Petrol.* **66**, 113–7.

GROSS, G. A. 1973. The depositional environment of principal types of Precambrian iron-formations. *In: Genesis of Precambrian Iron and Manganese Deposits. UNESCO Earth Sci. Ser.* **9**, 15–21.

GRAHAM, C. M. & POWELL, R. 1984. A garnet–hornblende geothermometer: calibration, testing and application to the Pelona schist, Southern California. *J. metamorphic Geol.* **2**, 13–31.

HARLEY, S. L. 1984a. An experimental study of the partitioning of Fe and Mg between garnet and orthopyroxene. *Contrib. Mineral. Petrol.* **86**, 359–73.

—— 1984b. The solubility of alumina in orthopyroxene coexisting with garnet in FeO-MgO-Al$_2$O$_3$-SiO$_2$ and CaO-FeO-MgO-Al$_2$O$_3$-SiO$_2$. *J. Petrol.* **25**, 665–96.

—— & GREEN, D. H. 1982. Garnet-orthopyroxene barometry for granulites and garnet peridotites. *Nature, London,* **300**, 696–700.

HODGES, K. V. & SPEAR, F. S. 1982. Geothermometry

and geobarometry and the Al$_2$SiO$_5$ triple point at Mt. Moosilauke, New Hampshire. *Am. Mineral.* **67**, 1118–34.

HOLDAWAY, M. T. & LEE, S. M. 1977. Fe–Mg cordierite stability in high grade pelitic rocks based on experimental, theoretical and natural observations. *Contrib. Mineral. Petrol.* **63**, 175–98.

HUANG, C. C. 1978. An outline of the tectonic characteristics of China. *Eclogae geol. Helv.* **71**, 611–35.

JAHN, B. M. & ZHANG, Z. Q. 1984. Archaean granulite gneisses from eastern Hebei province, China: rare-earth geochemistry and tectonic implications. *Contrib. Mineral. Petrol.* **85**, 224–243.

JOHNSON, C. A., BOHLEN, S. R. & ESSENE, E. J. 1983. An evaluation of garnet–clinopyroxene thermometry in granulites. *Contrib. Mineral. Petrol.* **84**, 191–8.

LI, J. L., CONG, B. L. & ZHANG, R. Y. 1982. Petrogenesis of early Archaean greenstone of Taipingzhai, Qianxi, Eastern Hebei. *In: Inst. Geol. Acad. Sin. Res. Geol.* 55–65.

LINDSLEY, D. H. 1983. Pyroxene thermometry. *Am. Mineral.* **68**, 477–93.

MA, X. Y. & WU, Z. W. 1981. Early tectonic evolution of China. *Precambrian Res.* **14**, 185–202.

NEWTON, R. C. & HASELTON, H. T. 1981. Thermodynamics of the garnet–plagioclase–Al$_2$SiO$_5$–quartz geobarometer. *In: NEWTON, R. C., NAVROTSKY, A. & WOOD, B. J. (eds) Thermodynamics of Minerals and Melts.* Springer, New York, 129–45.

—— & PERKINS, D. 1982. Thermodynamic calibration of geobarometers based on the assemblages garnet–plagioclase–orthopyroxene (clinopyroxene)–quartz. *Am. Mineral.* **67**, 203–222.

NUTMAN, A. P., BRIDGWATER, B., DIMROTH, E., GILL, R. C. O. & ROSING, M. 1983. Early (3700 my) Archaean rocks of the Isua supracrustal belt and adjacent gneisses. *Rapp. Grønlands geol. Unders.* **112**, 5–22.

PERKINS, D. & CHIPERA, S. J. 1985. Garnet–orthopyroxene–plagioclase–quartz barometry: refinement and application to the English River subprovince and the Minnesota River valley. *Contrib. Mineral. Petrol.* **89**, 69–80.

PIDGEON, R. T. 1980. 2480 Ma old zircons from granulite facies rocks from east Hebei Province, North China. *Geol. Rev.* **26**, 198–207.

PRASAD, C. V. R. K., SUBBA REDDY, N. & WINDLEY, B. F. 1982. Iron formations in Archaean granulite-gneiss belts with special reference to southern India. *J. geol. Soc. India*, **23**, 112–22.

QIAN, X. L. 1981. The tectonic evolutionary characteristics of the Pre-sinian basement in eastern Hebei. *G. Collection of struct. Geol.* **2**, 34–42 (in Chinese).

SUN, D. Z. & WU, C. H. 1981. The prinicpal geological and geochemical characteristics of the Archaean greenstone gneiss sequences in North China. *Spec. Publ. geol. Soc. Aust.* **7**, 121–32.

THOMPSON, A. B. 1976. Mineral reactions in pelitic rocks (2) calculations of some P–T–X(Fe–Mg) phase relations. *Am. J. Sci.* **276**, 425–54.

WANG, K. Y., YAN, Y. H., YANG, R. Y. & CHEN, Y. F. 1985. REE geochemistry of early Precambrian charnockites and tonalitic granodioritic gneisses of the Qianan region, eastern Hebei, North China. *Precambrian Res.* **27**, 63–84.

WEAVER, B. L. & TARNEY, J. 1983. Elemental depletion in Archaean granulite-facies rocks. *In*: ATHERTON, M. P. & GRIBBLE, C. D. (eds), *Migmatites Melting and Metamorphism*. Shiva, Nantwich, 250–63.

WELLS, P. R. A. 1977. Pyroxene thermometry in simple and complex systems. *Contrib. Mineral. Petrol.* **62**, 129–39.

WINDLEY, B. F. 1984. *The Evolving Continents*. Wiley. 399 pp.

WOOD, B. J. & BANNO, S. 1973. Garnet–orthopyroxene and orthopyroxene–clinopyroxene relationships in simple and complex systems. *Contrib. Mineral. Petrol.* **42**, 109–24.

XU, S. T. & ZHANG, W. M. 1984. Structural styles and deformation history of Archaean granulites near Taipingzhai, eastern Hebei Province, China. *Scientia Geol. Sinica*, **4**, 117–26 (in Chinese).

ZHANG, R. Y. & CONG, B. L. 1982. Mineralogy and *T–P* conditions of crystallisation of early Archaean granulites in Qianxi county, NE China. *Sci. Sin.* **25**, 99–112.

——, CONG, B. L., YING, Y. P. & LI, J. L. 1981. Ferrifayalite-bearing eulysite from Archaean granulites in Qianan county, Hebei, North China. *Tscherm. Min. Petr. Mitt.* **28**, 167–87.

J. D. SILLS, Department of Geology, Leicester University, Leicester LE1 7RH, UK.

K. WANG & Y. YAN, Institute of Geology, Academia Sinica, PO Box 634, Beijing, Peoples Republic of China.

B. F. WINDLEY, Department of Geology, Leicester University, Leicester LE1 7RH, UK.

Index